# WindEurope Annual Event 2023



Journal of Physics: Conference Series Volume 2507

Copenhagen, Denmark
25 – 27 April 2023

**Editor:**

**Amir R. Nejad**

ISBN: 978-1-7138-7463-8
ISSN: 1742-6588

**Printed from e-media with permission by:**

Curran Associates, Inc.
57 Morehouse Lane
Red Hook, NY 12571

**Some format issues inherent in the e-media version may also appear in this print version.**



Institute of Physics
Dirac House, Temple Back
Bristol BS1 6BE UK

Phone: 44 1 17 929 7481
Fax: 44 1 17 920 0979

techtracking@iop.org

**Additional copies of this publication are available from:**

Curran Associates, Inc.
57 Morehouse Lane
Red Hook, NY 12571 USA
Phone: 845-758-0400
Fax: 845-758-2633
Email: curran@proceedings.com
Web: www.proceedings.com

# TABLE OF CONTENTS

# PREFACE

This Special Issue presents selected contributions from the **WindEurope Annual Event 2023 Conference** that took place 25-27 April in Copenhagen. A total of 25 papers are included, addressing one (or more) of the three conference themes:

- Resource assessment
- Turbine technology
- Wind farm: installation and operations
- Floating offshore wind
- Digitalisation
- Environmental sustainability and social acceptance
- Grid and system integration
- Renewable hydrogen and Power-to-X.

**Conference Committee for the Scientific Program**

- Amir R. Nejad, Professor, Norwegian University of Science and Technology (NTNU)
- Stephan Barth, Managing Director, ForWind - Center for Wind Energy Research
- Athanasios Kolios, Professor, Technical University of Denmark (DTU)
- Simon Watson, Professor, Delft University of Technology
- Olimpo Anaya-Lara, Professor, Strathclyde University
- James Carroll, Reader (Associate Professor), Strathclyde University

We thank all, more than 30, reviewers for their engagement and effort, without which these proceedings would not have been possible. As with previous WindEurope events, the European Academy of Wind Energy (EAWE) has been responsible for organizing the review process for scientific contributions and has contributed to the development of the conference sessions. WindEurope has been responsible for the organization and logistics of the conference, and we thank their highly professional staff and their associates for the excellent collaboration.

**Proceedings editor**
Amir R. Nejad, Professor, Norwegian University of Science and Technology (NTNU)

# Peer Review Statement

All papers published in this volume have been reviewed through processes administered by the Editors. Reviews were conducted by expert referees to the professional and scientific standards expected of a proceedings journal published by IOP Publishing.

- **Type of peer review:** Single Anonymous
- **Conference submission management system:** Morressier
- **Number of submissions received:** 25
- **Number of submissions sent for review:** 25
- **Number of submissions accepted:** 25
- **Acceptance Rate (Submissions Accepted / Submissions Received × 100):** 100
- **Average number of reviews per paper:** 3
- **Total number of reviewers involved:** 19
- **Contact person for queries:**
  **Name:** Rébecca Brulé
  **Email:** conference@windeurope.org
  **Affiliation:** WindEurope

# Pattern mining based data fusion for wind turbine condition monitoring

**Xavier Chesterman[1,2], Timothy Verstraeten[2], Pieter-Jan Daems[2], Ann Nowé[1], Jan Helsen[2]**

[1]Artificial Intelligence Laboratory, Vrije Universiteit Brussel, Brussels, Belgium
[2]Acoustics and vibrations research group/OWI-Lab, Vrije Universiteit Brussel, Brussels, Belgium

E-mail: xavier.chesterman@vub.be, timothy.verstraeten@vub.be, pieter-jan.daems@vub.be, ann.nowe@vub.be, jan.helsen@vub.be

**Abstract.**
The profitability of wind turbine energy production is for an important part determined by the operation and maintenance costs of wind turbines. An important driver of these costs is currently the premature failure of components due to excessive wear. If it would be possible to accurately predict these failures, preventive maintenance can be made more effective, which should result in less downtime and expensive unexpected failures. This in turn should lower the operational and maintenance costs. The research presented here is a contribution to the research on condition monitoring and failure prediction for wind turbines. To this end, a methodology for failure prediction is designed that combines (fuses) multiple information sources (i.e. SCADA and status log data). The novelty of this research lies in the fact that pattern mining techniques are used to identify relevant rules for a rule-based failure classifier. The methodology is validated on generator bearing failure cases from a real operational wind farm. The results show that the methodology is able to predict generator bearing failures accurately well in advance. The rules on which the predictions are based are interpretable and correspond in general to expert knowledge on the matter.

## 1. Introduction
The current push towards renewable energy production has resulted in a significant increase in investments in the wind turbine sector. According to the Global Wind Report 2022, an additional 93.6 gigawatts (GW) of wind energy production capacity has been installed worldwide in 2021. This corresponds to a 12% increase compared to the previous year, which brings the total capacity to 837 GW [1]. The profitability of the investments is determined by a.o. the operation and maintenance costs of the wind turbines. Recent studies estimate that they account for 25-40% of the levelized cost of energy [2]. Premature failures due to excessive wear play an important role in this. These are partially the result of high loads caused by environmental conditions and aggressive control actions [3], [4]. Examples of components that suffer from this are generator and gearbox bearings. Their lifetime is often considerably less than the expected lifetime of 20 years [5], [6]. Being able to detect these premature failures should make preventive maintenance more efficient, which should in turn result in lower operational and maintenance costs.

This paper is a contribution to the research on condition monitoring and failure prediction for wind turbines. The goal is to identify and predict generator bearing failures on data from an operational offshore wind farm. Multiple data sources, i.e. Supervisory Control and Data Acquisition (SCADA) data and status log data are combined or fused. The methodology presented in this paper is however different from most other anomaly detection research. The focus lies here on the development of a model that is interpretable so that expert validation of the results can more easily be done. For this reason, pattern mining techniques are used for the extraction of patterns. The novelty of the methodology presented in this paper is the use of Symbolic Aggregation approXimation (SAX) and pattern mining techniques (i.e. contrast mining) for the construction of a rule-based failure classifier. The methodology is validated on generator bearing failure cases from a large operational wind farm.

## 2. Related work

The goal of this paper is to develop a rule-based classifier that can predict generator bearing failures with high accuracy. The rules for a rule-based classifier can be designed by experts. However, in situations in which the expert knowledge is not complete, the rules can be mined from data. The latter strategy is what is followed in this paper. In the literature, examples can be found where (in)frequent pattern mining algorithms are used to identify anomaly-related rules (for example [7], [8], [9],[10], ...). However, in this paper, a type of algorithm is used, i.e. contrast set mining, that specifically searches for rules that can best explain the differences between two or more groups. This corresponds well with the goal of this research, namely identifying the patterns or rules that best explain the differences between high and low failure-risk zones. The hypothesis is that the group of rules that explain well the difference between the two, contains a subset of rules that are useful for predicting high failure-risk zones. Furthermore, it has been shown in research that contrast set mining algorithms like TAR2, TAR3, and STUCCO tend to generate less complicated rules than traditional association rule mining algorithms (see [11], [12]). This facilitates the creation of a more interpretable rule-based classifier.

TAR3 is a further evolution of TAR2, which is described in [11]. The algorithm was designed with the purpose of generating rules with limited complexity. The philosophy behind it is that of the *narrow funnel effect*. This effect implies that a small number of critical variables control the remaining variables within a system, or formulated differently, what happens in the total space of a system can be controlled by a small critical region. According to [11], many domains are not characterized by very complex relations. For those domains, it is better to learn just enough so that the generated patterns remain interpretable. Treatment learners like TAR2 or TAR3 generate treatments or rules (which are conjunctions of attribute-value pairs), that return subsets of the training dataset with a higher frequency of the desired class and a lower frequency of the undesired classes. The desirability of each class is determined by class scores that are assigned by the user to each class. These scores can be considered hyperparameters for the model. A more thorough discussion of the algorithm is outside the scope of this paper. More information on TAR2 and TAR3 can be found in [13]. Examples of research where TAR3 is used are [14] and [15].

The Search and Testing for Understandable Consistent Contrasts (STUCCO) algorithm, presented in [12], is a contrast-set mining algorithm that does not use weighted classes. This means that contrary to the treatment learning algorithms it does not require user-defined class scores. It is designed to find the contrast sets for which the support differs meaningfully across the different groups. In that sense, it is similar to TAR2 and TAR3. However, the way it searches for patterns is different. STUCCO makes use of statistical techniques like minimum deviation size, expected cell frequencies, $\chi^2$-bounds, ... for the pruning of the contrast sets. The remaining contrast sets are filtered based on whether or not their support is surprisingly different from the support of their subsets. If it is, the contrast sets are considered "surprising", and are returned to the user. A more detailed analysis of the algorithm is outside the scope of this paper. More information can be found in [12] and [16].

## 3. Methodology

In this section, an overview is given of the different parts of the methodology, e.g. input data and the data enrichment, preprocessing of the data, pattern mining, post-processing of the patterns, and construction of the rule-based classifier that is used for the failure prediction. Figure 1 gives a schematic overview.

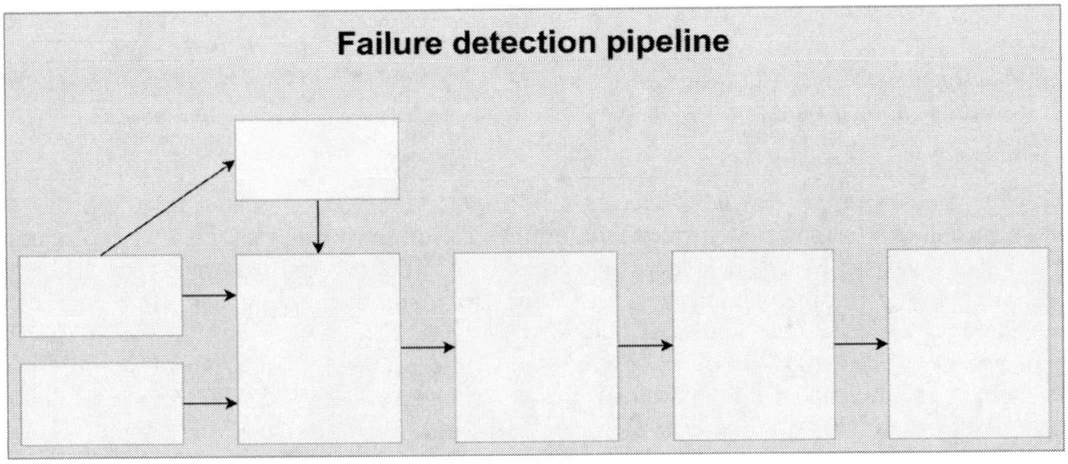


**Figure 1.** Schematic overview of the methodology.

### *3.1. Input data and data enrichment*

For the development and validation of the methodology, a historical batch of data from a large operational wind farm, consisting of 2MW turbines, is used. The batch stretches over a period of more than 10 years. For confidentiality reasons, no more details on the wind farm can be given. The batch consists of three different information sources: 1) 10-minute SCADA data, which contains information like component temperatures, wind turbine context (e.g. outside temperature, active power, ...), 2) status log data, which contains wind turbine alarms, and 3) generator bearing replacement information, which contains information on the generator bearings (i.e. bearing type, date, turbine) that were replaced. From the SCADA data, the following signals are used as input: generator front and rear bearing temperatures, nacelle temperature, wind speed, rotor speed, active power, and generator torque. These were selected based on an extensive literature review (see [17]). From the status log data, only the alarms associated with stops and warnings are used. This results in 289 different types of alarms. The data is further enriched with wind turbine state information. These states are deduced from the SCADA data by analyzing the active power behavior of the turbine and the fleet. A distinction is made between the following states: steady-state, full power, power down/offline, full power steady-state, and derated.

### *3.2. Preprocessing*

The preprocessing of the data consists of several steps. Firstly, the signals in the SCADA data are normalized using the fleet information. This is done according to the methodology described in [18]. Secondly, the SCADA and status log data are aggregated per day.

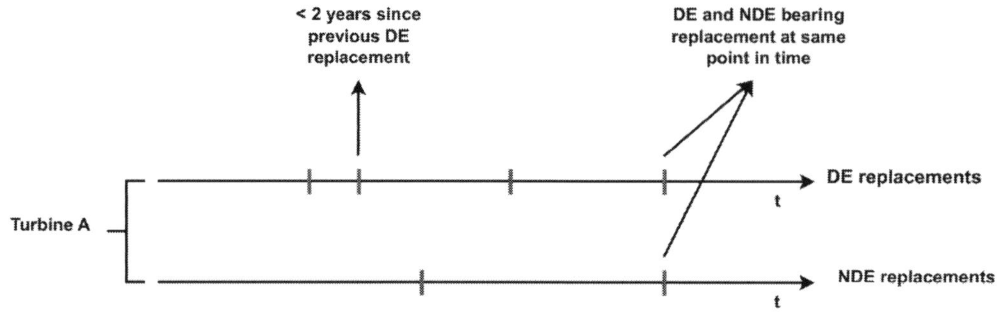


**Figure 2.** Schematic representation of replacement cleaning. Red bars are replacements that are not failures. Green bars are replacements that are failures.

Thirdly, the generator bearing replacement information is cleaned. This research is based on the assumption that a replacement is also a failure. To minimize the risk of using replacements that are not failures, all replacements are removed if they occur less than two years after the replacement of the same bearing, or if the replacement happens at the same time as the replacement of the other bearing (e.g. non-drive-end or NDE bearing is replaced at the same time as the drive-end or DE bearing, or vice versa) (see Figure 2). After cleaning, 55% of the replacements are considered failures, which is sufficient for the analysis. Fourthly, the different data sources, i.e. SCADA data, status log data, and wind turbine state information, are merged together on the wind turbine and date-time keys.

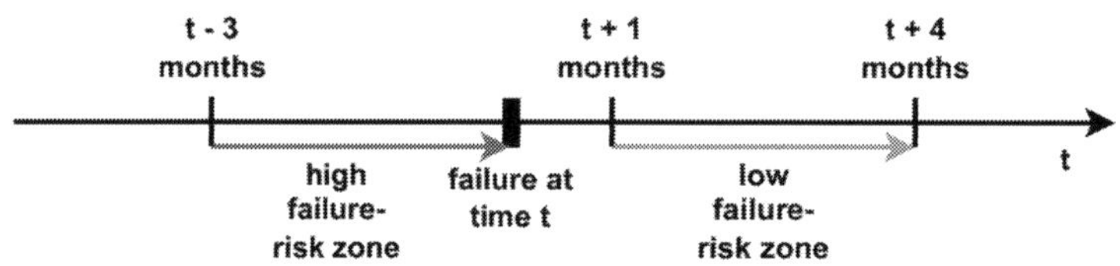


**Figure 3.** Schematic representation of low and high failure risk zones.

Fifthly, the data is divided into failure risk zones. Figure 3 shows a schematic representation of how this is done. Data that is generated 1-4 months after a failure is considered low failure-risk data. A run-in time of 1 month is used to make sure that the low failure-risk data is not polluted with start-up and test behavior. The three months that precede a failure are considered high failure-risk data. By dividing the data like this, the failure risk difference is maximized, which should help the pattern mining algorithms to find the relevant patterns or rules. Sixthly, the power down states of the turbines are removed.

Seventhly, the data is split into a training and testing dataset. Figure 4 shows a schematic representation of how this is done. For each replacement type (NDE or DE) there is a separate training and testing dataset. Each replacement is assigned an ID. Half of the IDs are randomly assigned to the training dataset, the other half is assigned to the testing dataset. The high and low failure-risk zones that are associated with the replacement ID are assigned to the respective dataset. This method ensures that the training and testing datasets contain more or less the same amount of data and that the training dataset contains more or less an equal amount of low and high failure-risk data.

The eighth and final preprocessing step is transforming the time series into a symbolic representation using Symbolic Aggregation approXimation (SAX) [19]. SAX was designed

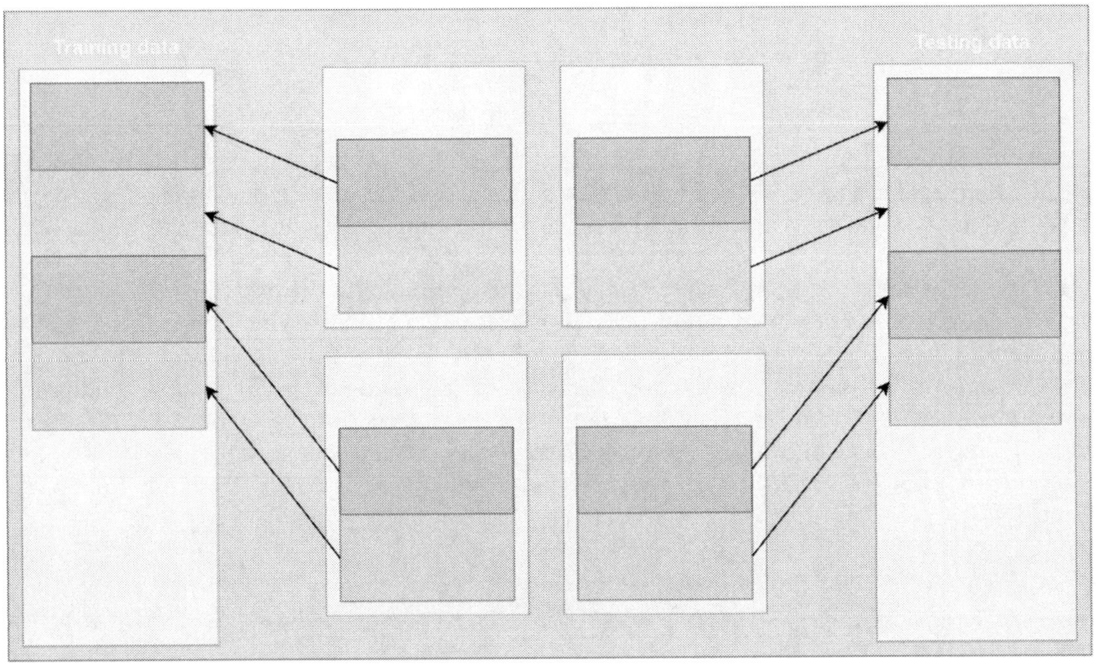


**Figure 4.** Schematic representation of splitting of data in training and testing.

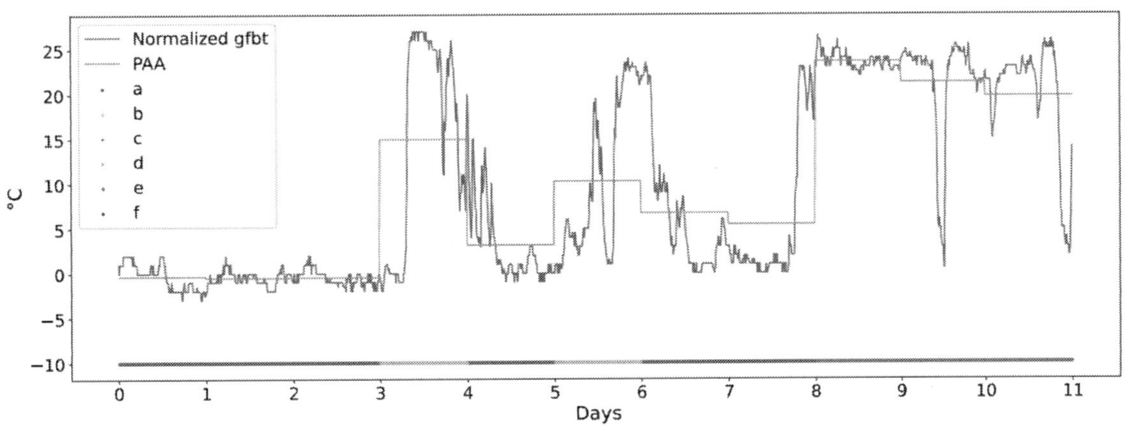


**Figure 5.** The normalized generator front bearing temperature, together with the Piecewise Aggregate Approximation (PAA) and symbolic transformation.

specifically for time series. Figure 5 shows an overview of the impact of the different steps of SAX. The transformation methodology first uses Piecewise Aggregate Approximation (PAA) which aggregates the data over a specified window by calculating the average. This results in a dimensionality reduction. In the next step, the new PAA-transformed time series is converted into a symbolic representation.

After preprocessing the data, the training and testing data both have a tabular format. The training data for DE failures consists of 2967 instances (observations) and 306 columns. The testing data has 2895 instances. For the NDE failures, the training dataset contains 767 instances and 306 columns, and the testing dataset contains 722 instances. The fact that the number of instances for the NDE failures is significantly smaller than for the DE failures has unfortunately an impact on the performance of the rule-based classifier (see results section).

### 3.3. Pattern mining

Once the data has been preprocessed, pattern mining algorithms are used to extract relevant patterns. The goal is to find patterns that best explain the difference between the high and low failure-risk zones. For this, optimised (non-) weighted contrast set mining algorithms (called respectively NWCSM and WCSM) extending from STUCCO and TAR3 are reasonable choices. Since these algorithms are actually supervised pattern mining algorithms, the patterns are only mined on the training dataset, not on the testing dataset. This is to avoid information leakage, which would inflate the accuracy of the final rule-based classifier on the test dataset. Both the NWCSM and WCSM can generate rules that have as consequent the high or low failure-risk zone (the *consequent* is the right-hand side of a rule, e.g. a rule of the form $X \implies Y$, which means in words "if X then Y", has as antecedent X and as consequent Y). However, the focus of this research lies on the rules with the high failure-risk zone as consequent. For this reason, the rules with low failure-risk zone as consequent are dropped.

### 3.4. Constructing the rule-based classifier

The next step is designing the rule-based classifier. This classifier is based on the rules that are identified by NWCSM and WCSM. Each algorithm generates multiple rules. Using only a single rule for constructing the classifier is suboptimal because a lot of information is lost. However, using all the rules is also not useful because it makes the classifier less transparent. Furthermore, some rules may have a high lift score (*lift* is defined as a measure of the prediction performance of an association rule compared to the performance of a random model (see Eq. 2)) but very low support (*support* is defined as the relative frequency that a pattern occurs in a dataset (see Eq. 1)). The latter can result in severe overfitting [20], something that was also observed during the analysis of the results for this research. There are three criteria for determining whether a rule will be used by the classifier or not, i.e. relevance, minimum support, and minimum confidence (*confidence* expresses the reliability of a rule, or how often the antecedent and consequent occur together compared to the total number of times the antecedent appears in the transactions (see Eq. 3)). A rule is considered relevant if it contains at least one item in its antecedent that is related to a generator bearing temperature. An overview of the thresholds for minimum confidence and support can be found in Table 1.

$$\text{support(X)} = \frac{\sharp \text{ transactions containing X}}{\sharp \text{ transactions}} \tag{1}$$

where:

X = A pattern.
$\sharp$ = Count.

$$\text{lift} = \frac{\text{P(X} \wedge \text{Y)}}{\text{P(X)P(Y)}} \tag{2}$$

where:

X = A pattern. In the case of association rules X is the antecedent of the rule.
Y = A pattern. In the case of association rules Y is the consequent of the rule.
P(.) = Probability function.
$\wedge$ = AND.

 IOP Publishing
**2507** (2023) 012001 doi:10.1088/1742-6596/2507/1/012001

| Model | Bearing type | Minimum confidence | Minimum absolute support |
|---|---|---|---|
| WCSM | DE | 0.7 | 10 |
| WCSM | NDE | 0.7 | 5 |
| NWCSM | DE | 0.7 | 30 |
| NWCSM | NDE | 0.7 | 10 |

**Table 1.** Confidence and support thresholds used for postprocessing of the patterns.

$$\text{conf(R)} = \frac{\sharp\ (\text{transaction containing } R_{\text{ante}} \wedge \text{transaction containing } R_{\text{cons}})}{\sharp\ \text{transaction containing } R_{\text{ante}}} \quad (3)$$

where:

R = Association rule.
$\sharp$ = Count.
conf(R) = Confidence of rule R.
$X_{\text{ante}}$ = Antecedent or body of rule R.
$X_{\text{cons}}$ = Consequent or head of rule R.
$\wedge$ = AND.

The rule-based classifier uses multiple rules. This means that it is possible that multiple rules indicate at the same time that an instance (or transaction) is high failure-risk. A good classifier is able to quantify the difference between instances where only a few rules fire, and those where many rules fire. The latter situation should get a higher score than the former since it is more likely that it is really associated with a high failure-risk zone. For this reason, the classifier is designed as a confidence-weighted voter combined with an anomaly threshold. If a rule is found in an entry or transaction of the training or testing dataset, then this rule votes that it is part of a high failure-risk zone. However, not all rules are equal. Some rules have a higher confidence than others. To take this into account, each rule has a number of votes that equals its confidence. This guarantees that the rules with the highest confidence can give the most votes. Once each rule has voted, the sum of the votes is taken (Eq. 4). If the sum is larger than the anomaly threshold, then the instance is classified as a high failure-risk zone.

$$\text{votes}_{\text{hfr}}(X) = \text{conf}(R_1)\ I_{R_{1\text{ante}} \in X} + ... + \text{conf}(R_n)\ I_{R_{n\text{ante}} \in X} \quad (4)$$

where:

$\text{votes}_{\text{hfr}}(X)$ = Sum of votes for high failure-risk zone for entry or transaction X.
$\text{conf}(R_i)$ = Confidence of rule i, with i $\in$ 1,...,n.
$I_{R_{i\text{ante}} \in X}$ = 1 if antecedent of rule i is in transaction X, 0 otherwise, with i $\in$ 1,...,n.

### *3.5. Calculating the anomaly threshold*

The anomaly threshold is determined through a grid search over sensible threshold values on the training dataset. To determine the accuracy of the classifier, a confusion matrix is constructed. This implies that the number of true positives (TP), true negatives (TN), false positives (FP), and false negatives (FN) need to be calculated. However, on real data, this is a non-trivial task. For this reason, a couple of definitions are introduced.

- TP = if at least one entry or transaction in the high failure-risk zone has a sum of votes larger than the anomaly threshold.

- TN = if no entries or transactions in the low failure-risk zone have a sum of votes larger than the threshold.
- FP = if at least one entry or transaction in the low failure-risk zone has a sum of votes larger than the threshold.
- FN = if no entries or transactions in the high failure-risk zone have a sum of votes larger than the threshold.

The anomaly threshold is set to the value that maximizes the accuracy of the rule-based classifier on the training dataset. The accuracy is calculated using Eq. 5. Due to the way that the training dataset is constructed, it contains the same amount of high failure-risk and low failure-risk zones. This means that accuracy measures that can handle unbalanced data are unnecessary.

$$\text{Accuracy} = \frac{\text{TP} + \text{TN}}{\text{TP} + \text{TN} + \text{FP} + \text{FN}} \tag{5}$$

*3.6. Validation*
The methodology is validated on the testing dataset. This is done by using the post-processed rules that were mined on the training dataset. The testing dataset is searched for occurrences of patterns that make up the antecedents of the rules. If an antecedent is found in an entry or transaction of the testing dataset, the rule votes for the high failure-risk category. The number of votes that each rule has corresponds to the confidence of the rule as it was determined on the training dataset. Once the test dataset has been searched, the sum of the votes is calculated using Eq. 4. If the sum is higher than the anomaly threshold that was determined on the training dataset, an anomaly flag is raised. The performance of the methodology is determined using the high failure-risk prediction accuracy of the model on the test dataset. The accuracy is calculated using Eq. 5, which is based on the TP, TN, FP, and FN counts as defined in the previous section.

## 4. Results
The results section consists of two parts. The first part analyses the rules generated by the WCSM and the NWCSM. More specifically, the focus lies on the interpretability of the rules, whether they make sense, and their predictive capabilities. The second part analyzes the prediction accuracy of the rule-based classifier.

*4.1. Results pattern mining*

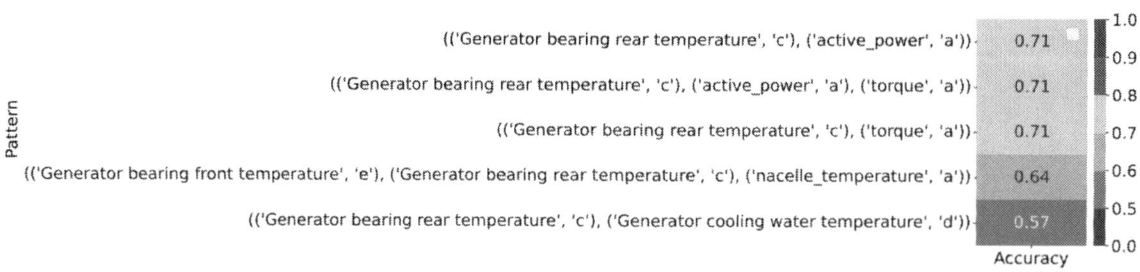


**Figure 6.** WCSM: best rule summary for NDE failures.

The WCSM has been configured to return the 200 rules (with as consequent the high failure-risk zone) with the highest lift. After post-processing, the number of rules is reduced to just

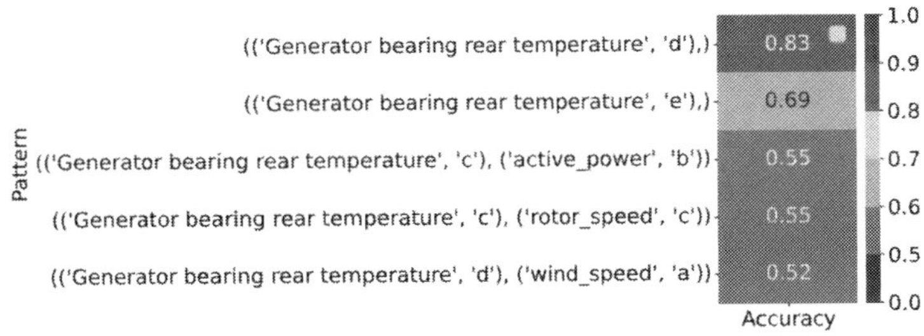


**Figure 7.** WCSM: best rule summary for DE failures.

5 for both the DE and NDE generator bearing failure cases. Figures 6 and 7 show the results for respectively the NDE and DE generator bearing failures on the test dataset. The patterns (which are the bodies of the rules) are relatively short. The most accurate rules for the NDE case achieve an accuracy of 0.71. The rules for the DE case are also explainable from an engineering point of view. The accuracy of the most accurate rule is quite high (0.83).

**Figure 8.** NWCSM: top-20 best rule summary for NDE failures.

Figures 8 and 9 show the results for the post-processed rules identified by the NWCSM. The first thing that can be noted is the fact that these rules are in general longer than those generated by the WCSM. This is due to the fact that the latter algorithm searches for narrow funnel effects, which assumes that the interactions that determine a system are of limited complexity. This results in simpler, but more comprehensible rules. A second thing is the fact that after post-processing more rules from the NWCSM remain (DE: 211 rules, NDE: 44 rules) than is the case for the WCSM (DE: 5 rules, NDE: 5 rules). Apparently, NWCSM generates more rules with high confidence and relatively high support. Figure 8 shows the results for the 20 rules with the best predictive accuracy for the NDE bearing failures. The rules are in general also easily

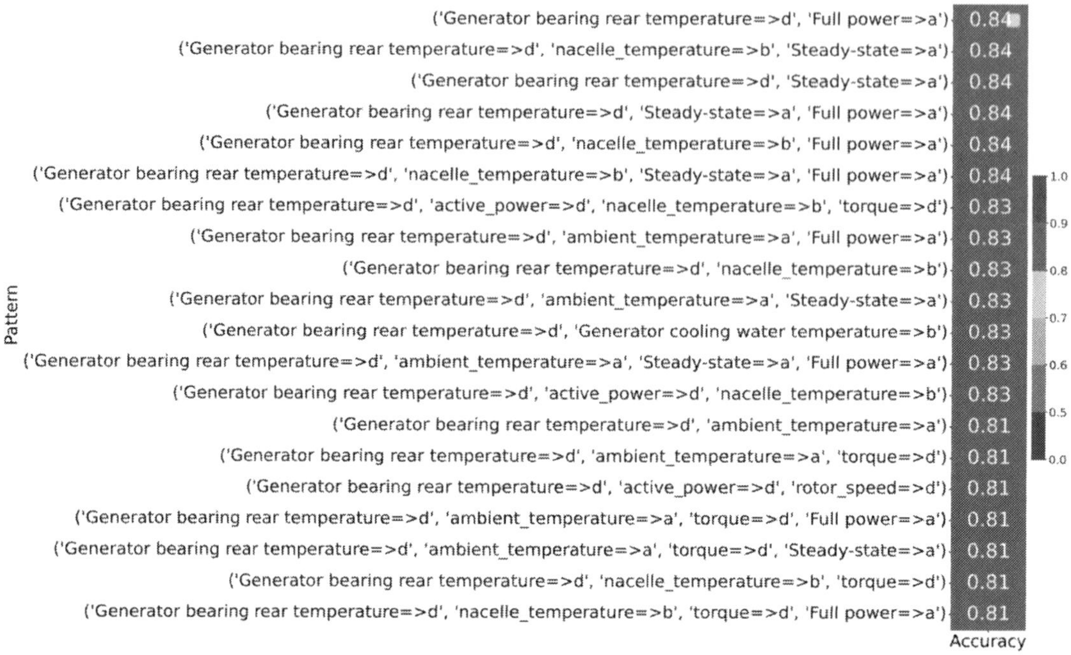


**Figure 9.** NWCSM: top-20 best rule summary for DE failures.

| Model type | Failure type | Training | | | Testing | | |
|---|---|---|---|---|---|---|---|
| | | Accuracy | TPR | TNR | Accuracy | TPR | TNR |
| WCSM | DE | 0.80 | 0.74 | 0.86 | 0.81 | 0.89 | 0.72 |
| WCSM | NDE | 0.77 | 0.83 | 0.71 | 0.79 | 0.57 | 1.00 |
| NWCSM | DE | 0.81 | 0.82 | 0.79 | 0.77 | 0.89 | 0.66 |
| NWCSM | NDE | 0.64 | 1.0 | 0.29 | 0.62 | 0.83 | 0.43 |

**Table 2.** Accuracy, TPR and TNR results for rule-based classifiers based on weighted or non-weighted contrast set mining algorithms for DE and NDE replacements.

interpretable.

### *4.2. Rule-based classifier prediction performance*

The rule-based classifier combines the predictions of the different rules that remain after the post-processing step. The goal is to develop a classifier that is able to predict the generator bearing failures as accurately as possible. Table 2 shows the results for the different classifiers. For the classifier based on the WCSM rules (called further weighted classifier), the accuracy on the DE bearing failures is 0.8. If this is compared to the best rule in Figure 7 then we see that the accuracy is slightly lower. For the classifier based on the rules generated by the NWCSM (called further non-weighted classifier), the accuracy is 0.77. This is substantially higher than the accuracy of the best rule that can be found in Figure 9. The weighted classifier applied to the NDE bearing failures results in an accuracy on the test dataset of 0.79. This is also a substantial improvement over the most accurate rule shown in Figure 6. For the non-weighted classifier the accuracy is only 0.62, which is substantially worse than for the best rules in Figure 8. The results show that in some cases the combination of the different rules by confidence-weighted voting is beneficial compared to using only a single rule. In other cases, it is unfortunately not.

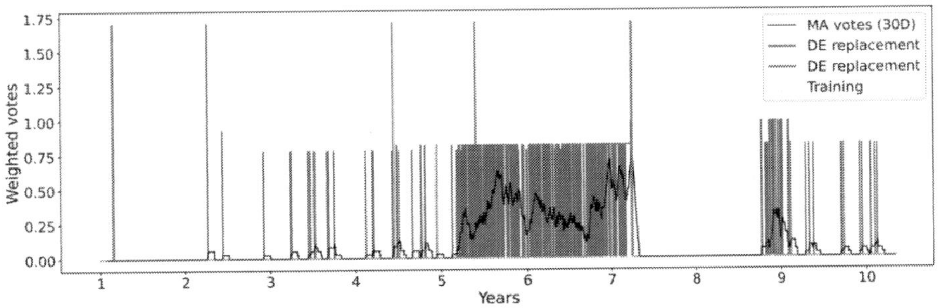


**Figure 10.** WCSM: DE failure prediction.

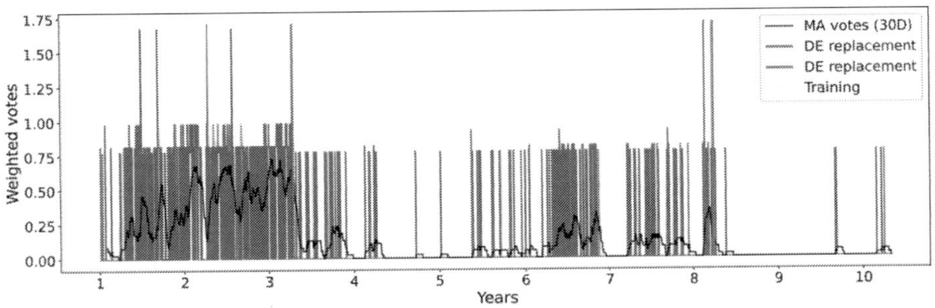


**Figure 11.** WCSM: DE failure prediction.

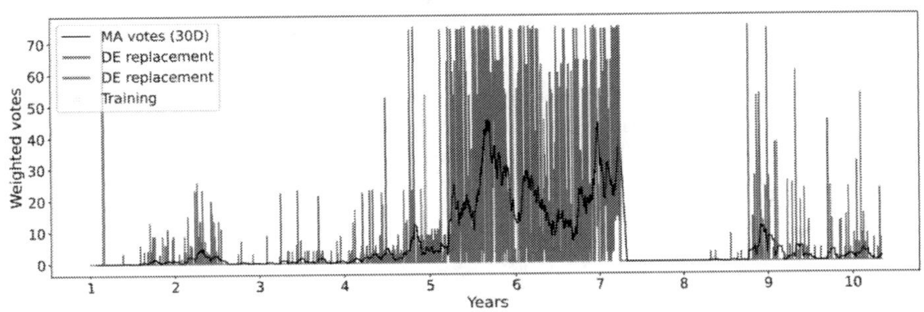


**Figure 12.** NWCSM: DE failure prediction.

Figures 10, and 11 show several DE generator bearing failure identifications. The moving average of the votes clearly increases until just before the failure. After the failure, when the problem has been fixed, the moving average drops back to 0 or close to it. Figures 12 and 13 show some of the detections by the non-weighted classifier. The results are for the same turbines as the ones in Figures 10 and 11. The failure detection pattern is more clear for the non-weighted classifier than for the weighted classifier. For the NDE bearing failures, the results are unfortunately less clear than for the DE bearing failures. This means for example that the increase in the moving average is less pronounced due to only sporadic occurrences of the post-processed rules. The weaker results for the NDE bearing failures can be attributed to several factors. Firstly, the dataset contains relatively few examples of NDE bearing failures

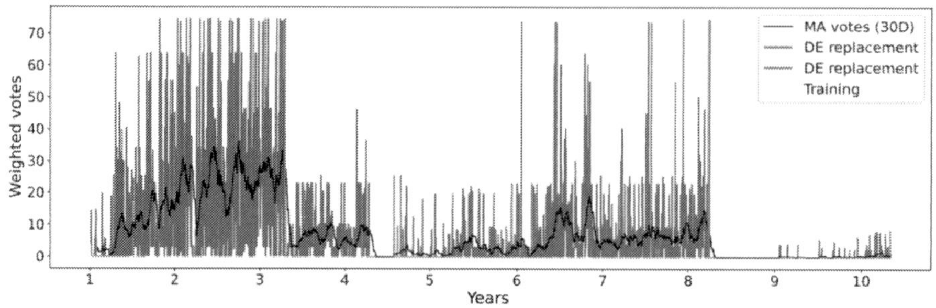


**Figure 13.** NWCSM: DE failure prediction.

that are clearly separated in time from the DE bearing failures. This means that it is more difficult to distinguish the fingerprint of the NDE bearing failures from those of the DE bearing failures. This probably also explains why the rules for the DE and NDE bearing failures look quite similar. Secondly, the number of observations in the training data for the NDE bearing failures is much lower compared to the DE case. Given the quality of the data, it might actually be better to treat the DE and NDE bearing failures together instead of separately.

## 5. Conclusion

The goal of this research is to identify failures in wind turbines using a rule-based classifier. The reason for selecting this methodology is the fact that a rule-based classifier is more easily interpretable by the user. The classifier requires one or more rules. One way to get these rules is to ask experts to formulate them. However, this is not always possible, due to the labor intensity of the effort, or the fact that there is no or very little expert knowledge on the subject. An alternative is to extract the rules in a data-driven way using data mining or machine learning. This is the method that is followed in this research. A specific type of pattern mining algorithm, called contrast set mining, is used to this end. These models have been developed specifically with the purpose to search for the patterns that best explain the difference between two or more groups. This corresponds well to the case that is being solved here. Once the patterns have been extracted, they are filtered, and rules are constructed. The rule-based classifier uses these rules through confidence-weighted voting and an anomaly threshold to predict whether an instance corresponds to a high failure risk or not. For the validation of the methodology, data from a large operational wind farm is used.

The results show that the methodology is able to reliably detect drive-end generator bearing failures. In general, the moving average of the votes shows a clear increasing trend as the bearing failure approaches. Once the problem has been fixed the moving average returns to a much lower level or 0. The results for the non-drive-end bearing failures are however less good. For the weighted classifier, the accuracy is comparable with the accuracy for the drive-end bearing failures. However, for the non-weighted classifier, there is clear performance degradation. The trends in the moving average of the votes are also much less clear. The cause of the performance degradation can be attributed to the characteristics of the data. The added value of a rule-based classifier that uses the weighted sum of the rules versus a classifier that only uses the rule with the highest accuracy is not always clear. In some cases, a clear performance improvement can be seen. However, in other cases, the performance is slightly worse compared to that of the best rule. All things considered, the methodology seems to show potential for anomaly detection and root-cause analysis. Future work will focus on several aspects of the methodology, e.g. the setting of certain design parameters, the construction of the rule-based classifier, the setting of the alarm threshold, ....

**Acknowledgements**
Xavier Chesterman, Timothy Verstraeten, Pieter-Jan Daems, Ann Nowé, and Jan Helsen received funding from the Flemish Government (AI Research Program). The research presented in this paper is partly financed by the European Union (H2020 PLATOON, Pr. No: 872592). The authors would also like to acknowledge FWO for the support through the SBO Robustify project (S006119N), and VLAIO ICON project Supersized 4.0.

## References

[1] Lee J and Zhao F 2022 *Global wind report 2022* (Global Wind Energy Council GWEC) 155
[2] Pfaffel S, Faulstich S and Rohrig K 2017 Performance and reliability of wind turbines. A review. *Energies* **10** 1904
[3] Verstraeten T, Nowé A, Keller J, Guo Y, Sheng S and Helsen J 2019 Fleetwide data-enabled reliability improvement of wind turbines. *Renew. Sust. Energ.* **109** 428-37
[4] Tazi N, Châtelet E and Bouzidi Y 2017 Wear analysis of wind turbine bearings. *Int. J. Renew. Energy Res.* **7(4)** 2120-9
[5] IEC 2022 Part 12-1: Power performance measurements of electricity producing wind turbines *Wind energy generation systems*
[6] IEC 2022 Wind turbines - Part 4: Design requirements for wind turbine gearboxes *Wind energy generation systems*
[7] Gan W, Chen L, Chen C 2021 Anomaly rule detection in sequence data, *arXiv:2111.15026* 1-14
[8] Feremans L, Vercruyssen V, Cule B and Meert W 2020 Pattern-based anomaly detection in mixed-type time series. *ECML PKDD* **11906** 240-56
[9] Rahman A, Xu Y, Radke K and Foo E 2016 Finding anomalies in SCADA logs using rare sequential pattern mining. *Netw. Syst. Secur.* 1-9
[10] Sweetlin C, Vaidehi V and Lakshmi R 2015 Minimal infrequent pattern based approach for mining outliers in data streams. *Expert Syst. Appl.* **42(4)** 1998-2012
[11] Menzies R and Hu Y 2006 Just enough learning (of association rules): the TAR2 "treatment" learner. *Artif. Intell. Rev.* **25** 211-29
[12] Bay S and Pazzani M 1999 Detecting change in categorical data: mining contrast sets. *KDD '99: Proceedings of the Fifth ACM SIGKDD* 302-6
[13] Hu Y 2003 *Treatment learning: implementation and application.* (The University of British Columbia)
[14] Gundy-Burlet K, Schumann J, Menzies T and Barrett A 2008 Parametric analysis of ANTARES re-entry guidance algorithm using advanced test generation and data analysis. *ISAIRAS 2008* 1-8
[15] Gay G, Menzies T, Davies M and Gundy-Burlet K 2010 Automatically finding the control variables for complex system behavior. *Autom. Softw. Eng.* **17** 439–68
[16] Bay S and Pazzani M 2001 Detecting group differences: mining contrast sets. *Data Min. Knowl. Discov.* **5** 213-46
[17] Chesterman X, Verstraeten T, Daems P-J, Nowé A, and Helsen J 2023 Overview of normal behavior modeling approaches for SCADA-based wind turbine condition monitoring demonstrated on data from operational wind farms *Wind Energ. Sci. discussions (Preprint)* 1-41
[18] Chesterman X, Verstraeten T, Daems P-J, Nowé A and Helsen J 2021 Condition monitoring of wind turbines and extraction of healthy training data using an ensemble of advanced statistical anomaly detection models. *PHM_CONF* **13(1)** 1-10
[19] Lin J, Keogh E, Wei L and Lonardi S 2007 Experiencing SAX: a novel symbolic representation of time series. *Data Min. Knowl. Discov.* **15** 107-44
[20] Cheng H, Yan X, Han J and Hsu C-W 2007 Discriminative frequent pattern analysis for effective classification. *2007 IEEE 23rd Int. Conf. Data Eng.* 716-25

# A use-case-driven approach for demonstrating the added value of digitalisation in wind energy

**S Barber[1], A M Sempreviva[2], S Sheng[3], D Farren[4] and D Zappalá[5]**

[1]Institute for Energy Technology, OST - Eastern Switzerland University of Applied Sciences, Oberseestrasse 10, CH-8640 Rapperswil.

[2]Technical University of Denmark - Department of Wind Energy and Energy Systems, Denmark.

[3]National Wind Technology Center (NWTC), National Renewable Energy Laboratory (NREL), Golden, USA.

[4]ServusNet Analytics, Cork, Ireland.

[5]TU Delft - Delft University of Technology, Delft, Netherlands.

E-mail: sarah.barber@ost.ch

**Abstract.** Digitalisation is one of the key drivers for reducing the costs and risks of wind energy. When considering whether to embark on a digitalisation initiative, two key questions arise. The first is what business or operational opportunities might feasibly be addressed and the second is which of the many potential aspects of digitalisation are relevant to those opportunities. In this work, we show how these questions can be answered with a use-case-driven approach, based around a survey aiming to collect and collate the main "pain points" (or everyday challenges) of people in the wind energy sector. Although the relatively low number of participants of the survey (46) means that the results should only be used indicatively, it is still possible to make some general recommendations for priorities for digitalisation efforts in the wind energy sector. Firstly, digitalisation efforts should focus both on supporting people carrying out cross-lifecycle tasks, in particular sharing data, managing data, undertaking general data analyses and accessing data. Tools to do this should deal with varying data formats and naming conventions, make metadata more accessible, define data and metadata standards, make more data publicly available and improve the quality of data. Secondly, efforts should also focus on supporting people in the wind farm operational phase, in particular with failure detection, fault diagnosis, failure rate modelling and predictive maintenance. Solutions to do this should focus on accessible and validated tools for fault detection, cloud or other data pipeline solutions for SCADA data and tools for exhaustive data documentation. Finally, digitalisation efforts should focus on better communicating and helping people become aware of existing solutions and tools, as well as on helping people to exert a stronger influence on possible solutions.

## 1. Introduction

Digitalisation, defined as "the organisational and industry-wide use of data and digital technologies to improve efficiency, create insights, and develop products and services" [1] is one of the key drivers for reducing costs and risks of wind energy due to the opportunities it offers [2]. These opportunities include new processes and business models resulting from large amounts of data becoming available at different phases of the wind energy project life cycle, and include digital twins, predictive maintenance, drones and decision support systems. These can all contribute to reducing maintenance costs, increasing energy production and increasing efficiency.

However, a number of challenges stand in the way of a successful exploitation of these opportunities. The three "Grand Challenges" of wind energy digitalisation have recently been defined in [1] as: (1) Creating findable, accessible, interoperable and reusable (FAIR) data frameworks [3]; (2) Connecting people and data to foster innovation; (3) Enabling collaboration and competition between organisations. IEA Wind Task 43 [4] aims to solve these challenges by developing solutions and recommendations for the adoption of digital technologies such as data standards, machine learning and Artifical Intelligence (AI), data analytics and visualisation, open-source tools and Internet of Things (IoT) instrumentation.

When considering whether to embark on a digitalisation initiative, two key questions arise. The first is what business or operational opportunities might feasibly be addressed and the second is which of the many potential aspects of digitalisation are relevant to those opportunities. It is not possible to prescribe an approach to every potential scenario, but a set of well-defined value-adding use cases, key inhibitors (or "pain points") and potential solutions to those inhibitors can provide a starting point upon which to build a business case. It is with this purpose in mind that IEA Wind Task 43 set out to research and map representative use cases, pain points and typical solutions. In addition to exploring these relationships, teams within IEA Wind Task 43 are also exploring specific use cases in further detail to identify the tangible benefits, data requirements and relevant analytics or modelling methods [5].

In this paper, we therefore present a use-case-driven approach for demonstrating the added value of digitalisation in wind energy, developed within IEA Wind Task 43. We define a "digitalisation use case" as "an activity that an organisation or consortium carries out - and the steps as part of this - in order to generate value/save costs/make decisions, to which digital solutions can be applied to improve it.". As well as demonstrating the value of digitalisation to the industry, this approach has the potential to compare reference methodologies, quantify the range of data types required for certain tasks, highlight implementation challenges and frame opportunities around key decisions. In Section 2 we introduce the approach, in Section 3 we present the results, in Section 4 a discussion of the resulting recommended priorities for digitalisation efforts for the wind energy sector as well as an evaluation of the approach. In Section 5 we draw the conclusions.

## 2. Approach

This work was carried out using a simplified version of the approach applied for identifying the "Grand Challenges in the digitalisation of wind energy" [1], shown in Figure 1. The approach was simplified and applied as follows:

(a) Exploit databases: we defined an initial list of "use cases" by carrying out a literature review and collecting inputs from IEA Wind Task 43 participants via brainstorming sessions. We focused on defining value-creating processes that we think are important in the wind energy sector today.

(b) Analysis: we analysed which existing digital solutions (from and beyond IEA Wind Task 43) could be used to add value to the processes from (a). The results showed that more information was required in order to prioritise which of the processes provide the most value and which have the highest potential to be improved by digital solutions. This was achieved in part (c).

(c) Enrichment: Instead of carrying out individual interviews, we opted for a survey in order to get a larger range of inputs from the sector. The aim of the survey was to collect and collate the main "pain points" of people in the wind energy sector, where "pain point" was defined as "anything that poses you with challenges, difficulties, problems, or even emotional pain", i.e. something that really frustrates people and gets in the way of reaching their goals or carrying out their tasks.

(d) Use cases: The results of the initial table and the survey from parts (a)-(c) were used to define a set of priorities for digitalisation efforts for the wind energy sector.

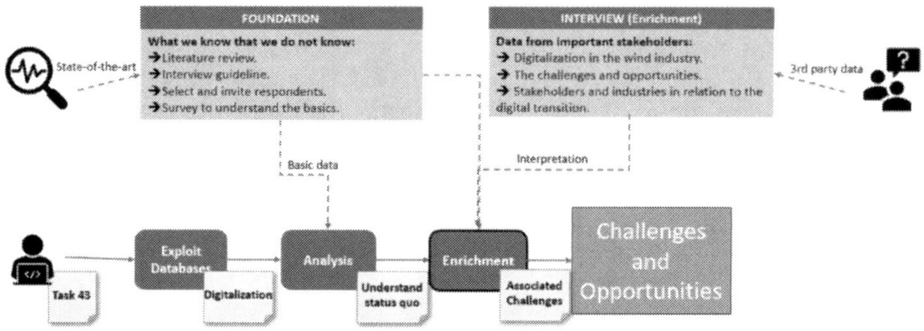


**Figure 1.** The data collection, processing and analysis approach applied for identifying the Grand Challenges in the digitalisation of wind energy [1].

## 3. Results

In this section, the results of the four steps of the approach described in Section 2 above are presented.

### *3.1. Exploit databases*

An excerpt from the table resulting from the first step "(a) Exploit databases" is shown in Table 1. The full table can be accessed in [6], and contains a total of 33 use cases. The first three columns of the table summarise the potential challenges people in the wind energy sector are facing for different wind energy project lifecycle phases, and what the related "use case" is according to the definition from Section 1. The fourth column is discussed below. We divided the use cases into the following wind project lifecycle phases:

A. Wind turbine design
B. Wind farm planning
C. Wind farm operation
D. Project selling / buying
E. End of life
F. General

The "general" category was defined for activities that cannot be assigned to a particular lifecycle phase, such as recruiting, project acquisition and data sharing.

### *3.2. Analysis*

An excerpt of the results of the phase "(b) Analysis" is shown in the right-hand column of Table 1. For each "use case", we assess which digital solutions (from and beyond IEA Wind Task 43) could be used to add value. The possible digital solutions were established by first creating a list of the activities and outputs of IEA Wind Task 43 and then combining this with the knowledge and experience of the IEA Wind Task 43 participants in other areas such as Digital Twins and Decision Support Systems.

**Table 1.** Excerpt from initial list of use cases [6].

| Lifecycle phase | Challenges people in the wind energy industry are facing | What's the "use case"? (the task that someone is doing) | How could digital solutions contribute to solving this? |
|---|---|---|---|
| A. Wind turbine design | Improving aerodynamic design tools (engineering models) for +10MW wind turbines | Designing +10 MW wind turbines | IoT monitoring systems, recommendations for data sharing |
| B. Wind farm planning | Efficiently comparing different scenarios and choosing the best project layout | Holistic wind farm layout planning | Digital WRA tools |
| C. Wind farm operation | Choice of predictive models with optimal balance of complexity and scalability for specific decisions | Model choice - operation | Decision Support Systems |
| D. Project selling / buying | Evaluating asset performance, maintenance and financial data to determine potential insurance risk | Asset risk assessment | Decision Support Systems |
| E. End of life | Deciding what to do at the end of life | Design standards | Digital logistics tools |
| F. General | Finding customers and project partners | Project acquisition | Digital matchmaking tools or data marketplaces |

### *3.3. Enrichment*

*3.3.1. Survey* The results of parts (a) and (b) showed that there are a large number of tasks and processes with a high potential to be improved through digitalisation, even though it was recognised that the list was not yet complete. However, it was not possible for a small group of IEA Wind Task 43 participants to fully understand and prioritise the most important "use cases" in the entire industry, and therefore a survey was designed and shared with people working in the wind energy sector across the entire value chain. The main question asked in the survey was "Describe a "pain point" in your everyday work and the related task (which can be either carried out by you or your team)". The survey allowed each participant to enter up to three "pain points". As well as this, for the "pain points" that were described, the survey asked "Do you have any ideas for how digital tools might be used to reduce or relieve the pain?" The results are described in the next four sections: first the general results, followed by more details of the two most important lifecycle phases, and then finally an analysis of the ideas for "pain relief".

*3.3.2. General results* A total of 46 people took part in the survey, with a total of 55 pain points being described. As shown in Figure 2, of these 46 people, five self-identified as only data scientists, 18 as only domain scientists, none as only data stewards (as defined in [7]), 12 as domain scientists and data scientists, and five as domain scientists and data scientists and data stewards. As shown in Figure 3, of these 46 people, five are involved only in wind farm planning, seven only in wind farm operation, two only in wind turbine design, eight in multiple lifecycle phases and 24 in R&D (21 of which work in multiple lifecycle phases). Due to the relatively small number of participants compared to the size of the entire sector (approximately 1.4 million people [8]), the results need to be treated with care and should be used indicitavely rather than quantitatively.

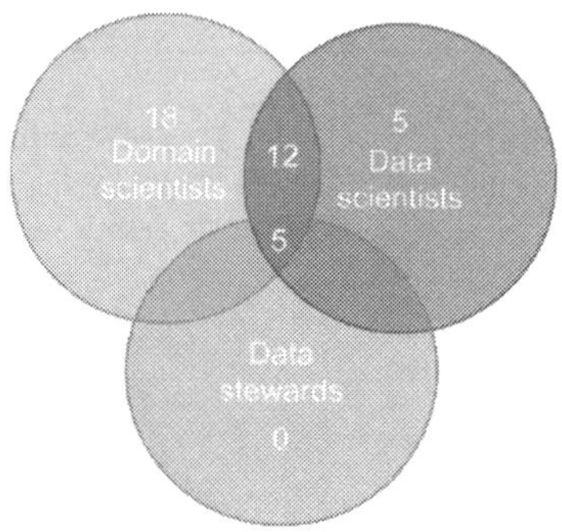


**Figure 2.** Summary of type of survey participants (domain scientists, data scientists and data stewards).

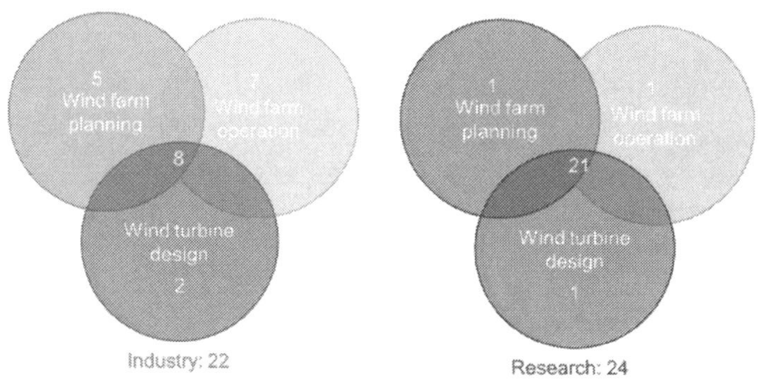


**Figure 3.** Summary of type of survey participants (industry and academia).

In order to analyse the large amount of data obtained, the pain points and use cases were mapped to each other in a manual process. During this process, additional use cases were created for activities that the respondents referred to but were not yet included in the existing table from phase "(a) Enrichment". This extended the list from 33 to 50 use cases, as can be seen in [6]. Some additional use cases that came up include choosing the best wake model for a given application, predictive design and operation, project acquisition and managing data. The full list of use cases that came up in the survey is given in Appendix A. The full list of pain points is given in Appendix B.

The total number of pain points for each use case is summarised in Figure 4. This highlights which use cases were associated with pain points most frequently, with the pain points grouped into the relevant lifecycle phase. Table 2 summarises the number of pain points per lifecycle phase, showing that most of the pain points were associated with the operational phase and with general tasks. These numbers need to be interpreted with care, because the total number of respondents was certainly not representative of the entire sector. However, there was no strong bias of participants towards the wind farm operational phase, and therefore it is possible to conclude that the wind farm operational phase seems to be associated with a particularly large number of pain points. The domination of the general pain points could be a result of the large number of respondents carrying out tasks across all lifecycle phases (nearly all of the academic respondents and approximately one third of the industry respondents). The completely missing (or almost completely missing) lifecycle phases "wind turbine design", "project selling / buying" and "end of life" indicate the lack of respondents dedicated to these phases. Future surveys should ensure a better distribution across all phases. Due to these results, the wind farm operation and the general use cases are examined in more detail below. Further analysis of all the results is underway but is beyond the scope of this paper.

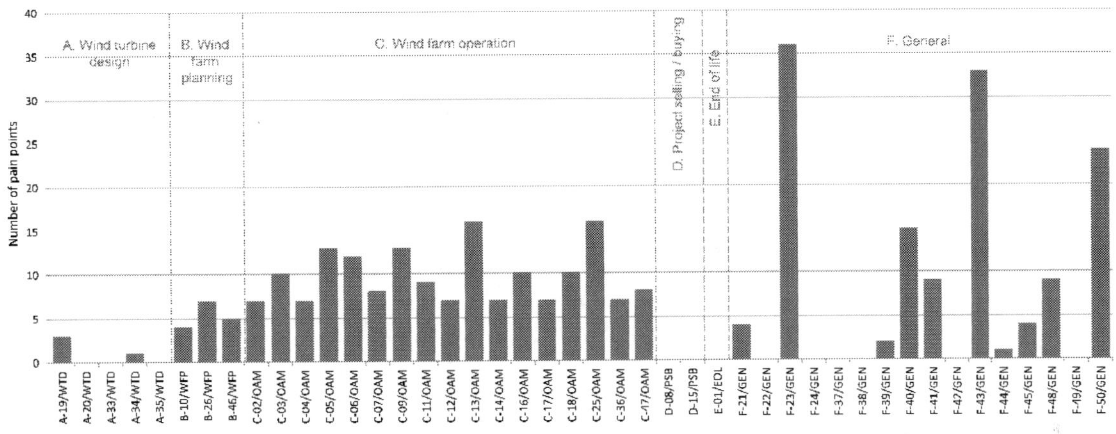


**Figure 4.** Mapping of pain points to use cases.

**Table 2.** Number of pain points per lifecycle phase

| Lifecycle phase | Number of pain points |
|---|---|
| Wind turbine design | 2 |
| Wind farm planning | 16 |
| Wind farm operation | 167 |
| Project selling / buying | 0 |
| End of life | 0 |
| General | 139 |

*3.3.3. General use cases* Within this category, the four use cases with the most number of pain points associated with them are "F-23/GEN: Sharing data" with 37 pain points, "F-43/GEN:

Managing data" with 33 pain points, "F-50/GEN: General data analysis" with 24 pain points and "F-40/GEN: Accessing data" with 17 pain points. This indicates that these four use cases should be the main focus of future digitalisation efforts. For these four use cases, the specific pain points and their frequencies are summarised in Figure 5.

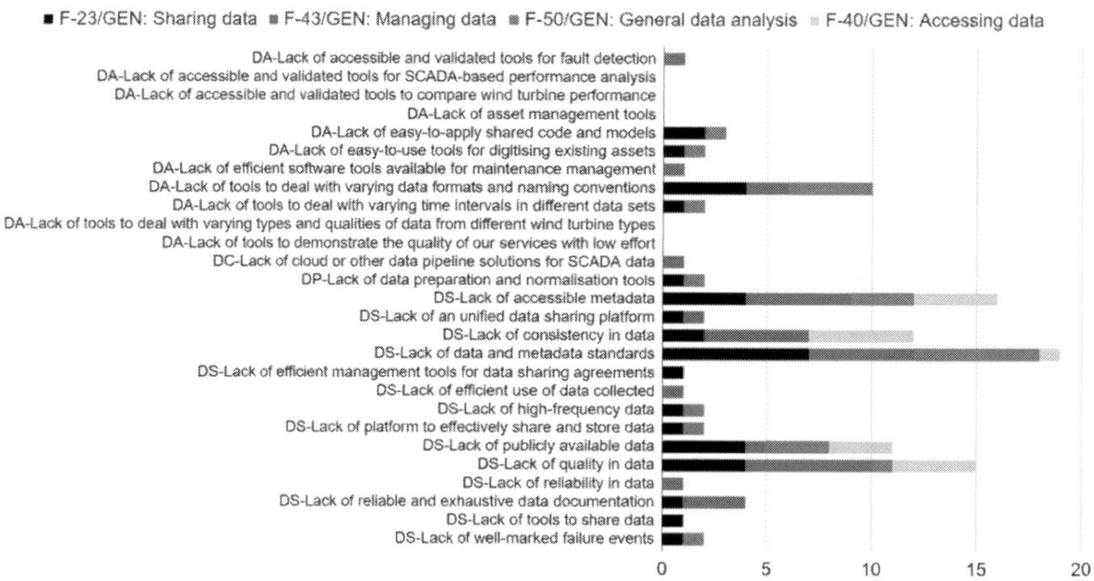


**Figure 5.** Mapping of pain points to use cases for the top four "general" use cases.

This shows that the dominating pain points in this category are the lack of tools to deal with varying data formats and naming conventions, a lack of accessible metadata, a lack of data and metadata standards, a lack of publicly available data and a lack of quality in data. These topics broadly agree with previous surveys carried out in IEA Wind Task 43 [1], and at the same time indicate that solutions for these problems should focus on the general use cases "F-23/GEN: Sharing data", "F-43/GEN: Managing data", "F-50/GEN: General data analysis" and "F-40/GEN: Accessing data".

*3.3.4. Wind farm operation use cases* The four use cases with the most number of pain points associated with them are "C-25/OAM: Failure detection" with 16 pain points, "C-13/OAM: Fault diagnosis" with 16 pain points, "C-09/OAM: Failure rate modelling" with 13 pain points and "C-05/OAM: predictive maintenance" with 13 pain points. This indicates that these four use cases should be the main focus of future digitalisation efforts. For these four use cases, the specific pain points and their frequencies are summarised in Figure 6.

This shows firstly that the top four use cases were mapped to the same pain points. This probably happened because the four use cases are very similar (they are all related to failure detection), and the inputs of the respondents were not detailed enough for differences between these four cases to be made in the analysis. To avoid this in the future, the survey needs to more clearly differentiate between exactly what is meant by a use case (an activity that someone is carrying out to bring value) and a pain point (anything that poses you with challenges, difficulties, problems, or even emotional pain).

As well as this, it can be seen that the dominating pain points in this category are a lack of accessible and validated tools for fault detection, a lack of cloud or other data pipeline solutions

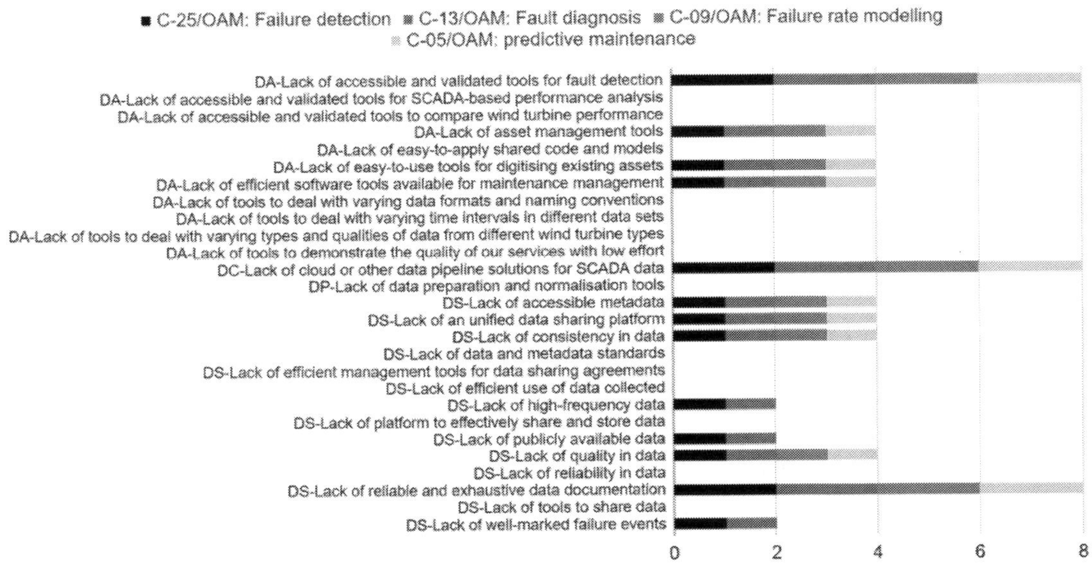


**Figure 6.** Mapping of pain points to use cases for the top four "operation" use cases.

for SCADA data and a lack of reliable and exhaustive data documentation. This is interesting, because it highlights particular needs of wind farm operators. These three topics should be focused on by future efforts to advance digitalisation in wind energy.

*3.3.5. Possible "pain relievers"* With multiple pain points per respondent, and multiple solutions per pain point, there were a total of 63 responses to the question "Do you have any ideas for how digital tools might be used to reduce or relieve the pain?". These were categorised according to the type of solution suggested, and the resulting profile is shown in Figure 7. It is interesting that the most common response is "None" (occurring 19 times), showing that many respondents did not have any ideas for solutions to relieve their pain points. This indicates that a priority for the future is to better communicate and help people become aware of existing solutions and tools.

Other frequent responses include suggestions related to data standards (10 occurrences), enhancing metadata (10 occurrences) and data sharing tools (6 occurrences). This corresponds well with the main pain points discussed in the previous two sections, many of which were related to data formats, metadata and data sharing. In the category "data standards", the suggestions included "Standardisation of data streams and data models, extending to information about the source of the data and expected inaccuracies or behaviour", "Further standardisation", "Getting OEMs and owner/operators to follow standards and best practices", "Data standardisation or automated data formatting tools", "Standard data formats", "Standardisation of data collection and reporting". In the category "enhancing metadata", the suggestions included "Knowledge base describing datasets", "Comprehensive metadata and schemas", "Standardised data and metadata", "Enhanced data and metadata", "Better metadata", "Data schema identifying data sources", "Enhanced metadata". In the category "data sharing tools", the suggestions including "Data sharing platform", "Accessible repositories for energy market data", "Tools to analyse energy market data", "Data exchange tools", "Data sharing framework". These responses indicate a high need for data standards, enhanced metadata and data sharing tools, but a low level of detail regarding which topics should be prioritised and, more importantly, how - and by whom - these data standards should be developed and enforced. In total, there are 44 suggested solutions, corresponding to 70% of the responses, indicating that while respondents have some ideas to alleviate pain points, they are not in a position to influence the solutions. Addressing this problem should be one of the priorities of future digitalisation efforts.

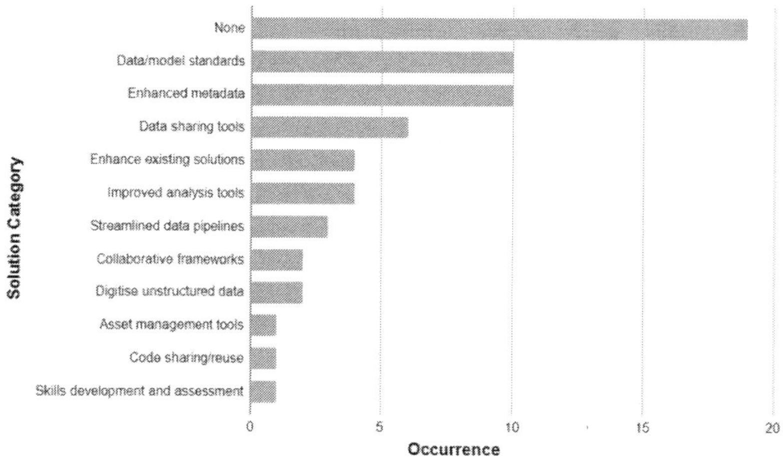


**Figure 7.** Categorisation of solutions suggested in the survey.

## 4. Discussion

In this section, the recommended priorities for future digitalisation efforts that could be defined in this work are introduced, followed by an evaluation of the use-case-driven approach.

### *4.1. Recommended priorities*

The results of this work have allowed some priorities for digitalisation efforts for the wind energy sector to be recommended, as summarised below.

Firstly, digitalisation efforts should focus both on supporting people in the wind energy sector carrying out cross-lifecycle tasks, in particular sharing data, managing data, undertaking general data analyses and accessing data. Tools to do this should focus on dealing with varying data formats and naming conventions, making metadata more accessible, defining data and metadata standards, making more data publicly available and improving the quality of data.

Secondly, digitalisation efforts should also focus on supporting people in the wind farm operational phase, in particular carrying out failure detection, fault diagnosis, failure rate modelling and predictive maintenance. Solutions to do this should focus on accessible and validated tools for fault detection, cloud or other data pipeline solutions for SCADA data and tools for exhaustive data documentation.

Thirdly, digitalisation efforts should focus on better communicating and helping people become aware of existing solutions and tools, as well as on helping people to exert a stronger influence on possible solutions. This could be realised through strengthening the dissemination and education activities of IEA Wind Task 43.

Further analysis is beyond the scope of this paper. However, the survey will be used in the future to develop further recommendations for the other lifecycle phases. Additional surveys will be carried out by focusing the questions for people from specific lifecycle phases. These surveys will more clearly differentiate between exactly what is meant by a use case and a pain point, in order to allow for a more detailed description of use cases for each pain point.

### 4.2. Evaluation of use-case-driven approach

The use-case-driven approach developed in this work has proven to be valuable in a number of different ways. The main value is related to the survey, which has allowed "use cases" to be mapped with "pain points" effectively, thereby making a prioritisation of future digitalisation efforts possible. The survey also allowed the state of knowledge of the respondents to be assessed, and recommendations for improving this in the future to be defined. As well as this, the approach of dividing the responses into different lifecycle phases was useful, and could be applied in future analyses on the topic of digitalisation. However, the study was limited by the fairly low number of survey participants, and the results should be treated with care. Further work to obtain more inputs is underway as part of IEA Wind Task 43.

## 5. Conclusions

In this work, we presented a use-case-driven approach for demonstrating the added value of digitalisation in wind energy, developed within IEA Wind Task 43. The approach involved firstly defining an initial list of use cases by carrying out a literature review and collecting inputs from IEA Wind Task 43 participants via brainstorming sessions, and then analysing which existing digital solutions could be used to add value to these use cases. The results showed that more information was required in order to prioritise which of the use cases provide the most value and which have the highest potential to be improved by digital solutions. This was achieved by implementing a survey aiming to collect and collate the main "pain points" of people in the wind energy sector, where "pain point" was defined as "anything that poses you with challenges, difficulties, problems, or even emotional pain", i.e. something that really frustrates people and gets in the way of reaching their goals or carrying out their tasks. The results were used to define a set of priorities for digitalisation efforts for the wind energy sector. The main value brought to the sector through this approach was the survey design, which has allowed "use cases" to be mapped with "pain points" effectively, thereby making a prioritisation of future digitalisation efforts possible. The survey also allowed the state of knowledge of the respondents to be assessed, and recommendations for improving this in the future to be defined. The survey will be used in the future to develop further recommendations for the other lifecycle phases. Additional surveys will be carried out by focusing the questions for people from specific lifecycle phases.

## References

[1] Clifton A, Barber S, Bray A, Enevoldsen P, Fields J, Sempreviva A M, Williams L, Quick J, Purdue M, Totaro P and Ding Y 2022 *Wind Energy Science* **In Review**

[2] WindEurope Wind energy digitalisation towards 2030 `https://windeurope.org/intelligence-platform/product/wind-energy-digitalisation-towards-2030/` accessed: 2022-09-28

[3] Wilkinson M, Dumontier M, Aalbersberg I and et al 2016 *Sci Data* **3** URL `https://doi.org/10.1038/sdata.2016.18`

[4] IEA Wind Task 43 website `https://www.ieawindtask43.org/` accessed: 2023-02-22

[5] IEA Wind Task 43 Risk-Based Maintenance Use Case `https://vimeo.com/721607313/4b44f1a5ab` accessed: 2023-03-03

[6] Barber S, Sempreviva A M, Sheng S, Farren D and Zappalá D 2023 A use-case-driven approach for demonstrating the added value of digitalisation in wind energy - extended version of Table 1 URL `https://doi.org/10.5281/zenodo.7716476`

[7] Teperek M, Cruz M J, Verbakel E, Böhmer J K and Dunning A 2018 Data stewardship – addressing disciplinary data management needs URL `osf.io/mjk9t`

[8] IRENA and ILO Renewable energy and jobs: Annual review 2022 `https://www.irena.org/publications/2022/Sep/Renewable-Energy-and-Jobs-Annual-Review-2022` accessed: 2023-02-22

## Appendix A. Inventory of Use Cases

| Lifecycle Stage | Unique ID | Use Case |
|---|---|---|
| Wind turbine design | A-19/WTD | Benchmarking simulation tools |
| | A-20/WTD | Root Cause Analysis |
| | A-33/WTD | Design tools |
| | A-34/WTD | Designing large wind turbines |
| | A-35/WTD | Designing for site-specific conditions |
| Wind farm planning | B-10/WFP | Design for reliability |
| | B-26/WFP | Wind resource assessment |
| | B-46/WFP | Wake modelling |
| Wind farm operation | C-02/OAM | Energy Market Participation |
| | C-03/OAM | AEP Assessment |
| | C-04/OAM | Turbine Parameter Optimisation |
| | C-05/OAM | Predictive Maintenance (of gear boxes) |
| | C-06/OAM | Risk-Based maintenance |
| | C-07/OAM | Evaluate Potential Turbine Performance Enhancements |
| | C-09/OAM | Failure Rate Modelling |
| | C-11/OAM | Curtailment management |
| | C-12/OAM | Digital Twin(s) |
| | C-13/OAM | Fault Diagnosis |
| | C-14/OAM | Performance Assessment with External Parties |
| | C-16/OAM | Performance Benchmarking |
| | C-17/OAM | Availability Benchmarking |
| | C-18/OAM | Detecting under-performance |
| | C-25/OAM | Failure detection |
| | C-36/OAM | Predictive design and operation |
| | C-47/OAM | Reliability based forecasting |
| Project selling/buying | D-08/PSB | Asset Risk Assessment |
| | D-15/PSB | Asset Valuation |
| End of life | E-01/EOL | End-of-life decision |
| General | F-21/GEN | Project acquisition |
| | F-22/GEN | Recruiting |
| | F-23/GEN | Sharing data |
| | F-24/GEN | Finding metadata |
| | F-37/GEN | Increasing the diversity of the workforce |
| | F-38/GEN | Making sure the workforce has the right skills needed today |
| | F-39/GEN | Making sure research gets transferred to the industry effectively |
| | F-40/GEN | Accessing data |
| | F-41/GEN | Validating models |
| | F-42/GEN | Accessing published methods |
| | F-43/GEN | Managing data |
| | F-44/GEN | Code and Model Sharing/Reuse |
| | F-45/GEN | General admin tasks |
| | F-48/GEN | Homogenization and digitalisation of data from existing assets |
| | F-49/GEN | Standard data formats, data streams and models |
| | F-50/GEN | General data analysis |

## Appendix B. Pain Points by Category

| Category | Pain Point |
|---|---|
| Data Analysis | Lack of accessible and validated tools for fault detection<br>Lack of accessible and validated tools for SCADA-based performance analysis<br>Lack of accessible and validated tools to compare wind turbine performance<br>Lack of asset management tools<br>Lack of easy-to-apply shared code and models<br>Lack of easy-to-use tools for digitising existing assets<br>Lack of efficient software tools available for maintenance management<br>Lack of tools to deal with varying data formats and naming conventions<br>Lack of tools to deal with varying time intervals in different data sets<br>Lack of tools to deal with varying types and qualities of data from different wind turbine types<br>Lack of tools to demonstrate the quality of our services with low effort |
| Data Collection | Lack of cloud or other data pipeline solutions for SCADA data |
| Data Preparation | Lack of data preparation and normalisation tools |
| Data Sharing | Lack of accessible metadata<br>Lack of an unified data sharing platform<br>Lack of consistency in data<br>Lack of data and metadata standards<br>Lack of efficient management tools for data sharing agreements<br>Lack of efficient use of data collected (?)<br>Lack of high-frequency data<br>Lack of platform to effectively share and store data<br>Lack of publicly available data<br>Lack of quality in data<br>Lack of reliability in data<br>Lack of reliable and exhaustive data documentation<br>Lack of tools to share data<br>Lack of well-marked failure events |
| Mindset | Lack of willingness to share data |
| Resources | Lack of easy-to-use recruiting tools<br>Lack of efficient paperwork management<br>Lack of good funding opportunities<br>Lack of good people<br>Lack of prioritisation of technical work and more emphasis on general administration<br>Lack of time to write proposals |

# Can data sharing really provide added value? Practical data sharing recommendations for the wind energy sector

**S Barber[1], F Hammer[1], C Henderson[2]**

[1]Institute for Energy Technology, OST - Eastern Switzerland University of Applied Sciences, Oberseestrasse 10, CH-8640 Rapperswil.
[2]Stacker Group, Charlottesville, Virginia, USA.

E-mail: `sarah.barber@ost.ch`

**Abstract.** The digital era offers many opportunities to the wind energy industry and research community and digitalisation is one of the key drivers for reducing project costs and risks. The WeDoWind framework has been developed in order to address one of the main challenges to a successful exploitation of digitalisation in wind energy - data sharing and collaboration. The main innovation of this framework is the way it creates tangible incentives to motivate different types of people to actually share data and knowledge in practice. In this work, we carry out a detailed analysis of the strengths and weaknesses of the WeDoWind framework based on a survey filled out by participants of two use case studies and observations from the WeDoWind development team. The results show that the framework successfully enhances collaboration and data sharing in the sector. The results allowed a set of practical data sharing recommendations for the wind energy sector to be developed, which are being continuously improved based on our experience with the WeDoWind framework. They can be applied by anyone wishing to share data effectively and efficiently.

## 1. Introduction

The digital era offers many opportunities to the wind energy industry and research community and digitalisation is one of the key drivers for reducing project costs and risks [1]. The opportunities arise through new processes and business models brought about by the availability of large amounts of data. These can include drones, predictive maintenance, digital twins expert systems. A successful exploitation of these opportunities raises a number of challenges, which were recently examined in [2]. The resulting three "Grand Challenges" of wind energy digitalisation were defined as: (1) Creating findable, accessible, interoperable and reusable (FAIR) data frameworks [3]; (2) Connecting people and data to foster innovation; (3) Enabling collaboration and competition between organisations. A recent literature review of previous work related to these challenges by the present authors showed many existing efforts (e.g. [4], [5], [6]), but that there is a large research gap related to the second two challenges, and in particular with the humanistic aspects of digitalisation [7]. These could include, for example, methods for changing organisational culture and techniques for incentivising people to collaborate with each other in practice, particularly between organisations, e.g. [8], [9], [10], [11], [12], [13].

Based on the results of the above-mentioned literature review, a new framework for enhancing data sharing and collaboration in the wind energy sector, called the WeDoWind framework, has recently been developed and tested on a case study by the present authors [7]. The main innovation of this framework is the way it creates tangible incentives to motivate different types of people to actually share data and knowledge in practice. The value creation process involved is shown in Fig. 1. Value is created by bringing together WeDoWind Challenge Providers (for example, wind farm owner/operators, hardware suppliers, measurement service providers and asset managers), who provide challenges and data, with Solution Developers (for example, data scientists, researchers or students), who solve the WeDoWind Challenges using the provided data. A WeDoWind Challenge is defined as a fixed problem with a motivation, goal, expected outcome and a deadline. Motivation to participate is created as follows:

- The Challenge Providers receive diverse state-of-the-art solutions to their WeDoWind Challenges from international teams, as well as increased visibility and contact with the research community.
- The Solution Developers get access to new data and to real problems from the industry, as well as increasing their visibility within the wind energy community.

A digital platform allows all the knowledge and information (including code, data, discussions and meeting documentation) to be collected in one central location. It can therefore be built upon in future WeDoWind Challenges and be easily accessed by lots of different people from all over the world. This results in a community - or ecosystem - of active and passive WeDoWind Challenge participants from academia and industry interested in open science, open innovation as well as generally sharing data and code, as well as learning from each other.

Through the possibility to accumulate different data sets from multiple data providers in a unified format, providing a more realistic environment for developing and benchmarking new models, the framework ultimately allows industry to adopt new approaches developed by academia much more effectively. Furthermore, it enables testing on how well the developed models scale to a large database, which is an integral requirement in practice. Finally, it can enforce transparency and robustness requirements for challenge solutions.

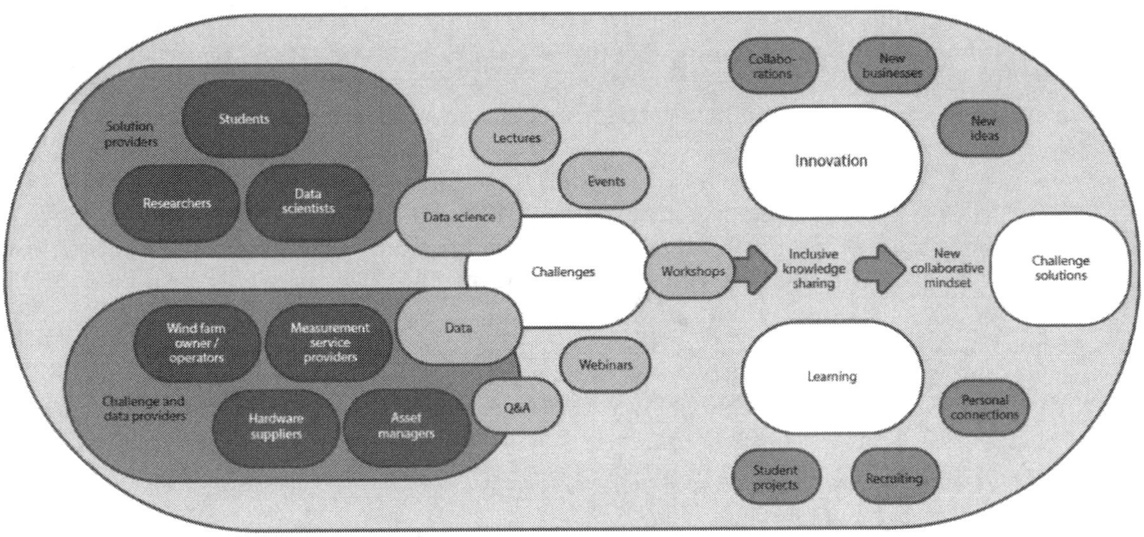


**Figure 1.** The value creation process of the WeDoWind framework.

In this present paper, the strengths and weaknesses of the WeDoWind framework are analysed, based on surveys filled out by participants of two use case studies and is complemented with observations from the WeDoWind development team over the last two years. The results of these analyses are then combined into a traditional SWOT (Strengths-Weaknesses-Opportunities-Threats) analysis, which is finally used to define some practical data sharing recommendations for the wind energy sector. The approach is described in Section 2 and the results are presented in Section 3. Then the data sharing recommendations are presented in Section 4.

## 2. Approach

The work presented in this paper was carried out in the following steps:

(i) Design and implementation of a survey.
(ii) Collection of observations from the WeDoWind development team.
(iii) Combination of the results from steps (i) and (ii) into a SWOT analysis.
(iv) Transfer of the results of step (iii) into general data sharing recommendations.

The approach was based on the results of the following two use case studies, which were run as WeDoWind Challenges using the WeDoWind framework:

**Use Case 1: The EDP Wind Turbine Fault Detection Challenge** The goal of this WeDoWind Challenge was "to identify the failures in five of the major wind turbine components and advise an intervention to the wind farm operators in order to reduce corrective maintenance costs." Two years of SCADA data from five wind turbines and data from the meteorological mast, as well as a list of SCADA signal names, the data sheet of the wind turbine type and the manufacturer's power curve were provided. Six solutions using Normal Behaviour Models, Combined Local Minimum Spanning Tree and Cumulative Sum of Multivariate Time Series Data, Combined Ward Hierarchical Clustering and Novelty Detection with Local Outlier Factor, Normal Behaviour Model with Lagged Inputs, Canonical Correlation Analysis and Kernel Change-Point Detection were submitted. Evaluation of the results showed that two of the solutions performed significantly better than EDP's existing method in terms of total prediction costs. Additionally, several challenges related to data sharing and model evaluation were identified and discussed, including the need to provide a clear optimisation goal at the start as well as the need for the Challenge Provider to play an active role during the running of the Challenge. A detailed description and discussion of this use case can be found in [7].

**Use Case 2: The WinJi Gearbox Fault Detection Challenge** The goal of this WeDoWind Challenge was "to make use of the provided SCADA data in order to train, test and validate methods that will provide clear indicators of an upcoming gear box related fault, as well as/or a horizon-based probability of the event occurring". Over two years of 10-minute SCADA were provided, for five wind turbines in the same site. Six different solutions were submitted and compared, using a Convolutional Autoencoder with a Particle Swarm Optimization, Performance monitoring using Deep Neural Networks, Direct Error Code Prediction using DNNs, T-SNE Projection for clustering, Combined Ward Hierarchical Clustering and Novelty Detection with Local Outlier Factor and Time-to-failure Prediction through Random Forest Regression. A comparison and evaluation of the results showed that, in general, some of the approaches had a high potential to reach the goals of the challenge. However, there were some things missing in the Challenge organisation, due to its confidential nature, that prevented its successful solution. For example, not enough detail of the different failure types and not enough data sets from wind turbines experiencing gearbox failure was provided. Furthermore, a model or rule relating fault detection times or remaining useful lifetime to the estimated costs for repairs, replacements and inspections was missing, as well as a clear strategy for training and test periods in advance. A detailed description and discussion of this use case can be found in [14].

For each case study, the WeDoWind framework was applied in the following steps:

- A dedicated space for the WeDoWind Challenge was created on the digital platform together with the Challenge Provider. The WeDoWind Challenge description, including direct links to download the data, was developed together with the Challenge Provider and posted inside this space.
- A public "call for participants" website was created with a direct link to the registration form. This was shared within the wind energy community using social media.
- A process for allowing the Challenge Provider to decide who may participate or not was set up. This process was not meant to reduce accessibility, but instead to ensure that applicants were real people interested in contributing and not robots, bots or imposters.
- A "Getting Started Guide" to using the digital platform was created and explainer videos were recorded in order to help users interact on the platform.
- A series of online workshops were organised for the participants - a launch workshop, interim workshops every month and then a final workshop. These involved brainstorming sessions in small groups as well as question and answer sessions with the Challenge Provider. The sessions were documented on a digital whiteboard and recordings were posted in the digital space.
- Regular email updates were sent with specific questions and actions to encourage interaction. This included requests to summarise and comment on different possible methods, as well as discussions of evaluation methods.
- The space was regularly checked, cleaned and coordinated by the WeDoWind developers to ensure that the information was up-to-date and understandable.
- Regular updates were communicated on social media.

## 3. Results

In this section, the results of the four different steps described in Section 2 above are presented.

### *3.1. Design and implementation of the survey*

A survey for the WeDoWind Challenge participants was designed using a survey design guideline from HAL Open Science [15]. The survey was split into several sections related to motivation, value added and suggestions for improvements. Some sections involved quantifying the participants' experiences on a scale of one to five, and some were qualitative. The qualitative questions were:

- What motivated you to sign up for the challenge?
- What was your main benefit from participating in this challenge?
- What was the main negative part of the challenge?

The specific implementation and results for the two use case studies are described below.

*3.1.1. EDP Challenge survey results* For the EDP Challenge, answers were received from seven Solution Providers. In general, the feedback was positive. Table 1 shows a summary of the quantitative answers, where answers of 1 and 2 have been given the label "Disagree", 3 = "Neutral", 4 and 5 = "Agree". In the "general" section, the answers show that the majority of participants received new insights or ideas (57%), learned about the challenges of using real data from the industry (72%) and got to compare their work with others and evaluate its success (72%). However, less than half (43%) reported that they made some useful new contacts and increased their visibility in the wind energy sector. This is expected to improve as more Challenges are run and the ecosystem effect takes over. They were also mixed feelings about the data, with less than half (43%) finding that the provided data was of sufficient quality and was sufficiently documented and labelled for solving the challenge. However, almost everyone (86%) found the challenge topic realistic and interesting. Regarding the support, less than half of the participants (43%) thought that the Challenge Providers were active and supportive during the process, whereas nearly all of them (86%) reported that the WeDoWind operators were active and supportive during the process.

The majority of the participants found the digital platform useful for summarising and centralising the knowledge relevant for the challenge (57%), that the webinars were a useful way of sharing ideas (57%) and that the regular email updates were motivating (57%). Unfortunately, none of the participants agreed that the digital platform was easy to use, and less than half (43%) said that the tech support of the digital platform was sufficient. Regarding the evaluation, the majority would have preferred a formal evaluation method to have been defined by the challenge providers at the beginning (86%) and to have defined a formal evaluation method together with the other participants at the beginning (71%).

Most of the participants thought that WeDoWind has a high potential for the future, 71% believing that WeDoWind could help the wind energy sector benchmark and evaluate ML methods for various applications in the future, 57% thinking that WeDoWind could provide a central knowledge hub for wind energy in the future, and 83% intending to take part in a WeDoWind Challenge in the future. Finally, 71% of the participants would like future WeDoWind Challenges to include more collaboration components.

Additional qualitative feedback included positive aspects, such as seeing the performance and different methodologies of other people's models, accessing data, comparing solution to others, publishing a paper, creating new connections, exchanging knowledge and sharing thoughts, as well as things to improve, including the lack of feedback from the Challenge Provider and the low frequency of the data provided.

*3.1.2. WinJi Challenge survey results* For the WinJi Challenge, answers were received from six Solution Providers. In general, the feedback was even more positive than the EDP Challenge. This was partly due to several improvements made to the process based on the feedback from the EDP Challenge, including improved usability of the digital platform, improved regular emails to motivate the participants and better coordinated webinars.

Table 2 shows a summary of the quantitative answers, where answers of 1 and 2 have been given the label "Disagree", 3 = "Neutral", 4 and 5 = "Agree". In the "general" section, the answers show that the majority of participants made some useful new contacts (60%), learned about the challenges of using real data from the industry (80%) and got to compare their work with others and evaluate its success (100%). However, less than half reported that they had received new insights or ideas (40%) or increased their visibility in the wind energy sector (20%). Again, this is expected to improve as more Challenges are run and the ecosystem effect takes over. As opposed to the EDP Challenge, there were very clear feelings about the data, with none of the participants finding that the provided data was of sufficient quality or quality, or was sufficiently documented and labelled for solving the challenge. In fact, this was the main topic of the evaluation part of this Challenge. The paper summarising the results ended with a set of best practice data sharing guidelines for wind turbine fault detection model evaluation. However, everyone found the challenge topic realistic and interesting. Regarding the support, less than half of the participants (20%) thought that the Challenge Providers were active and supportive during the process, whereas all of them reported that the WeDoWind operators were active and supportive during the process. It should be noted that the feedback about the

Challenge Providers is not entirely understandable to the authors of this paper (the WeDoWind operators) because our perception was that they were far more supportive than the Challenge Providers in the EDP Challenge. This topic is being further investigated.

The majority of the participants found the digital platform useful for summarising and centralising the knowledge relevant for the challenge (60%), that the webinars were a useful way of sharing ideas (100%) and that the regular email updates were motivating (100%). Furthermore, 80% of the participants found the digital platform easy to use, compared to 0% for the EDP Challenge. However, a similar proportion (40% compared to 43%) said that the tech support of the digital platform was sufficient. Regarding the evaluation, a similar feedback was observed as for the EDP Challenge; the majority would have preferred a formal evaluation method to have been defined by the challenge providers at the beginning (80%) and to have defined a formal evaluation method together with the other participants at the beginning (80%).

The potential value of WeDoWind in the future was rated even higher than for the EDP Challenge, with 100% believing that WeDoWind could help the wind energy sector benchmark and evaluate ML methods for various applications in the future, 100% thinking that WeDoWind could provide a central knowledge hub for wind energy in the future, and 80% intending to take part in a WeDoWind Challenge in the future. Finally, 80% of the participants would like future WeDoWind Challenges to include more collaboration components.

Additional qualitative feedback included positive aspects, such as learning about several methods, meetings to discuss the results and understand the difficulties, networking, group-based working, learning how other experts approached the challenge, first-hand collaboration with several experts in the field, as well as things to improve, including the lack of quality and quantity of the provided data set and the need to include more collaboration components in the process.

*3.1.3. Summary of survey results* The survey results were used to define the main strengths and weakness of the WeDoWind framework by calculating the average proportion of "Agree" answers across both use case studies. The main strengths were found to be:

- Enabling participants to compare and evaluate their work.
- Providing realistic and interesting topics to work on together.
- Enabling productive collaboration through a moderated WeDoWind framework.
- Allowing ideas to be shared through regular webinars.
- Motivating successful collaboration through regular email updates.

The main weaknesses were found to be:

- The participants not not think that their visibility in the sector was increased.
- There is no method for ensuring that the provided data is of sufficient quality or quantity, or that it is sufficiently documented for solving the challenge.
- No formal evaluation method was defined at the beginning of the Challenges.
- The digital platform was not easy to use.
- The tech support of the digital platform was insufficient.

### *3.2. Observations from the development team*

The results of a brainstorming workshop carried out by the WeDoWind development team showed the following main strengths:

- The framework provides people from all over the world with any background unrestricted access to real problems in the wind energy industry, leading to a diverse range of ideas and inputs.
- Researchers seem to be motivated to participate and submit solutions.
- The Challenge Providers benefit from new ideas and solutions.

Furthermore, the main improvement priorities were defined as:

- More work is required on the user activities and engagement patterns in the digital platform.
- More work is required on the digital platform.
- Collaboration could be enhanced even more by requiring collaborative solutions, rather than comparing individual solutions.
- Further case studies are required in order to build up a valuable network of experts.
- The importance of FAIR data or at least data with a certain amount of quality has to be stressed and challenge providers need to put more effort into this.
- The effort for the WeDoWind moderation team are relatively high, and therefore this process needs to be made scalable through training and toolboxes for moderators.

### *3.3. SWOT analysis*

Finally, the results of the previous sections have been combined in a Strengths-Weaknesses-Opportunities-Threats (SWOT) analysis, as summarised in Figure 2. The top half shows the strengths and weaknesses listed in the previous two sections, whereas the bottom half shows the main external opportunities (left) and threat (right).

We defined the main external opportunities and threats based on our experience as well as on the Grand Challenges in the Digitalisation of Wind Energy [2]. The opportunities were: Digitalisation is key driver for reaching net zero; Data sharing and collaboration need improving; There are few existing solutions for incentivising data sharing, as described in Section 1. Furthermore, our experience shows us that there is a general push to improve diversity and inclusion at work. The threats were: The challenge of working on humanistic aspects combined with technical aspects; The lack of readiness of some people to make the necessary fundamental mindset shift or cultural change; The general fear surrounding data and knowledge sharing; The resistance to supporting under-represented groups by certain people.

In order to use the strengths to exploit the opportunities and minimise the threats, the following future steps were then defined:

- Develop and test further use case WeDoWind Challenges based on diverse types of measurement data and relevant topics together with pioneer partners.
- Use the results to demonstrate the benefits of data and knowledge sharing to the wider community.
- Focus on providing unrestricted access to a diverse range of people from all over the world and connect the WeDoWind Challenges to teaching resources.
- Engage with social scientists to try and understand and remove the barriers related to humanistic aspects.

## 4. Data sharing recommendations

The results of the previous sections allowed the following data sharing recommendations to be defined:

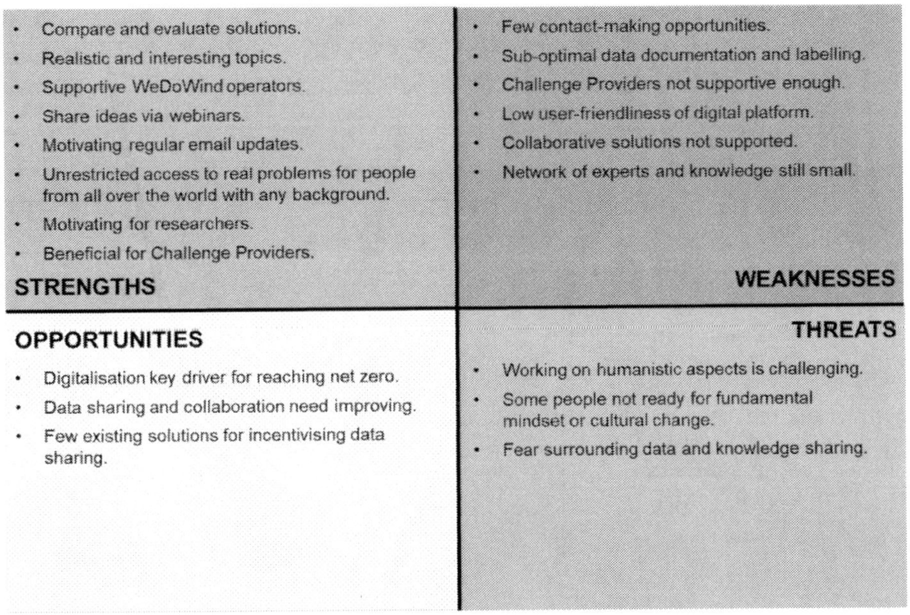


**Figure 2.** Results of the SWOT analysis.

- Think of data and knowledge sharing on a spectrum – there is a large range of opportunity between the extremes of "not sharing any data" and "sharing all your data publicly".
- Define and create "win-win situations" when sharing data and knowledge – think about how multiple parties can mutually benefit from each other.
- If you want a say in how data is shared in the future, make sure to contribute to industry-wide efforts to agree upon data and metadata standards, such as the IEA Wind Task 43.
- Instead of reinventing the wheel, share and publish your non-critical code for tasks such as data filtering, cleaning and preparing.
- If you want to be truly innovative, try to get as many different inputs from a diverse range of people with different backgrounds and experiences.

These data sharing recommendations can be used by anyone in the sector and are continuously being updated based on experience with the WeDoWind framework.

## 5. Conclusions

The WeDoWind framework has been developed in order to address the main challenges related to a successful exploitation of digitalisation in wind energy. The main innovation of this framework is the way it creates tangible incentives to motivate different types of people to actually share data and knowledge in practice. A detailed analysis of the strengths and weaknesses of the WeDoWind framework based on a survey filled out by participants of two use case studies and complemented with observations from the WeDoWind development team showed that the framework successfully enhances collaboration and data sharing in the sector. The experience allowed a set of practical data sharing recommendations for the wind energy sector to be developed, which are being continuously improved based on experience with the WeDoWind framework.

**Table 1.** Summary of the quantitative feedback from seven Solution Providers in the EDP Challenge.

| Question | Agree | Neutral | Disagree |
|---|---|---|---|
| **General benefits** | | | |
| Participation in this challenge gave me some new insights or ideas I can use for my research | 57% | 29% | 14% |
| Participation in this challenge resulted in some useful new contacts | 43% | 29% | 29% |
| Participation in this challenge increased my visibility in the wind energy sector | 43% | 29% | 29% |
| Participation in this challenge helped me understand the challenges of using real data from the industry | 72% | 0% | 29% |
| Participation in this challenge helped me compare my work with others and evaluate its success | 72% | 14% | 14% |
| **The data and the challenge** | | | |
| The provided data was of sufficient QUALITY for solving the challenge | 43% | 14% | 43% |
| The provided data was of sufficient QUANTITY for solving the challenge | 57% | 29% | 14% |
| The provided data was sufficiently documented and labelled | 43% | 43% | 14% |
| The challenge topic was realistic and interesting | 86% | 0% | 14% |
| **Support** | | | |
| The challenge providers were active and supportive during the process | 43% | 0% | 57% |
| The WeDoWind operators were active and supportive during the process | 86% | 0% | 14% |
| **The process** | | | |
| The digital platform was useful for summarising and centralising the knowledge relevant for the challenge | 57% | 29% | 14% |
| The webinars were a useful way of sharing ideas | 57% | 29% | 14% |
| The digital platform was easy to use | 0% | 43% | 57% |
| The tech support of the digital platform was sufficient | 43% | 14% | 43% |
| The regular email updates were motivating | 71% | 29% | 0% |
| **Evaluation** | | | |
| I would have preferred a formal evaluation method to have been defined by the challenge providers at the beginning | 86% | 14% | 0% |
| I would have preferred to have defined a formal evaluation method together with the other participants at the beginning | 71% | 29% | 0% |
| **Future potential** | | | |
| WeDoWind could help the wind energy sector benchmark and evaluate ML methods for various applications in the future | 71% | 0% | 29% |
| WeDoWind could provide a central knowledge hub for wind energy in the future | 57% | 29% | 14% |
| I intend to take part in a WeDoWind challenge in the future | 83% | 0% | 14% |
| I would like future WeDoWind challenges to include more collaboration components | 71% | 19% | 0% |

**Table 2.** Summary of the quantitative feedback from six Solution Providers in the WinJi Challenge.

| Question | Agree | Neutral | Disagree |
|---|---|---|---|
| **General benefits** | | | |
| Participation in this challenge gave me some new insights or ideas I can use for my research | 40% | 40% | 20% |
| Participation in this challenge resulted in some useful new contacts | 60% | 20% | 20% |
| Participation in this challenge increased my visibility in the wind energy sector | 20% | 60% | 20% |
| Participation in this challenge helped me understand the challenges of using real data from the industry | 80% | 20% | 0% |
| Participation in this challenge helped me compare my work with others and evaluate its success | 100% | 0% | 0% |
| **The data and the challenge** | | | |
| The provided data was of sufficient QUALITY for solving the challenge | 0% | 20% | 80% |
| The provided data was of sufficient QUANTITY for solving the challenge | 0% | 0% | 100% |
| The provided data was sufficiently documented and labelled | 0% | 20% | 80% |
| The challenge topic was realistic and interesting | 100% | 0% | 0% |
| **Support** | | | |
| The challenge providers were active and supportive during the process | 20% | 80% | 0% |
| The WeDoWind operators were active and supportive during the process | 100% | 0% | 0% |
| **The process** | | | |
| The digital platform was useful for summarising and centralising the knowledge relevant for the challenge | 60% | 20% | 20% |
| The webinars were a useful way of sharing ideas | 100% | 0% | 0% |
| The digital platform was easy to use | 80% | 0% | 20% |
| The tech support of the digital platform was sufficient | 40% | 20% | 40% |
| The regular email updates were motivating | 100% | 0% | 0% |
| **Evaluation** | | | |
| I would have preferred a formal evaluation method to have been defined by the challenge providers at the beginning | 80% | 20% | 0% |
| I would have preferred to have defined a formal evaluation method together with the other participants at the beginning | 80% | 20% | 0% |
| **Future potential** | | | |
| WeDoWind could help the wind energy sector benchmark and evaluate ML methods for various applications in the future | 100% | 0% | 0% |
| WeDoWind could provide a central knowledge hub for wind energy in the future | 100% | 0% | 0% |
| I intend to take part in a WeDoWind challenge in the future | 80% | 20% | 0% |
| I would like future WeDoWind challenges to include more collaboration components | 80% | 20% | 0% |

## References

[1] Wind energy digitalisation towards 2030 https://windeurope.org/intelligence-platform/product/wind-energy-digitalisation-towards-2030/ accessed: 2022-09-28

[2] Clifton A, Barber S, Bray A, Enevoldsen P, Fields J, Sempreviva A M, Williams L, Quick J, Purdue M, Totaro P and Ding Y 2022 *Wind Energy Science* **In Review**

[3] Wilkinson M, Dumontier M, Aalbersberg I and et al 2016 *Sci Data* **3** URL https://doi.org/10.1038/sdata.2016.18

[4] Barber S, Clark T, Day J and Totaro P 2022 The IEA Wind Task 43 Metadata Challenge: A roadmap to enable commonality in wind energy data URL https://doi.org/10.5281/zenodo.6457039

[5] Bresciani S, Ciampi F, Meli F and Ferraris A 2021 *International Journal of Information Management* **60** 102347 ISSN 0268-4012 URL https://www.sciencedirect.com/science/article/pii/S0268401221000402

[6] Maria S A, Allan V, Christian B, Robert V D, Gregor G, Kjartansson D H, Pilgaard M L, Mattias A, Nikola V, Stephan B, Javier S R, Pawel G, Inge R T, Christian B H, Willem W J and W H K 2017 Taxonomy and metadata for wind energy Research &Development Integrated Research Programme on Wind Energy, IRPWIND Grant agreement no 609795, , collaborative project, Start date: 01st December 2013 Work Package 2 - Deliverable D2.3 Lead Beneficiary: DTU Delivery date: 12 December 2017 Dissemination level: PU The research leading to these results has received funding from the European Union Seventh Framework Programme under the agreement 609795. URL https://doi.org/10.5281/zenodo.1199489

[7] Barber S, Lima L A M, Sakagami Y, Quick J, Latiffianti E, Liu Y, Ferrari R, Letzgus S, Zhang X and Hammer F 2022 *Energies* **15** ISSN 1996-1073 URL https://www.mdpi.com/1996-1073/15/15/5638

[8] Chesbrough H 2010 *Long Range Planning* **43** 354–363 ISSN 0024-6301 business Models URL https://www.sciencedirect.com/science/article/pii/S0024630109000569

[9] Pisano G 2015 *Harvard business review* **93** URL https://www.econbiz.de/Record/you-need-an-innovation-strategy-pisano-gary/10011296658

[10] Saragih H S and Tan J D 2018 *International Journal of Business Innovation and Research* **17** 361–377

[11] Chae B K 2019 *International Journal of Information Management* **45** 83–94

[12] Janardhanan N 2021 *Leveraging Co-innovation Model for Energy Transition: Examining India's Engagement with Japan and China* (Singapore: Springer Singapore) pp 21–40 ISBN 978-981-15-8905-8 URL https://doi.org/10.1007/978-981-15-8905-8$_2$

[13] Lee S M, Olson D L and Trimi S 2012 *Management decision*

[14] Barber S, Aizpitarte U, Serradilla O, Alberdi J, Zugasti E, Aizpurua J, Milani A, Sehnke F, Sakagami Y and Henderson C 2023 *Preprints.org 2023* **2023030239**

[15] Taherdoost H 2016 *International Journal of Academic Research in Management* **5** URL https://hal.science/hal-02546800

# Social acceptance "in my backyard" - What drives social acceptance of renewable energy projects?

**O San Martin**[1]

[1] Statkraft, Lilleaker, Norway

E-mail: orlando.sanmartin@statkraft.com

**Abstract**. This paper aims to present a general overview of the social acceptance of wind energy developments in Europe and identify influential social acceptance factors. First, we show social acceptance levels for renewable energy (onshore wind) projects in selected European countries and how it varies across and within countries. In addition, we produce regional maps showing within country variations in social acceptance indicators. Second, using an econometric model, we study how different factors influence social acceptance levels. Our investigation assesses social acceptance of renewable energy developments using primary data from two comprehensive opinion surveys. The first opinion survey -conducted in September/October 2021- contains more than 16 000 observations from 8 European countries and allows us to assess how social acceptance is affected by the distance to the wind parks. The second opinion survey – conducted in June 2022 - contains more than 18 000 observations from 9 European countries and allows us to assess -through an econometric model how social acceptance is affected by a set of relevant influential factors, including perceptions, preferences towards energy suppliers, preferences for community benefits schemes, and demographic factors among others. The analysis of the information gathered for this investigation shows variations across European countries and within each of the countries covered by this study. The findings from this study might be helpful to take into consideration during the planning and development of renewable energy projects and improve targeting the work towards community engagement aiming to obtain the social license to build and operate renewable energy projects.

## 1. Introduction

While there is widespread public support for increasing renewable energy supply in general, wind farm projects often face different degrees of opposition. Issues related to lack of social acceptance continue to impede plans for the expanded deployment of renewable energy facilities in Europe [1]. The lack of social acceptance is often seen as a major obstacle to achieving the renewable energy deployment rates needed to reach climate mitigation targets.

Among the most cited motivations for lack of social acceptance are high local costs compared with perceived local benefits, the inappropriate scale of development or cumulative impacts, limited public involvement in local energy planning and decision-making [2], or unfair distribution of the costs and benefits to the affected neighbor communities [3]. There is extensive literature on the social acceptance of wind power [5]. Research on this topic is influenced by a seminal paper [6] which defines three dimensions of public acceptance to disentangle the apparent dilemma of general public acceptance for the wind as a renewable energy source but often combined with opposition or low acceptance levels for specific wind farm projects [7]. The three dimensions or acceptance categories are labeled: *socio-political*, *market*, and *community acceptance*. Using these three dimensions, we can try to understand the dilemma faced by wind developers, given that despite high levels of approval for wind power at the national level, reflecting the *socio-political acceptance*, specific wind energy projects face a lack of *community acceptance* at the local level.

A widely cited article [8] proposed a conceptual framework to understand the apparent divergence or "gap" between *socio-political* and *community acceptance*. This article defines a 'social gap' the situation when there is high support for wind power – in general – as often reported in surveys but low success rates or low acceptance levels for specific wind farm projects, and an 'individual gap' when an individual supports wind power in general but opposes a local wind farm (i.e., a situation often linked to NIMBYism). This apparent inconsistency or "social gap" is widely described in media and economic literature and specific cases (e.g., from United States, Canada, the UK, and Finland) are documented in research across the globe [9] [10] [11]. The "social gap" experienced elsewhere and described in the literature can be illustrated with the recent debate in Norway, where a government initiative to provide a national framework for onshore wind development had to be discarded due to opposition from local and national levels. Researchers coined this as a "not-in-anybody's-yard" case [12]. On the one side, there is a general public opinion in favor of renewable power as a means to achieve climate targets, but at the same time, local stakeholders oppose the deployment of wind facilities. To achieve the renewable energy and climate targets, the "social gap" must be bridged to mitigate, accommodate, or work through the concerns of local communities regarding specific renewable energy projects [13]. It is also essential to be cautious when interpreting national opinion polls eliciting social acceptance for interventions such as wind parks [14]. Responses to public opinion polls do not always map the respondents' true preferences. Their answers might occasionally depend on contextual factors, which might then influence the divergence between the stated preferences for the technology in general and specific projects in particular. In the first part of this article, we report the results of the stated preferences for wind farms from an opinion survey replicated in several European countries.

Several potential drivers might influence social acceptance for wind projects. Distance and proximity effects, as well as the "place attachment" effect and the role of other externalities, e.g., visual intrusion on local landscape, are elements to consider as determinants of social acceptance [15] [16] [17] [18]. Attitudes and perceptions towards renewable energy might also drive peoples' preferences for wind technology in general and specific wind farm projects [4]. Environmental and climate awareness and attitudes [19] might also influence the willingness to accept wind farms in their vicinity. The role of community benefits and perceptions about distributive justice and community investments [4] community investments [20] [21] also play a role in determining social acceptance by local communities [22] [23] [24]. There are also initiatives promoting financial participation schemes to allow local households to become part of the investment as a vehicle to promote community acceptance. Still, the evidence is not yet conclusive [25]. In the second part of this article, we present the results of an econometric model for the determinants of social acceptance of wind farms.

Finally, another dimension to interpret the "social gap" might be related to the fact that the social acceptance concept used in assessing the social license for renewable energy projects is not necessarily a dichotomous decision and allows for different degrees of acceptance. Scholars have proposed an ordered categorical classification ranging from very low levels of acceptance or radical opposition to high levels of acceptance or active acceptance [26] [27] [28]. Aligned with this, in this investigation, we map respondents' preferences to host a wind farm 5 km from their residence using an ordinal variable with five acceptance levels.

This paper aims to present a general overview of social acceptance levels for renewable energy developments in Europe and identify key influential factors. This article assesses social acceptance of renewable energy developments using primary data from two sets of comprehensive opinion surveys. The first opinion survey -conducted in September/October 2021- contains more than 16 000 observations from 8 European countries and allows us to assess how public acceptance is affected by the distance to the wind parks. The second opinion survey – conducted in June 2022 - contains more than 18 000 observations from 9 European countries and allows us to assess -through an econometric model how social acceptance is affected by a set of relevant influential factors, including perceptions, preferences towards energy suppliers, preferences for community benefits schemes, and demographic characteristics among others.

The paper is organized as follows. In the next section, we briefly present the data survey and methodology. Section 3 discusses distance effects on public acceptance for renewable energy projects in Europe. In this section, we produce public acceptance maps to illustrate the spatial distribution of public acceptance levels for renewable energy projects -in 8 different countries- disaggregated into 66 regions. Section 4 presents and comments on the results from the econometric models aiming to identify key influential factors of social acceptance. The final section concludes the paper and presents key lessons.

## 2. Survey and methodology

Our investigation assesses public acceptance of renewable energy developments using primary data from two comprehensive opinion surveys. The first opinion survey -conducted in September/October 2021- contains more than 16 000 observations from 8 European countries and allows us to assess how public acceptance is affected by the distance to the wind parks. The survey item for polling public acceptance of renewable energy developments was "how happy or unhappy would you be if a wind (or solar) farm was constructed within a 5 km radius from your current address". The same question was repeated for the case of a 1 km radius. The survey used a 5-point Likert scale with values ranging from 1 ("very unhappy") to 5 ("very happy") to gauge respondents' level of acceptance.

A second opinion survey – conducted in May 2022 - contains more than 18 000 observations from 9 European countries and allows us to assess -through an econometric model how public acceptance is affected by a set of relevant influential factors, including environmental and climate awareness, information and knowledge about renewable power, energy supplier preferences, perceptions and concerns about renewable energy, preferences for community benefits schemes, and demographic factors. Since our dependent variable (i.e., public acceptance level) is ordered, we use an ordered choice model for our econometric analysis.

Table 1 presents the descriptive statistics for the variables used in our investigation. On the top of the table on the first row, our primary dependent variable is the level of acceptance for wind farms at 5 km from the respondents' residences. The following rows in the table present the explanatory variables used in our analysis in the coming sections classified by the main influential factors' categories.

**Table 1: Descriptive statistics – influential factors**

| Variable | Obs | Mean | Std. Dev. | Min | Max | Type |
|---|---|---|---|---|---|---|
| | | | | | | |
| Wind 5K preferences | 18 714 | 3,372 | 1,111 | 1 | 5 | ordinal |
| *Environmental/Climate Awareness* | | | | | | |
| Climate worried | 18 714 | 2,960 | 0,841 | 1 | 4 | ordinal |
| Fossil fuel companies | 18 714 | 0,409 | 0,492 | 0 | 1 | binary |
| *Supplier preferences* | | | | | | |
| Cheapest price | 18 714 | 0,431 | 0,495 | 0 | 1 | binary |
| *Information on renewables* | | | | | | |
| Understand energy origin | 18 714 | 2,904 | 0,805 | 1 | 4 | ordinal |
| Information on goals | 18 714 | 0,104 | 0,306 | 0 | 1 | binary |
| *Perceptions on renewables* | | | | | | |
| Perception: expensive | 18 714 | 0,230 | 0,421 | 0 | 1 | binary |
| Perception: noisy | 18 714 | 0,074 | 0,261 | 0 | 1 | binary |
| Perception: visual | 18 714 | 0,090 | 0,287 | 0 | 1 | binary |
| Perception: land use | 18 714 | 0,092 | 0,290 | 0 | 1 | binary |
| Perception: create jobs | 18 714 | 0,187 | 0,390 | 0 | 1 | binary |
| *Community benefits preferences* | | | | | | |
| Preferred el-price | 18 714 | 0,382 | 0,486 | 0 | 1 | binary |
| Skills & jobs | 18 714 | 0,285 | 0,451 | 0 | 1 | binary |
| Wildlife protection | 18 714 | 0,282 | 0,450 | 0 | 1 | binary |
| Monetary compensation | 18 714 | 0,256 | 0,436 | 0 | 1 | binary |
| Community services | 18 714 | 0,247 | 0,431 | 0 | 1 | binary |
| Schools support | 18 714 | 0,187 | 0,390 | 0 | 1 | binary |
| Local area improvements | 18 714 | 0,147 | 0,354 | 0 | 1 | binary |
| *Demographics* | | | | | | |
| Age group | 18 714 | 2,595 | 1,364 | 1 | 5 | ordinal |
| Female | 18 714 | 0,550 | 0,498 | 0 | 1 | binary |
| Income category | 16 838 | 3,227 | 1,965 | 1 | 8 | ordinal |
| Level of education | 18 174 | 4,016 | 1,408 | 1 | 7 | ordinal |

## 3. Social acceptance for onshore wind projects: distance and proximity effects

### 3.1. Social acceptance: socio-political dimension

The stated social acceptance levels obtained from the survey covering 9 European countries are shown in Figure 1. The higher levels of acceptance are represented by those responding to be "happy" or "very happy" with a wind farm located 5 km from their residence. The figure shows significant variations (i.e., 35% to 54% of the sample) across countries among those reporting higher acceptance levels.

### 3.2. Distance and proximity effects

The survey participants, to a large extent, stated higher levels of acceptance (on the 5-point scale) for wind farms at 5 km than at 1 km. Figure 3 shows that for the eight countries included in the 2021 survey more than 50% of the respondents in the 66 regions included in the regional breakdown reported higher acceptance levels for projects when increasing the hypothetical distance from 1 km to 5 km to their residence. The reported "distance effect" on public acceptance is illustrated by the percentage of the

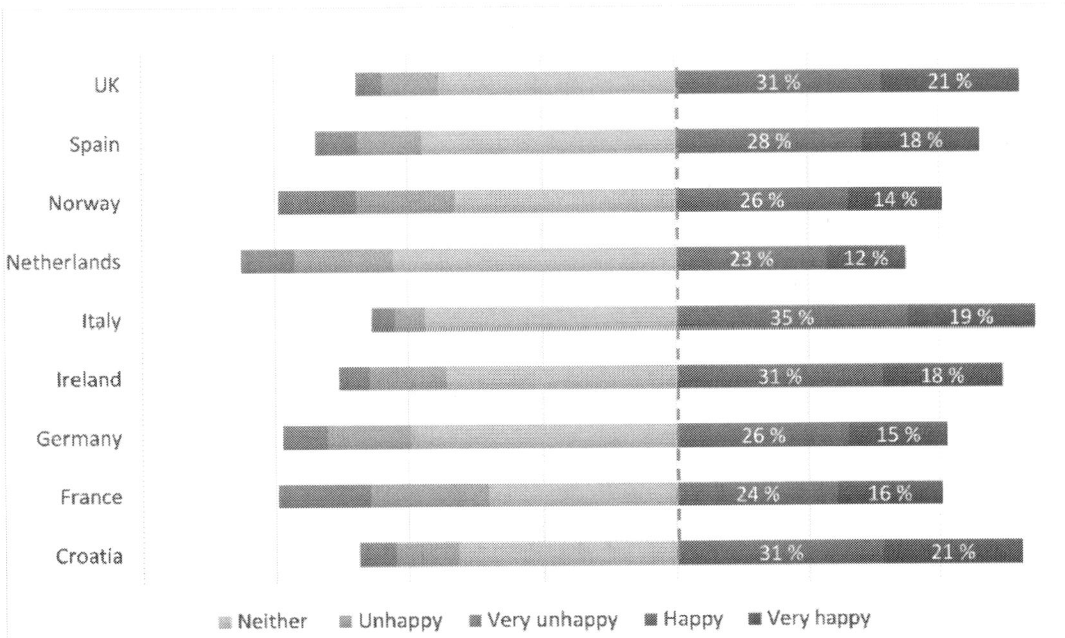


Figure 1: Social acceptance levels for onshore wind at 5 km by country

increase by moving away the wind park from 1 km to 5 km from the respondent's current address. In other words, it appears that the distance to the wind parks matters for an important share of the sample.

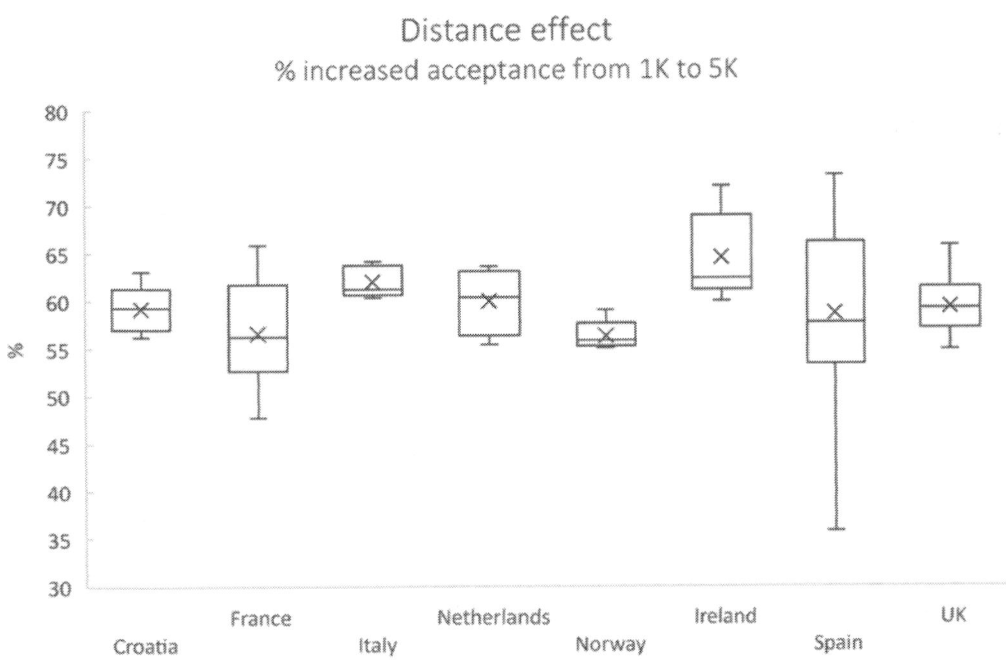


Figure 2: "Distance effect" – increased levels of acceptance with increased distance

### 3.3. Spatial distribution: acceptance and distance-sensitivity

Figure 3 shows the geographic distribution of respondents with higher acceptance levels for wind farms at a close distance from their current address (labeled as "wind lovers"). We label these cases as "wind lovers"; i.e., respondents who expressed the highest levels of acceptance (i.e., "somewhat happy" or "very happy" on the 5-point Likert scale) for wind parks at 1 km from their current address. The different (66) geographic units into which the sampled countries are divided are assigned a color code representing the percentage of the sample which stated a high level of acceptance for a wind park at 1 km

Figure 3. Geographical distribution of "wind lovers" (as a percent of the sample) across sampled countries.

from their residence. The darkest color in the map identifies those regions where 30% or more of the sample is characterized as "wind lovers." The legend at the bottom left of the figure shows the percentage value ranges of the other (lighter) colors.

## 4. Determinants of public acceptance: econometric model and results

This section presents and comments on the results of the econometric model proposed to analyze the determinants of public acceptance as a function of selected influential factors.

Previous investigations on public acceptance call for more nuanced approaches to understand public acceptance of energy projects and moving beyond notions of public acceptance -usually framed in an accept/reject dichotomy- in order to understand better the diverse spectrum of expression, engagement, and participation levels that inform public's attitudes to energy [2]. Following these suggestions, our investigation benefits from the information elicited through the opinion survey, which maps participants' preferences using a 5-point Liker scale. Given this information, our dependent variable representing public acceptance becomes a 5-level ordinal variable instead of the accept/reject dichotomy.

Consequently, we estimated an ordered logit model with a 5-level public acceptance variable as the dependent variable. We analyze the estimated regression coefficients to interpret the influence of the factors included in the model. These coefficients allow us to determine the direction of the relationship. Positive coefficients indicate that increased or higher levels of the corresponding factor or variable lead to increased levels of public acceptance (our dependent variable). In contrast, negative coefficients will reduce the probability of belonging to a high level of public acceptance (on the 5-point Likert scale).

**Table 2. Parameter estimates - ordered logit model**
Dependent variable: Social acceptance for wind park at 5 km

| Influencing factors | |
|---|---|
| *Environmental and climate awareness* | |
| Climate worried | 0,340*** |
| Fossil fuel companies | 0,084*** |
| *Supplier preferences* | |
| Cheapest price | -0,109*** |
| *Information on renewables* | |
| Understands energy origin | 0,237*** |
| Information on goals | 0,072 |
| *Perceptions on renewables* | |
| Perception: expensive | -0,277*** |
| Perception: noisy | -0,130** |
| Perception: visual | -0,357*** |
| Perception: land use | -0,372*** |
| Perception: create jobs | 0,089** |
| *Community benefits preferences* | |
| Preferred el-price | 0,082*** |
| Skills & jobs | 0,227*** |
| Wildlife protection | 0,084*** |
| Monetary compensation | -0,073** |
| Community services | 0,181*** |
| Schools support | 0,333*** |
| Local area improvements | 0,182*** |
| *Demographics* | |
| Age group | -0,120*** |
| Female | -0,301*** |
| Income category | -0,022*** |
| Level of education | 0,017 |
| Observations | 16,503 |

Standard errors not shown (available upon request)
*** p<0.01, ** p<0.05, * p<0.1

### 4.1. Environmental and climate awareness

In Table 2 we can see that two of the variables used to represent the respondents' level of environmental and climate awareness: climate worried and fossil fuel companies obtained positive and statistically significant coefficients in the proposed model. The positive and statistically significant coefficients mean that according to our proposed model, positive environmental and climate awareness contributes positively to respondents' public acceptance levels. In other words, there is no trade-off but complementarity between climate concerns and public acceptance of wind parks. Information about renewables also appeared to significantly contribute to social acceptance. This might suggest that marketing/ education campaigns will be better suited by focusing on the aspects which are significantly linked to public acceptance.

According to our results, environmental and climate awareness strongly contribute to increased social acceptance of wind projects. The research proposes that the analysis of wind farm projects should consider not only the negative effects of, for example, local landscape or wildlife but also the positive effects on global environmental issues such as the contribution to the reduction of global warming (i.e., social cost-benefit analysis). In such study, the value of such global good could be large enough to offset the negative externalities. This approach to analyzing public acceptance of wind farms might promote support for wind energy as a good solution towards carbon neutrality worldwide [29].

### 4.2. Supplier preferences

The variable cheapest price is a binary dummy variable that identifies those respondents who selected the most affordable price to the question "when choosing an energy supplier – what is more important for you?". The coefficient for cheapest price was negative and statistically significant. This means that respondents who consider the cheapest electricity price as their most important factor when choosing their electricity supplier tend to have lower public acceptance of wind farms.

### 4.3. Information on renewables

The coefficient of the variable understands energy origin resulted in positive and statistically significative. This means that respondents who stated to have a higher level of understanding about where the energy they use comes from tend to have a higher level of social acceptance for wind farms. The coefficient of the other variable used to represent the level of information and knowledge about renewable energy information on goals was not statistically significant in the model.

### 4.4. Perceptions on renewables

The influence of respondents' perceptions of renewable energy on social acceptance of wind farms is represented by their responses to several attributes. On the negative side, they are characterized as expensive, noisy, visually intrusive, and land-use intensive, whereas on the positive side, they recognize a job creation attribute. All the coefficients representing negative perceptions, such as it is expensive, takes too much land, is visually intrusive, and is noisy resulted negative and statistically significative. It means that those with negative perceptions of renewable energy are less likely to accept wind projects within 5 km of their residence. On the contrary, those who perceive that renewable energy projects contribute to job creation (positive and statistically significant coefficient) are more likely to have higher levels of public acceptance for wind projects within 5 km of their residence.

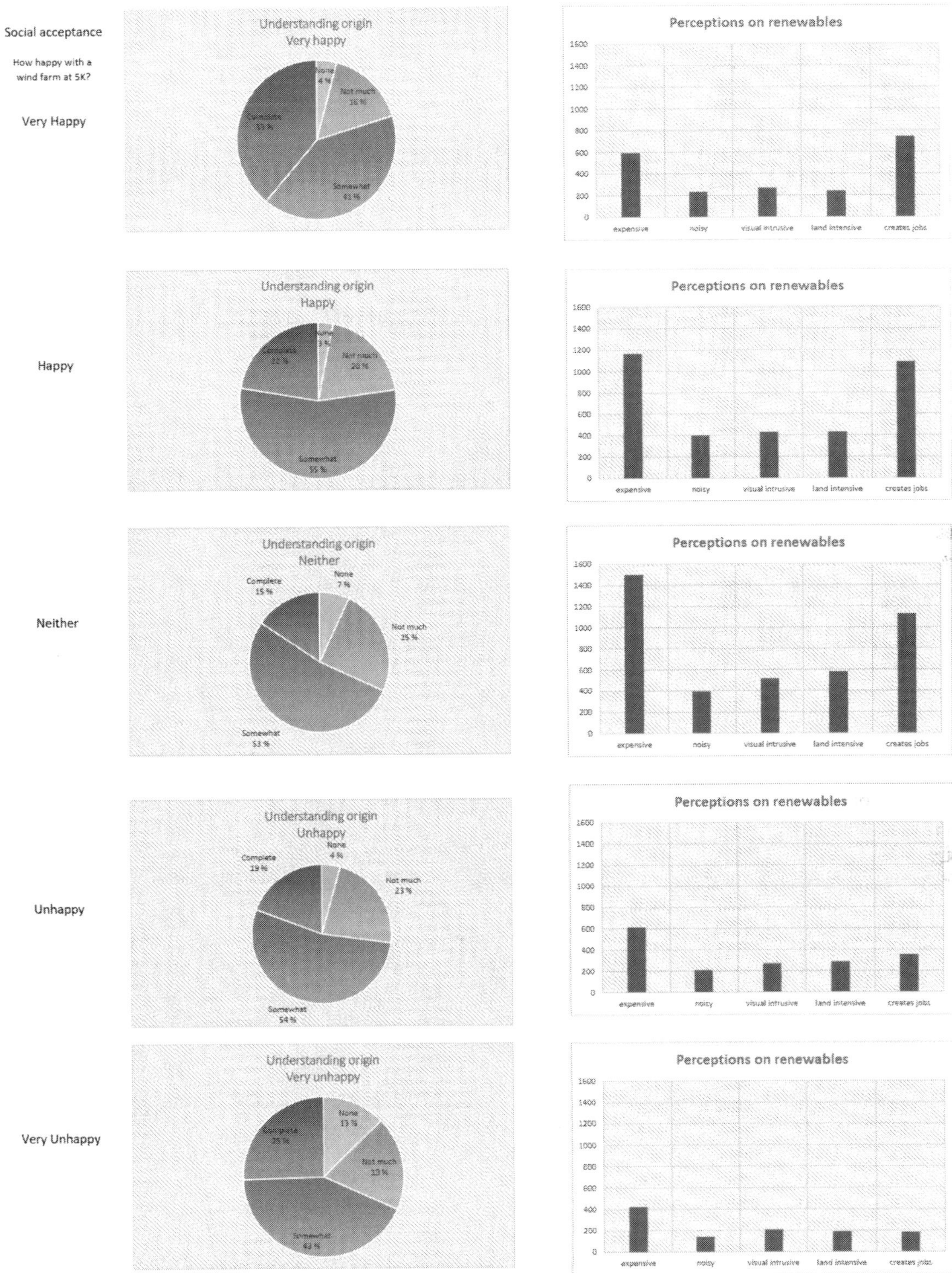


Figure 4. Understanding energy origin and perceptions on renewables by social acceptance level

### 4.5. Community benefits preferences and distributive justice

The next category of influential factors comprises different benefit-sharing schemes the respondents would like to see associated with constructing a wind farm within 10 km of their residence. The benefit-sharing schemes included in our model were preferred electricity tariffs, skills, and job-related programs, wildlife protection programs, monetary compensation, support to community service provision, school/education support programs, and local area infrastructure improvements. The coefficients for the variables representing all these schemes, except the one for monetary compensation, are positive and statistically significant. It means that the mentioned community benefits associated with the construction of a wind farm contribute positively to the acceptance of the projects. The coefficient for the monetary compensation appeared negative and statistically significant. It can be interpreted that the respondents who prefer direct monetary compensation over benefits in the form of common goods (or electricity prices) tend to have lower levels of public acceptance of wind farms.

Our results are aligned with those stating that the availability of community development funds results in higher levels of acceptance than financial participation offers for local citizens, implying that citizens prefer to apply the equality principle above the equity one (i.e., social/community vs private schemes) when deciding their level of acceptance for wind projects [7]. The negative coefficient on "monetary compensation" and positive coefficients on community services and local area improvements might support those findings.

### 4.6. Demographics

Finally, the model also considers the role of demographic characteristics on the public acceptance of wind energy projects. We note that the coefficient for the age group is negative and statistically significant. It means that the higher the age group the respondent belongs to (i.e., the older), the less likely to accept wind projects within 5 km of their residence. The coefficient representing the gender (female) of the respondent also is negative and statistically significant. It means that females are less likely to accept wind projects at 5 km of residence. The coefficient of the income category is also negative and statistically significant, meaning that those belonging to higher income level groups are less likely to accept wind projects at 5 km of their residence. The coefficient of the variable representing the respondents' education level did not achieve statistically significant value.

## 5. Final remarks

This investigation presents a general overview of social acceptance levels for European renewable energy developments and identifies some of its key influential factors. First, we give an overview of social acceptance levels for renewable energy (onshore wind) projects in selected European countries and how they vary across and within countries. As suggested in the literature, we analyze the issue by looking at both local-wide as well as nationwide. We produce regional maps showing within-country variations in social acceptance indicators. We also revisit the proximity hypothesis by analyzing the effect of the distance to the wind parks on social acceptance.

Second, using an econometric model we study how different factors influence social acceptance levels. The selection of influential factors was informed by reviewing relevant literature on this subject. Our study shows the effect of influential factors, such as environmental and climate awareness, electricity supplier preferences, information on renewables, perceptions on renewables, distributive justice as expressed by preferences for community benefit-sharing mechanisms and socio-demographic characteristics on social acceptance of wind energy projects. Our model results – by establishing statistically significant relationships between the corresponding influential factor and the social acceptance level – depart from the NIMBY (not-in-my-backyard) paradigm based on selfish behavior, and in line with other scholars suggests a group of influential factors that might be worth looking at when promoting new onshore wind projects. Modeling social acceptance as an ordinal variable with different acceptance levels instead of a dichotomous variable might also help to understand the complexities and "non-linearity" of this decision-making process.

Social acceptance to renewable energy projects in general and for onshore wind farms in particular become increasingly important for the success in achieving the climate targets and ambitions agreed upon in Europe. The results from this investigation help us to understand key determinants of social acceptance of renewable energy projects -beyond the strict selfish-motivated NIMBY behavior- using primary data sources. This information can be used to design and implement targeted efforts to promote the development, deployment and use of renewable energy while understanding the existence of a wide spectrum of factors influencing acceptance levels. The regional heterogeneity in preferences and acceptance levels might indicate the need for targeted efforts and to revisit existing "one-fit-all" policies and mechanisms.

## References

[1] García J H, Cherry T L, Kallbekken S and Torvanger A 2016 Willingness to accept local wind energy development: Does the compensation mechanism matter? *Energy Policy*, **99**, 165-73. https://doi.org/10.1016/j.enpol.2016.09.046

[2] Lennon B, Dunphy N P and Sanvicente E 2019 Community acceptability and the energy transition: a citizens' perspective. *Energy, Sustainability and Society*, **9** (1), 1–18. https://doi.org/10.1186/s13705-019-0218-z

[3] Markantoni M and Aitken M 2016 Getting low-carbon governance right: learning from actors involved in Community Benefits. *Local Environment*, **21**(8), 969–90. https://doi.org/10.1080/13549839.2015.1058769

[4] Stephens S and Robinson B M K 2021 The social license to operate in the onshore wind energy industry: A comparative case study of Scotland and South Africa. *Energy Policy*, **148**, 111981. https://doi.org/10.1016/j.enpol.2020.111981

[5] Ellis G and Ferraro G 2016 *The social acceptance of wind energy: where we stand and the path ahead*, European Commission, Joint Research Centre, Publications Office, https://data.europa.eu/doi/10.2789/696070

[6] Wüstenhagen R, Wolsink M and Bürer M J 2007 Social acceptance of renewable energy innovation: An introduction to the concept. *Energy Policy*, **35**(5), 2683–91. https://doi.org/10.1016/j.enpol.2006.12.001

[7] Walter G 2014 Determining the local acceptance of wind energy projects in Switzerland: The importance of general attitudes and project characteristics. *Energy Research & Social Science*, **4**, 78–88. https://doi.org/10.1016/j.erss.2014.09.003

[8] Bell D, Gray T and Haggett C 2005 The 'Social Gap' in Wind Farm Siting Decisions: Explanations and Policy Responses. *Environmental Politics*, **14**(4), 460–77. https://doi.org/10.1080/09644010500175833

[9] Bell D, Gray T, Haggett C and Swaffield J 2013 Revisiting the 'social gap': public opinion and relations of power in the local politics of wind energy. *Environmental Politics*, **22**(1), 115–35. https://doi.org/10.1080/09644016.2013.755793

[10] Cousse J, Wüstenhagen R and Schneider N 2020 Mixed feelings on wind energy: Affective imagery and local concern driving social acceptance in Switzerland. *Energy Research & Social Science*, **70**, 101676. https://doi.org/10.1016/j.erss.2020.101676

[11] Janhunen S, Hujala M and Pätäri S 2018 The acceptability of wind farms: the impact of public participation." *J. Environ. Pol. & Plan.* **20** (2) 214–35 https://doi.org/10.1080/1523908X.2017.1398638

[12] Dugstad A, Grimsrud K, Kipperberg G, Lindhjem H and Navrud S 2020 Acceptance of wind power development and exposure – Not-in-anybody's-backyard. *Energy Policy*, **147**, 111780. https://doi.org/10.1016/j.enpol.2020.111780

[13] Klick H, and Smith E R A N 2010 Public understanding of and support for wind power in the United States. *Renewable Energy*, **35**(7), 1585–91. https://doi.org/10.1016/j.renene.2009.11.028

[14] Klain S C, Satterfield T, MacDonald S, Battista N and Chan K M A 2017 Will communities "open-up" to offshore wind? Lessons learned from New England islands in the United States. *Energy Research & Social Science*, **34**, 13–26. https://doi.org/10.1016/j.erss.2017.05.009

[15] Mattmann M, Logar I and Brouwer R 2016 Wind power externalities: A meta-analysis. *Ecological Economics*, **127**, 23–36. https://doi.org/10.1016/j.ecolecon.2016.04.005

[16] Gibbons S 2015 Gone with the wind: Valuing the visual impacts of wind turbines through house prices. *J. Environ. Econ. Manag.* **72**, 177–96. https://doi.org/10.1016/j.jeem.2015.04.006

[17] Guo Y, Ru P, Su J and Anadon L D 2015 Not in my backyard, but not far away from me: Local acceptance of wind power in China. Energy (Oxford), 82, 722–33. https://doi.org/10.1016/j.energy.2015.01.082

[18] Jones C R and Eiser J R 2010 Understanding locals' opposition to wind development in the UK: How big is a backyard? *Energy Policy*, **38**(6), 3106–17. https://doi.org/10.1016/j.enpol.2010.01.051

[19] Hoyos D, Mariel P and Hess S 2015 Incorporating environmental attitudes in discrete choice models: An exploration of the utility of the awareness of consequences scale. *The Science of the Total Environment*, **505**, 1100–11. https://doi.org/10.1016/j.scitotenv.2014.10.066

[20] Teisl M F, McCoy S, Marrinan S, Noblet C L, Johnson T, Wibberly M, Roper R and Klein S 2015 Will Offshore Energy Face "Fair Winds and Following Seas"?: Understanding the Factors Influencing Offshore Wind Acceptance. *Estuaries and Coasts*, **38**(Suppl 1), 279–286. https://doi.org/10.1007/s12237-014-9777-6

[21] International Finance Corporation 2010 *Strategic Community Investment. A Good Practice Handbook for Companies Doing Business in Emerging Markets*, (Washington DC).

[22] Aitken M 2010 Wind power and community benefits: Challenges and opportunities. *Energy Policy*, **38**(10), 6066–75. https://doi.org/10.1016/j.enpol.2010.05.062

[23] Cowell R, Bristow G and Munday M 2011 Acceptance, acceptability and environmental justice: the role of community benefits in wind energy development. *J. Environ. Plan. Manag.* **54**(4), 539–57. https://doi.org/10.1080/09640568.2010.521047

[24] Vuichard P, Stauch A and Dällenbach N 2019 Individual or collective? Community investment, local taxes, and the social acceptance of wind energy in Switzerland. *Energy Research & Social Science*, **58**, 101275. https://doi.org/10.1016/j.erss.2019.101275

[25] Slee B 2015 Is there a case for community-based equity participation in Scottish onshore wind energy production? Gaps in evidence and research needs. *Renewable & Sustainable Energy Reviews*, **41**, 540–49. https://doi.org/10.1016/j.rser.2014.08.064

[26] Hofinger G 2001 Formen von "Akzeptanz": Sichtweisen auf ein Biosphärenreservat. *Umweltpsychologie*. **5**. 10–27. https://www.researchgate.net/publication/255730470_Formen_von_Akzeptanz_Sichtweisen_auf_ein_Biospharenreservat

[27] Langer K, Decker T, Roosen J and Menrad K 2018 Factors influencing citizens' acceptance and non-acceptance of wind energy in Germany. *J. Cleaner Production*, **175**, 133–44. https://doi.org/10.1016/j.jclepro.2017.11.221

[28] Langer K, Decker T, Roosen J and Menrad K 2016 A qualitative analysis to understand the acceptance of wind energy in Bavaria. *Renewable & Sustainable Energy Reviews*, **64**, 248–59. https://doi.org/10.1016/j.rser.2016.05.084

[29] De Salvo M, Notaro S, Cucuzza G, Giuffrida L and Signorello G 2021 Protecting the Local Landscape or Reducing Greenhouse Gas Emissions? A Study on Social Acceptance and Preferences towards the Installation of a Wind Farm. *Sustainability* (Basel, Switzerland), **13**(22), 12755. https://doi.org/10.3390/su132212755

# Offshore wind in the race for ocean space: A forecast to 2050

**S S Pettersen[1], Ø Aarnes[1], B Arnesen[1], B Pretlove[1], A K Ervik[2], M Rusten[2]**

[1] Ocean Space Programme, Group Research and Development, DNV, Høvik, Norway
[2] DNV Energy Systems, DNV, Høvik, Norway

Sigurd.pettersen@dnv.com

**Abstract**. This paper reports on recent results on the race for space in our ocean, based on DNVs forecasting efforts into the Blue Economy. We find that the world will see a large increase in the usage of ocean area by offshore installations for energy and food production, with the European area for installations growing close to five-fold to 2050. If not carefully managed, the energy transition in the ocean risks triggering a race for space and conflicts with other stakeholders. By introducing the *Spatial Competition Index* (SCI), we propose a new indicator to measure the level of competition among ocean industries and nature. SCI forecasts to 2050 reveal that shallow waters close to shore will face significant increases in pressure from ocean industries. This indicates that there is a need for co-existence to be considered in new offshore wind development projects, and for developers to increasingly consider floating structures.

## 1. Introduction

The coming era for the blue economy will be shaped by humanity's pressing need for transitioning the energy system and harvesting renewable energy from the sea. A rapid energy transition introduces new risks for the energy sector related to the impact on other ocean stakeholders as well as nature. As humans encroach further into the ocean space, the management of trade-offs between energy and food production, transportation, ocean conservation, and the aesthetic, cultural and ethical concerns among local communities and in the tourism sector, becomes critical.

Over the last few years, DNV has published a set of forecasts of the energy transition [1], and the development in the Blue Economy [2, 3, 4]. This paper elaborates on some key findings for the analysis of the North Sea, from the most recent report in DNVs *Ocean's Future to 2050* project, the *Spatial Competition Forecast* [4]. The latter report forecasts global estimates of area utilized by ocean industries and presents a deep dive into the busiest sea basins in both Europe and North America.

With the rise in spatial competition, the development of new offshore wind projects needs to consider the needs of other stakeholders at an early stage, and properly involve these stakeholders. This is critical to establish trust and transparency, establish a common knowledge basis on environmental impacts and interlinkages between the industries, and thereby reduce risk of conflict and identify synergies and win-win solutions [5].

The paper is structured as follows: First, we introduce central literature relating to spatial co-existence in the ocean. Then we briefly present our methodology, before presenting the main results and evaluate model sensitivities and robustness to uncertainty. We discuss our findings and introduce our research agenda on developing scenarios for co-existence between the ocean industries.

## 2. Literature Review

There is an extensive literature addressing spatial competition in the Blue Economy and the marine environment. The Marine Spatial Planning (MSP) research community has actively addressed the need for managing trade-offs arising between objectives relating to economic development and nature conservation in the ocean, with a clear foundation in ecosystem-based management, at least since the 1960s [6]. Today, MSP is part of a suite of approaches for ocean management that contribute to the sustainable development of a Blue Economy [7] and has been adopted in many countries [6].

In the EU, the Maritime Spatial Planning Directive [8] requires that each coastal member state details national marine spatial plans, defining MSP as "the process by which the relevant Member State's authorities analyse and organise human activities in marine areas to achieve ecological, economic and social objectives" [8]. Among the main challenges for current marine spatial planning is the need for early stakeholder inclusion, the development of proper performance metrics and monitoring methods, and incorporating socio-economic and ecological data, including climate change effects [9].

A new study from Nordic Energy Research [10] focuses on governmental instruments to inspire successful co-existence and highlights the need for government to set the framework for stakeholder dialogue. This dialogue should from the outset be founded in a plan defining all stakeholders, communication channels and information forming the basis for decisions. Gissi et al. [11] highlight the importance of incorporating change and adaptive capabilities in the MSP process. They argue that MSP needs to consider more thoroughly temporal aspects relating to climate change, and include corresponding ecological and economic development trajectories, in addition to managing the spatial distribution among ocean uses.

Already addressing the rising potential for competition among ocean industries, several EU projects have already investigated the potential for ocean multi-use, and even multi-purpose platform concepts [12, 13]. For instance, Van den Burg et al. [14] report on the geographic potential of alternative multi-use concepts, by reviewing what area is available for specific types of ocean structures as determined by bathymetric constraints and distance to shore.

In response to the growing area requirements and spatial competition, new forms of collaboration and multi-use strategies are likely to be realized, for instance driven by non-price, qualitative criteria in offshore wind tendering processes [10]. The term "multi-use" covers a broad array of strategies aiming to facilitate shared use of ocean space, that all represent a shift from the exclusive zoning of ocean area for specific uses. The EU Maritime Spatial Planning directive [8] already encourages multi-use, but the concept for now remains the exception rather than the rule.

In Schupp et al.'s [15] framework, multi-use ranges from (1) fully integrated multi-purpose platforms in which several users share the same marine structure, to (2) symbiotic use with the same peripheral infrastructure and services, to (3) activities simply occurring at the same time at the same place without significant loss of performance in either activity, to finally – the (4) repurposing of structures from one use to another. Table 1 introduces this typology with a set of relevant examples. The fully integrated structures face numerous barriers, both technically, economically, and regulatory [16], and defy core tenets in engineering design methodology like functional independence [17, 18].

Beyond the perspective of the combined industrial uses of ocean space, as outlined in the multi-use terminology, advances are also being made in combining nature conservation or restoration efforts with offshore wind. For instance, the Rich North Sea initiative of the Netherlands contribute to flat oyster restoration [19], and the design catalogues for nature-inclusive design provided by Wageningen University and Research [20] provide a first step into a world where offshore wind not only co-exists but has a positive impact on nature.

Our paper contributes to the understanding of where marine spatial competition is most likely to prevail, and thereby can serve as recommendations on where to focus efforts for co-existence both between industries, and between industries and nature.

**Table 1.** Multi-use combining industrial uses at different levels of system integration (based on [15]).

| Typology | Spatial | Temporal | Provisional | Functional | Description |
|---|---|---|---|---|---|
| **Multi-purpose** | X | X | X | X | Same area, same time, sharing core infrastructure and services |
| Examples | Combined floating offshore wind structure and finfish cage aquaculture [12, 13].<br>Floating desalination plant powered by wave power [12, 13, 21].<br>Energy islands acting as hubs for grid connection and green hydrogen production plants [1, 3, 4]. | | | | |
| **Symbiotic use** | X | X | X | | Same area, same time, sharing peripheral infrastructure and services |
| Examples | Shared logistics systems and service vessels for offshore wind and aquaculture operations in the same area [4].<br>Electricity from offshore wind to replace gas turbines on offshore oil and gas installations [22].<br>Offshore wind farms to act as charging stations for electric ships [23].<br>Floating solar photovoltaics replacing diesel generators at fish farms [24].<br>Integrated multi-trophic aquaculture: Fish farming combined with farming of low-trophic species like molluscs and seaweed [25]. | | | | |
| **Co-location** | X | X | | | Same area, same time |
| Examples | Adoption of passive fishing gear to reduce risk of gear entanglement [26].<br>Requirements to reduce risk for trawling over pipelines and subsea structures [27]. | | | | |
| **Repurposing** | X | | | | Same area, subsequently |
| Examples | Ships and offshore structures decommissioned to become artificial reefs [28]. | | | | |

## 3. Analysis

To analyse the future spatial competition, we apply spatial data analyses based on GIS (Geographic Information Systems) and combine this with system dynamics (SD) modelling that captures the long-term, feedback driven dynamics of the Blue Economy. The key novelty of our approach lies in the coupling of spatial and temporal analysis.

### *3.1. GIS analysis*

GIS techniques like spatial overlay and suitability analysis are used to quantify the available area for development of the main ocean industries in geographically well-defined sea basins taking into consideration marine protected areas (MPAs) and areas of particular ecological and biological significance. The high-level geographical breakdown is consistent with the world's Large Marine Ecosystems (LMEs).

Following previous research [14], the main dimensions used to constrain the viability of offshore installations generally are water depth and distance to shore. These two dimensions are used to parametrize ocean space and parse it into a set of 15 discretely defined ocean zones. The rationale behind this split, is that the areas that are most attractive to offshore wind also share characteristics with areas favorable to other users. This includes activities that depend on relatively shallow water for fixed structures, the mooring of floating structures, and activities relying on specific features of the ocean environment (like the fisheries). Area reserved as MPAs are also excluded from the measure of available area if these are categorized as highly protected, and thus exclude offshore wind development.

Additional data layers related to wind resource assessments impacting LCOE, metocean conditions impacting support vessel operability at the wind farms, and so on, would result in even smaller estimates of available area, indicating that competition could be even more pressing than as shown by our results.

### 3.2. *System dynamics model*

System dynamics (SD) is used to model the main feedbacks driving the spread of industry to deeper waters and new LMEs as activity fills up the most attractive zones. For offshore wind, the average levelized cost of electricity (LCOE) on the sea-basin level is used to determine the sea basins where it is most attractive to place the offshore wind production capacity forecasted. The distribution of industrial activity is calibrated against historical and current farms operating.

Based on earlier SD-based forecasts of future developments of the ocean industries [1-3] in each of the LMEs [4], the spatial pressure in each zone will rise due to the limitations on available area, creating an upward pressure on LCOE causing a spillover effect moving activity into nearby LMEs and into deeper waters further from shore. This emulates a risk-reward trade-off where offshore wind developers accept lower return on investment for a reduction in the risk of spatial conflicts with other ocean stakeholders.

### 3.3. *Spatial Competition Index*

The Spatial Competition Index (SCI) is the key indicator developed to address the level of competition between ocean uses. In its simplest form it is a gross measure that considers the sum of area needed by all users of the ocean, divided by the available area. Considering that some of the included ocean uses are inherently mobile, such as fisheries and shipping, the SCI can reach above 1, as several users may make use of the same area, but for shorter periods at a time.

Equation 1 defines the $SCI_z(t)$ at each time step $t$ as a sum of areas $A_{i,z}$ needed by an ocean industry $i$ in each zone $z$, with available area $A_z$, delimited by water depth and distance to shore, like the zonal approach used in [14].

$$SCI_z(t) = \frac{\sum_{i=1}^{n} A_{i,z}(t)\,)}{A_z(t)} \tag{1}$$

Running the SD simulation model results in area requirements estimates, corresponding changes in geographical distribution of ocean industries as resulting from spatial pressure and hence SCI measures for each zone.

## 4. Case description

We test the approach on four key sea basins (LMEs) within Europe; the North Sea, the Baltic Sea, the Celtic-Biscay Shelf (West of UK, West of France, Ireland), and the Mediterranean. Among these four, we here focus on the North Sea. The North Sea currently is the region seeing the most offshore wind development, being an area with excellent wind resources, as well as being the major hub for other maritime activity in Europe. Additionally, the North Sea is adjacent to many of Europe's major population centres in countries that have introduced ambitious targets for renewables. For the North Sea, area availability in the discretized water depth and distance to shore zones is shown in Table 2.

**Table 2.** Area [1000 km] at different water depth and distance to shore in the North Sea.

| Distance to shore [km] | | 0-2 | 2-50 | 50+ |
|---|---|---|---|---|
| Water depth [m] | 0-50 | 14 | 115 | 126 |
| | 50-100 | 1 | 53 | 143 |
| | 100-200 | 1 | 28 | 109 |
| | 200-400 | 1 | 27 | 38 |
| | 400+ | 1 | 7 | 33 |

The distribution of ocean industry activity and their forecast to 2050 is founded in the demand-driven, long-term, global forecast of the Blue Economy first presented in [1-4]. The baseline production forecasts to 2050 for Europe as a whole are coupled with data on the distribution of production and infrastructure per LME, and their current and historical distribution per zone as defined by water depth and distance to shore. The assumed initial zonal distribution for offshore wind in the North Sea, both fixed and floating, is shown in Table 3. For fixed offshore wind, this distribution is based on the 4C Offshore database [29], whereas the zonal distribution for floating offshore wind is based on the availability of area in the different zones that are considered technically feasible for floating offshore wind structures.

**Table 3.** Distribution [%] of installed offshore wind capacity in the North Sea by zone.

| | | Fixed offshore wind | | | Floating offshore wind | | |
|---|---|---|---|---|---|---|---|
| Distance to shore [km] | | 0-2 | 2-50 | 50+ | 0-2 | 2-50 | 50+ |
| **Water depth [m]** | 0-50 | 0.3 | 60.7 | 20.3 | 0 | 0 | 0 |
| | 50-100 | 0 | 9.2 | 9.6 | 0 | 7.8 | 20.8 |
| | 100-200 | 0 | 0 | 0 | 0.3 | 8.2 | 31.7 |
| | 200-400 | 0 | 0 | 0 | 0.3 | 8.0 | 11.1 |
| | 400+ | 0 | 0 | 0 | 0.2 | 2.0 | 9.6 |

To provide the area estimate, we calculate the area efficiency of wind farms based on a bottom-up approach, using established relationships between turbine capacity and size, arranged in a square grid layout with five to eight rotor diameters between turbines. We assume that the number of rotor diameters between turbines decline to 2050, as the average turbine in operation grows from 150 m diameter and 7 MW capacity to 250 m diameter and 13 MW capacity.

## 5. Results

The results show a five-fold increase in the area in European waters required for stationary infrastructure, both fixed and floating, across ocean industries including offshore oil and gas, offshore wind, and marine aquaculture. In 2050, 68,000 km$^2$ will be taken up by installations, with around 55,000 km$^2$ fixed offshore wind, and almost 7,000 km$^2$ floating. Figure 3 compares offshore wind with other ocean industries.

The entire rise in area required for installations in European waters is due to offshore wind, which increases from a 50% share of the total area covered by installations in 2020, to more than 80% in 2050. In comparison, oil and gas installation will reduce its area footprint due to the energy transition. In aquaculture, area efficiency gains obtained through new technical solutions halts growth in area footprint whilst production continues growing [2].

Figure 4 shows the distribution of the area for installations divided by sea basins (LMEs). In the North Sea alone, 36,000 km$^2$ will be occupied by stationary infrastructure, constituting around 5% of the total area of the North Sea. Compared to this, the amount of area needed in other European sea basins will be relatively minor. In both the Celtic Biscay Shelf and in the Baltic Sea, around 11,000 km$^2$ will be required to support the forecasted development of offshore wind, while less than 5,000 km$^2$ is needed in the Mediterranean. The overall European production capacity forecasts are consistent with DNVs Energy Transition Outlook [1] and Spatial Competition Forecast [4].

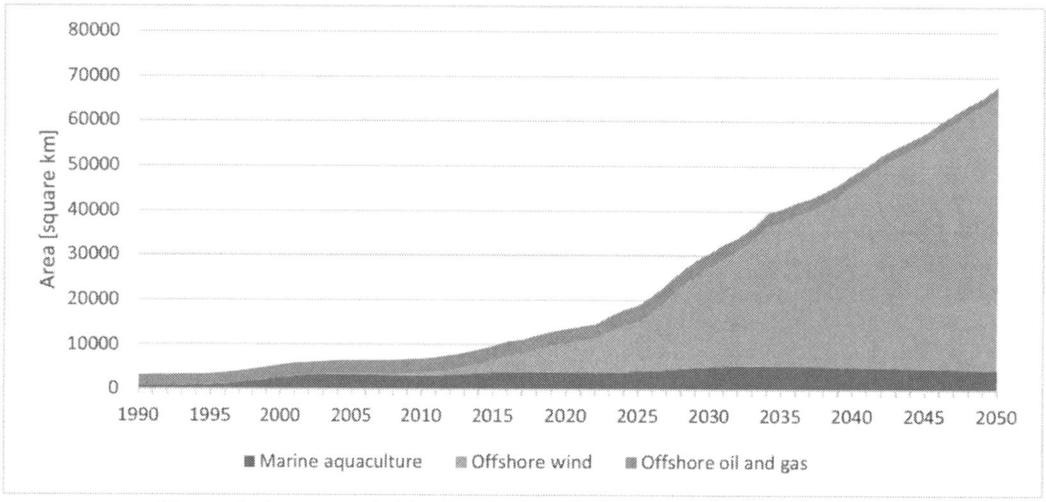


**Figure 3.** Area occupied by installations in Europe, split by industry [4].

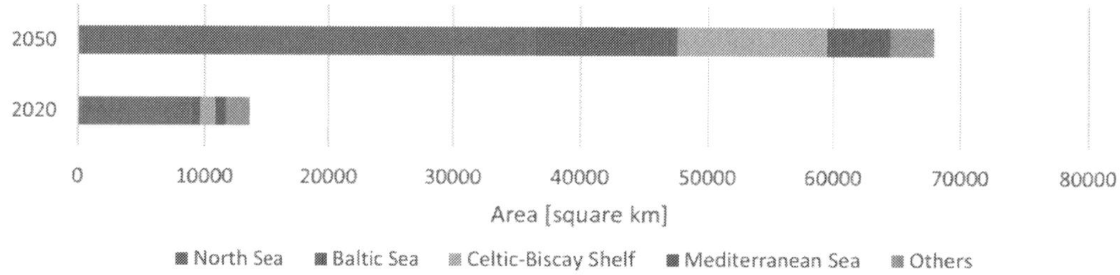


**Figure 4.** Area occupied by installations in Europe, split by sea basin [4].

The steep increase in demand for ocean area triggers a rising pressure on remaining available area. Figure 5 illustrates the Spatial Competition Index in the North Sea in 2050. The SCI considers the space needed for physical installations in offshore oil gas, offshore wind, and marine aquaculture, as well as the space utilization of shipping and fisheries, and conservation needs reflected in green (MPAs). As shown in red, the resulting SCI climbs to 1.15 in areas close to shore, where the water depth is less than 50 m. Areas further from shore in deeper waters face less spatial competition, but even here the SCI signals existing ocean users will experience higher pressure from new developments.

Figure 6 shows the SCI development for the zones within 2-50 km from shore for the North Sea, both when considering all ocean industries (as in the map), and when considering only those industries that require physical installations. The SCI considering only installations provides the more dramatic picture. As the SCI reaches 0.23 in 2050 for industries with installations up from 0.04, in the zone less than 50 km from shore and with less than 50 m water depth, this indicates that 23% of this area will be taken up by physical installations by then. As shown earlier, this is mostly attributed to offshore wind.

**Figure 5.** 2050 Spatial Competition Index mapped for the North Sea [4].

| | All ocean industries | | | | Industries with stationary infrastructure | | | |
|---|---|---|---|---|---|---|---|---|
| Water depth [m] | 2020 | 2030 | 2040 | 2050 | 2020 | 2030 | 2040 | 2050 |
| 0-50 | 1.02 | 1.07 | 1.11 | 1.15 | 0.04 | 0.11 | 0.17 | 0.23 |
| 50-100 | 0.74 | 0.79 | 0.81 | 0.85 | 0.01 | 0.03 | 0.06 | 0.08 |
| 100-200 | 0.76 | 0.80 | 0.83 | 0.87 | 0.00 | 0.00 | 0.01 | 0.01 |
| 200-400 | 0.60 | 0.63 | 0.67 | 0.70 | 0.00 | 0.00 | 0.01 | 0.01 |
| 400 + | 0.47 | 0.50 | 0.55 | 0.57 | 0.00 | 0.00 | 0.01 | 0.01 |

**Figure 6.** North Sea Spatial Competition Index from 2020 to 2050 for areas 2-50 km from shore [4].

Our results also reveal shifts in the distribution of offshore wind capacity to 2050, partly a consequence of limited room for new developments in the North Sea, as shown in Figure 5. Table 5 provides the distribution of fixed and floating offshore wind capacity in Europe to 2050. Currently, almost 85% of the capacity is installed in the North Sea. Towards 2050, we see this share greatly reducing as many attractive sites will be built out, and there will be increasing competition from other ocean uses. We forecast that the North Sea basin will hold around 50% of the installed capacity in Europe by 2050, as other regions gain market share, with wind developers trading slightly higher LCOE against a lower risk of conflict with other ocean stakeholders. The most attractive alternatives to the North Sea will be the Baltic and the Celtic-Biscay Shelf, the latter basin constituting 25% of floating wind capacity.

**Table 5.** Distribution of offshore wind capacity by LME

| | **Sea basins** | **2020** | **2030** | **2040** | **2050** |
|---|---|---|---|---|---|
| Fixed offshore wind | North Sea | 84% | 76% | 67% | 50% |
| | Baltic Sea | 6% | 12% | 16% | 17% |
| | Celtic-Biscay Shelf | 10% | 11% | 14% | 20% |
| | Mediterranean Sea | 0% | <1% | 3% | 9% |
| | Others | 0% | 0% | 0% | 0% |
| Floating offshore wind | North Sea | 79% | 56% | 53% | 49% |
| | Baltic Sea | 0% | 14% | 15% | 13% |
| | Celtic-Biscay Shelf | 21% | 24% | 25% | 25% |
| | Mediterranean Sea | 0% | 5% | 6% | 10% |
| | Others | 0% | 1% | 1% | 3% |

*5.1. Sensitivity analysis*

To investigate model robustness to uncertainty, we conduct sensitivity testing on key input parameters related to offshore wind. For instance, development in turbine size and average wind farm layout may have a large impact on the area efficiency of wind energy and therefore need to be understood. Table 6 presents some key results from these analyses.

**Table 6.** 2050 sensitivity results for Europe (base case values in bold).

| **Sensitivity run** | **Parameter value** | **Area efficiency [MW/km2]** | **Offshore wind area [km2]** | **Difference from base** | **Impact on SCI[a]** |
|---|---|---|---|---|---|
| 2050 average | 11.4 | 5.5 | 64,800 | +19% | 1.16; *0.26* |
| turbine capacity | **13.5** | **6.5** | **54,600** | **0%** | **1.15; *0.23*** |
| [MW] | 16.0 | 7.8 | 45,800 | -16% | 1.19; *0.20* |
| 2050 no. rotor | 3.75 | 11.6 | 30,700 | -44% | 1.12; *0.14* |
| diameters distance | **5.00** | **6.5** | **54,600** | **0%** | **1.15; *0.23*** |
| between turbines | 6.25 | 4.2 | 85,300 | +56% | 1.19; *0.33* |

[a] SCI score for the North Sea zone with depth 0-50 m and between 2-50 km from shore. SCI considering all industries shown in regular font, and SCI considering industries with installations only shown in italics.

The sensitivity analysis reveals that the model is far more sensitive to change in the 2050 layout than in the average 2050 turbine capacity. A reduction of 25% (from 5 to 3.75) in the number of rotor diameters between turbines triggers a 44% reduction in the area needed, while a 25% increase in this parameter causes a 56% increase in the area needed. On the other hand, a 19% increase in average turbine capacity causes only a 16% reduction in the area needed. The corresponding changes in SCI when considering all ocean activity is marginal, between 1% and 3%. Considering only installations, the impact on SCI is still smaller than the effect on area needed. Reducing turbine capacity by 16% causes a 13% reduction in SCI for installations only. Reducing the distance between turbines from 5 to 3.75 rotor diameters reduces SCI for installations only with 38%. The non-linear responses between these parameters are partly due to effects that spread installed capacity to deeper waters further from shore, or to other sea basins, when spatial pressure rises.

The analysis indicates that the model is sensitive to changes in key wind farm parameters. This has a two-fold consequence. First, it implies that there is significant uncertainty surrounding the estimation of area requirements from offshore wind and hence the SCI. Nevertheless, these forecasts can provide useful insights and valuable decision support, as well as communicate the risk of conflict with other users. Second, the large sensitivity implies that wind farm design decisions have a large impact on space use, and that innovations that improve the area efficiency of wind farms will greatly reduce the risk of conflict with other stakeholders.

## 6. Considering scenarios for co-existence in offshore wind development

In this paper, we have highlighted the importance of forecasting capabilities when considering the spatial planning aspects of offshore wind development projects. The results shown earlier reflect DNVs view of a 'most likely' future for the ocean space, but for proper risk management in the context of development projects, it is important to consider scenarios that account for key future uncertainties.

Broadly speaking, we can divide uncertainties into aleatoric and epistemic factors. Aleatoric uncertainty relates to the variability in outcomes beyond our 'most likely' forecast, for instance triggered by randomness and effects not considered in our system dynamics model. Examples include short term price fluctuations caused by temporary supply-demand imbalances for instance in the electricity markets, and regulatory/policy decisions that have a longer-term impact but appear to follow less predictable pattern on shorter time scales.

Epistemic uncertainty relates to the lack of knowledge about the complex causal interlinkages between phenomena. In the context of marine co-existence and multi-use, examples of such uncertainty include the impact of an offshore wind farm on the natural environment and fisheries closely linked to well-functioning ecosystem services, or how structurally coupling an offshore wind foundation with an aquaculture fish cage will impact the performance of each production system.

A great deal of the articulated concerns about future offshore wind developments among other ocean stakeholders exemplify epistemic uncertainty resulting from a lack of basic knowledge. The fisheries are concerned about losing access to key fishing grounds and about developments in spawning grounds and other areas that are particularly sensitive from an ecosystem perspective. With improvements in environmental monitoring, possibly also real-time monitoring made achievable by increasingly affordable sensor technologies, the state of knowledge about ecosystem and fisheries impacts will improve over time. However, monitoring impacts requires the wind farms to be installed, and does not negate stakeholder concerns ahead of development.

We believe that more extensive stakeholder management processes will be required in the process of opening areas for production of renewable energy, and in the following tendering processes. Qualitative criteria relating to co-existence are being tested in several countries around the North Sea [10, 30], with an upcoming example being the Norwegian licensing rounds [31].

By involving stakeholders from other ocean industries, including the fisheries, as well as regulatory bodies and environmental organizations, in building co-existence scenarios, we can achieve some of the reduction in epistemic uncertainty that is needed for social acceptance. As a minimum, such a process would involve elicitation of key dynamics factors known to be uncertain and changing over time, implementation in the modelling framework, and participatory modelling of scenarios that consider these factors. Examples could include the area efficiency ($MW/km^2$) which could be impacted by new turbine technology, or the impact of key stressors like wake effects, underwater noise, electromagnetic fields, or bird strikes on the local biodiversity. Coupling the trajectories of industry growth and factors like those mentioned above, within stakeholder defined narratives, can be a key tool for establishing common knowledge about the impacts of offshore wind.

DNV plans to investigate the role of scenarios in achieving co-existence further, partially building on the work presented in this paper. Our new Norwegian Research Council funded project MARCO –

Marine Co-existence scenario building, is currently (first half of 2023) being kicked off. The project consortium brings together stakeholders from across the ocean industries and academia, with Mainstream Renewable Power representing offshore wind, Salmar Aker Ocean representing marine aquaculture, and with the Norwegian Fishermen's Association representing the fisheries. The Norwegian Institute of Marine Research will contribute by anchoring the development of methodology within basic marine science. The main idea behind MARCO is illustrated in Figure 7.

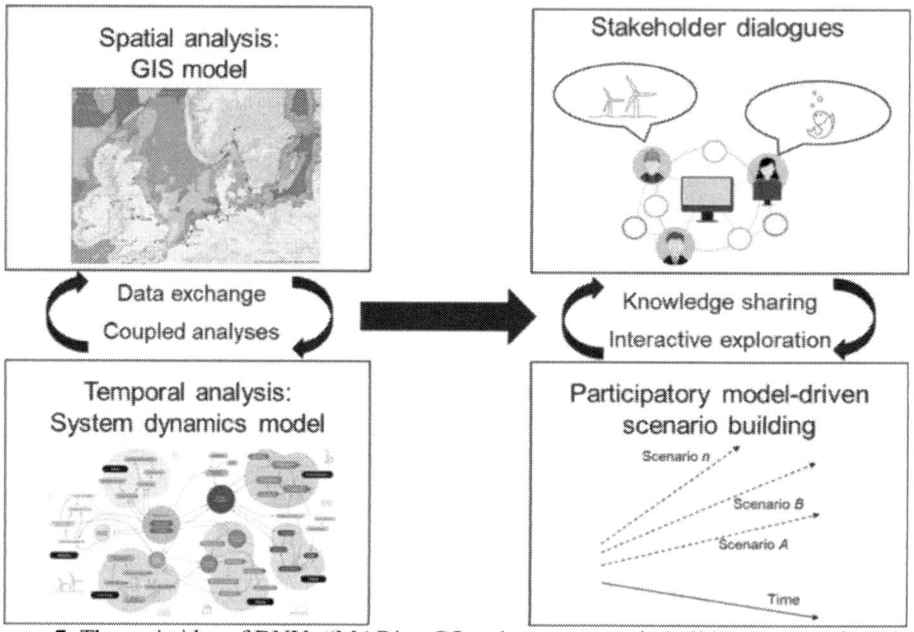


**Figure 7.** The main idea of DNVs "MARine CO-existence scenario building" research project.

As shown in Figure 7, MARCO will build on coupling of spatial and temporal models, building on the methodology explained in this paper. The project will then explore further how stakeholder participation in the development of scenarios can improve co-existence, by helping to establish a common knowledge base among ocean stakeholders.

## 7. Conclusion

Spatial competition will be rising to the forefront among concerns facing ocean-based industries, regulators and stakeholders concerned with conservation efforts. We propose the *Spatial Competition Index (SCI)* as an indicator of this and find that competition for space to be most critical in North Sea areas near shore in shallow water. Floating wind development in deeper water and in other sea basins will alleviate some of the increased pressure but we still see an increased risk of spatial conflicts.

Development processes in offshore wind will increasingly need to consider co-existence and multi-use opportunities to meet tendering requirements, but also to broadly manage stakeholder risk and obtain a social licence to operate. Consideration of multi-use will likely foster new opportunities and force innovation into solutions that seek synergies with other ocean businesses.

With project partners, DNV will conduct further research into the model-driven analysis of future co-existence scenarios through the MARCO project, thereby accounting for the considerable uncertainty surrounding key future developments in the energy markets, technical parameters, and interlinkages between sectors and with nature. Stakeholder participation in the framing of these future scenarios will be an essential component in building trust and transparency among ocean stakeholders in a blue economy driven by the energy transition.

**References**

[1] DNV. (2022). *Energy Transition Outlook.*
[2] DNV. (2021). Marine Aquaculture Forecast. *Ocean's Future to 2050.*
[3] DNV. (2021). *Ocean's Future to 2050.*
[4] DNV. (2023). Spatial Competition Forecast. *Ocean's Future to 2050.*
[5] Stuchtey, M., A. Vincent, A. Merkl, M. Bucher et al. (2020). *Ocean Solutions That Benefit People, Nature and the Economy.* Washington, DC: World Resources Institute. www.oceanpanel.org/ocean-solutions
[6] Ehler, C. N. (2021). Two decades of progress in Marine Spatial Planning. *Mar. Pol.*, **132** (June 2020), 104134. https://doi.org/10.1016/j.marpol.2020.104134
[7] Winther, J.-G., Dai, M., Douvere, F., Fernandes, L., Halpin, P., Alf, H., Juinio-Meñez, A., Li, Y., Morrissey, K., Rist, T., Scarano, R., Trice, A., Unger, S., & Whitehouse, S. (2020). *Integrated Ocean Management.* https://oceanpanel.org/publication/integrated-ocean-management
[8] Directive 2014/89/EU of the European Parliment and of the Council of 23 July 2014 establishing a framework for maritime spatial planning, *Official Journal of the European Union* (2014).
[9] Frazão Santos, C., Agardy, T., Andrade, F., Crowder, L. B., Ehler, C. N., & Orbach, M. K. (2021). Major challenges in developing marine spatial planning. *Mar. Pol.*, **132** (September 2018). https://doi.org/10.1016/j.marpol.2018.08.032
[10] Nordic Energy Research, DNV, & NIVA. (2023). *Co-existence and nature inclusive design in Nordic offshore wind farms.* https://www.nordicenergy.org/publications/coexistence-and-nature-inclusive-design-in-nordic-offshore-wind-farms/
[11] Gissi, E., Fraschetti, S., & Micheli, F. (2019). Incorporating change in marine spatial planning: A review. *Env. Sci. Pol.* **92**(3), 191-200.
[12] Abhinav, K. A., Collu, M., Benjamins, S., Cai, H., Hughes, A., Jiang, B., Jude, S., Leithead, W., Lin, C., Liu, H., Recalde-Camacho, L., Serpetti, N., Sun, K., Wilson, B., Yue, H., & Zhou, B. Z. (2020). Offshore multi-purpose platforms for a Blue Growth: A technological, environmental and socio-economic review. *Sci. Tot. Env.*, **734**, 138256.
[13] Dalton, G., Bardócz, T., Blanch, M., Campbell, D., Johnson, K., Lawrence, G., Lilas, T., Friis-Madsen, E., Neumann, F., Nikitas, N., Ortega, S. T., Pletsas, D., Simal, P. D., Sørensen, H. C., Stefanakou, A., & Masters, I. (2019). Feasibility of investment in Blue Growth multiple-use of space and multi-use platform projects; results of a novel assessment approach and case studies. *Renewable and Sustainable Energy Reviews, 107*(January), 338–359. https://doi.org/10.1016/j.rser.2019.01.060
[14] van den Burg, S. W. K., Aguilar-Manjarrez, J., Jenness, J., & Torrie, M. (2019). Assessment of the geographical potential for co-use of marine space, based on operational boundaries for Blue Growth sectors. *Mar. Pol.*, *100*(June 2018), 43–57.
[15] Schupp, M. F., Bocci, M., Depellegrin, D., Kafas, A., Kyriazi, Z., Lukic, I., Schultz-Zehden, A., Krause, G., Onyango, V., & Buck, B. H. (2019). Toward a common understanding of ocean multi-use. *Front. Mar. Sci.*, *6*(APR), 1–12. https://doi.org/10.3389/fmars.2019.00165
[16] van den Burg, S. W. K., Schupp, M. F., Depellegrin, D., Barbanti, A., & Kerr, S. (2020). Development of multi-use platforms at sea: Barriers to realising Blue Growth. *Ocean Eng.*, 217, 1-10.
[17] Braha, D. & Maimon, O. (1998). The measurement of a design structural and functional complexity. *IEEE Trans. Syst., Man, and Cyb.*, **28**(4).
[18] Suh, N. P. (1990). The Principles of Design, Oxford University Press.
[19] Rich North Sea. (2022). *Innovation for restoring oyster reefs installed in Luchterduinen wind farm.* https://www.derijkenoordzee.nl/en/news/innovation-for-restoring-oyster-reefs-installed-in-luchterduinen-wind-farm. Accessed 09.03.2023.
[20] Hermans, A., Bos, O., & Prusina, I. (2020). *Nature-Inclusive Design: a catalogue for offshore*

*wind infrastructure*. https://doi.org/10.13140/RG.2.2.10942.02882

[21] Offshore Energy. (2022). *Ocean Oasis unveils wave energy-driven desalination prototype*. https://www.offshore-energy.biz/ocean-oasis-unveils-wave-energy-driven-desalination-prototype/

[22] Equinor. (2022). *Enova supporting pioneer project*. https://www.equinor.com/news/archive/enova-supporting-pioneer-project. Accessed 09.03.2023.

[23] The Maritime Executive. (2023). *UK and Norway Advance Offshore Vessel Charging with Wind Power*. https://maritime-executive.com/article/uk-and-norway-advance-offshore-vessel-charging-with-wind-power. Accessed 09.03.2023.

[24] PV Magazine. (2023). *Floating solar tech for aquaculture*. https://www.pv-magazine.com/2023/01/04/floating-solar-tech-for-aquaculture/. Accessed 09.03.2023.

[25] Chopin, T. (2021). Integrated Multi-Trophic Aquaculture (IMTA) is a concept, not a formula. *International Aquafeed*. February 2021. https://www.researchgate.net/publication/349695427_Integrated_Multi-Trophic_Aquaculture_IMTA_is_a_concept_not_a_formula

[26] DNV. (2017). Interference between trawl gear and pipelines. *Recommended practice - DNV-RP-F111*.

[27] Stelzenmüller, V., Diekmann, R., Bastardie, F., Schulze, T., Berkenhagen, J., Kloppmann, M., Krause, G., Pogoda, B., Buck, B. H., & Kraus, G. (2016). Co-location of passive gear fisheries in offshore wind farms in the German EEZ of the North Sea: A first socio-economic scoping. *J. Env. Man.,* **183**(1).

[28] Ramm, L. A. W., Florisson, J. H., Watts, S. L., Becker, A., & Tweedley, J. R. (2021). Artificial Reefs in the Anthropocene: a review of geographical and historical trends in their design, purpose and monitoring. *Bull. Mar. Sci.,* **97**(4).

[29] 4C Offshore. *Global Offshore Wind Farm Database*. https://www.4coffshore.com/windfarms/

[30] WindEurope. (2022). *WindEurope position on non-price criteria in auctions*. https://windeurope.org/wp-content/uploads/files/policy/position-papers/20220413-WindEurope-Position-paper-non-price-criteria-in-auctions.pdf

[31] Regjeringen. (2022). *Høring av kvalitative kriterier og støtteordning for Utsira Nord*. https://www.regjeringen.no/no/dokumenter/horing-av-kvalitative-kriterier-og-stotteordning-for-utsira-nord/id2949768/?expand=horingsnotater. Accessed 07.12.2022.

# New insights into the influence of turbines on the behaviour of migrant birds: implications for predicting impacts of offshore wind developments on wildlife

**J Robinson Willmott[1], G Forcey[1], and M Vukovich[1]**
[1]Normandeau Associates, Inc., Gainesville, Florida, USA

E-mail: jwillmott@normandeau.com

**Abstract**. Knowledge of the movement and behaviour of birds and bats around turbines in the offshore marine environment is critical for assessing the environmental impacts of offshore wind developments in the eastern USA. To address the problem of gathering high-quality, long-term data on these species in this remote environment, we designed a multi-sensor system that was recently deployed for 6 months in 2021 and 2022. Two Acoustic and Thermographic Offshore Monitoring (ATOM™) systems were deployed on wind turbines 23 nautical miles off the coast of Virginia, USA. The systems were operational during the day and night and recorded 1,581 detections of birds and bats, with 99% of detections occurring in the fall. Most detections were of birds, including 5 shorebird species, 3 gull species, 1 tern species, 3 raptor species, 1 woodpecker species, and 18 passerine species. Skuas, corvids, and swallows were also observed. There were 521 detections of bats. Differences between species detected and identified in each sensor confirms that a multi-sensor approach for monitoring is beneficial. There were no observed collisions; two individuals (1 bird and 1 bat) suffered air displacement, causing them to fall, but they recovered and continued flying. ATOM also collected novel data on insects, tracking over 7,000 insects around the turbine rotor swept zone and revealed foraging behaviour in 596 of the 1,581 bird and bat detections. Offshore wind turbines thus provide potential sites for perching and foraging. Although these turbine sites provide a new opportunity to feed, which may be beneficial for insectivores and omnivores in enabling them to reach migration destinations in better condition, the consequences of a potentially delayed arrival are unknown (positive, negative, or neutral). Overall, our approach produced the first detailed insights into terrestrial land bird and bat activity around offshore turbines, providing novel information on changes in behaviour when turbine blades are moving and during higher wind speeds. Moreover, our data show that foraging activity appears to be conducted with an awareness of the moving blades and in safe zones close but parallel to blade movements. We recorded 113 observations of activity within 10 m of the moving blades and 70 observations where interactions with moving turbine blades were within 1 m; we call these latter avoidance measures nanoavoidance. No collisions were observed.

## 1. Introduction

The offshore wind industry in the USA has a goal of 30 gigawatts (GW) of deployed offshore wind by 2030 [1], with a currently predicted capacity of 86 GW expected by 2050 [2]. The principal areas of development include the eastern seaboard from Maine to North Carolina, the central and western Gulf of Mexico, and several areas along the Pacific coast and Hawaii.

As part of the National Environmental Policy Act (NEPA) process, the US Fish and Wildlife Service (USFWS) and Bureau of Ocean Energy Management (BOEM) are responsible for evaluating and determining how proposed offshore wind energy development in federal waters could impact species listed under the Endangered Species Act and Migratory Bird Treaty Act through completion of a Biological Assessment. During the permitting process, agencies request developers to complete research on wildlife within the area of development to fill knowledge gaps and assess risk.

In terms of species diversity and abundance, birds and bats constitute two groups of potential concern in the offshore environment. Broadly, birds include diurnal and nocturnal migrants, moving to and from overwintering and breeding sites, and resident seabirds. Migrant shorebird and songbird species are of particular interest because they are small and often migrate nocturnally, and little is known of their movements and use of offshore environments. Few datasets exist for understanding the movements of terrestrial land birds offshore. A dataset collected 29 miles offshore North Carolina, USA, in 2012–2013 is one of few publicly available reports and contains detections of 26 species of terrestrial land birds [3]. This study shows seasonality, weather, and wind speeds as being the main drivers of bird activity. Otherwise, there are limited data on migrant land bird individuals from gps- and vhf-tagged birds on movebank.org and motus.org. None of these datasets contain data on bird and bat behaviours around operational turbines. Similarly, although bats are known to be found offshore and the drivers of activity appear to be similar to those of birds (such as seasonality, weather, and wind speeds [4], [5], [6], [7]), activity and behaviour at operational offshore turbines is under-studied.

During both construction and operation, offshore wind developments may impact bird populations directly through mortality from collisions and indirectly through displacement or attraction, which may affect population fitness [8], [9], [10], [11], [12], [13]. Bird collisions with offshore wind turbines appear to be rare [14], [15], [16], but relevant studies are very limited due to logistical difficulties, and, in particular, very little is known about collision impacts on small bird species. More broadly, there is a strong need to better understand how birds interact with and are influenced by wind turbines daily and at small scales. The goal of this study was to provide the most detailed data to date on bird movements in the vicinity of offshore wind turbines and document bird behaviour around turbine blades (and possible collisions with turbines) using a novel multi-sensor system.

## 2. Approach

We designed a system with multiple sensors to collect information about bird and bat activity in the rotor-swept zone (RSZ) of offshore turbines. The Acoustic and Thermographic Offshore Monitoring (ATOM™) system combines four types of wildlife sensors analysed in combination: thermal cameras operating in stereo, a visible-light camera to allow species identification during the day, acoustic detectors for birds and bats, and a VHF receiver to detect birds fitted with VHF radio tags. The system is deployed on platforms underneath offshore wind turbines and continually collects data within the RSZ and the vicinity of the wind turbine during the monitoring period. The core ATOM components are mounted to a chassis attached to the turbine platform, the location of which is optimised for the best available view of the RSZ without constraining turbine maintenance operations. Acoustic detectors and VHF antennas are mounted away from the chassis (Figure 1).

Two ATOM systems were deployed on two adjacent turbines in the Dominion Energy Research lease area 23 nautical miles off the Virginia coast (Figure 2). The systems were deployed from 1 April to 15 June 2021, 15 August to 31 October 2021, and 15 January to 15 March 2022. Despite a remote connection via satellite modem, the connection speed and data transfer limits precluded us from remotely transferring data; nevertheless, the satellite connection was used to monitor system functionality and institute remote repairs when required. Data retrieval was done manually by swapping drive boxes and data storage cards every few months.

Figure 1. ATOM systems deployed on offshore turbines showing camera box (left) and acoustic sensors (right).

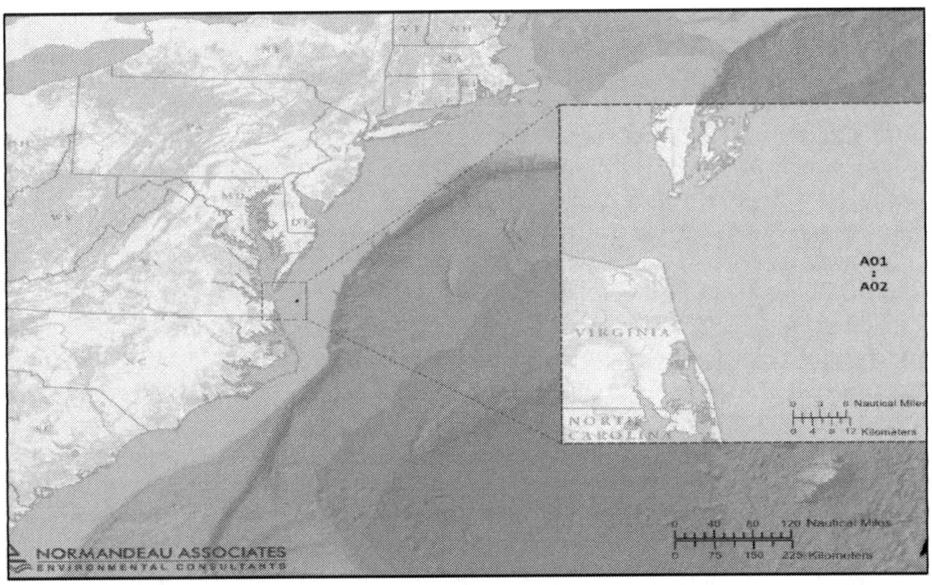


Figure 2. Location of the two Dominion Energy wind turbines off the coast of Virginia.

We reviewed 100% of video data using a combination of automatic target detection software and manual review of potential targets using our online data portal and analysis tool (ReMOTe). Using ReMOTe, analysts simultaneously reviewed both thermal and visible-light video. Determinations of target-type and behaviour were saved automatically into a central database. Birds and bats were sent to taxonomic experts (>10 years of experience) for identification when individuals were detected by both the thermographic and the visible-light video. Identifications were made to the lowest taxonomic level possible. Birds and bats marked as unidentified were those that were only recorded in the thermographic cameras or those for which key morphological characteristics needed for identification were not clear in the visible-light camera. During identification, it was also noted whether the turbine blades were moving and behavioural observations were noted as the following: Attraction (individual comes to check-out turbine then continues); Hawking (sallies from perch on short flights to capture flying insects); Aerial foraging (prolonged continuous flight capturing prey items); Monopole gleaning (taking insects off the turbine monopole); Microavoidance (blade interactions when blades are moving); Low patrol (direct flight below the RSZ); High patrol (direct flight within or above the RSZ); Flyover (very high flight visible above turbine, usually large birds for detection reasons); Thermaling (no flapping); and Perching.

Flight height and speed calculations were based on a track detection and particle analysis process within the stereo-thermographic video. Once tracks from the left and right cameras were paired, the distance of the object from the cameras was determined from the relative position of the object in each camera. Object velocities were determined by comparing location in sequential video frames. It was not possible to calculate distance and speed if targets were detected in only one camera in the stereo pair.

Insect detections were quantified along with bat and bird activity for the monitoring period. We examined relationships of insect detections with bird and bat detections by using Spearman's rank correlations.

Bird and bat acoustic data were reviewed by expert acousticians, and calls were ascribed to the lowest taxonomic level possible. Tag information from the VHF receivers were uploaded to the Motus website (Motus Wildlife Tracking System; motus.org) and were processed on motus.org.

To relate bat and bird activity to weather variables, we used modeled wind speed, wind direction, temperature, and sea level pressure data from StormGeo [17]. Weather variables were related to the bird and bat data by matching the animal detection timestamps to the closest value found in the weather data.

## 3. Results

The system was reliable throughout deployment with a few notable challenges: during the spring, there was a system short that caused 3 weeks of lost data on ATOM 2 (A02), and during the winter, a satellite modem was damaged by water intrusion preventing remote repair of a disk storage issue on ATOM 1 (A01), causing 15 days of lost data. Minor issues such as software bugs could be fixed remotely via satellite modem. Other periods of downtime were small and could mostly be attributed to power outages at the turbine, during which time the blades were not spinning.

Across all ATOM sensors and the entire monitoring period, there were 1,581 detections of birds and bat detections (521 bats, 1,011 birds, and 49 bird/bat) and over 7,000 insect detections. Bird detections included 5 shorebird species, 3 gull species, 1 tern species, 3 raptor species, 1 woodpecker species, and 18 passerine species. Skuas, corvids, and swallows were also identified but no individuals were identified to species (see Table A1). Of the bird detections, 522 occurred at turbine A01 and 489 occurred at A02 and most occurred during the fall, with only 9 birds observed in the spring and 5 during the winter. Only 2 bat detections occurred in spring and the remaining 519 detections occurred in fall; no bats were detected in winter. Bat detections include three species: Silver-haired Bat (*Lasionycteris noctivagans*), Hoary Bat (*Lasiurus cinereus*), and Eastern Red Bat (*Lasiurus borealis*) (see Table A1). Insects included many butterflies and moths (Lepidoptera) and dragonflies (Odonata), although only a few detections were identified to species. Insect detections occurred during all monitoring periods.

Most detections were recorded by video sensors (n=1,085; 70.9%) followed by acoustic detections (n=443, 28.9%) with only 0.2% made by the Motus receivers (n=3) (see Table A1). Ninety-one percent of bird detections and 45% of bat detections were during the day (Figure 3). Birds were active at lower median wind speeds compared to bats and insects, while insects were active at a higher median wind speed and a wider range of wind speeds than birds or bats (Figure 4). Bird activity dropped sharply at wind speeds above 5 m/s (Figure 5) and was minimal above 8 m/s, while bat activity dropped sharply above 6 m/s and was minimal above 10 m/s (Figure 6). Bird, bat, and insect activity occurred within similar temperature ranges (Figure 7). Birds were primarily active in air temperatures of 19–22°C (Figure 8), while bats were primarily active between 20 and 24°C (Figure 9).

Boxplots (Figure 4 and Figure 7) show the distribution of data among the animal types. The dark horizontal line is the median wind speed, and the box represents the middle 50% of data values. The lines above and below the box represent the data points that are within 1.5 times the length of the box above or below the box. Data beyond this range are shown as individual points.

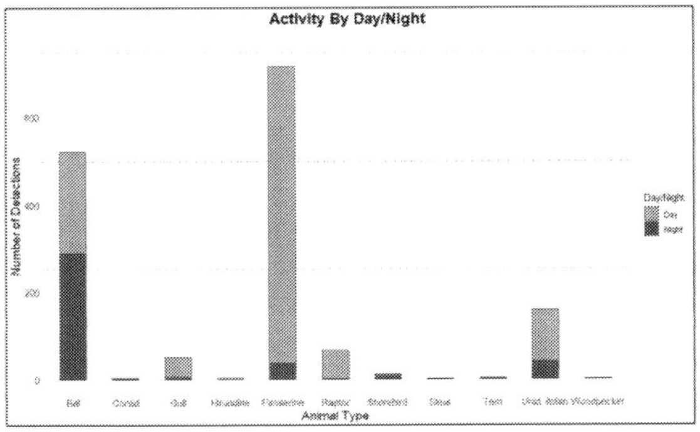


Figure 3. Day and night activity by bird and bat species groups.

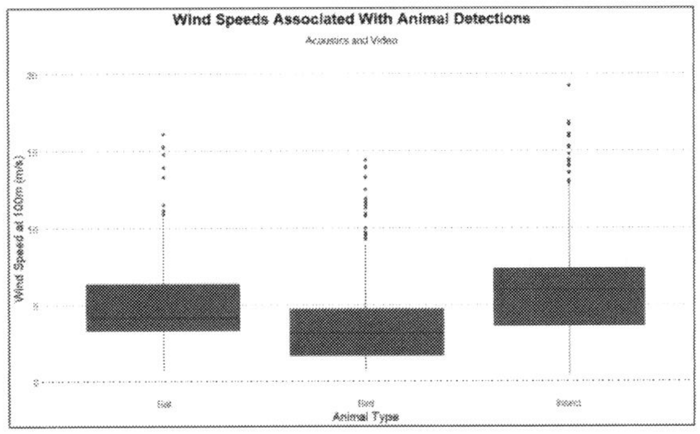


Figure 4. Bird, bat, and insect activity in relation to wind speed at 100 m above sea level.

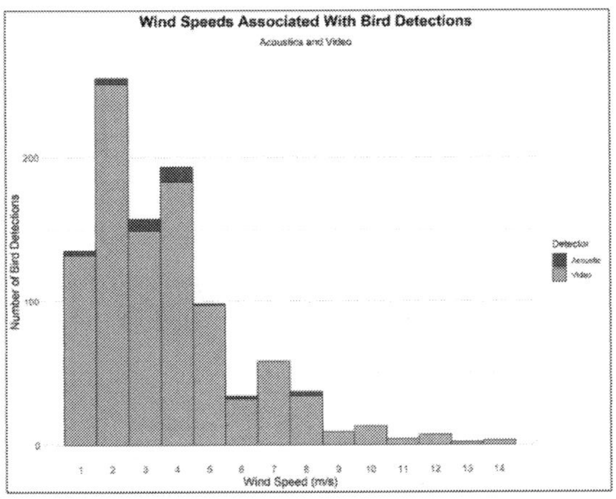


Figure 5. Number of bird detections at various wind speeds at the Coastal Virginia Offshore Wind Pilot Project.

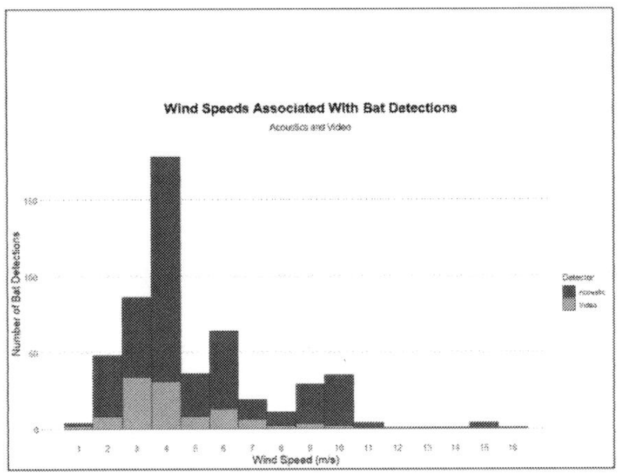


Figure 6. Number of bat detections at various wind speeds at the Coastal Virginia Offshore Wind Pilot Project.

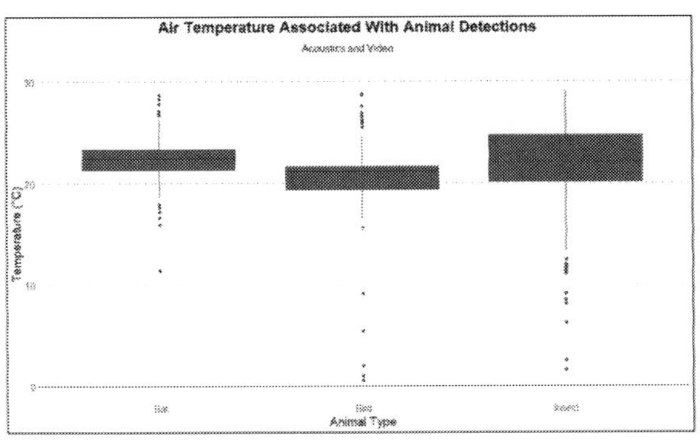


Figure 7. Bird, bat, and insect activity in relation to ambient air temperature.

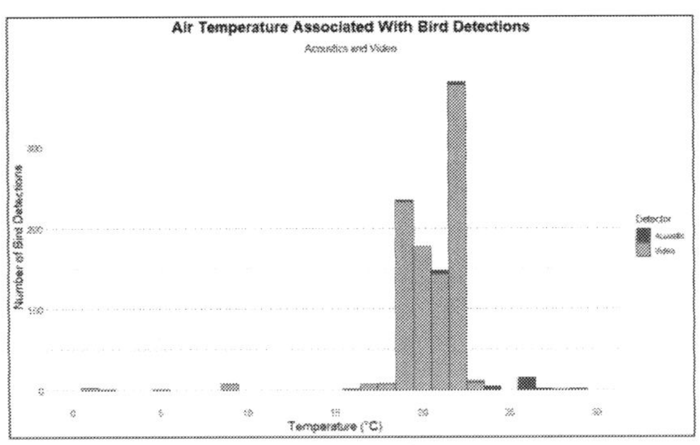


Figure 8. Number of bird detections at various air temperatures at the Coastal Virginia Offshore Wind Pilot Project.

Foraging in general was the most frequently observed behaviour (n=596 detections), executed by 21 bird species/groups and 2 bat species/group (Table 1). Aerial foraging (n=463) was the most frequently observed, followed by hawking (n=104) and monopole gleaning (n=29). Perching was sometimes associated with hawking or, in the case of Peregrine Falcons (*Falco peregrinus*), with resting and plucking prey. Feathers were observed drifting across the camera when a Peregrine Falcon was staying at the turbine, and remains of a freshly plucked corpse of a Dickcissel (*Spiza americana*) was found at the turbine the following day. Peregrine Falcons were seen patrolling the turbines (Figure 11). For both birds and bats detected by video, most foraging was associated with non-moving blades (n=483; 81%) (Figure 10; Figure 12) despite the blades spinning an estimated 81% of the time based on review of wind regime data and a cut-in speed of 5.0 m/s for the turbines. Foraging behaviours on Figure 10 include aerial foraging, hawking, and monopole gleaning.

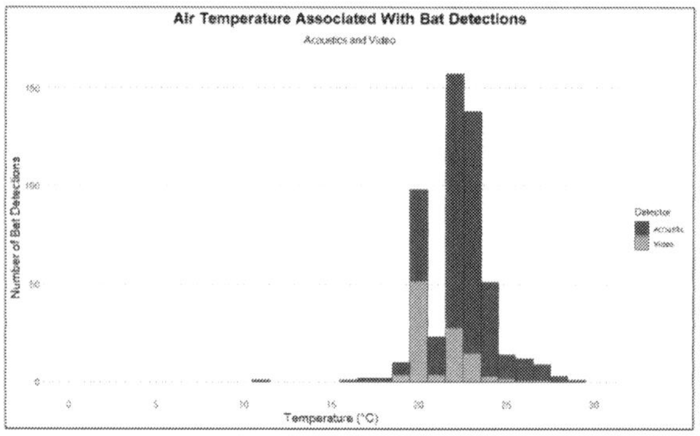


Figure 9. Number of bat detections at various air temperatures at the Coastal Virginia Offshore Wind Pilot Project.

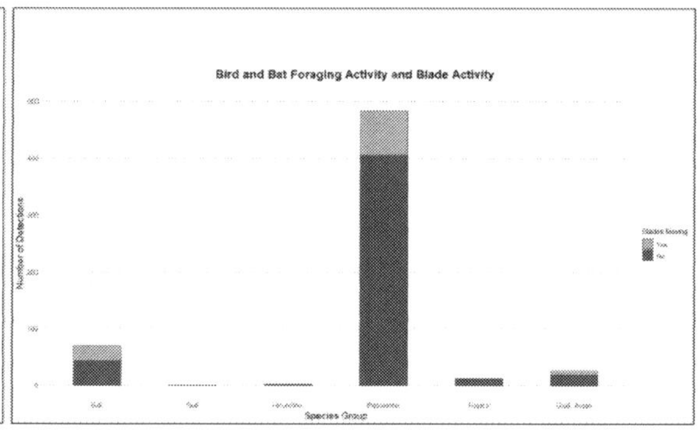


Figure 10. Number of foraging observations of bird and bat species groups when the blades were and were not moving.

Table 1. List of species and species groups seen foraging in video.

| Common Name | Scientific Name |
|---|---|
| Peregrine Falcon | *Falco peregrinus* |
| Hirundine species | |
| Brown Creeper | *Certhia americana* |
| Winter Wren | *Troglodytes hiemalis* |
| Wren species | |
| American Robin | *Turdus migratorius* |
| Blue-winged Warbler | *Vermivora cyanoptera* |
| Black-and-white Warbler | *Mniotilta varia* |
| American Redstart | *Setophaga ruticilla* |
| Cape May Warbler | *Setophaga tigrina* |
| Magnolia Warbler | *Setophaga magnolia* |
| Bay-breasted Warbler | *Setophaga castanea* |

| Common Name | Scientific Name |
|---|---|
| Blackburnian Warbler | *Setophaga fusca* |
| Palm Warbler | *Setophaga palmarum* |
| Pine Warbler | *Setophaga pinus* |
| Yellow-rumped Warbler | *Setophaga coronata* |
| *Setophaga* species | |
| *Parulidae* species | |
| Rose-breasted Grosbeak | *Pheucticus ludovicianus* |
| Passerine species | |
| Unidentified bird species | |
| Eastern Red Bat | *Lasiurus borealis* |
| Bat species | |

There were 70 observations of microavoidance from 18 species or species group (Table 2), where activity involved avoiding moving turbine blades. Microavoidance has been defined as a "bird behavioural responses to single blade(s) within the RSZ (including a 10-m buffer); it is considered as the bird's 'last-second' action taken to avoid collision" [16]. In our study, these 70 observations were individuals that manoeuvred around the turbine blades using similar behaviours as defined in Skov et al. [16]. These include an adjustment of direction where the bird or bat flies parallel to the rotor (n=39; bat=14, bird=25) (Figure 15), non-visible-adjustment where the bird or bat moves through the moving blades (n=19; bat=6, bird=13) (Figure 14), or avoidance involving an adjustment of speed where the bird or bat stalls flight with only slight adjustment of direction while waiting for the blade to pass (n=12;

bat=6, bird=6) (Figure 13). With avoidance involving adjustments in speed and direction, the bird or bat would afterwards either go through the blades or fly away from the turbine. Of the 113 foraging flights involving manoeuvring while the blades were moving, 6 were gleaning at RSZ height (within 10 m of the blades), 24 were hawking at RSZ height, again at times within 10 m of the blades, and the remaining 83 observations were of aerial foraging at various heights. All behaviours were angled such that they avoided directly interacting with the rotating blades, and these behaviours could also be defined as microavoidance. Hereon, we consider the submeter avoidance as nanoavoidance.

Figure 11. Peregrine Falcon patrolling at the turbine (blades were not moving).

Figure 12. Cape May Warbler chasing a moth (blades were not moving).

Table 2. Species or species groups observed showing nanoavoidance with moving blades.

| Common Name | Scientific Name | # |
|---|---|---|
| Shorebird species | | 1 |
| Great Black-backed Gull | *Larus marinus* | 1 |
| Peregrine Falcon | *Falco peregrinus* | 5 |
| Corvid species | | 1 |
| Brown Creeper | *Certhia americana* | 3 |
| Winter Wren | *Troglodytes hiemalis* | 2 |
| Wren species | | 1 |
| American Pipit | *Anthus rubescens* | 1 |
| American Redstart | *Setophaga ruticilla* | 1 |
| Cape May Warbler | *Setophaga tigrina* | 1 |

| Common Name | Scientific Name | # |
|---|---|---|
| Bay-breasted Warbler | *Setophaga castanea* | 1 |
| Palm Warbler | *Setophaga palmarum* | 1 |
| *Setophaga* species | | 3 |
| Passerine species | | 13 |
| Bird species | | 9 |
| Silver-haired Bat | *Lasionycteris noctivagans* | 1 |
| Hoary Bat | *Lasiurus cinereus* | 1 |
| Bat species | | 24 |
| TOTAL | | 70 |

Gulls were seen to approach the turbine then turn away. On 7 occasions, a gull approached the nacelle to perch and, on all occasions, the blades were not moving. There were 15 instances of gulls making a high flyover above the RSZ most (n=9) of which were when the blades were moving. There were 32 instances where gulls were seen within reach of the RSZ of which 28 were when blades were not moving. Great Black-backed Gull (*Larus marinus*) was also observed successfully navigating moving blades (nanoavoidance) although it was buffeted by the air draught.

Besides gulls, there were 9 other species or species groups observed approaching the turbine to perch (Table 3) including a woodpecker species and an Osprey (*Pandion haliaetus*).

No bird or bat collisions were observed. When the turbine blades were moving, all observed birds and bats avoided collisions while foraging within the RSZ. Two individuals (1 bird and 1 bat) appeared to be pushed off course from the turbine blade by the force of air movement. Both individuals recovered and continued flying. The bat revisited the blades before leaving the turbine.

Flight heights and flight velocities were generated for 33 species/species groups (see Table B1). Sample sizes are small, but, unsurprisingly, because the system was monitoring the RSZ, most flight heights generated were at rotor height.

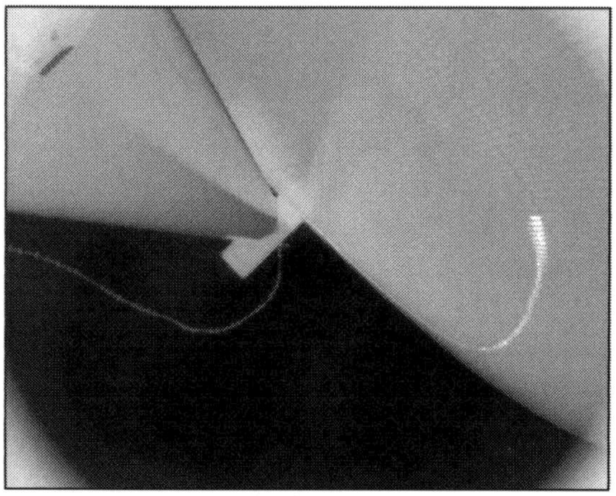

Figure 13. Nanoavoidance using adjustment of direction—the track goes parallel to the moving blades until the animal goes through the rotor swept area (image generated by a composite of thermographic images).

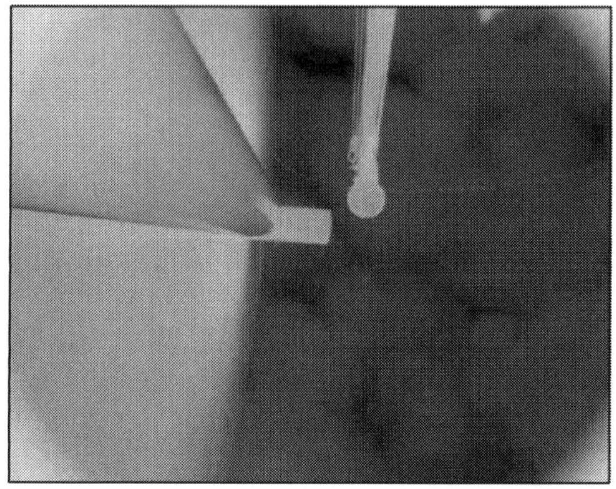

Figure 14. Nonvisible nanoavoidance (image generated by a composite of thermographic images).

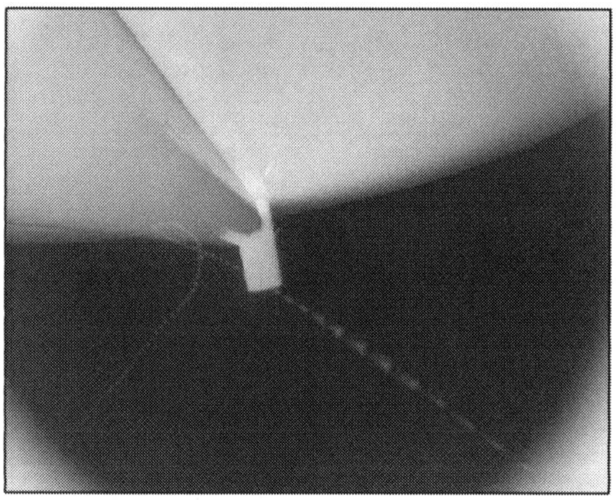

Figure 15. Nanoavoidance using adjustment of speed (image generated by a composite of thermographic images).

Table 3. Species or species groups observed perching.

| Common Name | Scientific name | # | Common Name | Scientific name | # |
|---|---|---|---|---|---|
| Laughing Gull | *Leucophaeus atricilla* | 1 | Cape May Warbler | *Setophaga tigrina* | 4 |
| Large Gull species | | 2 | Pine Warbler | *Setophaga pinus* | 5 |
| Small Gull species | | 1 | Yellow-rumped Warbler | *Setophaga coronata* | 1 |
| Osprey | *Pandion haliaetus* | 8 | *Setophaga* species | | 25 |
| Peregrine Falcon | *Falco peregrinus* | 17 | Passerine species | | 117 |
| Raptor species | | 2 | Bird species | | 28 |
| Northern Flicker | *Colaptes auratus* | 1 | | | |

## 4. Discussion

In this study we successfully used a novel multi-sensor system for monitoring bird and bat movement in the offshore environment. This approach provided unprecedented detail on bird movement offshore and provided new and surprising observations of land bird species using turbines to rest or forage. Such species included Northern Flicker and Brown Creeper (*Certhia americana*), neither of which have been recorded this far from shore (23 nautical miles) in the USA. There were other migrant passerines that might not be expected to be found so far from shore, such as American Robin (*Turdus migratorius*), but the shape of the coastline might encourage such species to make a shortcut when traveling between northern US states such as Massachusetts and Rhode Island to Virginia and North Carolina. In addition, the system provided new insights into bird behavior around turbines—we documented a high abundance of insects around the turbines, which provided a potentially important food source for birds and bats. At the same time, birds showed a high degree of avoidance of turbines with no recorded instances of collision in the study. These results have important implications for assessing exposure and collision risk in this remote and poorly studied environment.

Across bats and birds and all sensor types, video recorded 1,133 (72%) detections (see Table A1). For birds, terns were only recorded by the acoustic sensors and were not in the video viewshed, which is smaller than the reach of the acoustic sensors. All behaviours observed in gulls suggest that gull species can navigate safely around wind turbines, are seemingly more likely to approach turbines when the blades are not moving, and are more likely to keep above the RSZ when the blades are moving. These demonstrations of avoidance and apparent low collision rates for gulls are supported by other research [18], [19], [20], [21], [22], [23].

The presence of insects in the vicinity of turbines is assumed to be at least partially responsible for bird and bat activity around turbines [6], [24]. Nevertheless, we are unaware of studies that have documented insects and their possible influence on birds and bats around offshore turbines. Here, we recorded an unexpectedly high number of insect observations (>7,000) along with a high frequency of foraging behaviours associated directly or indirectly with this insect biomass. Long-distance migrations over the ocean have been documented in a number of insect species, especially among relatively large species in the orders Lepidoptera, Orthoptera, and Odonata [25], [26], [27]. Nevertheless, because of the obvious logistical challenges of recording insects in the offshore environment, very little is known about the precise routes, timing, and ecology of these migrations. Furthermore, surveys show that these larger insects comprise only a tiny fraction, perhaps less than 5%, of aerial insects in offshore waters, with smaller species of Diptera, Hymenoptera, and Homoptera being dominant [25]. Therefore, overall insect abundance around the turbines was clearly much higher than documented by our study and further research on the insect community composition, source, and seasonality could be valuable in understanding how the presence of this food source impacts bird and bat species around offshore turbines.

We recorded 113 observations of activity within 10 m of the moving blades and 70 observations where interactions with moving turbine blades were within 1 m. We call these avoidance measures within 1 m of the blade nanoavoidance. As research continues over the next 2 years and with continuous coverage, a significant number of new observations are anticipated, and a closer scrutiny of foraging and avoidance behaviours should be feasible.

Migrant songbirds and shorebirds, which would otherwise fly directly to their wintering sites, now encounter potential sites for perching and foraging. Although these turbine sites provide a novel opportunity to feed, which may benefit insectivores and omnivores by enabling them to reach migration destinations in better fitness, the consequences of a potentially delayed arrival are unknown (positive, negative, or neutral). As such, more work is needed to determine how these interactions with turbines impact the overall fitness of individual birds and bird populations. Our results suggest a high level of micro- and nanoavoidance of turbine blades by birds, which has potential implications when assessing risk. These turbine platforms are continuously lit at night as required by 33 CFR 67.05-15 which states "Obstruction lights shall be displayed at all times between the hours of sunset and sunrise". These lights appear to be flashing amber lights. Without doubt, the drivers of insect activity at offshore wind turbines deserve further investigation.

## 5. Conclusions

This initial study comprised only 6 active monitoring months. However, these unique data already provide key information on the timing and location of bird migrations, attraction, and foraging activities in the vicinity of wind turbines and the species involved. The results increase both our knowledge of bird ecology and our understanding of which bird species might be sensitive to future developments in offshore wind. Thus far this short study, which spanned the main period for fall migratory movements offshore along the eastern US Atlantic coast, has shown high avoidance by migratory songbirds of moving turbine blades and is the first study to incorporate a camera resolution sufficient to record small songbird activity around offshore turbines.

## Appendix A

Table A1. Bird and bat detections by sensor recorded and by day or night (highlighted species were observed foraging)

| | | | | | Total | | |
|---|---|---|---|---|---|---|---|
| Common Name | Scientific Name | Acoustic | MOTUS | Video | Day | Night | Total |
| **BIRD** | | | | | | | |
| Semipalmated Plover | *Charadrius semipalmatus* | | 2 | | 0 | 2 | 2 |
| Semipalmated Sandpiper | *Calidris pusilla* | | 1 | | 0 | 1 | 1 |
| Spotted Sandpiper | *Actitis macularius* | 1 | | | 0 | 1 | 1 |
| Solitary Sandpiper | *Tringa solitaria* | 1 | | | 0 | 1 | 1 |
| Upland Sandpiper | *Bartramia longicauda* | 3 | | | 1 | 2 | 3 |
| Shorebird species | | | | 3 | 3 | 0 | 3 |
| Skua species | | | | 1 | 1 | 0 | 1 |
| Laughing Gull | *Leucophaeus atricilla* | | | 10 | 9 | 1 | 10 |
| Herring Gull | *Larus argentatus* | 1 | | 8 | 9 | 0 | 9 |
| Great Black-backed Gull | *Larus marinus* | | | 3 | 3 | 0 | 3 |
| Large Gull species | | | | 16 | 14 | 2 | 16 |
| Small Gull species | | | | 3 | 2 | 1 | 3 |
| Gull species | | | | 10 | 9 | 1 | 10 |
| Royal Tern | *Thalasseus maximus* | 1 | | | 0 | 1 | 1 |
| Osprey | *Pandion haliaetus* | | | 8 | 8 | 0 | 8 |
| Merlin | *Falco columbarius* | | | 1 | 1 | 0 | 1 |
| Peregrine Falcon | *Falco peregrinus* | | | 53 | 52 | 1 | 53 |
| Raptor species | | | | 3 | 3 | 0 | 3 |
| Northern Flicker | *Colaptes auratus* | | | 1 | 1 | 0 | 1 |
| Corvid species | | | | 2 | 1 | 1 | 2 |
| Hirundine species | | | | 3 | 3 | 0 | 3 |
| Brown Creeper | *Certhia americana* | | | 10 | 10 | 0 | 10 |
| Winter Wren | *Troglodytes hiemalis* | | | 17 | 17 | 0 | 17 |
| Wren species | | | | 1 | 1 | 0 | 1 |
| American Robin | *Turdus migratorius* | 2 | | 2 | 4 | 0 | 4 |
| American Pipit | *Anthus rubescens* | | | 1 | 1 | 0 | 1 |
| Northern Waterthrush | *Parkesia noveboracensis* | 1 | | | 1 | 0 | 1 |
| Blue-winged Warbler | *Vermivora cyanoptera* | | | 1 | 1 | 0 | 1 |
| Black-and-white Warbler | *Mniotilta varia* | 2 | | 13 | 13 | 2 | 15 |
| American Redstart | *Setophaga ruticilla* | 1 | | 3 | 3 | 1 | 4 |
| Cape May Warbler | *Setophaga tigrina* | | | 112 | 110 | 2 | 112 |
| Northern Parula | *Setophaga americana* | 2 | | 1 | 2 | 1 | 3 |
| Magnolia Warbler | *Setophaga magnolia* | 1 | | 4 | 4 | 1 | 5 |
| Bay-breasted Warbler | *Setophaga castanea* | 2 | | 7 | 7 | 2 | 9 |
| Blackburnian Warbler | *Setophaga fusca* | | | 5 | 5 | 0 | 5 |
| Palm Warbler | *Setophaga palmarum* | 1 | | 13 | 14 | 0 | 14 |
| Pine Warbler | *Setophaga pinus* | | | 27 | 27 | 0 | 27 |
| Yellow-rumped Warbler | *Setophaga coronata* | | | 16 | 16 | 0 | 16 |
| Kirtland's Warbler | *Setophaga kirtlandii* | | | 1 | 1 | 0 | 1 |
| Setophaga species | | | | 171 | 167 | 4 | 171 |
| Parulidae species | | | | 6 | 6 | 0 | 6 |
| Rose-breasted Grosbeak | *Pheucticus ludovicianus* | 12 | | 10 | 21 | 1 | 22 |
| Passerine species | | | | 271 | 249 | 22 | 271 |
| Unidentified bird species | | | | 158 | 120 | 38 | 158 |
| **BAT** | | | | | | | |
| Silver-haired bat | *Lasionycteris noctivagans* | 233 | | 1 | 155 | 79 | 234 |
| Hoary bat | *Lasiurus cinereus* | 80 | | 2 | 9 | 73 | 82 |
| Eastern Red bat | *Lasiurus borealis* | 86 | | 4 | 49 | 41 | 90 |
| Unknown low frequency species | | 13 | | | 6 | 7 | 13 |
| Bat species | | | | 103 | 15 | 88 | 103 |
| **TOTAL** | | 443 | 3 | 1085 | 1154 | 377 | 1531 |
| **Percent of TOTAL** | | 28.9% | 0.2% | 70.9% | 75.4% | 24.6% | |

Journal of Physics: Conference Series **2507** (2023) 012006 doi:10.1088/1742-6596/2507/1/012006

## Appendix B

Table B2. Summary of flight heights and velocities

| Subtype | Common Name | N | No. Null Values | No. with Value | Height (m above sea level) Median | Min | Max | Velocity (m/s) Median | Min | Max |
|---|---|---|---|---|---|---|---|---|---|---|
| Shorebird | Shorebird species | 2 | 1 | 1 | 35.1 | 35.1 | 35.1 | 5.0 | 5.0 | 5.0 |
| Skua | Skua species | 1 | 0 | 1 | 107.9 | 107.9 | 107.9 | 32.1 | 32.1 | 32.1 |
| Gull | Laughing Gull | 5 | 3 | 2 | 100.0 | 86.7 | 113.4 | 30.5 | 19.3 | 41.7 |
| Gull | Herring Gull | 7 | 3 | 4 | 100.2 | 91.9 | 151.0 | 34.9 | 22.9 | 61.2 |
| Gull | Great Black-backed Gull | 3 | 2 | 1 | 106.4 | 106.4 | 106.4 | 58.3 | 58.3 | 58.3 |
| Gull | Large Gull species | 8 | 3 | 5 | 131.0 | 78.7 | 174.0 | 36.9 | 16.8 | 71.7 |
| Gull | Gull species | 6 | 3 | 3 | 86.9 | 85.8 | 174.0 | 25.8 | 17.4 | 28.1 |
| Raptor | Merlin | 1 | 1 | 0 | | | | | | |
| Raptor | Peregrine Falcon | 24 | 10 | 14 | 74.4 | 33.0 | 114.2 | 21.6 | 4.0 | 35.8 |
| Corvid | Corvid species | 1 | 0 | 1 | 59.9 | 59.9 | 59.9 | 12.2 | 12.2 | 12.2 |
| Hirundine | Hirundine species | 2 | 0 | 2 | 46.8 | 45.4 | 48.1 | 6.7 | 6.3 | 7.1 |
| Passerine | Brown Creeper | 8 | 3 | 5 | 32.0 | 28.0 | 78.8 | 9.8 | 4.8 | 35.1 |
| Passerine | Winter Wren | 6 | 3 | 3 | 27.2 | 27.1 | 28.6 | 3.5 | 3.0 | 5.6 |
| Passerine | Wren species | 1 | 0 | 1 | 31.0 | 31.0 | 31.0 | 9.1 | 9.1 | 9.1 |
| Passerine | American Robin | 1 | 1 | 0 | | | | | | |
| Passerine | American Pipit | 1 | 1 | 0 | | | | | | |
| Passerine | Blue-winged Warbler | 1 | 1 | 0 | | | | | | |
| Passerine | Black-and-white Warbler | 12 | 8 | 4 | 32.3 | 26.9 | 39.0 | 3.6 | 2.3 | 6.7 |
| Passerine | American Redstart | 3 | 1 | 2 | 44.8 | 40.4 | 49.2 | 20.8 | 11.5 | 30.0 |
| Passerine | Cape May Warbler | 34 | 22 | 12 | 29.9 | 26.7 | 35.7 | 5.7 | 3.8 | 8.2 |
| Passerine | Magnolia Warbler | 4 | 4 | 0 | | | | | | |
| Passerine | Bay-breasted Warbler | 7 | 2 | 5 | 31.1 | 28.2 | 37.7 | 4.8 | 3.3 | 11.4 |
| Passerine | Blackburnian Warbler | 4 | 2 | 2 | 29.1 | 26.7 | 31.5 | 7.0 | 6.4 | 7.6 |
| Passerine | Palm Warbler | 10 | 7 | 3 | 28.6 | 28.5 | 29.3 | 4.5 | 4.2 | 6.9 |
| Passerine | Pine Warbler | 3 | 1 | 2 | 27.3 | 27.0 | 27.6 | 3.6 | 3.0 | 4.2 |
| Passerine | Yellow-rumped Warbler | 11 | 8 | 3 | 37.7 | 28.8 | 41.9 | 5.9 | 4.0 | 6.7 |
| Passerine | Setophaga species | 37 | 25 | 12 | 37.2 | 27.5 | 55.3 | 7.4 | 2.7 | 11.4 |
| Passerine | Parulidae species | 6 | 3 | 3 | 33.4 | 31.4 | 46.9 | 6.1 | 5.0 | 6.6 |
| Passerine | Rose-breasted Grosbeak | 9 | 4 | 5 | 32.4 | 26.8 | 48.3 | 5.4 | 3.4 | 8.3 |
| Passerine | Passerine species | 59 | 33 | 26 | 37.8 | 24.0 | 110.0 | 7.9 | 0.1 | 49.1 |
| Unid. Avian | Unidentified bird species | 42 | 15 | 27 | 50.5 | 25.5 | 127.4 | 10.1 | 1.0 | 53.2 |
| Bat | Bat species | 36 | 10 | 26 | 97.8 | 39.7 | 130.4 | 29.2 | 5.8 | 50.0 |

**Acknowledgments**
We would like to thank the Dominion Energy team and the CVOW project for their continuing support of this research, particularly Scott Lawton, Tony Taylor, Stewart Lamerdin, and Matt Overton. We would also like to thank SGRE particularly Adam Cross and Francis Ackerman for coordinating site visits, and Charlie Donadio and his team from Fast Ferry who so expertly and safely get our team to the turbines for these deployments and retrievals. We thank BOEM for supporting the initial development of the first ATOM system and our Normandeau team including our hardware and software engineers lead by Karen Gilland and Chris Ribe for helping us move development of the system forward.

**References**

[1] https://www.whitehouse.gov/briefing-room/statements-releases/2021/03/29/fact-sheet-biden-administration-jumpstarts-offshore-wind-energy-projects-to-create-jobs/
[2] US Department of Energy 2016 Wind vision: a new era for wind power in the United States. Available from: https://www.energy.gov/eere/wind/wind-vision-1
[3] Normandeau Associates Inc 2014 *Acoustic Monitoring of Temporal and Spatial Abundance of Birds Near Outer Continental Shelf Structures: Synthesis Report* (Herndon, VA: U.S. Dept. of the Interior, Bureau of Ocean Energy Management) BOEM 2014-004
[4] Johnson J B, Gates J E and Zegre N P 2011 Monitoring seasonal bat activity on a coastal barrier island in Maryland, USA *Environ. Monit. Assess* **173** 685–99
[5] Pelletier S and Peterson T 2013 *Wind Power and Bats Offshore: What are the Risks? A Current Understanding of Offshore Bat Activity* (Providence, RI: Presentation to the American Wind Power Association Offshore Wind Power) October 2013
[6] Pelletier S K, Omland K, Watrous K S and Peterson T S 2013 *Information Synthesis on the Potential for Bat Interactions with Offshore Wind Facilities, Final Report* (Herndon, VA: U.S. Dept. of the Interior, Bureau of Ocean Energy Management, Headquarters) OCS Study BOEM 2013-01163 p 119
[7] Peterson T 2016 *Long-term Bat Monitoring on Islands, Offshore Structures, and Coastal Sites in the Gulf of Maine, mid-Atlantic, and Great Lakes* Report by Stantec Consulting for US Department of Energy
[8] Desholm M and Kahlert J 2005 Avian collision risk at an offshore wind farm *Biol. Lett.* **1** 296–98 Available from: https://doi.org/10.1098/rsbl.2005.0336
[9] Drewitt A L and Langston R H W 2006. Assessing the impacts of wind farms on birds *Ibis Lond* **148** 29–42 Available from: https://doi.org/10.1111/j.1474-919X.2006.00516.x
[10] Everaert J and Stienen E W M 2007 Impact of wind turbines on birds in Zeebrugge (Belgium) *Biodivers. Conserv.* **16** 3345–59 Available from: https://doi.org/10.1007/978-1-4020-6865-2_8
[11] Masden E A, Haydon D T, Fox A D and Furness R W 2010 Barriers to movement: modelling energetic costs of avoiding marine wind farms amongst breeding seabirds *Mar. Pollut. Bull.* **60** 1085–91 Available from: https://doi.org/10.1016/J.MARPOLBUL.2010.01.016
[12] Furness R W, Wade H M and Masden E A 2013 Assessing vulnerability of marine bird populations to offshore wind farms. *J. Environ. Manag.* **119** 56–66 Available from: https://doi.org/10.1016/j.jenvman.2013.01.025
[13] Vanermen N, Onkelinx T, Courtens W, van de walle M, Verstraete H and Stienen E W M 2015 Seabird avoidance and attraction at an offshore wind farm in the Belgian part of the North Sea. *Hydrobiologia* **756** 51–61 Available from: https://doi.org/10.1007/s10750-014-2088-x
[14] Pettersson J 2005 *The Impact of Offshore Wind Farms on Bird Life in Southern Kalmar Sound, Sweden, a Final Report Based on Studies 1999–2003* (Sweden: Lund University) pp 128
[15] Desholm M 2006 *Wind Farm Related Mortality Among Avian Migrants: a Remote Sensing Study and Model Analysis* PhD thesis (Denmark: University of Copenhagen) 132 pp
[16] Skov H, Heinänen S, Norman T, Ward R M, Méndez-Roldán S and Ellis I 2018 *ORJIP Bird Collision and Avoidance Study, Final report April 2018* (United Kingdom: The Carbon Trust)

[17] StormGeo 2022 Availablve from: https://www.stormgeo.com/company/who-we-are/

[18] Krijgsveld K L, Fijn R C, Japink M, van Horssen P W, Heunks C, Collier M P, Poot M J M, Beuker D and Dirksen S 2011 *Effect Studies Offshore Wind Farm Egmond aan Zee Final Report on Fluxes, Flight Altitudes and Behaviour of Flying Birds* (Culemborg: Bureau Waardenburg) Rapport 10–219

[19] Thaxter C B, Ross-Smith V H, Bouten W, Masden E A, Clark N A, Conway G J, Barber L, Clewley G C and Burton N H K 2018 Dodging the blades: new insights into three-dimensional space use of offshore wind farms by lesser black-backed gulls Larus fuscus *Mar. Ecol. Prog. Ser.* **587** 247–53

[20] Furness R W 2019 Avoidance rates of herring gull, great black-backed gull and common gull for use in the assessment of terrestrial wind farms in Scotland *SNH* Research Report No 1019

[21] Thaxter C B, Conway G J, Burton N H K, Ross V H, Willem S, Masden E A, et al 2019 Avian vulnerability to wind farm collision through the year: insights from lesser black-backed gulls (Larus fuscus) tracked from multiple breeding colonies. *J. Appl. Ecol.* **2019** 1–13

[22] Leemans J J, van Bemmelen R S A, Middelveld R P, Kraal J, Bravo Rebolledo E L, Beuker D, Kuiper K and Gyimesi A 2022 *Bird Fluxes, Flight- and Avoidance Behaviour of Birds in Offshore Wind Farm Luchterduinen* (Culemborg: Bureau Waardenburg) Report 22-078

[23] Tjørnløv R S, Skov H, Armitage M, Barker M, Cuttat F and Thomas K 2023 *Resolving Key Uncertainties of Seabird Flight and Avoidance Behaviours at Offshore Wind Farms. Final Report for the study period 2020-2021* Prepared for Vattenfall Available from: https://group.vattenfall.com/uk/contentassets/1b23f720f2694bd1906c007effe2c85a/aowfl_aberdeen_seabird_study_final_report_20_february_2023.pdf

[24] de Jong J, Millon L, Håstad O and Victorsso J 2021 Activity pattern and correlation between bat and insect abundance at wind turbines in south Sweden *Animals* **11** 3269 Available from: https://doi.org/10.3390/ani11113269

[25] Bowden J, Johnson C G 1976 *Migrating and Other Terrestrial Insects at Sea* pp 97–117 ed L Cheng *Marine Insects* (Amsterdam-Oxford: North-Holland Publishing Company; New York: American Elsevier Publishing Company)

[26] Russell R W, May M L, Soltesz K L and Fitzpatrick J W 1998 Massive swarm migrations of dragonflies (Odonata) in eastern North America *Am. Midl. Nat.* **140** 235–342

[27] Srygley R B and Dudley R 2008 Optimal strategies for insects migrating in the flight boundary layer: mechanisms and consequences *Integr. Comp. Biol.* **48** 119–33

# Sustainable end-of-life value chain scenarios for wind turbine blades

**S Fayyaz[1,3], K W Lund[2], B Khoshnevisan[1], E S Madsen[2], and M Birkved[1]**

[1] SDU Life Cycle Engineering, Department of Green Technology, University of Southern Denmark, Campusvej 55, Odense M 5230, Denmark

[2] SDU Engineering Operational Management, Department of Technology and Innovation, University of Southern Denmark, Campusvej 55, Odense M 5230, Denmark

**Abstract.** This study presents a sustainable end-of-life (EoL) value chain scenario assessment framework for decommissioned wind turbine blades (WTBs) to address the challenge of increased volumes of WTBs reaching their EoL. Findings from the previous studies highlight that WTBs EoL scenarios and their upscaling are yet to be addressed environmentally and economically. The scenarios investigated herein are mechanical shredding, pyrolysis, and cement co-processing that can be industrially upscaled. Together with the industrial partners, end-of-life scenario value chains are identified, to assess their sustainability through material flow analysis (MFA), life cycle assessment (LCA), and techno-economic assessment (TEA). A prospective consequential LCA model is proposed for scenarios with different technology readiness levels (TRL) expected to be commercialized at different timeframes. IPCC's Shared Socio-economic Pathways (SSPs) will be used to describe foreground and background systems in 2030, 2040, and 2050. More specifically, SSP1 (i.e., green road), SSP2 (i.e., middle road), and SSP5 (i.e., fossil-fueled development) will be employed and quantified based on integrated assessment models (IAM). Furthermore, environmental impacts, economic criteria, Social sustainability, and circularity cannot directly be compared to evaluate the scenarios. Thus, this research proposes multi-criteria decision-making (MCDM) method to evaluate the three end-of-life scenario value chains considering a prospective scheme and addressing the key challenges related to the assessment of emerging technologies. Furthermore, a full conceptual framework of the methodology is presented.

## 1. Introduction

The wind energy sector has undergone tremendous development in the last four decades (a 75-fold growth of capacity from 1997 to 2018) [1]. Therefore, many wind turbines are reaching their end-of-life (EoL) in the coming years considering the typical service life of 20-25 years [2]. Hence, the management of composite wind turbine blades (WTBs) at their end-of-life is becoming an increasing challenge.

WTBs are made of glass fiber reinforced plastic (GFRP), foam, plywood and/or wood, and some metal components i.e., lightning conductors[3]. Carbon fiber-reinforced plastic (CFRP) is also increasingly used in WTBs to create higher stiffness and must thus be considered in future EoL solutions [4]. However, due to the complexity of the materials, the uncertainty of material composition of WTBs, and the lack of well-established recycling/reuse options for recovered materials from WTBs, sustainable solutions for EoL management of WTBs are yet to be designed and industrially implemented. WTBs are resistant to sunlight, moisture, and heat and will take hundreds of years to degrade when landfilled

[3] Corresponding author (sfay@igt.sdu.dk)

[5]. However, the organic polymer and balsa wood could release methane or volatile organic compounds, of which, on average, 75% are collected by landfill gas collection systems [5]. So far, composite wastes have mainly ended up in a landfill, but the European Union has issued several directives regarding composite waste control (75/442/EEC) amendment (91/156/EEC), landfilling (1999/31/EC), and incineration (2000/76/EC) to ensure minimizing waste generation and increasing the rate of recycling/material recovery. Besides landfilling being an unattractive solution in terms of material circularity and environmental impact, both Germany and the Netherlands banned landfilling and later as part of the Wind Europe 2022, it was proposed a complete landfill ban of fiber-reinforced plastics (FRPs) in Europe [6]. Thus, it is important to establish sustainable alternatives to landfill to create a higher level of material circularity [7].

The future waste streams of WTB waste are important to determine where, when, and how much FRP waste from WTBs is to be handled. Several research studies have developed models to provide quantities of waste flows over time. These models have been tested on different geographical areas based mostly on public databases based on the commissioning dates of wind turbines [8]–[15]. The geographical areas that have been studied range from the entire world [12], to Europe [11], [13] North America[9], [16] and country level [8], [15], [17], [18]. The findings from previous literature indicate that in Europe, 100.000 tonnes of decommissioned WTBs are to be handled yearly by 2034 [11]. Worldwide the prediction is that there will be 43 million tonnes of cumulative blade waste by 2050 and that China will account for 40% of the generated waste whilst Europe and the United States will contribute 25% and 16%, respectively [12]. These predictions highlight the magnitude of the problem and that different geographical areas will face the waste problem at different times.

Sustainable recycling technologies for WTBs are not yet widely available, cost-competitive, and commercialized but are still under development [2]. Three technological tracks are deemed scalable and mature to be considered as solutions i.e., mechanical shredding, cement co-processing, and pyrolysis [19] but at different TRLs due to technological barriers.

This research aims to develop a framework to evaluate the WTB waste recycling scenarios with different levels of TRL in terms of environmental, economic, social, and circularity aspects in a prospective framework.

### *1.1. Literature review*

Our comprehensive literature review on 30 out of 70 articles from 2018 to 2022 -Before 2018, landfilling and incineration were considered primary alternatives for WTBs EoL solutions [1]- with the keywords i.e., wind turbine blade, end of life, composite waste, life cycle assessment, techno-economic assessment, circular economy, and sustainability showed that 60% of the peer-reviewed publications are conceptual and review studies that are depicted in Figure 1. Furthermore, the case studies are more model/estimation/simulation-driven analyses dedicated to repurposing and mechanical recycling cases. Thus, there is a need for more comprehensive assessments based on real case studies/primary data on emerging recycling technologies. The overall suggestions of the review regarding the recycling method were mechanical and Cement co-processing, and repurposing for now and thermal Methods for the future. Policy support, producers' responsibility, and higher landfill costs were also proposed to support sustainable recycling. The key findings from the literature review will be elaborated on in the following sections.

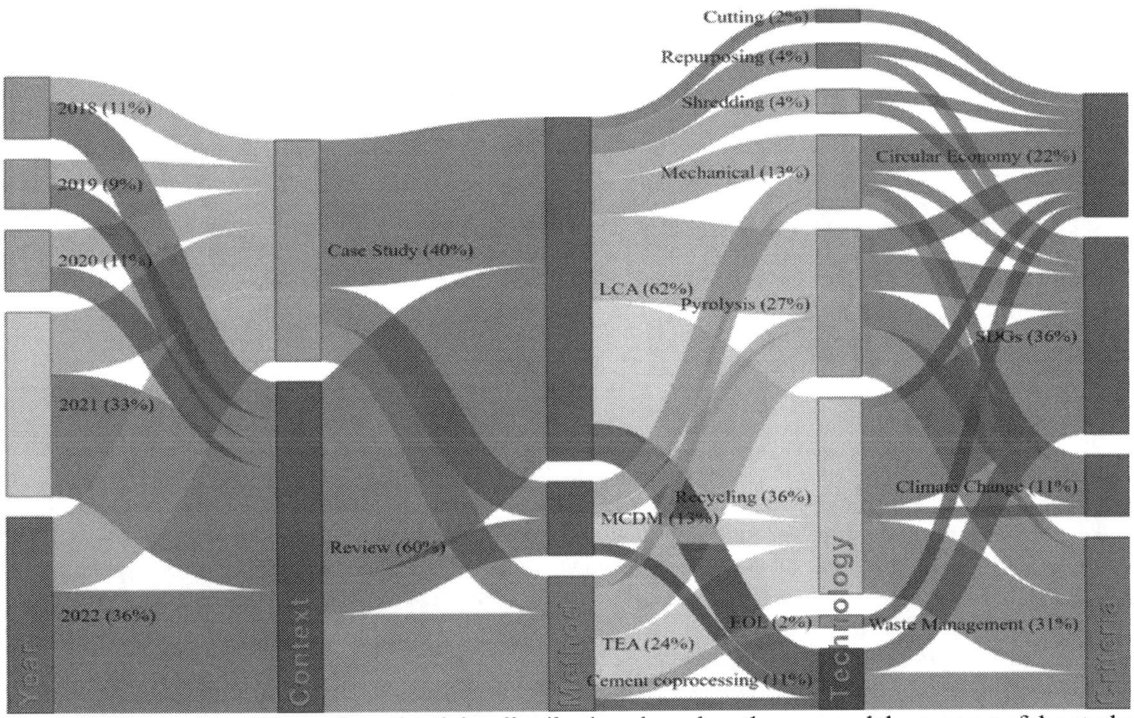


**Figure 1.** Illustration of the reviewed articles distributions based on the year and the context of the study, assessment method, intended technology, and assessment criteria

*1.2. WTBs EoL scenarios.*

Literature has so far focused on possible technologies for handling WTB waste EoL. The first step in all scenarios is pre-processing operations. Jensen and Skelton considered different alternatives for cutting operations such as wire cutting, water jet cutting, jaw cutting, and saw cutting[20]. However, these operations and their impacts on future recycling scenarios are yet to be covered in the literature both in terms of operational implications and environmental impact.

Structural repurposing is when sections of the blade are cut to size and used directly in making new products such as furniture [21]or bridges [22]. However, this EoL strategy is difficult to scale, and with future waste volumes in mind, more large-scale technologies must be implemented.

Mechanical recycling is primarily referred to in processes where WTB waste undergoes cutting, shredding, milling, or grinding [2], [23]. In these processes, the FRP blade material is reduced in size to smaller fractions, and other materials, such as metals and steel, can be removed while fibers and cured resin are still mixed [2], [23]. Therefore, the fractioned WTB material must either be used directly where the combination of cured resin and fibers are utilized e.g. noise barriers [3] or filling in asphalt [24]. The mechanical recycling technologies are a prerequisite for further processing e.g., pyrolysis or cement co-processing [2], which are addressed later in this section.

Cement co-processing and incineration are both thermal processes in which mechanically pre-processed materials are burned ideally with heat recovery. However, as only the organic fractions of the materials will be combusted, the thermal process leaves behind a significant unburnt fraction, i.e., the glass fibers, which become wastes [25]. For this reason, incineration is not considered a future solution for sustainable waste handling [26]. In the cement co-processing technology, the mechanically ground WTB is also burnt to recover the calorific value for cement kilns. In this process, the WTB waste thus substitutes Fuel as well as refuse-derived fuel (RDF) or solid recovered fuel (RDF). Contrary to incineration, the cement co-processing technology can utilize the inorganic material from the glass fibers to substitute silica in the cement [1], [27].

Thermal recycling processes cover the processes where the polymers in the matrix are decomposed under high temperature, high pressure, and no oxygen, such as pyrolysis [28]–[30] and microwave pyrolysis [24], and fluidized bed technology [31]. Pyrolysis has received increasing interest in academic literature since the process allows for the separation of cured resin and glass fibers. The mechanically recycled WTBs are fed into reactors that operate under high temperatures and pressure in the absence of oxygen, which results in recovered fibers, gas, and pyrolysis oil with a calorific value similar to fuel oil (30–40 MJ/kg) [30]. The process produces multiple products with multiple applications in other industries. However, the pyrolysis processing technology is yet to be tested on an industrial scale for WTB waste[28]. In the majority of the reviewed studies, fiber recycling is considered, but upcycling of higher-value products, e.g., fuel and chemicals, is scarcely investigated[32]. Pyrolysis is also considered a costly and energy-intensive process because of the high process temperatures applied [23]. However, there is still a lack of the overall trade-off of the pyrolysis impacts since the high value of potential products and a higher level of material circularity could justify the increased cost and energy consumption.

Despite the increasing attention to WTBs EoL solutions, the product data available on blades in terms of materials, geometries, and material layout in the blade are not available to the required level of detail [1], [4], [38]. The lack of knowledge of what the blades consist of largely affects how they can be treated at the EoL as the material type, quality, and quantity largely affect post-processing options and potential secondary applications. To address this problem, the Danish cross-sector consortium named DecomBlades launched a standardized material passport for blade disposal in mid-2022 [39].

### *1.3. Circularity and TRL level of the scenarios*
The 9R-ladder presented by Potting et al. [33] is a tool to classify strategies according to the level of circularity. However, at some point in time, blades can no longer be repaired or refurbished; therefore, EoL solutions must be designed. Concerning the 9R-ladder, structural repurposing is at level R7, and the thermal recycling method stands at level R8, whilst cement co-processing is a mix of recycling and energy recovery, leaving it between levels R8 and R9.

While EoL scenarios have different degrees of circularity, they also have different technology readiness levels (TRL). Paulsen and Enevoldsen [27] presented a TRL-level assessment of the EoL technologies, finding that the TRL level of mechanical recycling is at 9 (max), cement co-processing is at 8-9, pyrolysis is at 7, and solvolysis is between 5-6. Downstream processing of pyro-outputs to applicable products is also not well developed, and the corresponding TRL depends on the intended application. For instance, the TRL of process technologies for pyro-oil produced from waste plastic is 6-9, and that of pyro-gas is 2-3 [34]. Comparing the sustainability of EoL technologies that are not at the same TRL and circularity levels is exceptionally complex, especially when assessing future solutions, and is found to be overlooked in the literature.

### *1.4. EoL Value chains*
Even though EoL recycling technologies have been increasingly investigated in academic literature, complete supply chain solutions are still to be researched. EoL solutions have to be designed with a supply chain mindset since impacts on cost, environment, and industrial scalability depend not only on the material processing technologies but also on logistical and operational processes before and after. Liu et al. [35] propose a supply chain setup of four stages, i.e., 1) waste preparation, 2) transportation, 3) recycling, and 4) post-processing, to compare the environmental impact of EoL solutions using an Eco-audit approach. Also, Rentizelas et al. [36] studied a potential supply chain setup for mechanical recycling, and Krauklis et al. [37] presented the core supply chain elements such as material collection, disassembly, material selection, recycling, and application of recycled fibers.

The common shortcoming of the previous studies is that the supply chain setup has been simplified and has not been supported by empirical data. So far, no actual EoL projects for WTBs have been documented and discussed in academic literature.

DecomBlades consists of ten industrial and academic partners representing the entire value chain for future recycling routes for EoL WTBs. The shared aim of the three-year project is to design and assess future EoL scenarios.

### *1.5. literature gap and the way to address*

The main body of literature was dedicated to reviewing or model/estimation/simulation-driven analyses mostly on mechanical recycling or repurposing that don't answer the coming challenge. there is a need to consider the magnitude of coming WTB waste in the future. Moreover, the entire value chain scenarios supported by empirical data are needed to be assessed as the scenarios. There should be a focus on emerging recycling technics as scaled-up future scenarios as well as post-processing of the outputs to the final product. Assessing the sustainability of future EoL scenarios should consider the overall trade-off of the environmental, economic, and social indicators, the high value of potential products, and the level of material circularity on a multicriteria assessment scheme. There is no established framework for sustainability assessment of emerging recycling scenarios in the future.

To address the gap in the literature, the assessment framework including environmental, economic, social, and circularity aspects is proposed with the herein specialties. LCA-wise, the prospective consequential context has been taken remarking on the magnitude of the waste and its influences on the marginal supplies in the future. The shared socioeconomic pathways were relied on to project multiple future states that are not provided by the present prospective LCA databases. Two extremes of SSPs namely SSP1 and SSP 5 as well as the middle of the road, SSP2 were considered in 2030, 2040, and 2050. A comprehensive sustainability assessment, accounting for the three pillars of sustainability as well as circularity as a highlighted Sustainable development goal has been proposed by employing MCDM models for weighing and ranking. To date, no value chain recycling scenario sustainability assessment addressing the abovementioned challenges was proposed to account for future waste quantities remarking established and emerging recycling technologies supported by realistic data. The proposed sustainability assessment framework outcomes supplied by the actual operational data from the industrial partners in the consortium will also be released by the end of 2023.

## 2. Methodology and case description

In this research, the blade manufacturers have provided information on the specifications of blades while the recycling partners provided details on the EoL processes. A value chain approach was adopted to establish functional, sustainable full-scale EoL scenarios of WTBs. The resulting data were compiled and analyzed by the academia through Material Flow Analysis (MFA) to quantitatively tracks the distribution and trajectory of materials among the processes, Life Cycle Assessment (LCA) to quantify the environmental impacts of WTB EoL scenarios in four steps as described by ISO 14040 [40], ISO and Techno-Economic assessment (TEA) for economic analysis of scenarios. MCDM technics for weighing and ranking are supposed to evaluate the outcomes of the assessments to answer the WTB EoL challenge in the best way possible.

Four scenarios were developed through the assessment of feasible solutions for FRPs, workshops, and meetings with the project partners. At the preliminary assessment, low maturity of pyro-outputs (fiber, oil, and gas) processing to final products popped up as a challenge. This challenge led to the development of future scenarios for pyro-output processing as well as two other scenarios within a time frame of 2030, 2040, and 2050 in a prospective LCA scheme. Scenario-wise, the Shared Socio-economic Pathways (SSPs) developed by the intergovernmental panel on climate change (IPCC) will be relied upon for future scenario development [41]

### *2.1. Value chain scenarios*

A literature study identified the potential technological solutions for the EoL of WTBs[5]. Additionally, it has been identified that data on upscaling of EoL technologies and solutions to a full-scale operation are sparse. This study also includes the operations management perspective of the value chain from the wind turbine site to the processing plants. The research at hand, therefore, considers four EoL scenarios including all the steps in the relevant value chains and the design of every single handling, processing, and transportation of the WTB from the site and to the final processing plant.

Mechanical shredding is a method to grind WTBs into fragments for further applications as filling/gravel or input to pyrolysis and cement co-processing [42]. Cement co-processing is a recovery-recycling process that utilizes fiber fractions as mineral feed supplements and combustible polymer matrix as an alternative fuel [5]. Pyrolysis is an upcycling process to reclaim fiber, oil, and gas from the

FRP matrix [43]. The landfill was also included as a baseline scenario. The four scenarios are presented in Figure 3 through eight value chain steps and are utilized as input for further analysis.

*2.2. Scenarios assessment.*
The MFAs and LCAs were all scaled to one t of WTBs as reference flow enabling comparison of scenarios. The TEAs were conducted based on the capacity and size of the plants and harmonized calculation assumptions. Based on the expected application of results in decision-making and the macro scale nature of the WTBs EoL issue, consequential LCA was applied for the assessment [44]. Applying this approach influences on background systems were included in the assessment, and the outputs hence substitute other materials or products in the market. Net impacts/savings of each scenario are calculated by subtracting the avoided impacts of substitution from the induced impacts of the process.

In all the scenarios the environmental benefit of the avoided product compensates for or surplus the environmental impact of the processes to different extents. The initial assessments represent the importance of avoided products in the trade-off accounting. Given that there are no real markets and off-takers for the outputs, the substitution of the avoided products is based on the most relevant applications. Elaboration is particularly critical for the less mature pyro-output processing options. Additionally, some environmentally preferred pyro-product processing options are not well established yet but could emerge as competitive options in the future. It is therefore considered crucial to develop cost-effective chemical segregation processes to make pyrolysis profitable [32]. To address these challenges, SSP-aligned scenarios were developed based on each potential option, post-processing, and application in 2030, 2040, and 2050 for each scenario.

*2.3. Prospective LCA*
Due to the rapid changes in e.g. energy systems and industrial processes, traditional LCA based on a static database doesn't provide a representative insight into the performance of future technologies/current technologies under future conditions [45]. One of the major challenges of applying LCA to new technologies is modeling a consistent future foreground value chain that can be addressed by applying a scenario-based approach. Another concern is future background system modeling which ideally is answered by the transformation of existing databases to the future context, using Integrated Assessment Models (IAMs) to provide forecasted scenarios in line with the Shared Socioeconomic Pathways (SSPs). The uncertain nature of the future data also necessitates considerable attention to the discussion of both design and assessment uncertainties [45]. Projection in time was introduced to LCA to assess the performance of emerging technologies in the future as a prospective LCA (pLCA) framework. PREMISE is developed as a tool for the generation of a prospective inventory database based on IMAGE and REMIND IAM models for the SSP2 scenario[46]. PREMISE has some limitations making it misaligned with our needs for the DecomBlades project. It is only compatible with attributional LCA (Cut off) and merely the SSP2 baseline & RCPs are reflected in the prospective ecoinvent database[46]. The Energy and emission data provided by IAM based on the SSPs were thus implemented for the pLCA framework applied in this study.

*2.4. SSP scenarios*
Shared socioeconomic pathway scenarios developed by IPCC encapsulate the changes in technology and environment over time until 2100[47]. Five narrative-based descriptions of demographics, human development, economy and lifestyle, policies and institutions, technology, and environment, and natural resources in the future represent potential societal developments. The scenarios are Sustainable development [48], Middle-of-the-road development [22], Regional rivalry [50], Inequality [51], and Fossil-fueled development[52] including long-term demographic and economic changes with a multi-model approach to project energy, land-use, and emissions trajectories[53]. For this study, we consider SSP1 as the best case, SSP2 as the middle of the road, and SSP5 as the worst case to have a clear picture of the future window of opportunities.

*2.4.1. SSP1, SSP2, & SSP5 narratives.* Qualitative narratives could describe institutions, political stability, environmental awareness evolutions, and trends over large world regions to elaborate intended future scenarios. Quantified data of key variables can be implemented for energy use, land use, emissions, and other outcomes modeling [54]. We have taken the relevant narratives in the fields of economy and lifestyle, policies & institutions, Technology, and environmental & natural resources out of the three SSPs to consider in establishing the SSP-aligned scenarios. Integrated assessment models (IAMs) are implemented to develop quantified data based on the SSPs [54].

*2.4.2. IAM quantification models.* There are six IAM models all developed to determine energy use and emissions characteristics namely: AIM-CGE, GCAM, IMAGE, MESSAGE-GLOBIOM, REMIND-Magpie, and WITCH-GLOBIOM [55] by FEEM[4], IIASA[5], PBL[6], NIES[7], PIK, and PNNL[8] teams for the SSP scenario[56]. Each model covers some SSPs with more focus on specific fields. The data resulting from the IAM models are provided by the International Institute for Applied Systems Analysis database, Austria (IIASA) [57].

*2.4.3. IIASA database.* SSP public database provided by IIASA could help policymakers around the world with science-based policies. Different IAM projection models are utilized for the SSPs. A marker scenario is proposed for each SSP based on one IAM model. SSP1: IMAGE, SSP2: MESSAGE-GLOBIOM, SSP3: AIM, SSP4: GCAM, SSP5: REMIND-MAGPIE. Other IAM-quantified SSPs could be used as an uncertainty space [57]. The quantified data on energy, fuel, and emissions based on marker scenarios for SSP1, SSP2, and SSP5 for 2030, 2040, and 2050 are presented in table 1.

**Table 1.** Quantified data of energy, fuel, & emissions for SSP1, SSP2, and SSP5 based on marker scenario IAMs for 2030, 2040, & 2050.

<table>
<tr><th>Model</th><th></th><th colspan="3">IMAGE</th><th colspan="3">MESSAGE-GLOBIOM</th><th colspan="3">REMIND-MAGPIE</th></tr>
<tr><td>REGION</td><td>R5.2OECD</td><td colspan="3">SSP1-Baseline</td><td colspan="3">SSP2-Baseline</td><td colspan="3">SSP5-Baseline</td></tr>
<tr><td>VARIABLE</td><td>UNIT</td><td>2030</td><td>2040</td><td>2050</td><td>2030</td><td>2040</td><td>2050</td><td>2030</td><td>2040</td><td>2050</td></tr>
<tr><td>Capacity|Electricity</td><td>GW</td><td>2979.21</td><td>3241.81</td><td>3969.72</td><td>2963.27</td><td>3326.98</td><td>3793.07</td><td>2626.20</td><td>3133.00</td><td>3841.30</td></tr>
<tr><td>Capacity|Electricity|Biomass</td><td>GW</td><td>55.30</td><td>25.75</td><td>7.28</td><td>10.86</td><td>1.25</td><td>2.01</td><td>37.36</td><td>58.95</td><td>89.81</td></tr>
<tr><td>Capacity|Electricity|Coal</td><td>GW</td><td>415.77</td><td>377.57</td><td>390.25</td><td>226.55</td><td>210.60</td><td>209.44</td><td>571.91</td><td>769.41</td><td>1015.46</td></tr>
<tr><td>Capacity|Electricity|Gas</td><td>GW</td><td>995.96</td><td>1188.90</td><td>1364.02</td><td>1428.47</td><td>1902.40</td><td>2289.00</td><td>1130.07</td><td>1657.00</td><td>2116.70</td></tr>
<tr><td>Capacity|Electricity|Geothermal</td><td>GW</td><td></td><td></td><td></td><td>2.42</td><td>0</td><td>0</td><td>6.12</td><td>7.98</td><td>11.93</td></tr>
<tr><td>Capacity|Electricity|Hydro</td><td>GW</td><td>520.22</td><td>541.44</td><td>544.76</td><td>450.24</td><td>451.55</td><td>452.98</td><td>235.07</td><td>199.07</td><td>197.35</td></tr>
<tr><td>Capacity|Electricity|Nuclear</td><td>GW</td><td>326.13</td><td>208.53</td><td>55.03</td><td>293.75</td><td>159.03</td><td>38.32</td><td>244.91</td><td>182.04</td><td>126.56</td></tr>
<tr><td>Capacity|Electricity|Oil</td><td>GW</td><td>122.70</td><td>49.93</td><td>4.15</td><td>6.49</td><td>3.88</td><td>0.28</td><td></td><td></td><td></td></tr>
<tr><td>Capacity|Electricity|Other</td><td>GW</td><td>23.56</td><td>48.42</td><td>54.44</td><td>0</td><td>0</td><td>0</td><td></td><td></td><td></td></tr>
<tr><td>Capacity|Electricity|Solar</td><td>GW</td><td>213.73</td><td>331.31</td><td>697.33</td><td>145.18</td><td>128.13</td><td>73.62</td><td>157.01</td><td>108.63</td><td>10.66</td></tr>
<tr><td>Capacity|Electricity|Solar|CSP</td><td>GW</td><td>5.01</td><td>11.99</td><td>37.62</td><td>1.58</td><td>0</td><td>0</td><td>3.01</td><td>2.16</td><td>0.44</td></tr>
<tr><td>Capacity|Electricity|Solar|PV</td><td>GW</td><td>208.72</td><td>319.32</td><td>659.71</td><td>143.6</td><td>128.13</td><td>73.62</td><td>153.96</td><td>106.46</td><td>10.23</td></tr>
<tr><td>Capacity|Electricity|Wind</td><td>GW</td><td>305.85</td><td>305.86</td><td>852.46</td><td>399.29</td><td>461.73</td><td>694.00</td><td>233.89</td><td>149.57</td><td>272.71</td></tr>
<tr><td>Capacity|Electricity|Wind|Offshore</td><td>GW</td><td>26.45</td><td>105.29</td><td>216.43</td><td>0</td><td>0</td><td>0</td><td></td><td></td><td></td></tr>
<tr><td>Capacity|Electricity|Wind|Onshore</td><td>GW</td><td>279.39</td><td>364.67</td><td>636.03</td><td>399.29</td><td>399.29</td><td>694.00</td><td></td><td></td><td></td></tr>
<tr><td>Emissions|BC</td><td>Mt BC/yr</td><td>0.45</td><td>0.39</td><td>0.33</td><td>0.38</td><td>0.33</td><td>0.30</td><td>0.54</td><td>0.49</td><td>0.46</td></tr>
<tr><td>Emissions|$CH_4$</td><td>Mt $CH_4$/yr</td><td>72.06</td><td>72.42</td><td>68.50</td><td>70.55</td><td>74.37</td><td>79.24</td><td>79.65</td><td>96.26</td><td>112.62</td></tr>
<tr><td>Emissions|$CH_4$|Fossil Fuels and Industry</td><td>Mt $CH_4$/yr</td><td></td><td></td><td></td><td></td><td></td><td></td><td>23.02</td><td>35.64</td><td>47.46</td></tr>
<tr><td>Emissions|$CH_4$|Land Use</td><td>Mt $CH_4$/yr</td><td>29.14</td><td>27.37</td><td>25.57</td><td>31.22</td><td>32.27</td><td>33.12</td><td>30.71</td><td>31.58</td><td>31.62</td></tr>
<tr><td>Emissions|CO</td><td>Mt CO/yr</td><td>59.23</td><td>55.04</td><td>50.70</td><td>73.53</td><td>67.17</td><td>63.74</td><td>108.89</td><td>103.99</td><td>99.74</td></tr>
<tr><td>Emissions|$CO_2$</td><td>Mt $CO_2$/yr</td><td>9608.73</td><td>9170.82</td><td>8680.83</td><td>12631.6</td><td>13400.4</td><td>14251.9</td><td>16862.5</td><td>20633.0</td><td>25110.0</td></tr>
<tr><td>Emissions|$CO_2$|Fossil Fuels and Industry</td><td>Mt $CO_2$/yr</td><td>10854.1</td><td>10357.7</td><td>9748.9</td><td>12959.3</td><td>13664.6</td><td>14431.5</td><td>16933.0</td><td>20709.0</td><td>25171.0</td></tr>
<tr><td>Emissions|$CO_2$|Land Use</td><td>Mt $CO_2$/yr</td><td>-1000.1</td><td>-956.1</td><td>-855.5</td><td>-327.63</td><td>-97.02</td><td>-179.56</td><td>-70.94</td><td>-74.76</td><td>-50.90</td></tr>
<tr><td>Emissions|F-Gases</td><td>Mt $CO_2$-eq/yr</td><td>789.46</td><td>816.87</td><td>850.09</td><td>726.21</td><td>825.14</td><td>912.77</td><td>844.78</td><td>922.21</td><td>1002.06</td></tr>
<tr><td>Emissions|Kyoto Gases</td><td>Mt $CO_2$-eq/yr</td><td>12994.7</td><td>12572.3</td><td>11990.9</td><td>15990.1</td><td>17004.2</td><td>18100.6</td><td>20610.0</td><td>24832.0</td><td>29812.0</td></tr>
<tr><td>Emissions|$N_2O$</td><td>kt $N_2O$/yr</td><td>2667.87</td><td>2597.52</td><td>2508.51</td><td>2912.69</td><td>3083.52</td><td>3202.56</td><td>3115.08</td><td>2966.03</td><td>2998.46</td></tr>
<tr><td>Emissions|$N_2O$|Land Use</td><td>kt $N_2O$/yr</td><td>1632.14</td><td>1595.28</td><td>1553.45</td><td>1967.72</td><td>2055.52</td><td>2145.87</td><td>2057.14</td><td>1990.77</td><td>1940.57</td></tr>
<tr><td>Emissions|$NH_3$</td><td>Mt $NH_3$/yr</td><td>11.88</td><td>11.36</td><td>10.84</td><td>14.78</td><td>15.24</td><td>15.64</td><td>14.66</td><td>14.17</td><td>13.50</td></tr>
<tr><td>Emissions|$NO_x$</td><td>Mt $NO_2$/yr</td><td>11.87</td><td>10.90</td><td>9.48</td><td>15.00</td><td>13.06</td><td>11.49</td><td>16.19</td><td>16.44</td><td>16.22</td></tr>
<tr><td>Emissions|OC</td><td>Mt OC/yr</td><td>2.74</td><td>2.56</td><td>2.21</td><td>2.40</td><td>2.21</td><td>2.10</td><td>3.21</td><td>3.12</td><td>3.09</td></tr>
<tr><td>Emissions|Sulfur</td><td>Mt $SO_2$/yr</td><td>5.31</td><td>4.28</td><td>3.44</td><td>9.34</td><td>8.01</td><td>6.98</td><td>9.12</td><td>7.76</td><td>6.56</td></tr>
<tr><td>Emissions|VOC</td><td>Mt VOC/yr</td><td>9.63</td><td>8.33</td><td>7.13</td><td>20.42</td><td>19.64</td><td>19.17</td><td>25.66</td><td>23.58</td><td>21.64</td></tr>
<tr><td>Energy Service|Transportation|Freight</td><td>bn tkm/yr</td><td>17730.6</td><td>20037.4</td><td>22244.4</td><td></td><td></td><td></td><td>70927.0</td><td>79703.0</td><td>92050.0</td></tr>
</table>

[4] Fondazione Eni Enrico Mattei

[5] International Institute for Applied Systems Analysis,

[6] The Netherlands Environmental Assessment Agency, The Netherlands

[7] National Institute for Environmental Research, Japan

[8] Pacific Northwest National Laboratory, USA

Journal of Physics: Conference Series **2507** (2023) 012007 doi:10.1088/1742-6596/2507/1/012007

## 3. Results and discussion

### *3.1. SSP-aligned scenarios*

To develop the SSP-aligned scenarios for the study, a list of possible options for processing and post-processing was provided for each scenario. For each time frame, a set of options was selected as a scenario based on the literature, technical experience, and insights of SDU and the relevant partners [58] [43]. The qualitative and quantitative frameworks defined by each SSP were also reflected in the developing SSP-aligned scenarios for each timeframe. The feasible options for the SSP-aligned scenario are listed below in Figure 2.

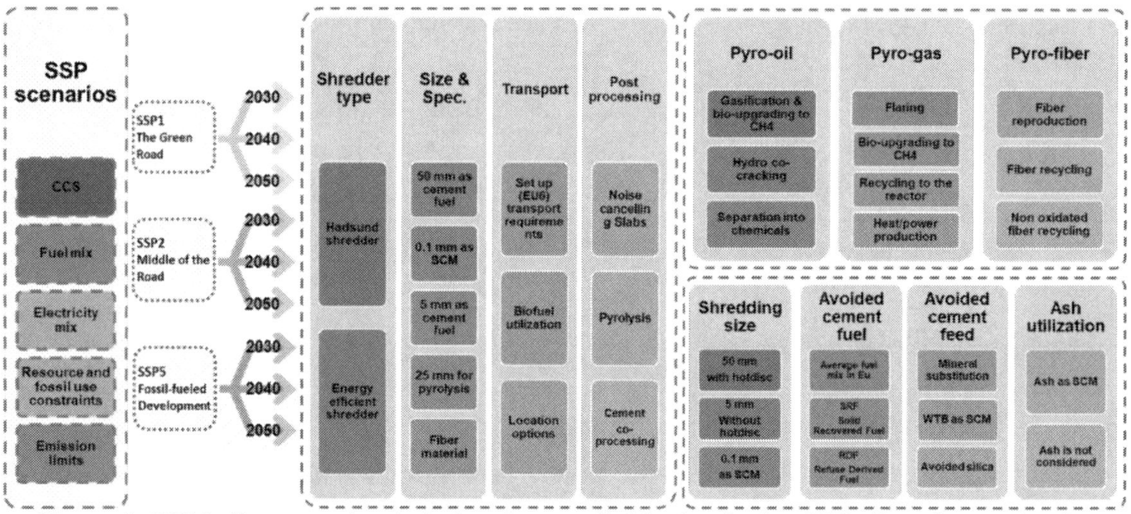


**Figure 2.** SSP indicators and technical options applied in developing SSP-aligned scenarios for mechanical shredding, pyrolysis, and Cement co-processing overtime

### *3.2. MCDM evaluation framework*

LCA-MCDM integration is a recommended decision-making approach [59]. LCA analyses the cradle-to-grave environmental impacts of a product or service in a multidimensional approach [60], [61] and the MCDM method would assist to assess the performance of a scenario out of varying indicators provided by LCA [62] as well as economic index and other sustainability indices. Economic growth, sustainable resource use, and maintaining the ecological balance now and in the future are the sustainability concerns. Ideal decision-making must appreciate these bottom-line concepts that lead to a complex trade-off situation. MCDM is especially helpful in multisectoral economic, and environmental criteria comparisons [61].

A weighing MCDM scheme like the best-worst method (BWM) method would be considered for the criteria based on the expert's viewpoints on the questionnaires. BWM [63] could be implemented with an advantage for weighting as it needs minimum pairwise comparisons and has fewer inconsistency issues [64]. A basic linear optimization model to define the ideal weights that have been employed in various decision-making and evaluation problems as well as sustainable supply-chain [65], [66].

After weighing the criteria, the MCDM ranking method would be implemented for a robust scenario assessment. It would be employed for the evaluation of the scenarios on each timeframe considering environmental impacts (i.e., climate change, human health, ecosystem quality, and resources), circularity, and cost.

### *3.3. Discussion*

Sustainable full-scale value chain-based scenarios based on empirical data are assessed in this project.

The developed framework addresses the challenges to assessing emerging immature technologies that should be considered for the future. The prospective LCA model is developed covering two extremes of SSPs and the middle road scenario for three points of time based on the predicted amount of waste WTB. The uncertainty due to less mature options for the future is resolved through developing SSP-aligned scenarios and implementing the pLCA approach.

Economic assessment supplements the environmental assessment outcomes and provides a good relation with reality. Circularity is considered to have some correlation with any scenario's sustainability. MCDM weighing and ranking methods are proposed for weighing multiple criteria and further assessment of each set of scenarios based on them. Given that actual WTBs EoL projects have not been documented so far in academic literature this cross-disciplinary large-scale empirical project, could be employed to good advantage for the wind community, wind turbine owners, producers, and researchers for their work on handling EoL WTBs. The case description, assessment methods, and the proposed framework are graphically illustrated in figure 3.

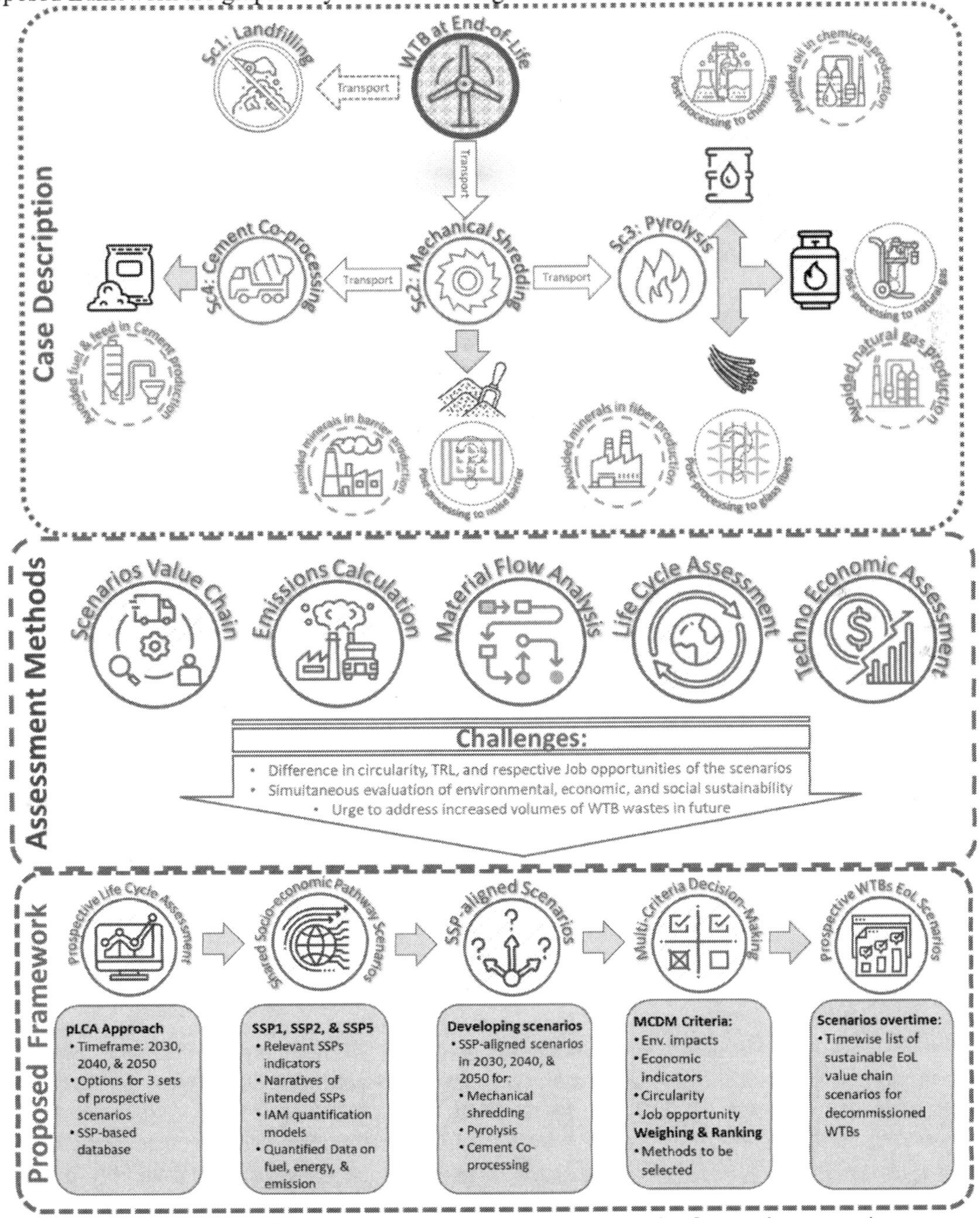


**Figure 3.** Case description, assessment methods, and the framework of emerging scenarios assessment

This study Develops an assessment framework addressing the challenges through future technologies evaluation and provides insight into EoL management over time until 2050. More empirical investigations on the feasible options for EoL management of WTBs in the future are yet to be investigated.

## 4. Conclusion

To establish the data foundation supporting quantitative sustainability assessment of industrial-scale EoL scenarios for decommissioned WTBs, potential challenges, data gaps, and technological shortages have been presented. To address these challenges SSP-aligned future scenarios were chosen as the most likely future pathways. Scenarios for 2030, 2040, and 2050 were developed accordingly thus supporting the collaborative prospective work of the consortium. In the next step, prospective consequential LCA, TEA, will be implemented to assess SSP-based scenarios. In addition, MCDM will be applied to weigh the criteria and identify the most optimal solutions over the proposed time.

In this cross-disciplinary large-scale executive project, the route to the establishment of sustainable industrial-scale waste management systems for spent WTBs and the challenges in each phase have been elaborated. The uncertainty of the pyrolysis scenario due to less mature pyro-output processing options is resolved mainly through developing SSP-based scenarios and implementing pLCA.

This study develops and presents an assessment framework addressing the challenges through future and emerging technologies scenario evaluation and provides insight into the EoL routes for WTBs and challenges associated with EoL solution design and assessment to the wind community, wind turbine owners, producers, and researchers for their work on handling EoL WTBs.

## Acknowledgments

This study has been done by SDU under the auspices of the DecomBlades project supported financially by Innovation Fund Denmark (grant number: 0177-00006B). The funders had no role in the study design, data collection, analysis, or preparation of the manuscript. We would also appreciate the technical support provided by the project partners.

## 5. References

[1] N. Sakellariou, "Current and potential decommissioning scenarios for end-of-life composite wind blades," *Energy Systems*, vol. 9, no. 4, pp. 981–1023, Nov. 2018, doi: 10.1007/S12667-017-0245-9.

[2] L. Mishnaevsky, "Sustainable end-of-life management of wind turbine blades: Overview of current and coming solutions," *Materials*, vol. 14, no. 5. MDPI AG, pp. 1–26, Mar. 01, 2021. doi: 10.3390/ma14051124.

[3] R. Fonte and G. Xydis, "Wind turbine blade recycling: An evaluation of the European market potential for recycled composite materials," *J Environ Manage*, vol. 287, p. 112269, Jun. 2021, doi: 10.1016/J.JENVMAN.2021.112269.

[4] L. Mishnaevsky, K. Branner, H. N. Petersen, J. Beauson, M. McGugan, and B. F. Sørensen, "Materials for Wind Turbine Blades: An Overview," *Materials 2017, Vol. 10, Page 1285*, vol. 10, no. 11, p. 1285, Nov. 2017, doi: 10.3390/MA10111285.

[5] A. J. Nagle, E. L. Delaney, L. C. Bank, and P. G. Leahy, "A Comparative Life Cycle Assessment between landfilling and Co-Processing of waste from decommissioned Irish wind turbine blades," *J Clean Prod*, vol. 277, Dec. 2020, doi: 10.1016/j.jclepro.2020.123321.

[6] "Wind industry calls for Europe-wide ban on landfilling turbine blades | WindEurope." https://windeurope.org/newsroom/press-releases/wind-industry-calls-for-europe-wide-ban-on-landfilling-turbine-blades/ (accessed Mar. 09, 2023).

[7] J. Beauson, A. Laurent, D. P. Rudolph, and J. Pagh Jensen, "The complex end-of-life of wind turbine blades: A review of the European context," *Renewable and Sustainable Energy Reviews*, vol. 155, p. 111847, Mar. 2022, doi: 10.1016/J.RSER.2021.111847.

[8] N. Andersen, O. Eriksson, K. Hillman, and M. Wallhagen, "Wind Turbines' End-of-Life: Quantification and Characterisation of Future Waste Materials on a National Level," 2016, doi: 10.3390/en9120999.

[9] H. Heng, F. Meng, and J. McKechnie, "Wind turbine blade wastes and the environmental impacts in Canada," *Waste Management*, vol. 133, pp. 59–70, Sep. 2021, doi: 10.1016/j.wasman.2021.07.032.

[10] A. Lefeuvre, S. Garnier, L. Jacquemin, B. Pillain, and G. Sonnemann, "Anticipating in-use stocks of carbon fibre reinforced polymers and related waste generated by the wind power sector until 2050," *Resour Conserv Recycl*, vol. 141, pp. 30–39, Feb. 2019, doi: 10.1016/J.RESCONREC.2018.10.008.

[11] G. Lichtenegger, A. A. Rentizelas, N. Trivyza, and S. Siegl, "Offshore and onshore wind turbine blade waste material forecast at a regional level in Europe until 2050," *Waste Manag*, vol. 106, pp. 120–131, Apr. 2020, doi: 10.1016/J.WASMAN.2020.03.018.

[12] P. Liu and C. Y. Barlow, "Wind turbine blade waste in 2050," *Waste Management*, vol. 62, pp. 229–240, Apr. 2017, doi: 10.1016/J.WASMAN.2017.02.007.

[13] V. Sommer, J. Stockschläder, and G. Walther, "Estimation of glass and carbon fiber reinforced plastic waste from end-of-life rotor blades of wind power plants within the European Union," *Waste Manag*, vol. 115, pp. 83–94, Sep. 2020, doi: 10.1016/J.WASMAN.2020.06.043.

[14] Y. Chen *et al.*, "Modeling waste generation and end-of-life management of wind power development in Guangdong, China until 2050," *Resour Conserv Recycl*, vol. 169, Jun. 2021, doi: 10.1016/J.RESCONREC.2021.105533.

[15] N. Tazi, J. Kim, Y. Bouzidi, E. Chatelet, and G. Liu, "Waste and material flow analysis in the end-of-life wind energy system," *Resour Conserv Recycl*, vol. 145, pp. 199–207, Jun. 2019, doi: 10.1016/J.RESCONREC.2019.02.039.

[16] A. Cooperman, A. Eberle, and E. Lantz, "Wind turbine blade material in the United States: Quantities, costs, and end-of-life options," *Resour Conserv Recycl*, vol. 168, p. 105439, May 2021, doi: 10.1016/J.RESCONREC.2021.105439.

[17] E. L. Delaney *et al.*, "An integrated geospatial approach for repurposing wind turbine blades," *Resour Conserv Recycl*, vol. 170, p. 105601, Jul. 2021, doi: 10.1016/J.RESCONREC.2021.105601.

[18] A. A. M. Sultan, P. T. Mativenga, and E. Lou, "Managing Supply Chain Complexity: Foresight for Wind Turbine Composite Waste," *Procedia CIRP*, vol. 69, pp. 938–943, 2018, doi: 10.1016/J.PROCIR.2017.11.027.

[19] ETIPWind Executive Committee, "An overview of composite recycling in the wind energy industry," 2020. [Online]. Available: www.formasdopossivel.com

[20] J. P. Jensen and K. Skelton, "Wind turbine blade recycling: Experiences, challenges and possibilities in a circular economy," *Renewable and Sustainable Energy Reviews*, vol. 97, pp. 165–176, Dec. 2018, doi: 10.1016/J.RSER.2018.08.041.

[21] J. Joustra, B. Flipsen, and R. Balkenende, "Structural reuse of high end composite products: A design case study on wind turbine blades," *Resour Conserv Recycl*, vol. 167, p. 105393, Apr. 2021, doi: 10.1016/J.RESCONREC.2020.105393.

[22] "Re-use of wind turbine blade for construction and infrastructure applications", doi: 10.1088/1757-899X/942/1/012015.

[23] K. Ramirez-Tejeda, D. A. Turcotte, and S. Pike, "Unsustainable Wind Turbine Blade Disposal Practices in the United States: A Case for Policy Intervention and Technological Innovation," *NEW SOLUTIONS: A Journal of Environmental and Occupational Health Policy*, vol. 26, no. 4, pp. 581–598, 2017, doi: 10.1177/1048291116676098.

[24] M. Rani, P. Choudhary, V. Krishnan, and S. Zafar, "A review on recycling and reuse methods for carbon fiber/glass fiber composites waste from wind turbine blades," *Compos B Eng*, vol. 215, p. 108768, Jun. 2021, doi: 10.1016/J.COMPOSITESB.2021.108768.

[25] Paul. Robinson, E. S. Greenhalgh, and Silvestre. Pinho, "Failure mechanisms in polymer matrix composites : criteria, testing and industrial applications," p. 450, 2012.

[26] M. C. S. Ribeiro *et al.*, "Recycling Approach towards Sustainability Advance of Composite Materials' Industry," *Recycling 2016, Vol. 1, Pages 178-193*, vol. 1, no. 1, pp. 178–193, Jun. 2016, doi: 10.3390/RECYCLING1010178.

[27] E. B. Paulsen and P. Enevoldsen, "A multidisciplinary review of recycling methods for end-of-life wind turbine blades," *Energies (Basel)*, vol. 14, no. 14, Jul. 2021, doi: 10.3390/en14144247.

[28] S. Hao *et al.*, "A circular economy approach to green energy: Wind turbine, waste, and material recovery," *Science of The Total Environment*, vol. 702, p. 135054, Feb. 2020, doi: 10.1016/J.SCITOTENV.2019.135054.

[29] S. R. Naqvi, H. M. Prabhakara, E. A. Bramer, W. Dierkes, R. Akkerman, and G. Brem, "A critical review on recycling of end-of-life carbon fibre/glass fibre reinforced composites waste using pyrolysis towards a circular economy," *Resour Conserv Recycl*, vol. 136, pp. 118–129, Sep. 2018, doi: 10.1016/J.RESCONREC.2018.04.013.

[30] Y. Yang, R. Boom, B. Irion, D. J. van Heerden, P. Kuiper, and H. de Wit, "Recycling of composite materials," *Chemical Engineering and Processing: Process Intensification*, vol. 51, pp. 53–68, Jan. 2012, doi: 10.1016/J.CEP.2011.09.007.

[31] "(21) (PDF) Developments in the fluidised bed process for fibre recovery from thermoset composites." https://www.researchgate.net/publication/301849557_Developments_in_the_fluidised_bed_process_for_fibre_recovery_from_thermoset_composites (accessed Mar. 10, 2023).

[32] W. Yang, K.-H. Kim, and J. Lee, "Upcycling of decommissioned wind turbine blades through pyrolysis: A review," *J Clean Prod*, p. 134292, Sep. 2022, doi: 10.1016/j.jclepro.2022.134292.

[33] PBL, "Circular economy: what we want to know and can measure Framework and baseline assessment for monitoring the progress of the circular economy in the Netherlands Policy Report".

[34] A. Al-Rumaihi, M. Shahbaz, G. Mckay, H. Mackey, and T. Al-Ansari, "A review of pyrolysis technologies and feedstock: A blending approach for plastic and biomass towards optimum biochar yield," *Renewable and Sustainable Energy Reviews*, vol. 167. Elsevier Ltd, Oct. 01, 2022. doi: 10.1016/j.rser.2022.112715.

[35] P. Liu, F. Meng, and C. Y. Barlow, "Wind turbine blade end-of-life options: An eco-audit comparison," *J Clean Prod*, vol. 212, pp. 1268–1281, Mar. 2019, doi: 10.1016/j.jclepro.2018.12.043.

[36] A. Rentizelas, N. Trivyza, S. Oswald, and S. Siegl, "Reverse supply network design for circular economy pathways of wind turbine blades in Europe," *https://doi.org/10.1080/00207543.2020.1870016*, vol. 60, no. 6, pp. 1795–1814, 2021, doi: 10.1080/00207543.2020.1870016.

[37] A. E. Krauklis *et al.*, "Composite Material Recycling Technology—State-of-the-Art and Sustainable Development for the 2020s," *Journal of Composites Science 2021, Vol. 5, Page 28*, vol. 5, no. 1, p. 28, Jan. 2021, doi: 10.3390/JCS5010028.

[38] L. Mishnaevsky, P. Brøndsted, R. Nijssen, D. J. Lekou, and T. P. Philippidis, "Materials of large wind turbine blades: Recent results in testing and modeling," *Wind Energy*, vol. 15, no. 1, pp. 83–97, Jan. 2012, doi: 10.1002/WE.470.

[39] "DecomBlades | Wind industry blade decomissioning." https://decomblades.dk/ (accessed Mar. 10, 2023).

[40] ISO, "ISO - ISO 14044:2006/Amd 2:2020 - Environmental management — Life cycle assessment — Requirements and guidelines — Amendment 2," *ISO*, 2006. https://www.iso.org/standard/76122.html (accessed Mar. 10, 2023).

[41] J. Rogelj *et al.*, "Scenarios towards limiting global mean temperature increase below 1.5 °c," *Nat Clim Chang*, vol. 8, no. 4, pp. 325–332, Apr. 2018, doi: 10.1038/S41558-018-0091-3.

[42] H. K. Jani, S. Singh Kachhwaha, G. Nagababu, and A. Das, "A brief review on recycling and reuse of wind turbine blade materials," *Mater Today Proc*, vol. 62, no. P13, pp. 7124–7130, Jan. 2022, doi: 10.1016/j.matpr.2022.02.049.

[43] A. S. Nielsen, J. D. Rathke, and P. Enevoldsen, "A multidisciplinary assessment of Pyrolysis for recycling of wind turbine blade waste material," 2021.

[44] JRC-IES, "ILCD-Handbook-General-guide-for-LCA-DETAILED-GUIDANCE," 2010.

[45] C. van der Giesen, S. Cucurachi, J. Guinée, G. J. Kramer, and A. Tukker, "A critical view on the current application of LCA for new technologies and recommendations for improved practice," *J Clean Prod*, vol. 259, Jun. 2020, doi: 10.1016/j.jclepro.2020.120904.

[46] R. Sacchi *et al.*, "PRospective EnvironMental Impact asSEment (premise): A streamlined approach to producing databases for prospective life cycle assessment using integrated assessment models," *Renewable and Sustainable Energy Reviews*, vol. 160, May 2022, doi: 10.1016/j.rser.2022.112311.

[47] Intergovernmental Panel on Climate Change. Working Group III., *Emissions scenarios. Summary for policymakers : a special report of IPCC Working Group III*. Intergovernmental Panel on Climate Change, 2000.

[48] D. P. van Vuuren *et al.*, "Energy, land-use and greenhouse gas emissions trajectories under a green growth paradigm," *Global Environmental Change*, vol. 42, pp. 237–250, Jan. 2017, doi: 10.1016/J.GLOENVCHA.2016.05.008.

[49] O. Fricko *et al.*, "The marker quantification of the Shared Socioeconomic Pathway 2: A middle-of-the-road scenario for the 21st century," *Global Environmental Change*, vol. 42, pp. 251–267, Jan. 2017, doi: 10.1016/J.GLOENVCHA.2016.06.004.

[50] S. Fujimori *et al.*, "SSP3: AIM implementation of Shared Socioeconomic Pathways," *Global Environmental Change*, vol. 42, pp. 268–283, Jan. 2017, doi: 10.1016/j.gloenvcha.2016.06.009.

[51] K. Calvin *et al.*, "The SSP4: A world of deepening inequality," *Global Environmental Change*, vol. 42, pp. 284–296, Jan. 2017, doi: 10.1016/j.gloenvcha.2016.06.010.

[52] E. Kriegler *et al.*, "Fossil-fueled development (SSP5): An energy and resource intensive scenario for the 21st century," *Global Environmental Change*, vol. 42, pp. 297–315, Jan. 2017, doi: 10.1016/j.gloenvcha.2016.05.015.

[53] K. Riahi *et al.*, "The Shared Socioeconomic Pathways and their energy, land use, and greenhouse gas emissions implications: An overview," *Global Environmental Change*, vol. 42, pp. 153–168, Jan. 2017, doi: 10.1016/j.gloenvcha.2016.05.009.

[54] B. C. O'Neill *et al.*, "The roads ahead: Narratives for shared socioeconomic pathways describing world futures in the 21st century," *Global Environmental Change*, vol. 42, pp. 169–180, Jan. 2017, doi: 10.1016/j.gloenvcha.2015.01.004.

[55] CarbonBrief, "How 'Shared Socioeconomic Pathways' explore future climate change," Apr. 19, 2016.

[56] Elmar Kriegler, "Model Description."

[57] K. Riahi *et al.*, "The Shared Socioeconomic Pathways and their energy, land use, and greenhouse gas emissions implications: An overview," *Global Environmental Change*, vol. 42, pp. 153–168, Jan. 2017, doi: 10.1016/j.gloenvcha.2016.05.009.
[58] SDU, "Electro fuel from bio-trickling filter (eFuel) ," 2019.
[59] R. G. de Souza, J. C. N. Clímaco, A. P. Sant'Anna, T. B. Rocha, R. de A. B. do Valle, and O. L. G. Quelhas, "Sustainability assessment and prioritisation of e-waste management options in Brazil," *Waste Management*, vol. 57, pp. 46–56, Nov. 2016, doi: 10.1016/J.WASMAN.2016.01.034.
[60] C. Castellini *et al.*, "A multicriteria approach for measuring the sustainability of different poultry production systems," *J Clean Prod*, vol. 37, pp. 192–201, Dec. 2012, doi: 10.1016/J.JCLEPRO.2012.07.006.
[61] T. Myllyviita, P. Leskinen, and J. Seppälä, "Impact of normalisation, elicitation technique and background information on panel weighting results in life cycle assessment," *International Journal of Life Cycle Assessment*, vol. 19, no. 2, pp. 377–386, Feb. 2014, doi: 10.1007/S11367-013-0645-6/METRICS.
[62] M. Bengtsson, "Weighting in Practice:Implications for the Use of Life-Cycle Assessment in Decision Making," *J Ind Ecol*, vol. 4, no. 4, pp. 47–60, Oct. 2000, doi: 10.1162/10881980052541945.
[63] J. Rezaei, "Best-worst multi-criteria decision-making method," *Omega (Westport)*, vol. 53, pp. 49–57, Jun. 2015, doi: 10.1016/J.OMEGA.2014.11.009.
[64] J. Rezaei, "Best-worst multi-criteria decision-making method: Some properties and a linear model," *Omega (Westport)*, vol. 64, pp. 126–130, Oct. 2016, doi: 10.1016/J.OMEGA.2015.12.001.
[65] H. Badri Ahmadi, S. Kusi-Sarpong, and J. Rezaei, "Assessing the social sustainability of supply chains using Best Worst Method," *Resour Conserv Recycl*, vol. 126, pp. 99–106, Nov. 2017, doi: 10.1016/J.RESCONREC.2017.07.020.
[66] W. N. K. Wan Ahmad, J. Rezaei, S. Sadaghiani, and L. A. Tavasszy, "Evaluation of the external forces affecting the sustainability of oil and gas supply chain using Best Worst Method," *J Clean Prod*, vol. 153, pp. 242–252, Jun. 2017, doi: 10.1016/J.JCLEPRO.2017.03.166.

# On a road map for technology qualification, innovation and cost reduction in floating offshore wind: learning from Hywind and Norwegian approach

**Michaela Ibrion, Amir R. Nejad**

Department of Marine Technology, Norwegian University of Science and Technology (NTNU), NO-7491, Trondheim, Norway

E-mail: Amir.Nejad@ntnu.no

**Abstract.** The main aim of this paper is to synthetize and to learn from the existing road maps and the Norwegian approach on the floating offshore wind. It targets to identify main priorities, key challenges, and technological qualification for the floating offshore wind development. The Norwegian approach is evaluated in the view of the key success factors of the offshore wind market highlighted by the World Bank. One particularity of the national Norwegian offshore landscape is the usage of the Norwegian floating wind for decarbonification and "greenification" of the oil and gas industry. Learning from the Hywind projects and Norwegian approaches and experiences for the floating offshore wind on the national and international level has potential in contributing to enhance the road maps for floating offshore wind in terms of technology qualification, innovation and cost reduction. This article offers a handful of key take away points for industry and decision makers about development of the floating offshore wind.

Keywords: offshore wind; floating offshore wind; road map; Hywind, Norwegian approach and experiences; offshore wind market pillars;

## 1. Introduction

The Green Deal has been seen by the European Commission (EC) as a blueprint for the reduction of greenhouse gas emissions - minimum 55 % by 2030 - reduction of energy dependence, facilitation of investments and new jobs, and increase of renewable sources in the energy mix by at least 40 % [1]. The dramatic geopolitical and energy market caused by the military invasion of Ukraine prompted the EC's plan - the REPowerEU - which aims to support development of clean energy, to diversify the energy supply, and to increase the resilience of the European energy system. [2].

In EU, the offshore wind is seen to have a huge potential and crucial for solving the urgent need for renewable energy. The North Sea is seen as the world's leading region for deploying capacity and expertise about offshore wind [3]. The first offshore wind project in the world was installed in 1991 in Denmark, and this has made Denmark, the Nordic countries and Europe as the birthplace of the offshore wind industry [4]. Nevertheless, in 2021, only 1 GW of offshore wind was installed in EU[5]. Europe continues to remain a technology hub for foundations and wind turbines. After three decades of development, the bottom-fixed offshore wind with a mature supply chain in countries around the North Sea and the Baltic Sea has become one of the cost-competitive energy in Europe [4].

The floating offshore wind is seen as a key towards the transition to green energy, predicted to achieve a higher profitability, and to produce by 2030, a breakthrough in renewable [6], [7] [8]. Definitely, "Floating offshore wind is no longer a niche technology" as highlighted by Giles Dickson , WindEurope CEO at FOWT 2020 event in Marseille[9]. Currently, the top five markets for floating wind installations are United Kingdom, Portugal, Norway, Japan and France[10].

The world's first floating offshore turbine, Hywind demo, was commissioned in 2009 in Norway [4], [11]. The offshore wind, particularly the floating wind, is seen as door opener for the next great industrial adventure in Norway [6]. The Norwegian government is taking initiatives to strongly promote the offshore wind power and to develop Norway as an offshore wind nation [12]. Norway has excellent wind resources, and the Norwegian Continental Shelf (NCS) and the North Sea are counted among the world's best wind resources in the water depths between 60 m to 1000 m [8], [13]. Floating wind turbines are technically feasible to be installed in water depth more than 60 m [14].

There are various studies and reports which offer road maps or visionary and forecasting frameworks about the development of offshore wind, particularly the floating offshore wind, in Norway [6, 15, 16, 17, 18, 19, 20]. However, there is no unity about the road map as an instrument or its systematic way of application to the Norwegian offshore market, as different approaches to the application of a road map are embraced. Moreover, learning further from these road maps is missing.

The aim of this study is to synthesize in a systematic manner and to learn from the existing road maps, particularly in terms of the Hywind projects, and the Norwegian approach towards the floating offshore wind. The study will also analyze the landscape of the offshore wind in Norway and will try to offer a clarity about how the road map as an instrument is anchored into the landscape of the Norwegian offshore wind. It targets to identify main priorities, key challenges, and technological qualification for the floating offshore wind development linked to the Norwegian approach and experiences.

## 2. Approach

The World Bank's Energy Sector Management Assistance Program (ESMAP) has highlighted four key factors for successful development of offshore wind in emerging markets [21]. In this paper, these interconnected key factors are applied to the Norwegian context named as four pillars as illustrated in the figure 1:

I. Strategy makes reference to a long-term planning of offshore wind development which is established by politicians, decisions makers, technocrats and energy planners.

II. Policy refers to law and agreements by lawmakers and bureaucrats.

III. Frameworks refer to a system of regulations, processes, and guidelines for enacting the policies; frameworks are implemented through government agencies and utilities.

IV. Delivery refers to the enabling environment and elements for obtaining the expected results through cooperation among stakeholders such as governmental organizations, industry, and the society.

In the following sections the paper dives into realities of the floating offshore wind in Norway, the Norwegian achievements on national and international arena, the Hywind, and the future plans in the perspective of these four pillars. A number of road maps developed by different stakeholders are also presented. Depending on the stakeholder and the scope, a road map sets goals and ambitions across different pillars, sometimes aiming for more practical manner. Discussions will then shed more light on these road maps with practical recommendations in the conclusions.

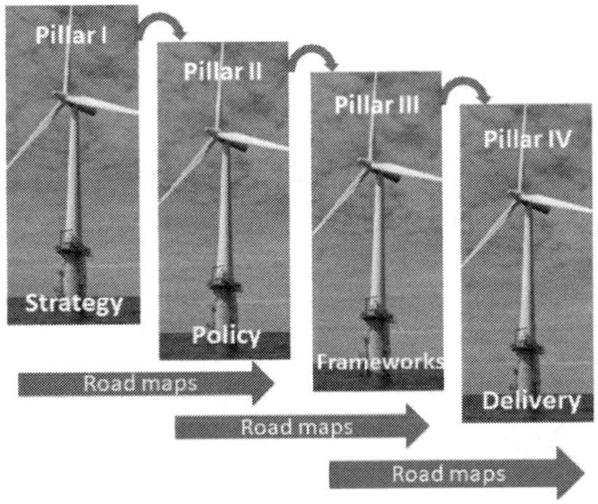


Figure 1: Research approach seen as combination of the pillars of the offshore wind market and road maps .

## 3. Floating offshore wind, the Norwegian experiences, current situation and future plans

Norway has been at forefront of technology development for the floating wind turbine with the first full-scale floating wind turbine in the world - the Hywind Demo - a 2.3 MW turbine which entered in operation in 2009 in Norway [11]. The Hywind technology is based on a spar type floating structure and the standard three blades, upwind pitch controlled horizontal axis wind turbine.

The lessons and experiences from Hywind Demo was taken further in developing the world's first full-scale floating wind farm, the Hywind Scotland with a capacity of 30 MW [22]. The Hywind Scotland entered is in operation since 2017 and was developed in UK by the Norwegian Equinor together with Masdar [11].

Inside Norway, the Hywind Tampen is the first floating wind farm which came in operation on 13 November 2022. The Hywind Tampen is currently the world's largest floating wind farm with a production capacity of 88 MW. The Hywind Tampen is located at 140 km from shore at a water depth between 260-300 metres. This wind farm comprises 11 concrete structures which were provided by the Aker Solutions and the wind turbines which were upgraded to 8.6 MW and were supplied by Siemens Gamesa. However, only seven out of eleven wind turbines came on stream in 2022 [23], [24]. Due to the supply chain challenges linked with global steel market, the four tower sections could not be delivered until September 2022, and this was too late for the 2022's installation weather window. The remaining four turbines for the Hywind Tampen will be installed in 2023 [25]. The total cost of the Hywind Tampen project reached to the amount of about 5 billion NOK, of which 2,3 billion NOK were provided by ENOVA, a governmental organization [15].

The Hywind Tampen is the first wind farm in the world which supplies power to the five oil and gas platforms - Snorre A and B, and Gullfaks A, B and C - located at the Norwegian North Sea. As per estimations, the Hywind Tampen wind farm will cover 35 % of the electricity demand of these five oil and gas platforms, and will reduce $CO2$ emissions from the fields by about 200,000 tonnes per year. The Hywind Tampen is seen as an important contribution of transforming the NCS from an oil and gas area to a broader energy area. It contributes to cut the emissions from oil and gas industry, and to increase the gas exports to Europe [24].

Furthermore, there are plans for development of the Trollvind wind farm with a capacity

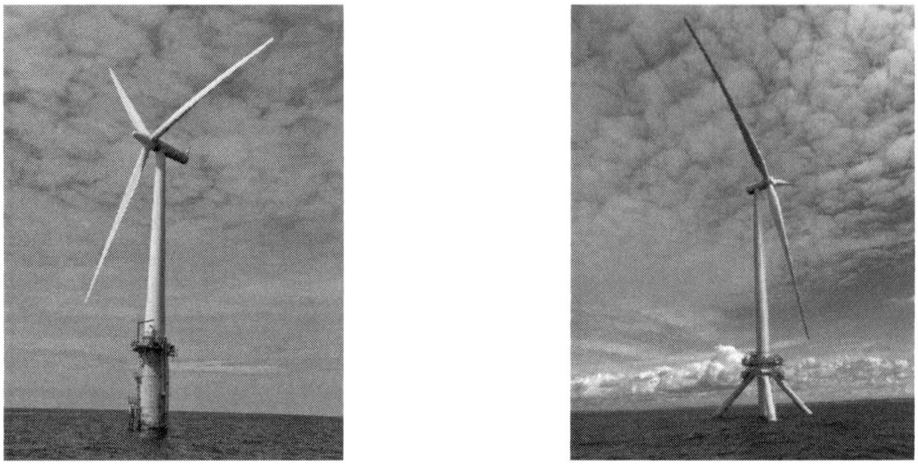

(a) Hywind Demo, installed 2009 (b) TetraSpar, installed 2021

Figure 2: Hywind Demo and TetraSpar in the test center at Karmøy, Norway (Photos by Amir R. Nejad, 2022)

of almost 1 GW and with an estimated annual production of nearly 4.3 TWh. This floating offshore wind farm will be situated around 65 km west of Kollsnes, Bergen. Trollvind will power the Troll and Oseberg oil and gas fields. The Troll gas field has very rich gas reserves and is one of the important gas fields on the NCS. The concessions for this project are in plan to start in 2025. Trollvind will not only contribute to the electrification of the oil and gas installations but also will help the onshore power grid for the Bergen region [6]. A possible investment decision can be taken in 2023, and a potential completion of the project can take place in 2027. As per estimations, Trollvind can deliver power for less than NOK 1/kWh. [6, 26].

In addition, two other areas - the Sørlige Nordsjø II and Utsira Nord with a capacity of 3GW and 1, 5 GW - are targeted to be opened for bottom-fixed and floating, respectively. The licence process is expected to be opened in 2023 and operation will not start before 2032 [6]. Development of a floating offshore wind project is planned for the Utsira Nord. Regarding the Sørlige Nordsjø II, two offshore wind projects of 1.5 MW, fixed and floating, which will provide power to the mainland Norway and to Europe are planned [8].

After 10 years of operation, the ownership of the Hywind Demo was taken over by the Unitech Offshore in 2019 which renamed the turbine as the Unitech Zefyros and made it available for research and development as a part of the METCentre test site, located outside of Karmøy near Stavanger [27]. Given the available infrastructure and local expertise, the Hywind demo site has nowadays converted to an international test center and a hub for testing different innovative floating concepts, for example the TetraSpar by a Danish company is under test operation since 2021 in this test facility - see Figure 2.

Moreover, out of Norway the Norwegian offshore experience is further linked with investment, development and operation of other offshore wind projects in areas like UK, US, Poland, France, Spain, Korea, Japan, and Vietnam [28].

## 4. Norwegian offshore wind in the view of key pillars for successful development

A non-exhaustive overview of the pillars of Norwegian offshore market - strategy, policy, framework, and delivery - as described in section 2 is presented in this section.

*4.1. Strategy - national long-term offshore wind development planning*
On 11 June 2021, the Ministry of Petroleum and Energy issued the "Energi til arbeid – langsiktig verdiskaping fra norske energiressurser" (the "Energy for work - long-term value creation from Norwegian energy resources"), an advisory document approved by the Norwegian Government and submitted for fial approval to the "Stortinget" (the Norwegian Parliament). This document offers an overview about the Norwegian energy history and its importance for the country and brings to attention the potential of the wind energy in creation of new jobs, contribution to a cleaner and decarbonised world and progress of technology and science. Within this document, two areas - the Utsira Nord and Sørlige Nordsjø II- were designated to award licenses to develop offshore wind farms [29]

The Norwegian strategical ambitions about development of a large scale offshore wind production were presented quite recently in May 2022 [19]. The Norwegian Government announced their strategy to transform Norway to one of the world leading nation in the offshore wind with the target to deliver 30 GW by 2040 and to have around 1500 wind turbines in operation. This ambition of the Norwegian Government to develop 30 GW of offshore wind production by 2040 corresponds to almost the same capacity of the current hydro-power production, meaning doubling the production just within 20 years[6, 12].

Moreover, in the autumn of 2022, the Norwegian Government issued a strategical map which contains its approach and vision about the implementation of the " Green Industrial Initiative" in Norway. Within this governmental strategy, seven areas were considered as national priorities, and the development of offshore wind is one of them [15].

*4.2. Policy - law and agreements*
The "Lov om fornybar energiproduksjon til havs" (Law relating to Renewable Energy Production at Sea - LOV-2010-06-04-21) known also as the "Havenergilova" or the "Offshore Energy Act" or the "Ocean Energy Law" has been in place since 2010. It regulates any offshore energy generation or project which are not being part of the offshore petroleum production. As per the Offshore Energy Act, the Norwegian state has the full right to utilize the offshore energy resources. The Offshore Energy Act applies to the territorial seas outside the baseline, to the NCS, but also provisions can be made about the internal waters. A licence is required for electricity generation, conversion and transmission for the areas under the jurisdiction of the Offshore Energy Act. Such type of licence can be obtained only after the government has carried out an environmental assessment of the area and made clear provisions which will be opened for licence applications. Nevertheless, the government can offer exemptions to pilot projects or to other particular projects with a limited time frame [30].

According to the the Ocean Energy Law, the estimated time for building an offshore wind farm is between 8 to 10 years [31]. The law opened the door for concessions to be granted, but in practice, it took a long time to do so. In the last years, the concessions which are targeted to be made are in the areas of the Utsira Nord and Sørlige Nordsjø II [32].

In 2022, the Government proposed amendments to the Offshore Energy Act. The proposed change concerns the permission to be given to the Ministry of Petroleum and Energy to advertise and invite competition for allocation of development areas in the Utsira Nord and Sørlige Nordsjø I [33].

The Norwegian policy environment has not yet developed sufficient legislation about offshore wind. The Hywind Tampen is seen to have the potential to contribute to refinement of the Norwegian legal framework for the offshore wind [34, 32].

*4.3. Frameworks - regulations, processes, guidelines for enacting the policies*
The Offshore Energy Regulations known also as "the Regulations of the Energy Act" or the "Forskrift til havenergilova" took a long time to be developed, as they were finalized just in

2020 and entered into force in 2021. These regulations offer details about the licensing process, and they are accompanied by guidelines. In addition to the act and regulations, the applicants for the offshore wind projects need also to follow the guidelines. The guidelines offer details about the procedures for the allocation of development areas and about application and licensing process itself [30], [32].

Norway has been among the leaders regarding good regulations of oil and gas, but the regulations for the offshore wind still present many deficiencies and many unclear and overlooked matters. Even after more than one decade, the rules and regulatory framework about the offshore wind needs further development and clarifications [32]. There are still many uncertainties related to the frameworks linked to a large Norwegian based offshore wind production. The processes are very slow and unclear for industry and increase uncertainty for stakeholders [19]. There is still uncertainty about the public strategy and governmental decisions linked with future concession rounds, support schemes, design for grid infrastructure, licensing and clear guidelines and regular awarding path [6].

A clear and well-developed regulatory framework is encouraged to be in place in order to support a faster development of the offshore wind, to attenuate conflicts among stakeholders and other interest groups, to support technological development and innovation, to contribute to the protection of environment, and to assure a stable and predictable landscape for investors [32]. Capgemini [6] recommends the sustainability assessments need to be financed by government before the tenders to be opened to industry. This is in order to increase the speed of process and to reduce the risk linked with the projects avoiding delays and to holistically consider a sustainability impact.

The process for the concession awarding and development is very long, as also seen for the areas of the Sørlige Nordsjø II and Utsira Nord. There is a 6 years period from when the area is awarded until the beginning of construction. The process lasts almost 10 years from the time area is opened for tendering until the commissioned area enters in operation [6].

In December 2022, the Norwegian Minister of Petroleum and Energy presented a consultation package with a couple of clarifications about the framework conditions for awarding offshore wind licences in the offshore wind areas of the Sørlige Nordsjø II and Utsira Nord. The package includes pre-qualification criteria for the Sørlige Nordsjø II, qualitative criteria for the Utsira Nord, and details about the allocation, auction and support scheme model. Pre-qualification criteria refer to ability to execute in terms of technical expertise and financial strength, sustainability approach by taking climate and environment in account and a positive effect on local industry by providing experience and competence development to the supply chain. The qualitative criteria include following: cost level in 2030; contribution to innovation and technology development; technical and financial execution ability; sustainability approach; and the positive effects for local industry. The Norwegian Government intends to announce the first phase of Sørlige Nordsjø II and Utsira Nord in the first quarter of 2023 [35].

### *4.4. Delivery - cooperation among stakeholders*

Stakeholders and players in the offshore wind industry, maritime and oil and gas industries, supply chain, investors and society need to collaborate in order to facilitate the commercialization of the floating wind [17]. The development of the floating offshore wind in Norway can be accelerated through targeted financial support schemes, and a coordination plan of efforts among governmental organizations and the industry [6].

About delivery, a coordinated plan for supporting development of infrastructures along the Norwegian coast is required in order to assure that Norwegian vessels, yards and ports can deliver in time on the 30 GW offshore wind within next 20 years [6].

ABB has emphasized that currently in Norway there is no subsidy plan or other established incentives which to support development on a large scale of both the floating and bottom-fixed offshore wind turbines. Impact assessments need to be done, state needs to open specific areas to applications for concessions, and auction-based arrangements are recommended to be employed for development of floating offshore wind [20].

The floating offshore wind projects are eligible for the Enova governmental subsidies and its program for full-scale innovative energy and climate technology, but only on condition these projects are individual innovation projects. Requirements for such projects are as follow: the projects have clear technological and financial risk; bring new solutions which generate energy; and present a significant environmental improvement [20].

In terms of delivery of a Norwegian-based large scale offshore industry, Menon [19] has emphasized the existing advantages: a favorable topography; a good cooperation among Norwegian stakeholders; short distance to European markets; good collaboration with international companies; existence of an innovation ecosystem based on clusters, test centres, collaboration with research and centres and academia; an advanced offshore expertise; and high quality of products and services. Nevertheless, Menon [19] brought to attention the significant barriers which can impact the delivery of the Norwegian-based large scale offshore industry, the market-specific and company-specific barriers. Markets-specific barriers refer to a lack of a domestic market and a limited access to market of small companies and industrial players. Company-specific barriers include high cost and wages, a limited production capacity, and lack of relevant skills [19].

A key stakeholder in the offshore wind arena such as Equinor - not only in Norway, but also on the European and international arena - targets to reach to 12-16 GW installed capacity by 2030 through its offshore wind projects in Norway, Europe, Asia and on the US East coast. The share of Equinor's gross CAPEX in renewable energy and low carbon solutions has increased from 4 % in 2020 to 11 % in 2021, and in 2025 is estimated to reach to more than 30 % [36].

## 5. Offshore wind road maps, the Norwegian approach

The road map presented by the Norwegian Government in 2022 [15] is a strategy road map which has identified the offshore wind as a priority area among other priority areas which are seen to contribute to the development of green industry in Norway. The Norwegian Government targets to allocate dedicated areas which will contribute to achievement of 30 GW offshore wind by 2040 on the NCS; 30 GW of offshore wind electricity corresponds to almost 75 percentage of today capacity for the Norwegian electric power system. Among the first areas to be developed is the 1,500 MW in the Southern North Sea II which will be connected to the Norwegian grid [15].

A pioneering road map for the Norwegian offshore wind is seen to be the roadmap about the deployment of the offshore wind energy in the Central and Southern North Sea (2020-2030), as a part of the European project, Windspeed [16]. This road map focuses on the challenges, opportunities, and potential of the North Sea countries in their pursuit for a rapid expansion of the offshore wind energy in the Central and Southern part of North Sea. The North Sea countries such as Norway, Denmark, Germany, UK, the Netherlands and Belgium have ambitious targets such as 135 GW for the development of the offshore wind in the North Sea. The road map tried to identify the actions, milestones, challenges, opportunities, uncertainty, and impacts in order to achieve the targets [16].

An interesting view about a current road map for the Norwegian offshore wind is conveyed by the technology and consultancy company, Capgemini [6]. Capgemini consulted more than 30 key stakeholders and experts for the offshore wind and identified that a road map for Norway needs to address the challenges linked to four main themes: predictability, sustainability and speed, industrial capacity and talent [6]. The Norwegian industry requires more predictability in order to commit to investments and to allocate adequate resources. Speed and efficiency of public processes needs to increase. Moreover, sustainability, biodiversity and co-existence with other offshore industries such as fishing and shipping need to be carefully considered. Industrial capacity in Norway needs to become stronger and to collaborate along the value chain through clusters and interest organizations. An accelerated transition from oil and gas to offshore wind industry needs to be implemented in order to secure competitiveness versus international players. An increased standardization will contribute also to industrialization of cost-efficient processes. Another important theme is to assure talent and workforce capacity for the offshore wind industry in Norway. A part of the competence gap will be covered by the workforce which will make a transition from the oil and gas industry. However, many gaps still will remain to fill in and the upskilling and attraction of talent from abroad is necessary [6].

A forecast or a vision road map for the global floating offshore wind including Norway over a timeline of five years, was brought to attention by the classification company DNV [17]. The DNV's forecast brought to attention the challenges linked with technology innovation as currently there are more than 40 floating wind structure concepts under developments and many others are waiting to be tested. A high number of designs and concepts presents the risk of increased high costs. A standardization of concepts can contribute to cost reduction, attract more investments and conduct to faster developments. Moreover, many fabrication approaches will create difficulties for supply chain in order to provide adequate fabrication/manufacturing facilities. Other technological challenges refers to the mooring systems and anchors which is common to all floating concepts, and significant developments are expected to be done in this area. Optimization of current technology, introduction of new methods and materials such as synthetic ropes, integrated tension monitoring systems, shared mooring, quick connection system, dynamic cables, maintenance of structures and mooring lines, all are just few examples of technological matters which require action, innovation, and cost reduction. [17]. A major challenge is linked with cost of the floating wind. The levelized cost of energy (LCOE) for bottom-fixed projects has reached to less than 50 USD/MWh, while the LCOE for the first floating wind farm passed 200 USD/MWh. Among the enablers for reduction of the LCOE are necessity for technology innovations, required development for supply chains, and the increase in size of the floating wind farms. DNV anticipates that by 2025 and 2040, the floating wind LCOE will drop under 100 USD/MWh, and under 40 USD/MWh, respectively. Solving challenges linked with technologies and cost reduction, adequate policies and regulatory frameworks, facilitation of investments, role and support from government, are among the key enablers for commercialization of floating offshore wind [17].

With the reference to the energy transition of Norway, DNV [18] offers also a focused national forecast or a national vision road map where is emphasizing that large scale offshore floating wind is seen as the most important instrument to ensure a green industry in Norway and to cut down carbon emissions. As per DNV's forecast, the production of a large-scale offshore wind will begin by 2028 [18]. The floating offshore wind will attract financial support in order to establish a local market of projects and to cover domestic energy demand. The financial support will reduce near 2050, as the price for floating offshore will go down and electricity will be exported to Europe.

The DNV's vision road map identified few drivers for the uptake of floating offshore wind in Norway. One driver is offered by the favourable geographical conditions for installation of floating wind and thus limiting the share of the bottom-fixed since on the Norwegian North Sea west coast the water deepens very steep. Another driver is the increase in the electricity demand as the hydropower cannot totally fill the gap between supply and an increased demand. Other driver for floating offshore wind is seen to be the electrification of offshore oil and gas production as the floating offshore wind will cover their energy demand of up to 56 % within the coming 30 years. Another driver will be the new interconnections to UK and Germany and the increased needs of the European electricity which will support the opportunities of high export revenue for floating wind energy [18].

The road ahead until 2030 for the floating offshore wind in Norway was discussed by the technology leader ABB [20]. The floating offshore wind in Norway can be seen as an instrument for reduction of the Norwegian's carbon emissions, but also as a new export opportunity. However, ABB emphasized that Norway needs to establish a strong national market for the Norwegian supplier industry before establishment of major export opportunities for the Norwegian business and deliveries to a global market. The current offshore oil and gas platforms are using power either from local gas turbines or from shore. The electrification of the the Norwegian offshore oil and gas by the floating offshore wind can inspire a new trend around the globe by creation of new renewable solutions and reduction of emissions from oil and gas [20].

Menon [19] also offers a preliminary road map for the Norwegian value chain which has argued the Norwegian industry having potential to obtain a market share between 5-14 % from the total global market of floating offshore wind. The lower level of market share hints there will be no active, clear and robust national frameworks and policy in order to support development of floating offshore in Norway until the market is more mature. Moreover, there will be only a limited number of Norwegian players which will act among the leading value chain in the international market. The upper level of market share suggests that the Norwegian players can obtain success in building a large scale floating offshore industry and can reach to a leading value chain on the international market [19]. As per Menon's estimations, the annual Norwegian offshore wind revenue can reach in 2050 between 21 to 96 billion NOK. Menon highlighted that there is a high potential in the floating offshore wind market in terms of revenue and employment for the Norwegian stakeholders. In order to put in practice this potential and to develop a competitive Norwegian-based floating offshore industry, Menon bring to attention the following key points: a required development for a Norwegian home market; existing strategy and targets needs to be supported by adequate policies, efficient measures and processes, policy instruments which facilitate scale-up; an early start for establishing a national supply chain; a Norwegian leading role in Europe; an adaptation from the Norwegian offshore oil and gas industry; focused development of required skills and transferable skills and expertise, particularly from the oil and gas industry; investment in production capacity and standardization, and in development of ports and infrastructure for building and assembly of offshore wind turbines; and finally investments in offshore wind from both government and industry [19]. It is important to highlight that the countries which took early actions in their domestic market for bottom-fixed offshore wind turbines are the those dominating the market today [19].

Moreover, Menon [37] pointed out that without adequate policy instruments in place, Norway will not develop a domestic market before commercialisation of the floating offshore wind. Menon [37] argues that a domestic market and a Norwegian based industry which includes the value chain related to development and operation of the floating offshore wind is essential for Norway to obtain a leading position in the international floating offshore wind market.

## 6. Discussions

As presented by the examples in the last section, a road map is seen as a key tool and instrument for offshore wind industry, policy and decision makers. A road map is an useful and required tool which supports the vision with concrete action steps. As an instrument, a road map offers coordination, directions and an overview for ongoing and future plans and projects. It may also focus on challenges, opportunities and potential for the offshore wind. A road map is about bringing an overview of the priority areas, critical steps, recommendations, decisions to be made, deadlines, and timelines with a highlight on the milestones which are at focus for industry and policy makers for a coming period of time (until 2040 or 2050, for example). Furthermore, there are road maps created by government, road maps as a result of deliverable for the European research projects, road maps which are offered by consulting companies, classification companies,

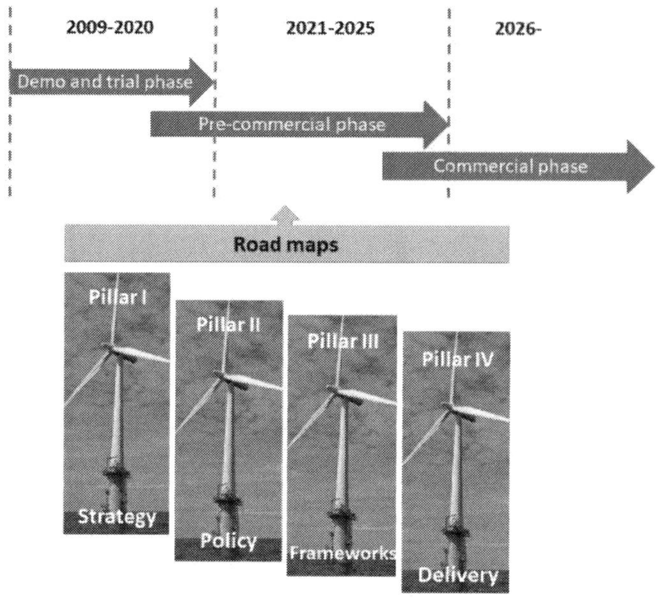


Figure 3: Road maps, offshore industry pillars, timescale and comercialisation stage for the floating offshore wind

and technology leader companies.

Synthesis of the different types of road maps for the Norwegian floating offshore and application of the offshore wind pillars to the Norwegian context brought to attention the important aspect of time and timeline. The figure 3 shows the road maps for the Norwegian floating offshore wind are an integral part of an ensemble which comprises the four pillars and the stages towards the commercialization. The road map needs to be directional and to reflect the national context. With regards to the timescale and commercialisation, the three stages from the Global Wind Energy Council are well applicable to the Norwegian floating offshore wind [10] as illustrated in figure 3.

As per the World Bank's Energy Sector Management Assistance Program (ESMAP)'s Report [21], all of the four pillars of the offshore wind industry present key factors in terms of success:
1. A successful strategy needs to establish a very clear national role for the offshore wind in terms of energy and socio-economic impacts such as energy independence, reduction of electricity prices, emission reduction, supply chain development, job creation, and foreign investments. Countries such as UK and Denmark have a successful strategy about the offshore wind which is a part of their long-term energy strategy [21].
2. A successful policy or policy environment needs to make a balance among different and competing interests of government, organizations, industry, and civil society. The successful policy /legislation should offer realistic milestones over a period of at least a decade. Furthermore, the policy environment needs to cover various aspects such as the followings: to support development of workforce including transition from other sectors; to offer incentives to offshore wind supply chain; to balance conflicting priorities about marine spatial planning; to put rules about the stakeholder engagement, especially, coastal communities and fisheries; to assure that environmental and social impact processes follow international standards; and to support development of infrastructures such as ports and transmission grids. Countries such Netherlands, Poland and Taiwan offer example of strong and successful offshore wind policy environment [21].

3. A successful framework refers to a system which aims to transform policies into realities by providing processes and rules and by making usage of agencies with well-defined mandates, clear roles, adequate budget, and prepared and sufficient staff. A successful framework covers seven key areas such as leasing, permitting, marine spatial planning, export system and grid connection, offtake and revenue, standards and certification, and health and safety. In order to be successful in all of these areas, the agencies which are in charge with implementation need to closely coordinate their approach, to engage with stakeholders, to follow international good practice, to make required adaptations, to minimize risks such as concerning the bankable offtake agreements, and to have clear rules about grid access and curtailment. In addition, the process needs to be transparent, with defined milestones, with a risk management in place and a health and safety culture instilled in the offshore wind industry [21].
4. A successful delivery needs to focus on continuous learning, flexibility, consultation with stakeholders, monitoring of timely implementation of frameworks, and a focus on the areas of supply chain, transmission grid, ports, and financing. A successful delivery is supported by a couple of factors: effective partnership among government, industry and stakeholders, particularly about supply chain and transmission grids; focus on bankability in order to reduce costs of manufacturing, ports, and logistics associated with offshore wind and also to attract finance and investments; focus and adaptation to changing condition and flexibility from both governments, stakeholders and industry; having a long view about deployment of offshore wind and looking to development of ports and transmission grids [21].

An analysis of the pillars of the Norwegian offshore market was performed earlier in section 4 which unveiled positive elements, but many improvements are required and encouraged to take place in order to develop successful key factors like those presented by the World Bank's Energy Sector Management Assistance Program (ESMAP)'s Report [21]. Keeping in mind the integration between road map, timelines and pillars of the Norwegian offshore market, a closer look into the floating offshore project Hywind Tampen can offer interesting perspectives and lessons about the Norwegian approach.

The Hywind Tampen represents the first floating offshore wind farm built on the NCS. This project is seen as opening for the future projects which target a green electrification of the Norwegian oil and gas platforms. The Hywind Tampen can be seen as initiator of a sort of trend in Norway about "the greenification of oil and gas production" as there are many gas and oil productions on the NCS and "plenty of opportunities" for the "greenification" [31]. Since the oil and gas production started in 1971, the NCS has accommodated a total of 120 fields oil and gas. In 2022, a total of 93 field were in production on the NCS: 70 in the North Sea area, 21 in the Norwegian Sea and 2 in the Barents Sea [38]. The Hywind Tampen is also seen to initiate further state support for the offshore wind in Norway in order to implement a green electrification of the oil and gas platforms on the NCS.

The Hywind Tampen floating offshore project benefited from the authorization granted by the Ministry of Petroleum and Energy based on previous licences for survey, exploratory drilling and petroleum activities as per the Norwegian Petroleum Act. The Hywind Tampen was authorized by the Norwegian Petroleum Act as a change in the plans for development and operation and as a modification of power supply to the 5 oil and gas platforms in the Snorre and Gullfaks. Therefore, the authorization from the "Havenergilova" was not required for the floating offshore wind Hywind Tampen [31, 34].

The Hywind Tampen project could not be possible without state aid, but the state support was rather an investment aid than an operational aid with a premium for electricity prices. The Hywind Tampen will not be connected to the Norwegian electricity transmission network and will not provide electricity to the Norwegian grid. The Hywind project will not have an effect on the Norwegian electricity market. The electricity produced by the Hywind Tampen will only cover a 35 % of electricity needs for the five oil and gas platforms situated in the fields of Gullfaks and Snorre. It seems this project will open the door for other floating offshore off-grid wind projects in Norway [34]. The process of decarbonization of the oil and gas industry in Norway making use of the floating offshore wind - the case of the Hywind Tampen - can be seen as an important aspect of learning from the Hywind projects and the Norwegian experience.

The road maps and the fundamental pillars of the offshore wind in Norway within a time perspective has brought to attention both favourable conditions and challenging elements for development of the floating offshore wind. On the positive side towards development of the floating offshore wind in Norway, deep water, very good wind sources, skilled workforce, long tradition working offshore, all of these offer important advantages [6]. The Norwegian floating offshore projects are being build using technologies and competencies which have been acquired for decades by the oil and gas industry [24]. Experienced companies in offshore oil and gas field have increased their engagement and interest for offshore wind industry and offer expertise for offshore structure, mooring, marine operations, logistics, consulting and many other areas[39]. Floating offshore wind can offer a smooth energy transition to countries with rich offshore oil and gas activities and experience such as Norway. Moreover, the floating offshore wind can benefit from the oil and gas skills and expertise in terms of structures, installations, floating technologies and delivery of projects in deep water locations. An illustrative example are the design for floating offshore structures or platform types which are combination of leaning from both the experience of oil and gas and offshore industry [10].

Regarding the challenges for the value chain of the offshore wind in Norway, there is no wind turbine manufacturing to be found in Norway, but there are sub-suppliers companies which deliver for the wind turbines manufacturers, for instance offshore cable manufacturing facilities [39]. As highlighted earlier, Capgemini [6] identified a couple of key challenges which need to be addressed by Norway in order to accelerate the offshore wind such as industrial capacity, predictability, speed, sustainability, and talent.

Technologies and innovations have played a critical role in the development of floating offshore wind in Norway and elsewhere. An example is offered by the high-voltage submarine cables and the dynamic cables like those ones provided to the Hywind Demo and to the Hywind Scotland. The aim for future is to develop high voltage dynamic cables which are more lighter, more flexible and can handle greater voltage and power and more smarter than today [9].

Demonstration projects such as the Flagship project is an example for the structural innovation and floating wind and targets to pave the way for the future floating wind farms in the North Sea by making use of the semi-submersible concrete structures and a 10 MW wind turbines which is accommodated by the METCentre in Norway. The Flagship project aims to reduce the LCOE to a range of 40-60/MWh Euro by 2030 [14].

Regarding the reduction of costs, the CAPEX/MW was manged to be reduced by 70 % from the Hywind Demo to the Hywind Scotland. As per estimations, it is expected that the CAPEX/MW will drop by at least 40 % between the Hywind Scotland and the Hywind Tampen [8].

The Hywind projects and the Norwegian experience has followed a technology agnostic approach towards the offshore wind projects. The best suited designs, substructures, installations and the wind technology have been selected for a given project and in order to match the geographical locations and places for installation and operation. This agnostic approach is perceived to limit bias towards usage of a specific design and technology and encourages adaptability and innovation solutions for particular problems and for regional clusters conditions. Employment of digitalisation and machine learning at a large scale will bring its benefits in the coming future [8]. Five decades of offshore experience in the oil and gas industry and almost two decades in offshore wind industry have contributed to establishment of a broad spectrum of technological concepts and solutions, and innovative technologies in Norway.

Strong national and international networks, interdisciplinary collaboration across different practice fields and sectors/units and drawing upon knowledge and experience from a variety of disciplines are essential for both the technological innovation and social innovation associated with the Hywind floating wind and the Norwegian approach.

Diversity of regional clusters, application of technology-agnostic approach, steady support to mature a proven technology for floating offshore wind farms, creation and development of new industrial opportunities on a regional and global scale, large scale for floating offshore wind farms, green energy transition plans and sustainable approaches are among the key parameters which encourage the innovation to flourish and learning to take place.

In addition, partnerships between industry and universities are recommended for developing different internship programs, educational programs, training, driving innovatory solutions. Moreover, the up-skilling of people working in offshore industries, education for new offshore workforce, and attraction of the right competencies from abroad needs to stay in focus [40], [6].

## 7. Conclusions

This paper presented learning from the existing road maps and the Norwegian approach on the floating offshore wind in the view of the key success factors for offshore wind development offered by the World Bank. A road map can offer a structured and holistic view regarding the development of the floating offshore wind industry. The Norwegian offshore wind industry does not have one comprehensive, with a clear path, high paced road map, but a multitude of road maps from government, consulting and technology leader companies, classification companies, and research projects.

Learning from the Hywind and the Norwegian experiences and approaches about offshore/floating offshore wind brought to attention that the Norwegian stakeholders are very good in initiation and pioneering of projects with illustrative examples: installation of the world's first demo floating offshore wind turbine (the Hywind Demo); investment and operation in the world's first floating offshore wind farm (the Hywind Scotland); the world's biggest floating offshore wind farm and the world's first floating farm for decarbonizing of the oil and gas industry (the Hywind Tampen).

However, learning from the Hywind, the Norwegian approaches, and the road maps of Norway for the offshore/floating offshore wind highlighted a paradoxical situation on national and international arena. On national level, the Norwegian governmental strategy is targeting 30 GW offshore wind until 2040 (still the proportion of the floating offshore wind is not clear). On the European and international arena, the targeted level of GW by the Norwegians for the offshore wind projects, including floating, can easily exceed the national Norwegian targets. Moreover, the role of the offshore/floating offshore wind in Norway is to "greenify" and to decarbonize the oil and gas industry, while on the international arena the focus is on the investment in existing and emerging markets for both bottom-fixed and floating offshore wind. Decarbonization of the oil and gas industry in Norway through the the development of the floating offshore wind is a national particularity of the road map for Norway and the offshore wind market. It has the potential to inspire an international trend for both the offshore wind industry and oil and gas industry.

This article offers a handful of key take away points for industry and decision makers, and which are not limited to the followings:

- A clear and comprehensive road map will contribute to the landscape of offshore wind, specifically, the floating wind energy in Norway and abroad and will help to evaluate future pathways for floating offshore industry. Moreover, a comprehensive and clear road map will offer incentives to stakeholders to invest in the offshore wind market.
- Norwegian academia, industry and governmental organizations need to collaborate to launch new and more tailored educational paths in order to help to fill the competence gaps for offshore wind which can become an important industry for job creation.

- The government needs to support and facilitate to keep up with the speed of other countries in terms of green transition, and particularly, in building and developing a robust local value chain for offshore wind industry by integrating and including large, medium and small size companies.
- The meaning of time and rhythm of action varies from one country to another; the time taken from announcement to production is a key challenge in Norway as elsewhere.
- A pioneering position in the floating offshore wind needs to be supported by a comprehensive road map and an updated analysis and plan of action about the pillars of the Norwegian offshore wind market.
- The Norwegian approach has followed until present a technology agnostic approach towards the offshore wind projects. This approach might raise challenges linked to technology standardisation and cost reduction of fabrication and manufacturing.
- Building and operating in large scale for offshore wind and particularly, floating offshore wind, is a key aspect in order to reduce cost and promote the industrialization of floating offshore wind turbines.
- Technological and social innovation is a fundamental element in achieving and maintaining high learning rates from the Hywind offshore wind development.

## Acknowledgement
The authors gratefully acknowledge the financial support of the Research Council of Norway through the InteDiag-WTCP project (Project Number 309205).

## References
[1] EU. Delivering the European Green Deal. `https://ec.europa.eu/info/strategy/priorities-2019-2024/european-green-deal/delivering-european-green-deal_en//`, 2021. [Online; accessed 10-Sept.-2022.

[2] European Union . Energy and the green deal, a clean energy transition. `https://ec.europa.eu/info/strategy/priorities-2019-2024/european-green-deal/energy-and-green-deal_en/`, 2022. [Online; accessed 12-OCT.-2022.

[3] Global Wind Energy Council . Global offshore wind report 2021. `https://gwec.net/global-offshore-wind-report-2021//`, 2021. [Online; accessed 6-Aug.-2022.

[4] Global Wind Energy Council . Global offshore wind report 2022. `https://gwec.net/gwecs-latest-reports/1///`, 2022. [Online; accessed 6-Aug.-2022.

[5] EU. Report from the commission to the European parliament and the council, progress on competitiveness of clean energy technologies. `https://energy.ec.europa.eu/system/files/2022-11/COM_2022_643_1_EN_ACT_part1_v5.pdf/`, 2022. [Online; accessed 26-Nov.-2022.

[6] Capgemini. Creating offshore winners, how Norway can become a global leader in offshore wind. `https://www.capgemini.com/no-no/research/creating-offshore-winners/`, 2022. [Online; accessed 25-Oct.-2022.

[7] Stiesdal. The vital role of floating wind. `https://www.stiesdal.com/offshore/the-vital-role-of-floating-wind//`, 2022. [Online; accessed 15-Sept.-2022.

[8] Equinor. Floating wind. `https://www.equinor.com/energy/floating-wind`, 2022. [Online; accessed 2-Jun.-2022.

[9] Giles Dickson, WindEurope . Floating offshore wind is gearing up for take-off. `https://windeurope.org/newsroom/news/floating-offshore-wind-is-gearing-up-for-take-off//`, 2020. [Online; accessed 6-Aug.-2022.

[10] Global Wind Energy Council. Floating offshore wind report 2022. `https://gwec.net/gwecs-latest-reports/1//`, 2022. [Online; accessed 6-Nov.-2022.

[11] Amir R Nejad and Jone Torsvik. Drivetrains on floating offshore wind turbines: lessons learned over the last 10 years. *Forschung im Ingenieurwesen*, 85(2):335–343, 2021.

[12] Norwegian Government. Ambitious offshore wind initiative. `https://www.regjeringen.no/en/aktuelt/ambitious-offshore-wind-power-initiative/id2912297/`, 2022. [Online; accessed 2-Aug.-2022.

[13] Cheynet, E. Bergen Offshore Wind Center and Geophysical institute, University of Bergen. Offshore wind potential in Norway and the North Sea. `https://www.uib.no/sites/w3.uib.no/files/attachments/presentation_cheynet_brazil.pdf`, 2021. [Online; accessed 2-Dec.-2022.

[14] Iberdrola. Floating offshore wind - floating offshore wind power: a milestone to boost renewables through innovation. https://www.iberdrola.com/innovation/floating-offshore-wind, 2022. [Online; accessed 23-Dec.-2022.

[15] Norwegian Government - Norwegian Ministry of Trade, Industry and Fisheries. Roadmap - the green industrial initiative. https://www.regjeringen.no/contentassets/1c3d3319e6a946f2b57633c0c5fcc25b/roadmap_the-green-industrial-initiative_spreads_web.pdf//, 2022. [Online; accessed 10-Febr.-2022.

[16] Veum, K. and Cameron, L. and Huertas Hernando, D. and Magnus Korpås, M. Roadmap to the deployment of offshore wind energy in the central and southern north sea (2020 – 2030). https://www.offshore-stiftung.de/sites/offshorelink.de/files/documents/Windspeed.pdf//, 2012. [Online; accessed 10-Oct.-2022.

[17] DNV. Floating wind: The power to commercialize, insights and reasons for confidence. https://www.dnv.com/focus-areas/floating-offshore-wind/commercialize-floating-wind-report.html//, 2022. [Online; accessed 10-Sept.-2022.

[18] DNV. Energy transition Norway 2022 - a national forecast to 2050. https://www.dnv.com/Publications/energy-transition-norway-2022-235535/, 2022. [Online; accessed 8-Dec.-2022.

[19] Menon Economics. Executive summary, floating offshore wind - state of market and the emerging Norwegian value chain. https://www.menon.no/wp-content/uploads/Floating-offshore-wind-1.pdf, 2022. [Online; accessed 12-Dec.-2022.

[20] ABB. Floating offshore wind - Norway's next offshore boom? https://new.abb.com/docs/librariesprovider50/media/tv1012-br-havvind-notat-til-zerokonferansen---engelsk.pdf, 2018. [Online; accessed 12-Nov.-2022.

[21] The World Bank's Energy Sector Management Assistance Program (ESMAP). Key factors for successful development of offshore wind in emerging markets. https://www.esmap.org/new-esmap-report-highlights-key-factors-dev-offshore-wind, 2021. [Online; accessed 2-Oct.-2022.

[22] Siemens Gamesa. Fantastic floating foundation: Siemens gamesa sails with tetraspar. https://www.siemensgamesa.com/en-int/explore/journal/2021/07/tetraspar-world-first-demonstration-industrialized-floating-offshore//, 2021. [Online; accessed 12-Sept.-2022.

[23] Hovland, K.M. Oppgraderer kapasiteten med 7,5 percentage: Equinor øker på hy-wind tampen. https://e24.no/olje-og-energi/i/0r099q/oppgraderer-kapasiteten-med-75-prosent-equinor-oeker-paa-hywind-tampen/, 2022. [Online; accessed 26-Sept.-2022.

[24] Equinor. First power from hywind tampen. https://www.equinor.com/news/20221114-first-power-from-hywind-tampen/, 2022. [Online; accessed 20-Nov.-2022.

[25] Offshore Magazine. North sea floating wind farm on track for q3 startup. https://www.offshore-mag.com/renewable-energy/article/14279667/north-sea-floating-wind-farm-on-track-for-q3-startup, 2022. [Online; accessed 3-Oct.-2022.

[26] Equinor. Equinor and partners consider 1 GW offshore wind farm off the coast of Western Norway. https://www.equinor.com/news/20220617-considering-1gw-offshore-wind-farm-off-western-norway/, 2022. [Online; accessed 20-Jan.-2023.

[27] METCenter. Unitech zefyros (hywind demo). https://metcentre.no/project/unitech-zefyros-hywind-demo///, 2022. [Online; accessed 15-Aug.-2022.

[28] Equinor. Offshore wind. https://www.equinor.com/energy/offshore-wind, 2022. [Online; accessed 2-Jun.-2022.

[29] The Norwegian Government. Meld. st. 36 (2020 – 2021), melding til stortinget, energi til arbeid – langsiktig verdiskaping fra norske energiressurser. https://www.regjeringen.no/contentassets/3d9930739f9b42f2a3e65adadb53c1f4/no/pdfs/stm202020210036000dddpdfs.pdf//, 2021. [Online; accessed 2-Dec.-2022.

[30] The Norwegian Government. Havenergilova. https://www.regjeringen.no/no/tema/energi/fornybar-energi/havenergiloven/id2876913//, 2021. [Online; accessed 3-Jan.-2023.

[31] Herrera Anchustegui, I. Hywind tampen: A regulatory gamechanger for (Norwegian) offshore wind? https://www.uib.no/sites/w3.uib.no/files/attachments/hywind_tampen_smi_29.09_.pdf//, 2020. [Online; accessed 10-Sept.-2022.

[32] Helle Nyhaeim, R. and Herrera Anchustegui, I. Where is the law in the wind? https://www.uib.no/en/bow/146923/where-law-wind, 2022. [Online; accessed 18-Dec.-2022.

[33] The Norwegian Government. Endringar i havenergilova. https://www.regjeringen.no/no/aktuelt/endringar-i-havenergilova/id2930027//, 2022. [Online; accessed 3-Jan.-2023.

[34] I. Herrera Anchustegui. Is Hywind Tampen's state aid approval a kickstart for the Norwegian offshore wind industry?". *European State Aid Law Quarterly*, 19:225–231, 2020.

[35] Thommessen. Framework conditions for offshore wind sent for consultation. https://www.thommessen.no/en/news/framework-conditions-for-offshore-wind-sent-for-consultation, 2022. [Online; accessed 12-Febr.-2023.

[36] Equinor. Equinor sustainability report 2021. https://www.equinor.com/content/dam/statoil/documents/sustainability-reports/2021/sustainaiblity-report-2021-equinor.pdf, 2021. [Online; accessed 2-July.-2022.

[37] Menon Economics. Policy instruments to realise floating offshore wind in Norway. https://offshore-wind.no/wp-content/uploads/2020/10/Policy-instruments-to-realise-floating-offshore-wind-in-Norway-MENON.pdf, 2020. [Online; accessed 12-Dec.-2022.

[38] Norwegian Petroleum. Fields. https://www.norskpetroleum.no/en/facts/field/, 2022. [Online; accessed 6-Jan.-2023.

[39] IEA. IEA Wind Anual Report 2021. https://iea-wind.org/wp-content/uploads/2022/12/IEA_Wind_TCP_Annual_Report_2021.pdf, 2021. [Online; accessed 23-Oct.-2022.

[40] Offshore Magazine. Offshore 2022 offshore wind - special report, an analysis of the offshore wind industry's challenges, solutions and opportunities. https://www.offshore-mag.com/renewable-energy/document/14284638/2022-offshore-wind-special-report, 2023. [Online; accessed 15-Jan.-2023.

# Profitability of hybrid power plants in European markets

**Hajar Habbou, Juan Pablo Murcia Leon, Kaushik Das**

Technical University of Denmark, Department of Wind Energy, 4000 Roskilde, Denmark
**Author contact email**: hajha@dtu.dk

**Abstract.** As markets continue to evolve, hybrid power plants (HPPs) are attracting the interest of plant operators and industry players alike. With their ability to provide flexible dispatchability, HPPs are poised to become a competitive solution in future energy markets, particularly in grid ancillary markets (such as frequency control, reactive power control and black-start). Moreover, resource complementarities present in some sites have the potential to significantly improve production predictability of collocated HPPs.To assess the profitability of HPPs in European markets, a hybrid sizing algorithm is applied to three locations across Europe with distinct resource distribution characteristics. The sizing tool implemented includes several novel features that are not typically incorporated into existing sizing software currently available on the market. This includes turbine selection, a simplified physical design of the wind power plant, a surrogate wake model, and a simplified solar panel degradation model. NPV-over-CAPEX optimal plant designs, tend to favor hybridization, by either collocating wind and solar power with storage, or only solar power with storage. On the hand, minimizing the levelized cost of energy generally results in single-technology power plants. The results show significant potential for hybrid power plants in European markets. However, to truly demonstrate their economic competitiveness, the focus should shift from LCOE to other optimization metrics that consider revenue from different electricity markets.

## 1. Introduction

There is an increasing interest in hybrid power plants (HPP) combining solar and battery, wind and battery, or a combination of all three. This trend is due to the continuously decreasing prices of Lithium-ion batteries and renewable energy technology. By the year 2020, 7 hybrid wind/solar power plants and 22 wind farms co-located with storage were in operation in Europe [1].

An increasing share of renewables integrated into the power grid has led to electricity markets shifting focus from mean energy production to value of energy delivered [2]. To adapt to this paradigm shift, design objectives which initially focused on minimization of levelized cost of energy should now consider net profit maximization from time varying revenue streams [3]. HPPs are increasingly being considered by energy providers, due to their ability to offer flexible dispatchability and ancillary services to the grid. In terms of reliability and flexibility, HPPs are more similar to traditional power plants than single renewable technology power plants.

Hybridization benefits also include economies of scope through shared grid connections, reduced land costs, and streamlined project planning resources. The joint probability distribution of the renewable energy resources may also be a driving factor, as it could enhance predictability and controllability of the supply from the plant.

The design considerations of the stand-alone wind and solar plant apply to the hybrid plant, in addition to those imposed by their colocation [4]. When designing an HPP, there is often a trade-off between designing multiple aspects as a whole and designing each individual technology within its field. On the one hand, optimizing the design of each technology independently, allows for more efficient systems within their specific domain. On the other, designing multiple aspects with a broader view leads to a more integrated and efficient system design.

The sizing and optimization of hybrid power plants are critical tasks for ensuring cost-effective and sustainable energy production. Fortunately, there are many commercial and open-source software tools available to support these tasks. Hybrid Optimization and Performance Platform (HOPP) is a design software for optimizing co-located, utility-scale hybrid plants comprising of wind, solar, battery, and Power-to-X [5]. The software provides optimal sizing, down to the component level. It takes into account physical design constraints, such as shadow flicker effects and irregular boundaries, when optimizing the layout of wind and solar power plants.

HOMER Pro is a micro-grid software, developed by HOMER Energy, to efficiently optimize micro-grid designs [6]. It simulates the optimal operation of the system by making energy balance calculations. Its main feature is providing the feasible system configuration with the least net present cost. Additionally, the software offers a sensitivity analysis that repeats the optimization process for each specified sensitivity variable.

GE's FLEXIQ is a modeling tool that evaluates the economics of hybrid renewable power plant projects and optimizes system configurations to maximize value. The tool provides optimal hybrid architecture and detailed optimal operation, optimizing plant configuration and providing a techno-economic evaluation. It also includes a power system management (PMS) and energy system management (EMS), allowing for active and reactive power control through the plant controller. The EMS enhances asset dispatch schedules to maximize profits, allowing for efficient and effective management of hybrid power plants [7].

This paper focuses on the sizing of utility-scale wind and solar hybrid plants coupled with battery, comparing the results of cost-based designs to value-based designs. While the utility sector has traditionally been driven by the LCOE metric, value-based metrics may offer a more comprehensive viewpoint [8] [9] [10].

## 2. Method

HyDesign is a state-of-the-art optimization tool that provides the optimal hybrid plant sizing based on a user specified financial metric [11], such as net present value over capital costs (NPV/CAPEX) or levelized cost of energy (LCOE). The associated workflow is shown in Figure 1. The design variables of the optimization include wind turbine design (blade tip to ground clearance, specific power, rated power), wind plant design (number of wind turbines, wind power density), solar plant design (AC power, surface tilt angle, surface azimuth angle, DC/AC ratio), battery sizing (power rating, energy storage duration).

The optimization engine sends design variables to wind power plant (WPP) and photovoltaic plant (PVP) and energy management system (EMS) model. The WPP and PVP models are informed by user-specified weather conditions. Based on this information, operational timeseries are estimated, and used to inform a finance model, which returns a quantity of interest to the optimization engine.

The sizing problem is implemented in OpenMDAO. It is an open-source optimization framework for efficient multidisciplinary optimization [12]. It is ideal for a sizing optimization due to its modular structure, which allows for independent modelling of components with different disciplines, and effectively handling their integration in the entire model.

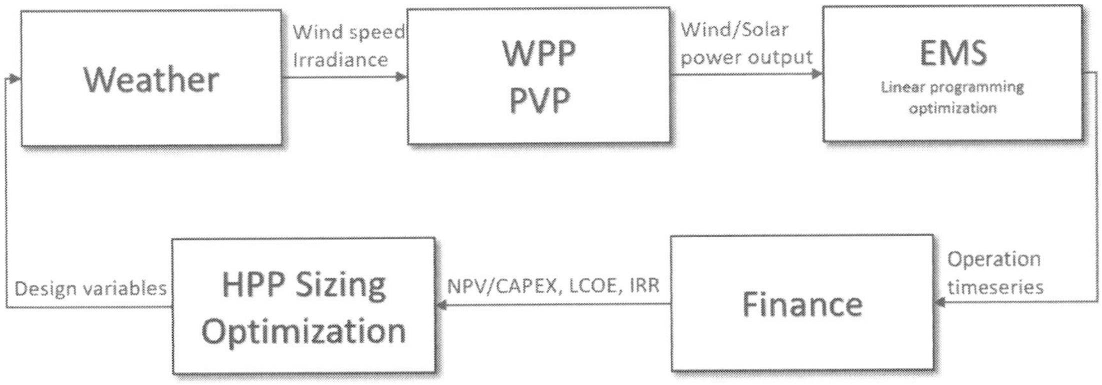


**Figure 1.** High level workflow of HyDesign

### *2.1. Weather*
The wind and solar resources are modelled in detail using the ERA5 and ERA5-land reanalysis datasets [13]. The mean wind speed from Global Wind Atlas 3 (GWA3) [14] is then used to augment the precision of the wind speed data, by considering the effects of the terrain.

To speed up the optimization, a user specified number of weeks per season are selected. The selected weather data is then transformed to match the same probabilistic distribution as the entire weather dataset.

### *2.2. Wind and PV power plant models*
To simulate the wind power production, a surrogate model was built using DTU's database of wind turbines. It generates the power and thrust curves of the turbine given its specific power. A surrogate model was also developed to estimate the wake losses as a function of the installation density, number of turbines and specific power of the turbine. The output of the surrogate model is a rectified power curve that takes into consideration the wake effect, providing a more realistic representation of the power output from the wind turbines in the plant.

PV production is modelled using a generic 1MW PV plant configuration. To account for PV panel degradation, a linear interpolation is applied to estimate the decrease in capacity throughout the panel lifespan, based on a yearly degradation rate.

### *2.3. Energy management system*
The sizing problem includes an energy management system (EMS) optimization, based on CPLEX (MILP optimization). The optimization is deterministic and assumes perfect forecasting of weather conditions. The EMS determines when to charge or discharge the battery with the aim of maximizing the revenues and minimizing penalty costs during peak hours when applicable. The model accepts the wind and solar power generation timeseries as input, and returns the optimal battery operation, to be considered in the financial evaluations. Figure 2 demonstrates how the EMS charges the battery during periods of low electricity price and discharges the battery during periods of high electricity price.

### *2.4. Financial evaluation*
A simple PV plant cost model estimates the total capital expenditure costs and operational and maintenance costs as a function of installed capacity and cost per MW of PV installed.

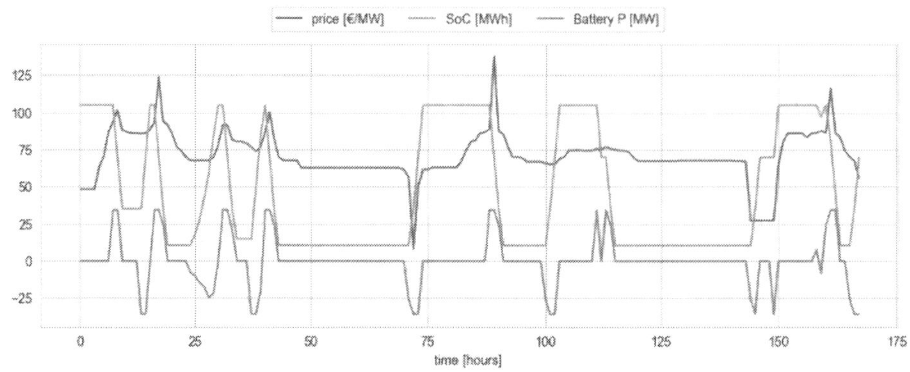


**Figure 2.** Electricity price and battery state of charge and power timeseries over a one-week period

WISDEM's cost and scaling model, developed in NREL [15], is used to evaluate the cost of the wind power plant. The model provides as output a cost scaling factor by specifying the unit costs and technical specifications of a reference wind turbine.

Battery costs are estimated using a simple battery cost model. The model calculates the total capital expenditure costs and operational and maintenance costs as a function of the battery energy and power capacity.

Costs of grid connection, balance of system, and land are also considered.

In the financial evaluation of the model, the net present value (NPV) and levelized cost of energy (LCOE) are calculated as followed:

$$LCOE = \frac{C_L}{AEP_L} \tag{1}$$

and

$$NPV = \sum_{\forall y} \frac{R_y}{(1 + WACC_{tx})^y} \tag{2}$$

where $R_y$ is defined as:

$$R_y = \begin{cases} -C_H \text{ for } y = 0 \\ \overline{i_y} \text{ for } y > 0 \end{cases} \tag{3}$$

$\overline{i_y}$ is the average revenue over the year and is defined as:

$$\overline{i_y} = (\langle pr(t)H(t) - l\rangle_y - O_H)\,(1 - r_{tax})\,(1 - \text{ WACC}_{tx}) \tag{4}$$

$C_L$ is defined as:

$$C_L = \sum_{\forall y} \frac{O_H}{(1+c)^y} \tag{5}$$

The $WACC_{tx}$ stands for the weighted average cost of capital after tax:

$$WACC_{tx} = \frac{C_W \text{ WACC }_W + C_S \text{ WACC }_S + C_b \text{ WACC }_b + C_{sh} \text{ WACC }_{sh}}{C_H} \tag{6}$$

$WACC_{sh}$ stands for shared costs weighted average cost of capital :

$$\text{WACC}_{sh} = \frac{\text{WACC}_W + \text{WACC}_S + \text{WACC}_b}{3} \tag{7}$$

Where $WACC_W$, $WACC_S$, $WACC_B$, $WACC_{sh}$ are the weighted average cost of wind, solar, battery and shared electrical costs. Total capital costs and operational costs are defined as followed:

$$C_H = C_W + C_S + C_b + C_{sh} \tag{8}$$

$$O_H = O_W + O_S + O_b + O_{sh} \tag{9}$$

where: $C_W$, $C_S$, $C_B$, $C_{sh}$ stand for CAPEX of wind, solar, battery and shared technology costs respectively. $O_W$, $O_S$, $O_B$, $O_{sh}$ stand for OPEX of wind, solar, battery and shared technology costs respectively

### *2.5. Optimization*
Surrogate based optimization is used to solve the sizing problem, using a modified parallel efficient global optimization algorithm [16]. Surrogate based optimization relies on building a surrogate (Gaussian process) as a function of all design variables. The algorithm is an iterative method that proposes new model simulations that balance exploration of the design space and exploitation of the trends discovered.

## 3. Case study
The hybrid sizing algorithm is applied to three locations in Europe: a site with high wind resources in Denmark (Lat: 55.23°, Long: 11.94°), a second site with high solar resources in France (Lat: 44.42°, Long: 4.22°), and a third site with average wind and solar resources situated in Germany (Lat: 49.31°, Long: 10.76°). The selection of these sites was based on the Global Wind Atlas [17] and Global Solar Atlas [18] maps, where darker colors indicate higher wind and solar resources, respectively.

Using the Balmorel model, electricity price data is predicted for the year 2030. Balmorel is a bottom-up partial equilibrium energy system optimisation model with a special focus on electricity and district heating sectors [19]. It can be used to forecast electricity prices across various regions in Europe for future years, typically up to 20 years in advance.

The price predictions generated using Balmorel were based on 2012 weather data assumptions. To maintain consistency, 25 years' worth of weather data was generated using the same dataset. 25 years corresponds to the projected lifetime of the power plant.

Figures 3, 4, and 5 display the hourly median and quantiles per season of unit wind and solar generation, as well as electricity price in the regions where the sites are situated. The figures illustrate the 5th, 15th, 25th, 35th, 50th (median), 65th, 75th, 85th, and 95th quantiles, with colours fading from the median. The plots provide insights into the seasonal variations of renewable energy generation and electricity prices in the different regions. The hourly median of electricity prices across all three locations and all seasons exhibits a consistent trend, with prices peaking generally between 4 PM and 8 PM. The data suggests that electricity prices are highest during the late afternoon and early evening hours, when there is typically higher demand for electricity due to people returning home and using more appliances for cooking, lighting, and heating/cooling.

Figure 3 highlights the first site's potential for high wind power output all year around. Wind power production levels are consistently high during the winter, spring, and fall seasons with a noticeable drop in wind production during the summer season.

The power production from wind resources in the chosen sunny site in France appears to be relatively low across all seasons, see Figure 4. However, the site boasts abundant solar resources

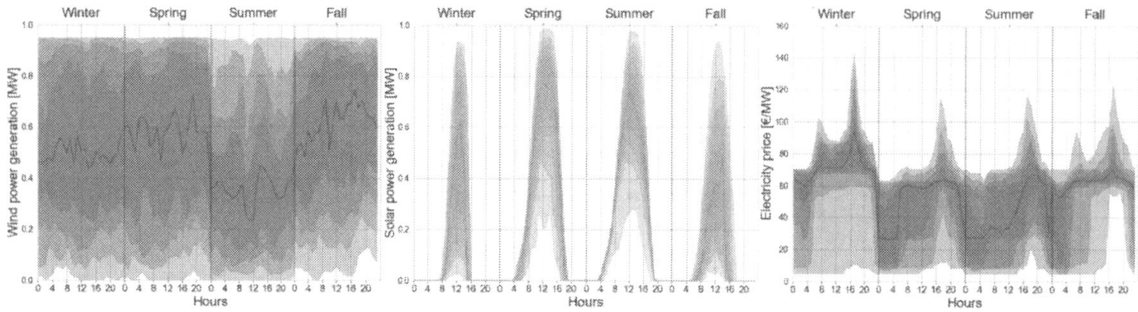


**Figure 3.** Hourly median and quantiles per season of a 1 MW wind turbine power generation (left), 1 MW installed PV power generation (middle), and electricity price (right) **in the good wind site situated in Denmark.** Wind power generation considers the following WPP specifications: clearance = 49, specific power = 321, rated power = 5, wind power density = 7. Solar plant generation considers the following panel specifications: tilt angle = 46, azimuth angle= 210. Darker colours represent higher probability.

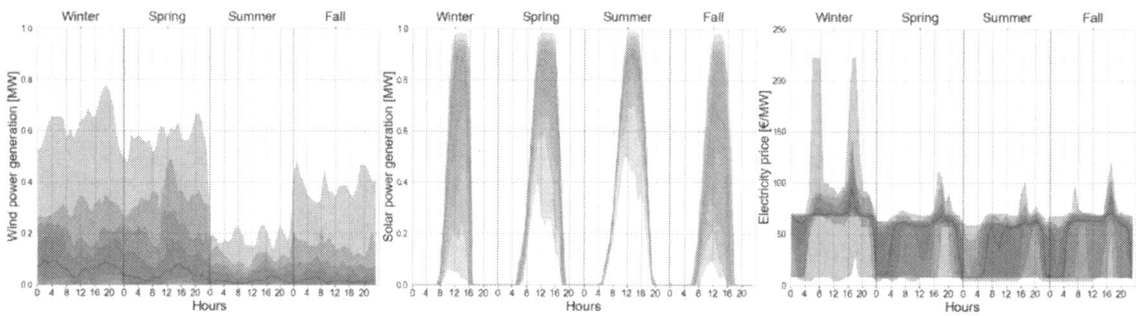


**Figure 4.** Hourly median and quantiles per season of a 1 MW wind turbine power generation (left), 1 MW installed PV power generation (middle), and electricity price (right) **in the good solar site situated in France.** Wind power generation considers the following WPP specifications: clearance = 49, specific power = 321, rated power = 5, wind power density = 7. Solar plant generation considers the following panel specifications: tilt angle = 44, azimuth angle= 210. Darker colours represent higher probability.

throughout the year, with peak production occurring during the summer when sunlight hours are longer compared to other seasons. Solar energy production dominates during the daytime hours, while wind energy production is consistently low throughout the day and night.

Figure 5 shows that the third site, located in Germany, has average wind resources that peak during the winter season. The solar production at this site is also relatively good, although lower than that of the second site. The plots show a complementary relationship between wind and solar resources at this site. Solar production peaks in the middle of the day when wind resources are low, and wind resources pick up again in the early evening when solar production begins to decline.

The wind and solar technology costs are derived from financial data extracted from the Danish Energy Agency technology data catalogue [20]. It is worth noting that a cheap battery scenario is considered. The technology costs assumptions are summarized in Table 1

In this case study, the primary objective function considered is the net present value of capital expenditures (NPV/CAPEX). The resulting optimal designs are then compared with

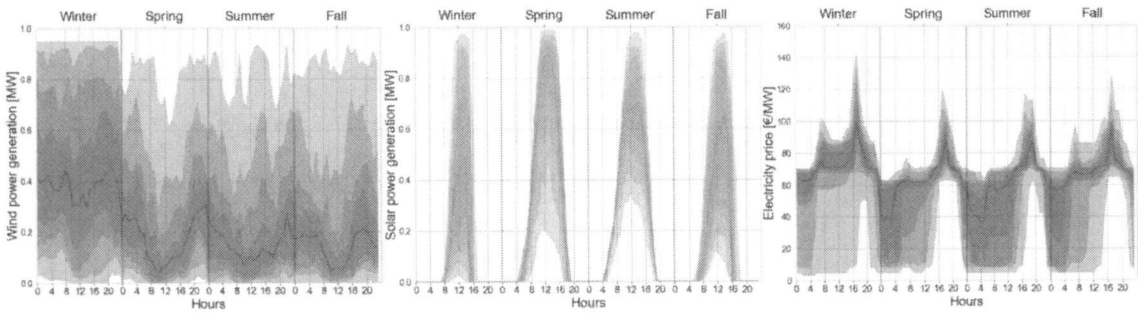


**Figure 5.** Hourly median and quantiles per season of a 1 MW wind turbine power generation (left), 1 MW installed PV power generation (middle), and electricity price (right) **in the average wind and solar site situated in Germany.** Wind power generation considers the following specifications: clearance = 49, specific power = 321, rated power = 5, wind power density = 7. Solar plant generation considers the following panel specifications: tilt angle = 48, azimuth angle= 210. Darker colours represent higher probability.

**Table 1.** Technology costs considered in the optimization.

| | |
|---|---|
| Wind technology costs | |
| Wind turbine cost | 640 k€/MW |
| Wind civil works cost | 80 k€/MW |
| Wind fixed operation/maintenance cost | 12.6 k€/MW/year |
| Wind variable operation/maintenance cost | 1.35 k€/MWh |
| Solar technology costs | |
| Solar PV cost | 110 k€/MW |
| Solar hardware installation cost | 100 k€/MW |
| Solar inverter cost | 20 k€/MW |
| Solar fixed operation/maintenance cost | 4.5 k€/MW |
| Battery technology cost | |
| Battery energy cost | 45 k€/MWh |
| Battery power cost | 16 k€/MW |
| Battery BOP/installation/commissioning cost | 18 k€/MW |
| Battery control system cost | 4.5 k€/MW |

plant designs that aim to minimize the levelized cost of energy (LCOE).

In the sizing optimization, NPV/CAPEX is the primary metric for economic evaluation instead of the internal rate of return (IRR) because the latter is not defined when NPV is negative, which is the case for a significant portion of the design space considered.

## 4. Results and discussion

The detailed sizing results based on NPV/CAPEX and LCOE in the three different locations are presented Table 2.

In the windy site situated in Denmark, the NPV/CAPEX optimal design is a hybrid power plant consisting of 275 MW of wind, 155 MW of solar, and 35 MW of battery with a storage duration of 3 hours. Minimizing LCOE, on the hand, recommends installing a 310 MW wind power plant with 27 MW of PV.

In France's sunny site, the NPV/CAPEX-based design resulted in a hybrid power plant comprising of 338 MW of solar and 37 MW of battery with a 2-hour storage duration, minimizing LCOE leads to a design made up of only 329 MW of PV with no battery installation. Similar to the sunny site results, the sizing optimization in the third site in Germany led to a hybrid power plant consisting of 380 MW of solar and 91 MW of battery with a storage duration of 2 hours when maximizing NPV/CAPEX, LCOE-based design consists of only 317 MW of PV.

In all three sites, optimizing NPV/CAPEX resulted in a hybrid power plant with a higher total capacity than the optimal plant obtained by minimizing LCOE. When the objective is set to NPV/CAPEX, the solver aims to maximize the overall profitability of the project, rather than just the cost of energy production. By integrating battery storage into the design of a hybrid power plant, the profitability of the project can be significantly improved.

The inclusion of batteries enables the shifting of energy production from periods of low electricity prices to periods of high electricity prices, thereby maximizing revenue. Additionally, batteries allow for over-planting, as excess energy produced during peak production can be stored and used during periods of low energy production. This avoids the need to curtail energy production during peak periods, which ultimately increases the overall efficiency of the plant. Overall, incorporating battery storage in the design of a hybrid power plant leads to a more efficient and profitable project. This is can be seen in Table 2, where the inclusion of battery in the design led to a higher NPV in all sites. In the first site, a 2.7 % increase in NPV was achieved, in the second a 5.8 % increase, and in the third site a 13 % increase.

Table 2 shows that the internal rate of return (IRR) of the project is similar for both the NPV/CAPEX optimization and the LCOE minimization, which is contrary to what would be expected. This result is due to the high electricity prices used in the analysis, resulting from the current situation in Ukraine which has disrupted energy markets. Consequently, a very favorable business case can already be achieved by considering LCOE as the objective function, where the solver aims to install the cheapest technology considering the available weather resources. If a data set with lower electricity prices were used, the impact of installing batteries would be more significant, leading to a greater difference in IRR between the NPV/CAPEX optimization and the LCOE minimization. Furthermore, if power purchase agreements (PPA) were considered instead of spot electricity markets, the impact on IRR would be even more pronounced between the two designs.

Figure 6 presents the hourly median and the $5^{th}$ and $95^{th}$ quantiles of the revenue per season in the windy site, for both the NPV/CAPEX and LCOE based designs. Darker colors indicate higher number of occurrences. The NPV/CAPEX optimal design generally generates more revenue than the LCOE based design in all seasons. This difference is particularly noticeable during the middle of the day, especially in the summer and spring seasons. The higher revenue generated by the NPV/CAPEX design can be attributed to the greater amount of PV installed, which allows it to take more advantage of high irradiance during the middle of the day.

Figure 7 indicates that the revenue generated by the NPV/CAPEX and LCOE designs are quite similar in the sunny site. As can be seen in Table 2, both designs have a similar PV installation. However, the NPV design generates a slightly higher revenue than the LCOE design, particularly during peak electricity price periods, thanks to the battery's ability to shift power to these periods. The $95^{th}$ quantile reveals that there are occurences in which the NPV/CAPEX design produces a greater revenue when the electricity price spikes, particularly between 4 pm and 8 pm, refer to Figure 4. For example, when the electricity price surges between 4 pm and 6pm in the fall, the median revenue is much higher with the NPV/CAPEX design.

Figure 8 presents the hourly median of the revenue per season for the German site. This plot reinforces the findings from the previous figure. The fall season provides a good example of the revenue differences between the LCOE and NPV designs. At the beginning of the day, the LCOE design generates slightly higher revenue than the NPV design. However, during peak electricity price periods, the NPV design generates more revenue thanks to the battery's ability to charge during low-price hours and discharge during high-price hours to maximize profits.

**Table 2.** Technology costs considered in the optimization.

| Country | Denmark | | France | | Germany | |
|---|---|---|---|---|---|---|
| Site description | Good Wind | | Good Solar | | Average Solar & Wind | |
| Latitude | 55.23 | | 44.42 | | 49.31 | |
| Longitude | 11.94 | | 4.23 | | 10.77 | |
| Elevation | 107 | | 204 | | 442 | |
| Optimization function | NPV | LCOE | NPV | LCOE | NPV | LCOE |
| Clearance (m) | 49 | 54 | 29 | 10 | 33 | 25 |
| Specific power (m²/W) | 321 | 316 | 276 | 330 | 246 | 234 |
| Rated power (MW) | 5 | 5 | 1 | 1 | 3 | 4 |
| Number of wind turbines | 55 | 62 | 0 | 0 | 0 | 0 |
| Wind power density (MW/km²) | 7 | 6 | 6 | 5 | 7 | 5 |
| Solar power (MW) | 155 | 27 | 338 | 329 | 380 | 317 |
| Surface tilt (degs) | 46 | 17 | 44 | 38 | 48 | 37 |
| Surface azimuth (degs) | 210 | 158 | 210 | 210 | 210 | 210 |
| DC/AC Ratio | 1.51 | 1.52 | 1.59 | 1.59 | 1.66 | 1.86 |
| Battery power (MW) | 35 | 0 | 37 | 0 | 91 | 0 |
| Battery storage duration (h) | 3 | 1 | 2 | 1 | 2 | 1 |
| NPV over CAPEX | 0.94 | 0.94 | 0.96 | 0.96 | 0.89 | 0.88 |
| NPV (Meuro) | 304.54 | 296.72 | 164.48 | 155.9 | 176.55 | 155.06 |
| LCOE (Euro/MWh) | 21.16 | 20.42 | 21.75 | 21.27 | 27.29 | 26 |
| CAPEX (Meuro) | 323.61 | 315.27 | 171.02 | 163.02 | 198.65 | 176.6 |
| OPEX (Meuro) | 6.16 | 6 | 2.41 | 2.35 | 2.84 | 2.66 |
| Grid (MW) | 300 | 300 | 300 | 300 | 300 | 300 |
| Wind (MW) | 275 | 310 | 0 | 0 | 0 | 0 |
| Solar (AC MW) | 155 | 27 | 338 | 329 | 380 | 317 |
| Solar (DC MW) | 233.8 | 41.14 | 536.13 | 521.5 | 632.13 | 590.84 |
| Battery Power (MW) | 35 | 0 | 37 | 0 | 91 | 0 |
| Battery Energy (MWh) | 105 | 0 | 74 | 0 | 182 | 0 |
| Total curtailment (GWh) | 40.39 | 5.14 | 7.02 | 12.93 | 16.82 | 4.48 |
| Rotor diameter (m) | 140.83 | 141.94 | 67.92 | 87.84 | 124.61 | 147.53 |
| Hub height (m) | 119.41 | 124.97 | 62.96 | 53.92 | 95.3 | 98.76 |
| Optimisation time (min) | 75.51 | 62.77 | 21.17 | 40.66 | 40.07 | 47.82 |

This finding highlights the importance of considering not only the initial investment costs but also the potential revenue benefits of storage in renewable energy projects.

## 5. Conclusion

The study examined the potential of hybrid power plants in European markets by applying a hybrid sizing algorithm to three locations with varying weather resources. The results are encouraging and indicate that hybrid power plants have promising prospects in European markets. The study evaluated two objective functions, NPV/CAPEX and LCOE. While NPV/CAPEX favors hybridization to maximize revenue generation, LCOE focuses on installing the cheapest technology based on weather resources. Overall, the study highlights the potential of hybrid power plants in Europe and provides valuable insights into the importance of considering multiple financial metrics for optimal plant sizing.

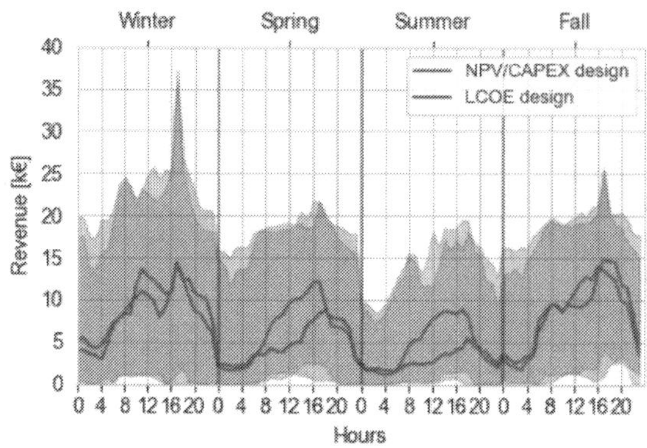


**Figure 6.** Hourly median and $5^{th}$ and $95^{th}$ quantiles of the revenue per season **in the good wind site in Denmark.**

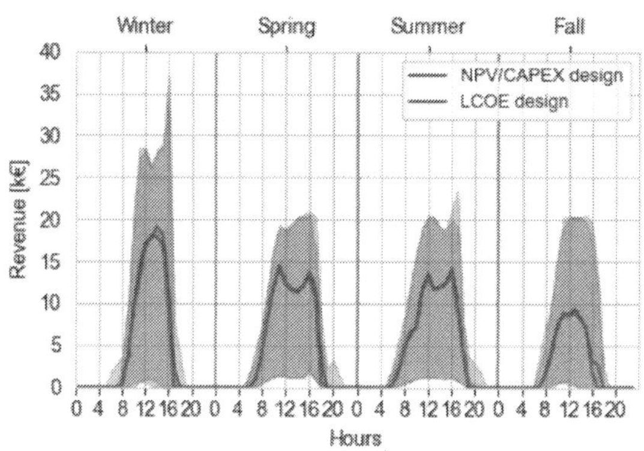


**Figure 7.** Hourly median and $5^{th}$ and $95^{th}$ quantiles of the revenue per season **in the good solar site in France.**

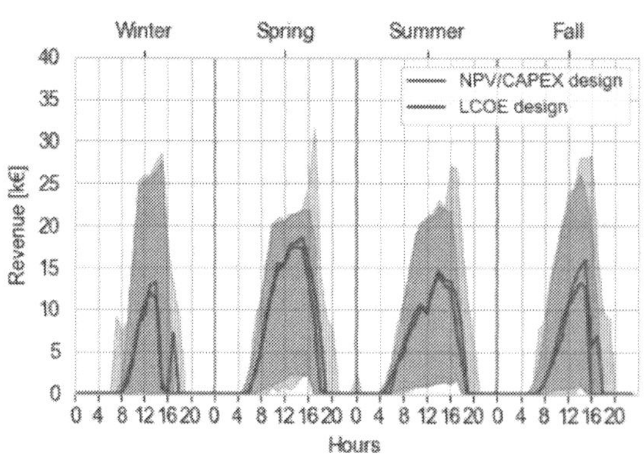


**Figure 8.** Hourly median and $5^{th}$ and $95^{th}$ quantiles of the revenue per season **in the average wind and solar resources in Germany.**

## References

[1] Hybrid renewable power plants make a good business case but need clearer legislation to become more widespread, Oct 2020. https://windeurope.org/newsroom/news/hybrid-renewable-power-plants-make-a-good-business-case/.

[2] Katherine Dykes, Lena Kitzing, Mattias Andersson, Cristian Pons-Seres de Brauwer, and Helena Canét. Beyond lcoe: New assessment criteria for evaluating wind energy r&i. In *SETWind workshop*, 2020.

[3] Katherine Dykes, Jennifer King, Nicholas DiOrio, Ryan King, Vahan Gevorgian, David Corbus, Nate Blair, Kate Anderson, Greg Stark, Craig Turchi, et al. Opportunities for research and development of hybrid power plants. Technical report, National Renewable Energy Lab.(NREL), Golden, CO (United States), 2020.

[4] Charles Tripp, Darice Guittet, Jennifer King, and Aaron Barker. A simplified, efficient approach to hybrid wind and solar plant site optimization. *Wind Energy Science*, 7(2):697–713, 2022.

[5] Darice Guittet, P. J. Stanley, Bill Hamilton, Jen King, and Aaron Barker. Hopp - hybrid optimization and performance platform.

[6] Homer pro help manual, April 2019. https://www.homerenergy.com/products/pro/docs/3.13/index.html.

[7] Flexiq: Design, operations, and fleet management solutions to optimize a hybrid project's customer value. https://www.ge.com/renewableenergy/hybrid/flexiqDISPATCHER.

[8] Robert Idel. Levelized full system costs of electricity. *Energy*, 259:124905, 2022.

[9] Juliet Simpson, Eric Loth, and Katherine Dykes. Cost of valued energy for design of renewable energy systems. *Renewable Energy*, 153:290–300, 2020.

[10] Eric Loth, Chris Qin, Juliet G Simpson, and Katherine Dykes. Why we must move beyond lcoe for renewable energy design. *Advances in Applied Energy*, 8:100112, 2022.

[11] Juan Pablo Murcia Leon, Hajar Habbou, Kaushik Das, Rujie Zhu, and Mikkel Friis-Møller. Dtuwindenergy/hydesign: Release of v1.0.3, January 2023.

[12] Justin S Gray, John T Hwang, Joaquim RRA Martins, Kenneth T Moore, and Bret A Naylor. Openmdao: An open-source framework for multidisciplinary design, analysis, and optimization. *Structural and Multidisciplinary Optimization*, 59:1075–1104, 2019.

[13] Hans Hersbach, Bill Bell, Paul Berrisford, Shoji Hirahara, András Horányi, Joaquín Muñoz-Sabater, Julien Nicolas, Carole Peubey, Raluca Radu, Dinand Schepers, et al. The era5 global reanalysis. *Quarterly Journal of the Royal Meteorological Society*, 146(730):1999–2049, 2020.

[14] Juan Pablo Murcia, Matti Juhani Koivisto, Graziela Luzia, Bjarke T Olsen, Andrea N Hahmann, Poul Ejnar Sørensen, and Magnus Als. Validation of european-scale simulated wind speed and wind generation time series. *Applied Energy*, 305:117794, 2022.

[15] Katherine Dykes, Andrew Ning, Ryan King, Peter Graf, George Scott, and Paul S Veers. Sensitivity analysis of wind plant performance to key turbine design parameters: a systems engineering approach. In *32nd ASME Wind Energy Symposium*, page 1087, 2014.

[16] Mohamed Amine Bouhlel, John T Hwang, Nathalie Bartoli, Rémi Lafage, Joseph Morlier, and Joaquim RRA Martins. A python surrogate modeling framework with derivatives. *Advances in Engineering Software*, 135:102662, 2019.

[17] Global wind atlas map. https://globalwindatlas.info/en.

[18] Global solar atlas map. https://globalsolaratlas.info/map.

[19] Frauke Wiese, Rasmus Bramstoft, Hardi Koduvere, Amalia Pizarro Alonso, Olexandr Balyk, Jon Gustav Kirkerud, Åsa Grytli Tveten, Torjus Folsland Bolkesjø, Marie Münster, and Hans Ravn. Balmorel open source energy system model. *Energy strategy reviews*, 20:26–34, 2018.

[20] Technology data for renewable fuels. https://ens.dk/sites/ens.dk/files/Analyser/technology-data-for-renewable-fuels.pdf.

# The Hydrogen Wind Turbine: Design of a wind turbine optimised for hydrogen production

**A Bechmann[1], T Barlas[1], H L Frandsen[2], L Jin[3], and R N Nakashima[2]**

[1] Department of Wind and Energy Systems, Technical University of Denmark (DTU)
[2] Department of Energy Conversion and Storage, Technical University of Denmark (DTU)
[3] Department of Industrial Eng. & Math. Sci., Università Politecnica delle Marche (UNIVPM)

E-mail: andh@dtu.dk

**Abstract.** "Green" hydrogen produced using electrolysis and zero-carbon electricity may be a path for the EU to reduce its dependence on natural gas imports and support the green transition. The EU uses 10 Mt of natural gas yearly for hydrogen production, representing a potential 120 GW market for the wind industry. Placing the hydrogen production (electrolysers) near the energy source (wind turbines) instead of the consumer (e.g. fertiliser producers) changes the energy transportation from power to hydrogen and opens new design possibilities. This work investigates how an off-grid wind turbine designed for hydrogen production may differ from a traditional one.

The paper first describes the numerical modelling framework used to estimate the hydrogen production and cost of a "hydrogen wind turbine." The main parameters of the system (generator rating, rotor diameter, electrolyser rating and battery capacity) are then optimised to reduce the levelised cost of hydrogen (LCOH). Results show that an LCOH-optimised wind turbine should have a lower specific power (i.e. a larger rotor) than an LCOE-optimised design. We find a 7% LCOH reduction compared to the reference system, opening the door for future wind turbines designed directly for hydrogen production.

## 1. Introduction

A year ago (March 2022), the European Council agreed to phase out dependence on Russian natural gas and become independent before 2030. Each year, the EU uses 10 Mt of natural gas to produce hydrogen for fertilisers, refining and other chemical applications [1]. The main alternative to "grey" hydrogen from natural gas is "green" hydrogen produced using electrolysis and zero-carbon electricity. Green hydrogen may be a path for the EU to reduce import dependence and support the green transition. As green hydrogen requires about 55 kWh/kg$H_2$, it also represents a potential 120 GW market for the wind industry (at a capacity factor of 0.5) just for this use case alone.

While placing electrolysers and Power-2-X plants on land provides the highest possible integration with other energy sources [2], placing them offshore close to the power source may still be an advantage. The main reason is that electrical cables are far more expensive than hydrogen pipes, and energy transportation becomes cheaper. [3] show that importing hydrogen to Germany is more affordable than producing it locally. This will be even more evident with the establishment of the European Hydrogen Backbone [4], which will provide a cost-effective option for long-distance hydrogen transport.

The costs and constraints of electrical infrastructure determine the boundary conditions for today's offshore wind turbine design. Changing the energy transportation to hydrogen eliminates electrical components and power conversion losses of traditional grid-connected electrolyser facilities and potentially allows for a simpler and cheaper wind turbine design. On a Hydrogen Wind Turbine (HWT), the electrolysis stack is integrated with the WT generator and operates off-grid. As the $H_2$ production requires water as feedstock, it is natural to think of offshore concepts that include a seawater desalination system [5, 6].

One of the main design choices for an HWT is the rating of the electrolysis stack ($P_e$) compared to the generator ($P_g$). Since the efficiency of the considered alkaline electrolyser stack drops at high loads [7], [8] suggest that it may be beneficial to "oversize" the electrolyser compared to the generator. They find that an electrolyzer rating 20% higher than the generator results in a drop of the Levelized Cost of Hydrogen (LCOH) of about 5%. However, the oversizing ratio is sensitive to the efficiency curve of the electrolysis system, which is not explicitly modelled by [8]. If the generator output exceeds the electrolyser capacity, it may be curtailed. Having battery storage can reduce the curtailment, but its size needs to be chosen wisely to minimise the LCOH.

Another critical parameter in the HWT design is the specific power, which is the ratio of the rated power to the swept area. Modern wind turbines have a relatively low specific power, designed to reach maximum rated power at relatively low wind speeds to maximise the capacity factor. However, [9] argues that an HWT should have a high specific power to increase electrolyser efficiency and lower the LCOH.

### *1.1. Research questions*
This paper investigates the design of an HWT. We first conceptualise an electrolyser system for the IEA 10 MW reference wind turbine [10]. Next, we evaluate how the size of the alkaline electrolysis stack and the battery impact the LCOH. Finally, a parametric study of the main wind turbine design parameters (specific power) is conducted to investigate the potential of reducing LCOH by optimising the wind turbine design. The paper tries to answer the following central questions:

(i) How should an electrolyser system for an HWT be designed?
(ii) Does hydrogen production change the boundary conditions for wind turbine design?
(iii) How does changing the main HWT components affect the LCOH?

## 2. Methodology
The HWT modelling framework consists of three main elements: the wind climate, the wind turbine (WT), and the electrolysis system (ES). A battery is also included to provide the grid-forming service for off-grid operation and to reduce curtailment when WT power exceeds the electrolyser rating. Each subsystem provides the input for the next subsystem until pressurised $H_2$ is finally output (Figure 1). As the paper focuses on the design of an isolated HWT, it does not consider the integration with the remaining energy system. The $H_2$ production is, therefore, not constricted to follow a demand profile and is simply exported when produced. Consequently, costs and losses due to wind farm infrastructure, $H_2$ transport and storage are not considered. The following sections describe each of the subsystems, followed by a section that describes how we evaluate the system's performance.

### *2.1. The wind climate*
The location of the planned energy island in the North Sea in Denmark is selected to get a realistic wind climate for the simulations. The hub-height wind climate for 2021 is estimated using the ERA5-GWA2 method [11] with the resulting all-sector Weibull parameters given in

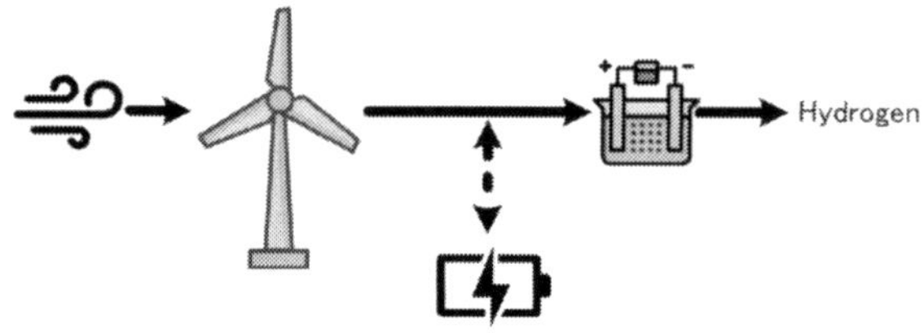


Figure 1: The subsystems of HWT model: the wind climate, the wind turbine with an integrated battery, and the electrolysis system.

Table 1. The wind climate is assumed to represent the average lifetime conditions of the wind turbine, i.e. no long-term correction of the wind climate has been performed. To estimate the wind climate for varying hub heights, we scale the Weibull-A parameter using a logarithmic velocity profile with a roughness length of $z_0 = 0.0002\,\mathrm{m}$. The Weibull-k parameter and the air density are kept fixed.

### *2.2. The reference wind turbine*

The IEA 10-MW off-shore WT [10] is used as a reference wind turbine (RWT). It has a rated power of 10 MW, a rotor diameter of 198.0 m, and a hub height of 119.0 m giving it a specific power of $SP = 325\,\mathrm{W/m^2}$. To evaluate the effects of optimising the main WT parameters (Table 2), we model the wind turbine as a simple parametric power curve. The power in the full load region is equal to the rated power, while we use the power equation in the partial load region, assuming optimal power coefficient ($C_p$=0.49):

$$P(V) = 0.5\rho V^3 C_p \pi (D/2)^2 \tag{1}$$

Knowing the wind turbine power curve and the wind climate, the gross Annual Energy production (AEP) and the capacity factor ($C_f$) can be calculated. Since this work only analyses a single wind turbine, the wake effects are ignored, and the RWT has a high capacity factor of 0.628 and an AEP of 55.0 GWh.

The electrical system for an HWT is very different to traditional WTs. The WT generator and a battery are connected to a DC bus through separate converters. The primary role of the battery is to provide grid-forming services necessary for the HWT to operate in off-grid/island mode [12]. However, the battery also serves as a reserve for "cold" upstarts and reduces curtailment in situations where power production exceeds the rating of the electrolysis system. The optimal battery capacity ($E_b$) is investigated in Section 3.1.

To dynamically model the electrolysis system, it is necessary to use realistic power time series as the fluctuating power may negatively influence $H_2$ production [5]. A super-capacitor can mitigate the high-frequency fluctuations from the wind, however, to analyse the most severe case, it has been omitted in this work. Instead, a 1-second resolution WT generator time series is simulated according to the wind conditions described by [13] and used directly as input for the electrolysis system without applying any low-pass super-capacitor filter.

Table 1: Parameters of the reference wind climate. The mean wind speed is $V_{ref} = 9.78\,\mathrm{m/s}$.

| | | | |
|---|---|---|---|
| $z_{ref}$ | Reference height | 119 | m |
| $A$ | Weibull scale parameter | 11.0 | m/s |
| $k$ | Weibull shape parameter | 2.28 | - |
| $\rho$ | Air density | 1.225 | kg/m$^3$ |

Table 2: The main parameters of the reference wind turbine. The rated wind speed is $V_{rated} = 11.0\,\mathrm{m/s}$ and the cut-in and cut-out wind speeds are $4\,\mathrm{m/s}$ and $25\,\mathrm{m/s}$ respectively.

| | | | |
|---|---|---|---|
| $P_g$ | Generator rating | 10 | MW |
| $D$ | Rotor diameter | 198 | m |
| $HH$ | Hub height | 119 | m |

*2.3. The electrolysis system*

The electrolysis system proposed in this study is illustrated in Figure 2. In this system, an alkaline electrolysis stack operates at nominal conditions of 30% wt. KOH (Potassium Hydroxide), 80 °C, 7 bar, and current density of $300\,\mathrm{mA/cm^2}$ (approx. 1.79 V/cell) generates the $H_2$ from water [14]. The partial load of the electrolysis stacks is restricted to 15-100% of the nominal load rating [15]. Once produced, $H_2$ is separated from the electrolyte and compressed in a two-stage process to a pipeline, which is kept pressurized at 70 bar [16]. We do not consider $H_2$ storage or onshore transport in the provided cost estimates, as these would be sensitive to location and the remaining infrastructure. A desalination unit (based on reverse osmosis) constantly replaces the water consumed in the electrolyser and the cooling towers.

The specific power consumption for hydrogen production for the entire electrolysis system at different partial loads is shown left in Figure 3. Based on the power consumption and the WT energy production time series, the Annual Hydrogen Production (AHP) can be estimated for different ratings of the electrolysis stack ($P_e$) and battery capacities ($E_b$). The power distribution between the different components of the fully loaded ES is shown to the right of Figure 3. The graph shows that $H_2$ compression is responsible for 2.6% of the system consumption, while the stack is responsible for 96.3, and the remaining 1% is attributed to the cooling and reverse osmosis systems, aligned with IRENA 2020's technical report [17].

The thermodynamic model for the electrolysis system is developed using Python with the libraries Numpy [18] and Scipy [19], and the system is solved using a mixed integer linear programming (MILP) optimization algorithm using Julia with the JuMP modelling framework [20] and the Gurobi solver [21].

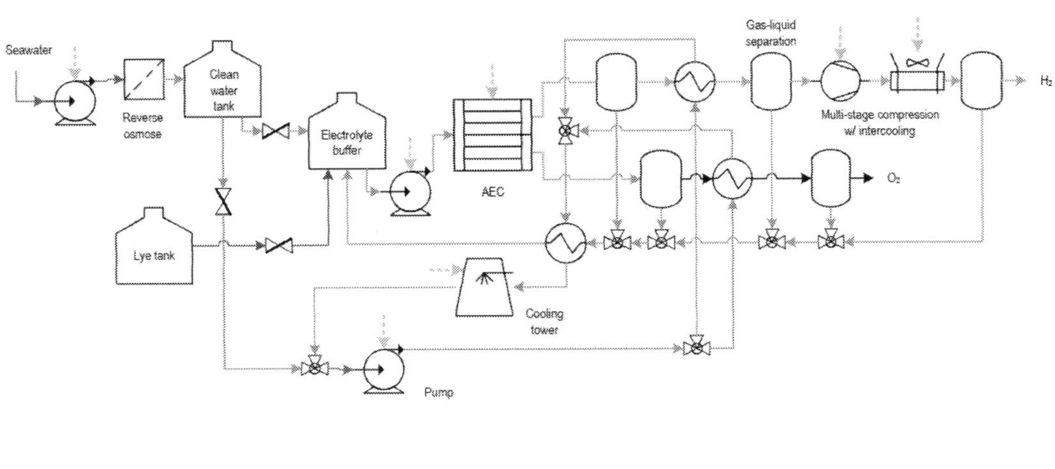


Figure 2: Flowsheet of the electrolysis system

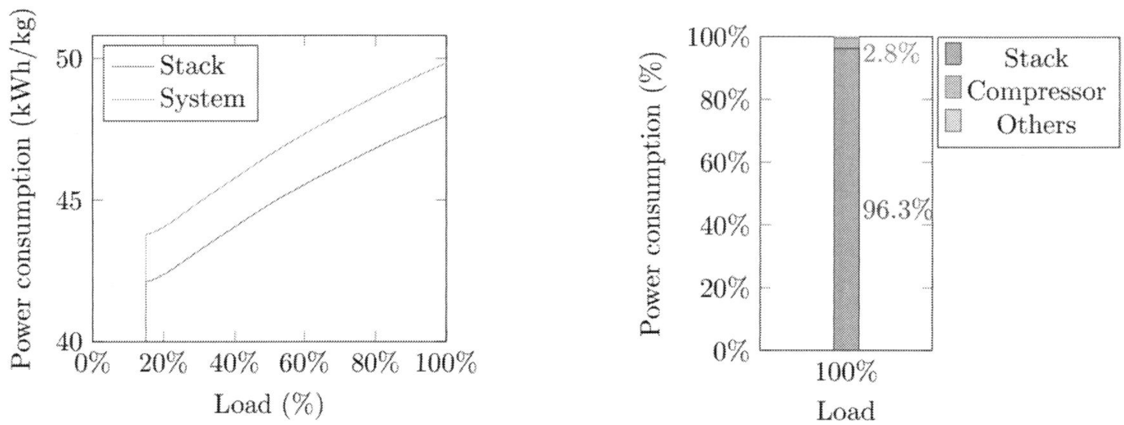


(a) Specific consumption (b) Power distribution

Figure 3: Left: Power consumption of alkaline stack and electrolysis system for different stack loads. Right: Power distribution between the different components of the fully loaded ES

### *2.4. System evaluation*

To evaluate the HWT performance for different configurations of electrolyser rating, generator rating, and rotor diameter, we define different key performance indicators (KPI).

*Energy curtailment:* If the power supply from the wind turbine generator exceeds the rating of the electrolysis system, the oversupply can charge the battery; otherwise, it must be curtailed. Energy curtailment may also occur when the power generation is less than the minimum power load of the AEC stack (15% of $P_e$). Curtailment is presented as a fraction of AEP, where $E_c$ is the annual energy curtailed:

$$\phi_c = \frac{E_c}{AEP} \tag{2}$$

*Energy efficiency:* The overall energy efficiency of the HWT system compares the energy content of the produced $H_2$ to the total energy supplied by the WT. $LHV$ is the lower heating value of $H_2$ (33.33 kWh/kg):

$$\eta = \frac{AHP \times LHV}{AEP} \tag{3}$$

*Levelised cost of hydrogen:* The LCOH measures the $H_2$ cost per unit $H_2$ produced:

$$LCOH = \frac{\sum_{i=1}^{t} (CAPEX + OPEX)/(1+r)^i}{\sum_{i=1}^{t} AHP/(1+r)^i}, \tag{4}$$

where, $CAPEX$ is the capital cost and $OPEX$ is the yearly operational cost, $t$ is the project duration (20 years), and $r$ (8%) is the discount rate.

To evaluate the costs, we utilise DTUs off-shore wind farm cost model [22] implemented in the TOPFARM Python package [23]. The model includes the CAPEX and OPEX of the wind turbine, foundation, and balance of the plant (BOP). For this work, simple cost models for the electrolyser and battery were added (Table 3) . The model inputs include the wind climate (Table 1), the WT configuration (Table 2), and the BOP (water depth, distance to shore,

Table 3: Battery and electrolyser cost assumptions [24]

| **Battery** | | **Electrolyser** | |
|---|---|---|---|
| $CAPEX_1$ | 160 EUR/kW | CAPEX | 1000 EUR/kW |
| $CAPEX_2$ | 142 EUR/kWh | OPEX | 4% of CAPEX/year |
| OPEX | 0.54 EUR/kW/year | | |

number of turbines). The analysis aims to investigate the trade-offs between efficiency and costs for different design choices rather than precisely estimating the cost of hydrogen. Thus, the AHP and LCOH are normalized relative to the results of a base case condition: the reference wind turbine with a 10 MW electrolysis stack system and no battery support. The normalized results are calculated as described in Eqs. (5) and (6).

$$AHP_n = \frac{AHP}{AHP_{base}} \tag{5}$$

$$LCOH_n = \frac{LCOH}{LCOH_{base}} \tag{6}$$

## 3. Results

### *3.1. Optimisation of the electrolysis system*

To determine the optimal size of the electrolysis system, we calculate the KPIs (Section 2.4) for varying ratings of the electrolysis stack while keeping wind climate (Table 1) and the WT configuration (Table 2) fixed. The results in Figure 4a indicate that the electrolysis system's optimal size depends on the chosen KPI. For instance, a minimal $LCOH_n = 0.987$ may be obtained for a 9.5 MW stack size, although lower curtailment (1.7 % for 9.7 MW) and higher $AHP_n$ (1.019 for 15.0 MW) can be achieved for larger systems. The relationship between the cost of the electrolysis system and the WT determines the optimum. Even though the AHP increases for larger electrolysis systems, the cost becomes too high as the design surpasses the minimal curtailment point. A similar trend is observed for different battery capacities (Figure 4b), where the minimum LCOH is estimated to be 97.6% of the base case for a storage capacity of 1.25 MWh and stack size of 9.5 MW.

### *3.2. Optimisation of the wind turbine*

This section explores the optimal wind turbine design for hydrogen production for the electrolysis/battery configuration derived from the previous section. The sensitivity of the wind turbine production and cost to the main top-level design parameters is studied. The main parameters comprise the rated power, rotor diameter and hub height. The range of parameters explored corresponds to realistic modern offshore wind turbine designs, although certain combinations result in infeasible designs. When optimising the main WT parameters, the electrolyser rating is set to $P_e = 0.9\,P_g$, and the battery capacity is set to $E_b = 0.125 P_g$. The parameters and their range are shown in Table 4.

Table 4: Range of wind turbine design parameters

| parameter | range |
|---|---|
| rated power | 5:2:15 [MW] |
| diameter | 130:10:240 [m] |
| hub height | 90:20:150 [m] |

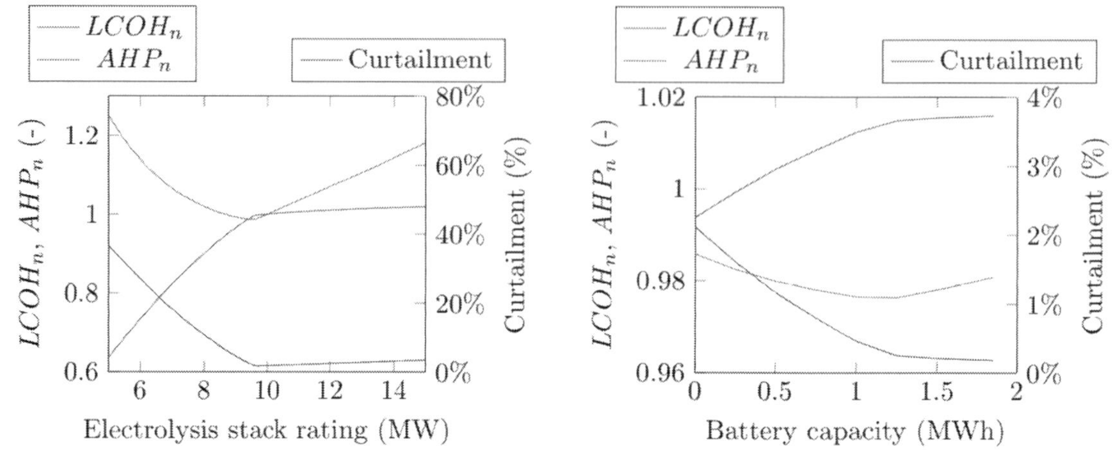


(a) Stack size (No battery) (b) Battery capacity (9.5 MW stack)

Figure 4: Impact of the electrolysis stack rating (left) and battery capacity (right) on AHP, curtailment and LCOH. The battery capacity and battery rating are assumed to be the same.

In Figure 5 left, the resulting LCOH is shown as a function of rated power and rotor diameter for a hub height of 110 m. The optimal design gives the minimum LCOH of 1.48 €/kg, for $P_g$ = 11 MW, $D$ = 240 m and $HH$ = 110 m. Compared to the initial design of the RWT ($P_g$ = 10 MW, $D$ = 198 m and $HH$ = 119 m) with an LCOH of 1.56 €/kg, this results in a 5% LCOH reduction. It is seen that, for the given design assumptions, the LCOH-optimised design moves towards a larger rotor. The specific power for the LCOH-optimised WT is $SP = 243\,\mathrm{W/m^2}$ compared to $SP = 325\,\mathrm{W/m^2}$ of the RWT.

It is interesting to compare the optimal design trends with the ones for a traditional LCOE-optimised wind turbine. In Figure 5 right, the resulting LCOE is shown as a function of rated power and rotor diameter for a hub height of 90 m. The optimal design gives the minimum LCOE of 0.0129€/kW for $P_g$ = 15 MW, $D$ = 240 m and $HH$ = 90 m. Although this design

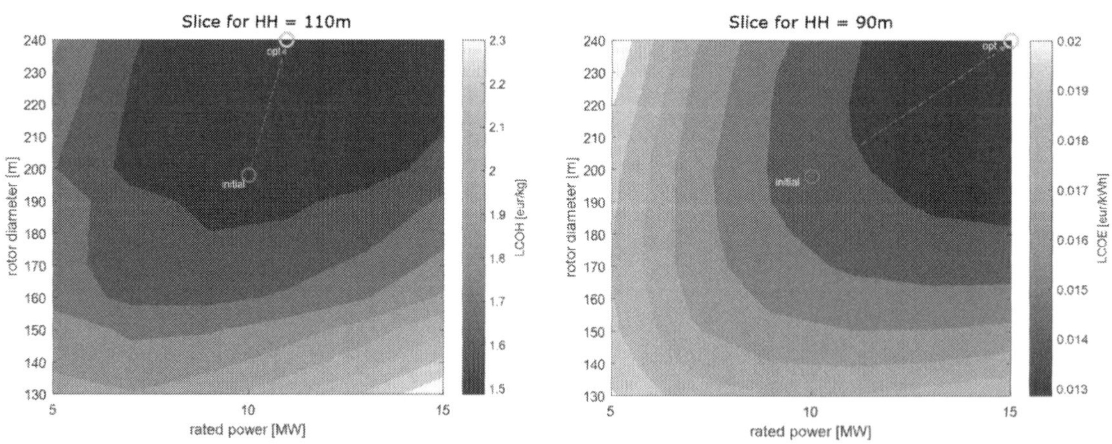


Figure 5: Left: LCOH as a function of rated power and rotor diameter for a hub height of 110m. The initial (RWT) and optimal (min LCOH) points are also indicated. Right: LCOE as a function of rated power and rotor diameter for a hub height of 90m.

combination is infeasible due to the low hub height, results are comparable to the closest feasible design for a hub height of 130 m. Compared to the initial design of the RWT ($P_g$ = 10 MW, $D$ = 198 m and $HH$ = 119 m) with an LCOE of 0.0144 €/kW, this results in a 10% LCOE reduction.

The specific power for the LCOE-optimised WT ($SP$ = 332 W/m$^2$) is close to the one of the RWT ($SP$ = 325 W/m$^2$), indicating that the RWT is an LCOE-optimised design, as expected. For the given design assumptions, the LCOH-optimized design moves towards a smaller generator than the LCOE-optimized design. This indicates that HWTs should have lower specific power ($SP \approx$ 240 W/m$^2$ ) than traditional LCOE-driven WT designs ($SP \approx$ 330 W/m$^2$).This is different from [9], who argues that an HWT should have a high specific power to increase electrolyser efficiency and lower the LCOH.

## 4. Conclusions

This work investigated how an off-shore wind turbine (WT) designed for hydrogen production (HWT) differs from a traditional WT. The analysis is based on a modelling framework that can estimate the hydrogen production and cost of an HWT for a given wind climate. The work includes a detailed thermodynamic model of the electrolysis system that can calculate the system efficiency at different stack loads. Using the IEA 10 MW WT as a reference (RWT), the main parameters of the HWT system (generator rating, rotor diameter, electrolyser rating and battery capacity) were changed to minimise the levelised cost of hydrogen (LCOH), and we compared the design to an LCOE-optimised WT. The following conclusions can be drawn:

(i) We found an electrolyser rating of 9.5 MW and a battery capacity of 1.25 MWh optimal for the 10 MW RWT. Therefore, our finding is similar to [2], who find the optimal electrolyser-to-generator ratio to be 0.92. [8], on the other hand, suggest "oversizing" the electrolyser compared to the generator and find a ratio of 1.2 suitable. The optimum balance depends on the efficiency and cost of the electrolysis system; increasing its cost will lead to a lower electrolyser-to-generator ratio, all else equal. For the electrolysis system developed in this work, the alkaline electrolysis cell stack is responsible for 96.3% of the total power consumption, $H_2$ compression 2.6%, and the remaining 1% is attributed to cooling and desalination.

(ii) We examined the effect on the LCOH and LCOE of changing the rotor diameter and rated power of the RWT ($P_g$ = 10 MW, $D$ = 198 m). Within the allowed parameter space, it is found that LCOE-optimisation moves the WT towards larger generators and rotor diameters ($P_g$ = 15MW, $D$ = 240 m). Nevertheless, the specific power for the LCOE-optimised design ($SP$ = 332 W/m$^2$) remains close to that of the RWT ($SP$ = 325 W/m$^2$), indicating that the RWT is also LCOE-optimised, as expected. However, when optimising for hydrogen production, the design moves towards a smaller generator ($P_g$ = 11MW, $D$ = 240 m) and a lower specific power ($SP$ = 243 W/m$^2$). This indicates that HWTs should have lower specific power ($SP \approx$ 240 W/m$^2$) than traditional LCOE-driven WT designs ($SP \approx$ 330 W/m$^2$). This conclusion differs from [9], who argues that an HWT should have a high specific power to increase electrolyser efficiency and lower the LCOH.

(iii) We found that using a 9.5 MW electrolyser and a 1.25 MWh battery lowered the LCOH by 2.4% compared to a 10 MW electrolysis stack without a battery. Furthermore, optimisation of the rotor diameter and generator rating gave an additional 4.6% LCOH reduction. We, therefore, conclude that there are opportunities for reducing hydrogen costs by designing wind turbines optimised for hydrogen production.

## References

[1] Nipper M 2022 Need for speed - How offshore wind and renewable power-to-X can help solve Europe's energy crisis White paper Ørsted URL https://orsted.com/en/about-us/whitepapers/renewables-can-solve-europes-energy-crisis
[2] Gea Bermúdez J, Pedersen R B B, Koivisto M J, Kitzing L and Ramos A 2023 *Energy Policy* **174** 19
[3] Moritz M, Schönfisch M and Schulte S 2022 *International Journal of Hydrogen Energy* 16 ISSN 03603199
[4] Rik van Rossum, Jaro Jens, Gemma La Guardia, Anthony Wang, Luis Kühnen and Martijn Overgaag 2022 European Hydrogen Backbone Tech. rep. Guidehouse The Netherlands URL https://www.ehb.eu/
[5] He W, Zheng Y, You S, Strbac G, Therkildsen K T, Olsen G P, Howie A, Byklum E and Sharifabadi K T 2022 *Journal of Physics: Conference Series* **2265** 042035 ISSN 1742-6588, 1742-6596 URL https://iopscience.iop.org/article/10.1088/1742-6596/2265/4/042035
[6] Caine, David, Iliffe, Molly, Kevin Kinsella, Widya Wahyuni and Laura Bond 2019 Dolphyn Hydrogen - phase 1 final report Tech. rep. Department for Business, Energy & Industrial Strategy
[7] Nami H, Rizvandi O B, Chatzichristodoulou C, Hendriksen P V and Frandsen H L 2022 *Energy Conversion and Management* **269** ISSN 01968904 URL https://linkinghub.elsevier.com/retrieve/pii/S0196890422009438
[8] Mehta M, Zaaijer M and Terzi D v 2022 *Journal of Physics: Conference Series* **2265** 042061 ISSN 1742-6588, 1742-6596 URL https://iopscience.iop.org/article/10.1088/1742-6596/2265/4/042061
[9] Langeraar J W 2021 Double the energy from wind, with hydrogen as primary energy carrier URL https://hy-gro.net/en/newsitem
[10] Bortolotti P, Tarres H C, Dykes K, Merz K, Sethuraman L, Verelst D and Zahle F 2019 IEA wind task 37 on systems engineering in wind energy – WP2.1 reference wind turbines Tech. rep. International Energy Agency tex.howpublished: NREL/TP-73492 URL https://www.nrel.gov/docs/fy19osti/73492.pdf
[11] Murcia J P, Koivisto M J, Luzia G, Olsen B T, Hahmann A N, Sørensen P E and Als M 2022 *Applied Energy* **305** 1–14 ISSN 03062619 URL https://linkinghub.elsevier.com/retrieve/pii/S0306261921011296
[12] Ibrahim O S, Singlitico A, Proskovics R, McDonagh S, Desmond C and Murphy J D 2022 *Renewable and Sustainable Energy Reviews* **160** 112310 ISSN 13640321 URL https://linkinghub.elsevier.com/retrieve/pii/S1364032122002258
[13] Murcia Leon J P, Koivisto M J, Sørensen P and Magnant P 2021 *Wind Energy Science* **6** 461–476 ISSN 2366-7451 URL https://wes.copernicus.org/articles/6/461/2021/
[14] Ulleberg O 2003 *International Journal of Hydrogen Energy* **28** 21–33 ISSN 03603199
[15] Nel Hydrogen 2021 Nel Hydrogen Electrolysers: The World's Most Efficient and Reliable Electrolyzers Tech. Rep. PD-0600-0125 Nel ASA URL https://nelhydrogen.com/wp-content/uploads/2020/03/Electrolysers-Brochure-Rev-D.pdf
[16] Taibi E, Miranda R, Carmo M and Blanco H 2020 Publisher: IRENA, Hydrogen Knowledge Centre URL https://www.h2knowledgecentre.com/content/researchpaper1613
[17] IRENA 2020 Green hydrogen cost reduction Tech. rep. URL https://www.irena.org/-/media/Files/IRENA/Agency/Publication/2020/Dec/IRENA_Green_hydrogen_cost_2020.pdf
[18] Harris C R, Millman K J, van der Walt S J, Gommers R, Virtanen P, Cournapeau D, Wieser E, Taylor J, Berg S, Smith N J, Kern R, Picus M, Hoyer S, van Kerkwijk M H, Brett M, Haldane A, del Río J F, Wiebe M, Peterson P, Gérard-Marchant P, Sheppard K, Reddy T, Weckesser W, Abbasi H, Gohlke C and Oliphant T E 2020 *Nature* **585** 357–362 publisher: Springer Science and Business Media LLC URL https://doi.org/10.1038/s41586-020-2649-2
[19] Virtanen P, Gommers R, Oliphant T E, Haberland M, Reddy T, Cournapeau D, Burovski E, Peterson P, Weckesser W, Bright J, van der Walt S J, Brett M, Wilson J, Millman K J, Mayorov N, Nelson A R J, Jones E, Kern R, Larson E, Carey C J, Polat I, Feng Y, Moore E W, VanderPlas J, Laxalde D, Perktold J, Cimrman R, Henriksen I, Quintero E A, Harris C R, Archibald A M, Ribeiro A H, Pedregosa F, van Mulbregt P and Contributors S 2020 *Nature Methods* **17** 261–272 tex.adsurl: https://rdcu.be/b08Wh
[20] Dunning I, Huchette J and Lubin M 2017 *SIAM Review* **59** 295–320
[21] Gurobi Optimization, LLC 2023 Gurobi Optimizer Reference Manual URL https://www.gurobi.com
[22] Thomsen K and Lind S O 2019 DTU offshore cost model URL https://topfarm.pages.windenergy.dtu.dk/TopFarm2
[23] Larsen G C and Réthoré P E 2013 *Energy Procedia* **35** 317–324 ISSN 18766102 URL https://linkinghub.elsevier.com/retrieve/pii/S1876610213012708
[24] Tahernejadledari S 2021 *Design and operation of wind turbine for hybrid power plant application including P2X* M-0446 (DTU Wind Energy)

# The Co-development of Offshore Wind and Hydrogen in the UK – A Case Study of Milford Haven South Wales

**Fulin Fan[1], John Nwobu[2,*], David Campos-Gaona[1]**

[1] Department of Electronic and Electrical Engineering, University of Strathclyde, G1 1XW Glasgow, United Kingdom
[2] Offshore Renewable Energy Catapult, G1 1RD Glasgow, United Kingdom

[*] E-mail: john.nwobu@ore.catapult.org.uk

**Abstract**. Green hydrogen produced from renewable energy resources can not only contribute to the decarbonisation of different energy sectors, but also serve as a carrier for long-distance delivery of renewable generation, offering a cost-effective way to exploit the renewables far from electrical grids. To facilitate the co-development of offshore wind and hydrogen, the paper develops a modelling framework to dispatch power and hydrogen flows across dedicated offshore wind hydrogen production systems to meet onshore hydrogen demands while keeping similar state of charge levels between multiple systems. Then the hydrogen supply to shore and the system investments and ongoing costs are discounted to their present values to calculate the levelised cost of hydrogen, which is minimised by the particle swarm optimsiation algorithm to suggest the best capacities of hydrogen system components including converters, desalination devices, electrolysers, compressors and storage assets. The proposed modelling framework is tested based on a case study at Milford Haven South Wales which is evaluated to have massive offshore wind resources in the Celtic Sea and comparable demands for hydrogen by 2040. The optimisation results are presented based on the techno-economic input parameters projected for 2030 and 2050 scenarios and discussed alongside the influences of technology advances on the system optimisation and resulting metrics including the levelised costs of hydrogen, net present values and potential levels of green hydrogen supply to Milford Haven.

## 1. Introduction

The global end of reliance on fossil fuels for power and efforts towards achieving a net zero economy are driving a clean energy revolution [1]. Conventional $CO_2$ producing energy processes are currently being replaced with carbon-free solutions presenting a promising growth area in the energy transition. Low carbon hydrogen is one of the main alternative energies powering the energy industry's transition and offers a huge potential for carbon free energy [2]. The UK has outlined a comprehensive roadmap for its low carbon hydrogen sector development in the 2020s [3] and doubled the hydrogen production ambition to up to 10 GW by 2023, at least half of which would come from electricity hydrogen subject to affordability and value for money [4]. In addition, up to 20 GW of potential hydrogen projects have been identified in the UK pipeline through to 2037 [5], most of which select the renewables-powered electrolysis and the carbon capture, usage and storage (CCUS)-enabled methane reformation [6].

In order to achieve true carbon emission reductions, it is necessary to ensure electrolysis hydrogen production being powered by low carbon electricity generation such as fully dedicated renewables and otherwise curtailed renewable generation [6]. Furthermore, Green hydrogen produced from dedicated renewables such as offshore wind not only ensures the low carbon nature of hydrogen production but will also allow hydrogen to act as an energy carrier for transporting and distributing renewable energy over long distances, especially when it is impractical or expensive to build or reinforce electricity grids [7]. For a 1.2 GW offshore wind farm requiring three to four 220 kV submarine cables for electricity delivery to shore, it was estimated that the supply and installation costs of hydrogen pipelines to shore were only around a third of those for laying submarine cables [8]. Given the need of 75 GW operating offshore wind capacity for the UK to reach net-zero carbon emissions in 2050 [9], the co-development of offshore wind and hydrogen can facilitate the integration of future high-level renewable energy into the energy systems. However, this poses many technical and commercial challenges [10] including but not limited to the integration of electrolysers (and fuel cells) within offshore wind farm infrastructures, the optimal system operation under varying offshore use case scenarios, and the ideal location/capacity of an offshore wind hydrogen system that can make the best business case for pilot and future projects.

To promote the investment into offshore wind hydrogen projects, the techno-economic simulation of an offshore wind and hydrogen co-location system for a specific offshore use case is required. This not only informs project developers of the techno-economics of the co-location project but can also be used in conjunction with an optimisation algorithm for the co-location project planning. Three system topologies have been investigated in [11] for offshore wind hydrogen production, including centralised electrolysis conducted onshore or at offshore central platforms and decentralised electrolysis placed at individual offshore wind turbines. Assuming the electrolyser capacity to be 80% of a 1.2 GW offshore wind farm that is 80 km from shore, the levelised costs of hydrogen (LCOH) produced by centralised onshore or offshore electrolysis were evaluated in [8] for 2020, 2030 and 2050 scenarios respectively; while the LCOH of the two topologies was forecast to reduce by almost 85% by 2030 and even further by 2050, the increased costs of installation, maintenance and operation for the offshore electrolysis led to a higher LCOH which, however, would reach comparable as the LCOH of the onshore electrolysis by 2050 [8]. For the decentralised offshore electrolysis, the ERM has implemented detailed bottom-up financial modelling of the first 10 MW Dolphyn commercial demonstrator that incorporates a polymer electrolyte membrane (PEM) electrolyser into a semi-submersible floating wind turbine, and estimated that a LCOH of around £1.5/kg would be available for bulk scale production from Dolphyn projects by 2040 [12]. In addition, the techno-economic overview and simulation of the three topologies along with varying electrolyser technologies and electricity/hydrogen co-generation modes were undertaken in [13] based on a reference case of 12 GW offshore wind hubs in North Sea. However, these research was mainly conducted by using a specific electrolyser capacity without optimisation.

The sizing problem of energy storage systems (ESSs) can be addressed by performing an economic optimisation subject to a set of technical constraints [14]. The optimal sizes of hydrogen-, ammonia- or battery-based ESSs co-located with a 1.5 GW hypothetical offshore wind farm were determined in [15] by maximising the net profit of the co-location system, i.e., the rise of the revenue from relevant energy markets above the investments into the ESSs. The operation of an offshore wind and hydrogen co-location system participating in the German electricity spot markets, ancillary service markets and the sale of hydrogen was designed in [16], based on which the hydrogen system was sized to either maximise the net present value or minimise the LCOH. The size and operation of an onshore hydrogen system co-located with offshore wind for the frequency response service provision were co-optimised in [17] to maximise the net present value of the co-location project based on the UK perspective. The offshore wind hydrogen system configuration for electricity market arbitrage or hydrogen production was designed separately in [18]; for each configuration, the operating strategies and hydrogen system capacities were determined to maximise the revenue and the return on investment in inner and outer optimisation layers respectively. Even though the sale of hydrogen has been considered a key revenue stream for offshore wind hydrogen systems, most research related to hydrogen system sizing problems did not take into account the local demand for hydrogen nor the diversity of offshore wind sources that might require coordinating the delivery of hydrogen from multiple hydrogen systems.

The contribution of this paper is to develop a modelling framework to optimise hydrogen system capacities for fully dedicated offshore wind hydrogen production systems which generate and store hydrogen at offshore central platforms and transport hydrogen to shore via pipelines. In addition to reflecting the entire process of offshore wind hydrogen production and transportation, the modelling framework dispatches hydrogen from multiple systems to fulfil onshore demands and maintain similar state of charge (SOC) levels between their storage assets. The present values of hydrogen supply to various energy sectors are compared with the total present costs of offshore wind hydrogen systems in order to estimate their average LCOH at the end of a 20-year project lifespan. Then the particle swarm optimisation (PSO) algorithm is used to minimise the average LCOH by optimising hydrogen system capacities for a given wind farm scale. The effectiveness of the modelling framework is presented here through a case study at Milford Haven (South Wales) which will deliver a hydrogen-enabled multi-vector energy system to assist the UK in achieving net zero by 2050 [19]. The optimisation of offshore wind hydrogen production systems performed for 2030 and 2050 scenarios not only suggests the technology improvement required for developing feasible projects but can also help understand the potential level of green hydrogen supply to Milford Haven in the future.

The paper is structured as follows: Section 2 describes the estimation of offshore wind resources and hydrogen offtake options in the Milford Haven case study and the technical modelling of offshore wind hydrogen systems; Section 3 implements the PSO algorithm based on the techno-economic input parameters of the systems projected for 2030 and 2050 scenarios; Section 4 discusses the hydrogen system sizing results and the optimisation-based system operation and cost-benefit analysis; Section 5 presents conclusions and recommendations for further work.

## 2. Technical modelling of offshore wind hydrogen production system

### *2.1. Offshore wind resources in Celtic Sea*

Milford Haven will witness huge installed capacity of offshore renewable generation in the Celtic Sea, with five zones identified as more promising regions for floating offshore wind (FLOW) development, as shown in Figure 1(a) [20]. Zone 1 and Zone 5 closer to the coast of South Wales have a total area of about 10,283 km$^2$. Given a FLOW turbine deployment capacity of 3 or 4.8 MW/km$^2$ in the medium or high case respectively, the two zones might allow deploying multiple FLOW farms with total installed capacity ranging from around 31 to 49 GW. More than ten FLOW projects totalling around 2.2 GW have been planned in the Celtic Sea, with their approximate locations shown in Figure 1(b) [21]. The time-varying FLOW resources are evaluated here based on the MERRA-2 (Modern-Era Retrospective Analysis for Research and Applications, Version 2) reanalysis data of wind speeds which has a spatial resolution of 0.5° latitude (~55 km) and 0.625° longitude (~69 km) [22]. Considering that a maximum of 18.5 GW FLOW capacity could be deployed in a 3,800 km$^2$ MERRA square in the high case, two suitable MERRA squares following the planned FLOW projects are adopted here to approximate the regions of the future FLOW projects (see Figure 1(b)). The straight distances from the centres of the two squares, denoted by MERRA-S1 and MERRA-S2, to the onshore Pembroke substation at Milford Haven are about 122.5 and 150.6 km respectively. It is presumed here that 1,200 Vestas wind turbines V236-15.0 MW™ [23] are deployed in each square with 18 GW FLOW capacity in total. Then the hourly reanalysis data of wind speeds recorded for each square over 2016-2019 is converted into the time series of available FLOW power outputs by using a virtual wind farm model which considers the wind power smoothing effect across the square [24]. Figures 2(a) and 2(b) show the wind power curve for the 18 GW FLOW capacity and the resulting wind power data in each MERRA square respectively. The shift of wind power profiles in time between the two squares reflects the travel of wind from one square to another.

### *2.2. Hydrogen offtake options around Milford Haven*

The FLOW hydrogen production delivered to Milford Haven will not only be consumed locally within Pembrokeshire but can also be transported to neighbouring regions. Table 1 lists the timeline and daily hydrogen usage estimated for various hydrogen offtake options within Pembrokeshire or neighbouring regions. According to the purpose of hydrogen use, the offtake price of each option is determined here by its break-even point at which the specific hydrogen use becomes cost competitive relative to a zero-carbon alternative [8]. Since the hydrogen production and storage might not always meet the required hydrogen demands, the priority of hydrogen supply is determined here based on the locations of the offtake options, followed by their break-even prices (see Table 1). In order to reflect the time-varying nature of hydrogen offtake, the (sub-) hourly hydrogen demands of power stations, vehicle hydrogen refuelling and marine vessels are synthesised here based on their daily usage in combination with final physical notifications (over 2016-2019), busy hours of petrol stations and time slots of vessel docking respectively. The daily hydrogen usage of the other offtake options is assumed to be evenly distributed across 24 hours. Figure 3(a) shows the profiles of aggregate hydrogen demands within Pembrokeshire and neighbouring regions synthesised over the four years. Assuming a hydrogen production efficiency of 22.2 kg/MWh, the total hydrogen production rates are calculated from FLOW power outputs in the two MERRA squares and compared with the total hydrogen demands, as shown in Figure 3(b). Their time-varying imbalances are induced by the intermittent nature of FLOW generation, highlighting the need of hydrogen storage assets for the time shift of hydrogen production.

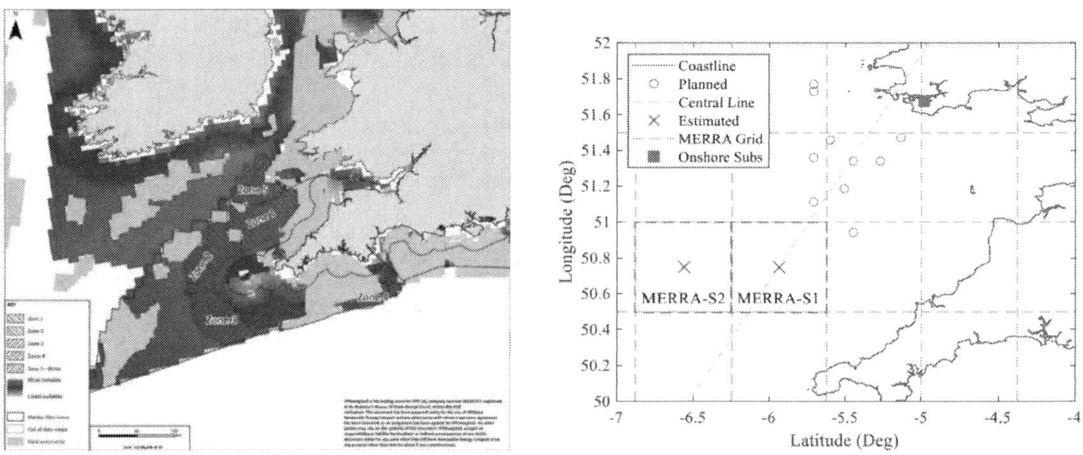


(a) (b)

**Figure 1.** Maps showing (a) five key zones identified for FLOW development and (b) planned FLOW projects and two MERRA squares selected for future FLOW development in the Celtic Sea.

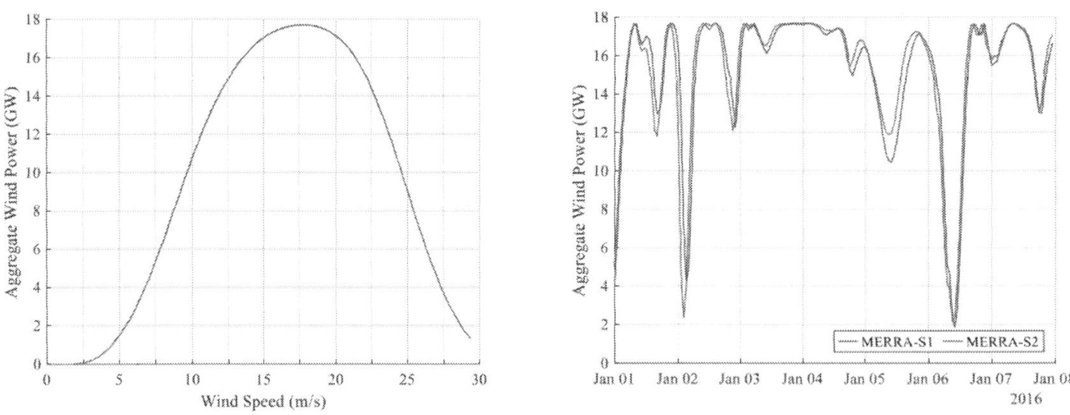


(a) (b)

**Figure 2**. (a) The power curve for 18 GW FLOW capacity and (b) the resulting wind power estimates (GW) over the first week of 2016 in each MERRA square.

**Table 1.** Hydrogen offtake options within Pembrokeshire or neighbouring regions and their estimated timeline, daily hydrogen usage, break-even prices, and offtake priority.

| Option | Purpose | Timeline | Usage (ton/day) | Price (£/kg) | Offtake Priority |
|---|---|---|---|---|---|
| Pembroke Oil Terminal | Bulk production & storage of liquid organic $H_2$ carrier or $NH_3$ for export | 2040 | 4,940.5 | 7.7 | 1 |
| Pembroke Refinery | Low carbon synthetic fuels | 2040 | 1,500.0 | 7.7 | 1 |
| Pembroke Dock | $H_2$ supply to marine vessels | 2035 | 17.1 | 3.5 | 3 |
| RWE Power Station | To fuel future $H_2$ gas turbines | 2040 | 1500.0 | 2.3 | 4 |
| Local Gas Network (Wales & West) | Potentially 100% into regional gas distribution system | 2032 | 45.0 | 2.2 | 5 |
| National Grid | Potentially inject to 100% $H_2$ backbone | 2030 | 250.0 | 2.2 | 5 |
| Pembroke Refinery | Industrial heat/grey $H_2$ replacement | 2030 | 200.0 | 1.5 | 7 |
| Milford Haven Port | Transport and heating requirements | 2030 | 2.5 | 1.5 | 7 |
| Pembroke Council | Vehicle fleet and $H_2$ refuelling hub | 2024 | 1.7 | 1.5 | 7 |
| Fishguard Dock | $H_2$ supply to marine vessels | 2035 | 5.2 | 3.5 | 10 |
| 520 MW Baglan Bay | To fuel future $H_2$ gas turbines | 2040 | 357.8 | 2.3 | 11 |
| 850 MW Severn Power | To fuel future $H_2$ gas turbines | 2040 | 584.9 | 2.3 | 11 |
| Tata Steel Port Talbot | $H_2$ requirement for steel production | 2030 | 721.4 | 1.8 | 13 |
| Celsa manufacturing | $H_2$ requirement for steel production | 2030 | 187.6 | 1.8 | 13 |
| Liberty Steel New | $H_2$ requirement for steel production | 2030 | 144.3 | 1.8 | 13 |
| Neighbouring Ports | Transport and heating requirement | 2030 | 0.6 | 1.5 | 16 |
| Neighbouring Councils | Vehicle fleet and $H_2$ refuelling hub | 2024 | 28.7 | 1.5 | 17 |

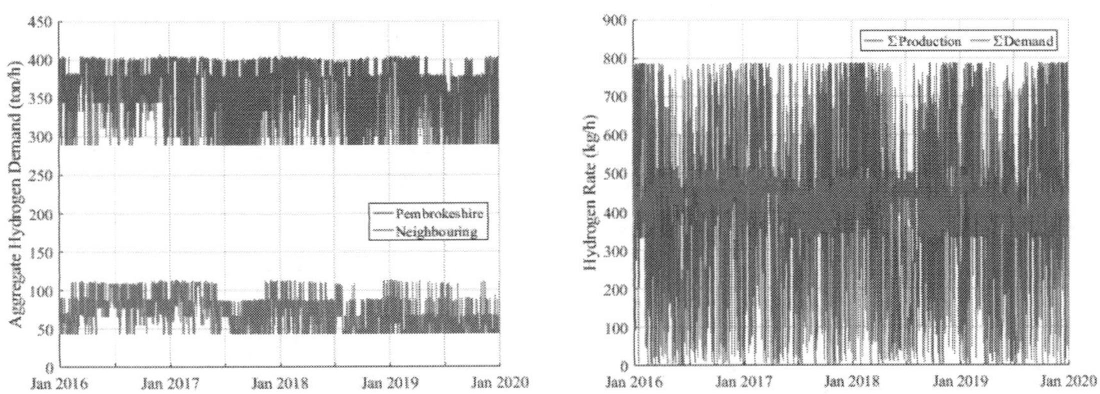


(a) (b)

**Figure 3**. (a) Time series (ton/hr) of aggregate hydrogen demands of Pembrokeshire and neighbouring regions and (b) their total demands against the total hydrogen production rates within the two MERRA squares synthesised based on historic data over 2016-2019.

### 2.3. *Offshore wind hydrogen system modelling*

*2.3.1. Schematic.* Figure 4 shows the schematic of a centralised offshore wind hydrogen system where power outputs of FLOW turbines are collected by inter-array AC cables and transferred to an offshore central platform for green hydrogen production. Given the smoothing effect and intermittent nature of FLOW power outputs, an offshore central platform with an expected export capacity of no greater than 500 MW [25] is designed here to connect 40 Vestas 15 MW wind turbines, totalling 600 MW. This means that each MERRA square can comprise 30 offshore wind hydrogen systems which are assumed to be configured and operated in the same way since the wind resource diversity across a single square is not modelled in this work. Since the layout optimisation of FLOW turbines and inter-array cables is outside the scope of this work, FLOW turbines are evenly distributed with a space $S_{WT}$ of 7 times the rotor diameter (i.e., ~2 km). Given the use of 630 mm$^2$, 81.7 MVA submarine AC cables, five 15 MW wind turbines are placed along each of the eight cable strings, forming a 600 MW wind turbine group. The power output of the 600 MW group delivered to the central platform is converted into DC power via an converter and then used by other hydrogen system components including a desalination device for seawater purification, an electrolyser for hydrogen production, and two compressors that pressurise hydrogen to reach the inlet pressure of 12 inch export pipeline or a higher pressure level for storage assets for later transportation to shore. In addition, a chemical storage device such as batteries requires to be deployed alongside the hydrogen system as backup power supply, though this is not modelled here for simplicity.

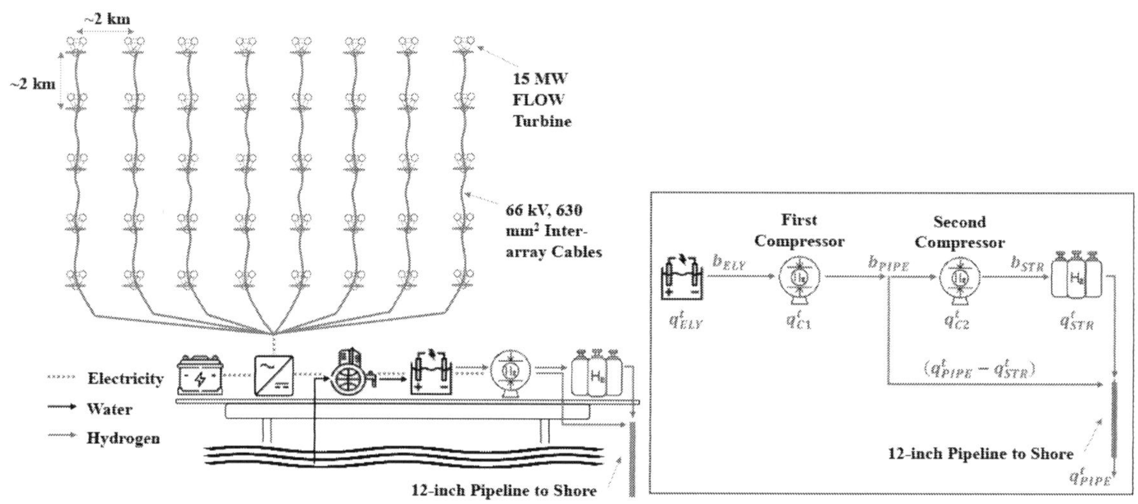


**Figure 4**. The schematic of a centralised offshore wind hydrogen system.

*2.3.2. Power flow balance.* Assuming that the FLOW turbines of each 600 MW group have the same outputs $P^t_{WT}$ (MW) at the time step $t$, the power delivered to the offshore central platform $P^t_{OCP}$ (MW) after cable losses is estimated by equation (1) subject to the AC/DC converter capacity $P^R_{CON}$:

$$P^t_{OCP} = \min\left(P^R_{CON},\ 40 \cdot P^t_{WT} - 8 \cdot \left((5 \cdot P^t_{WT}/66)^2 \cdot 2.3 + \textstyle\sum_{i=1}^{4}(i \cdot P^t_{WT}/66)^2\right) \cdot S_{WT} \cdot r_{AC}\right) \quad (1)$$

where $r_{AC}$ denotes the AC resistance (Ω/km) of the 66 kV cable per unit length, and the distance from a cable string end to the central platform is assumed to be about 2.3 times the space $S_{WT}$ between wind turbines on average. After subtracting conversion losses, the remaining power is distributed among the desalination device $P^t_{DEL}$, electrolyser $P^t_{ELY}$, compressors $P^t_{C1}$ and $P^t_{C2}$:

$$P^t_{OCP} \cdot \eta_{CON} = P^t_{ELY} + P^t_{DEL} + P^t_{C1} + P^t_{C2} \quad (2)$$

where $\eta_{CON}$ is the efficiency of the converter, and

$$P^t_{ELY} = q^t_{ELY}/\eta^{P2H}_{ELY} \quad (3)$$

$$P^t_{DEL} = \eta_{DEL} \cdot q^t_{ELY}/\eta^{W2H}_{ELY} \quad (4)$$

$$P_{C1} = 10^{-6} \cdot \left(\frac{q^t_{C1}}{3600}\right) \cdot \frac{u \cdot Z_{C1} \cdot T}{M \cdot \eta_C} \cdot \frac{N_C \cdot \gamma}{\gamma - 1} \cdot \left(\left(\frac{b_{PIPE}}{b_{ELY}}\right)^{(\gamma-1)/(N_C \cdot \gamma)} - 1\right) \quad (5)$$

$$P_{C2} = 10^{-6} \cdot \left(\frac{q^t_{C2}}{3600}\right) \cdot \frac{u \cdot Z_{C2} \cdot T}{M \cdot \eta_C} \cdot \frac{N_C \cdot \gamma}{\gamma - 1} \cdot \left(\left(\frac{b_{STR}}{b_{PIPE}}\right)^{(\gamma-1)/(N_C \cdot \gamma)} - 1\right) \quad (6)$$

where $q_{ELY}^{t}$ (kg/h), $\eta_{ELY}^{P2H}$ (kg/MWh) and $\eta_{ELY}^{W2H}$ (kg/L) denote the hydrogen production rate, power- and water-to-hydrogen efficiencies of the electrolyser respectively; $\eta_{DEL}$ (MWh/L) is the power usage of the desalination device per unit of seawater purified; $q_{C1}^{t}$ or $q_{C2}^{t}$ (kg/h) is the hydrogen flow rate of the first compressor that pressurises hydrogen from the production pressure $b_{ELY}$ (bar) to the inlet pressure of the pipeline $b_{PIPE}$ (bar) and the second compressor that further pressurises hydrogen to the pressure for storage $b_{STR}$ (bar); $u$ is the universal constant of ideal gas equalling 8.314 J/mol-K; terms $T$, $M$ and $\gamma$ are the temperature, molecular mass and heat capacity ratio of hydrogen that equal 288.15 K, 2.15 x $10^{-3}$ kg/mol and 1.41 respectively; $Z_{C1}$ and $Z_{C2}$ are the hydrogen compressibility factors determined by $T$ and associated compressor pressure levels; and the two compressors are presumed to have the same efficiency $\eta_C$ of 75% and a single compression stage ($N_C = 1$) [26]. In addition, the degradation of the electrolyser stacks with operating time is simulated here by linearly reducing the efficiencies $\eta_{ELY}^{P2H}$ and $\eta_{ELY}^{W2H}$ from their respective nominal levels to 90% of the nominal levels at the end of the stack lifetime [17]; then the electrolyser will be replaced to restore $\eta_{ELY}^{P2H}$ and $\eta_{ELY}^{W2H}$ to the nominal levels.

*2.3.3. Hydrogen flow balance.* Equation (7) depicts the hydrogen flow balance within the hydrogen system that delivers $q_{PIPE}^{t}$ to shore via the 12 inch pipeline (see Figure 4). The rate of hydrogen injected into the storage $q_{C2}^{t}$ or released from the storage $q_{STR}^{t}$ is determined by the difference between $q_{PIPE}^{t}$ and $q_{C1}^{t}$. The resulting hydrogen storage level $Q_{STR}^{t}$ (kg) is updated by equation (8) where $\Delta t$ (h) is the time step length in the simulation.

$$q_{ELY}^{t} = q_{C1}^{t} = q_{PIPE}^{t} + q_{C2}^{t} - q_{STR}^{t} = q_{PIPE}^{t} + \min(q_{C1}^{t} - q_{PIPE}^{t}, 0) - \min(q_{PIPE}^{t} - q_{C1}^{t}, 0) \quad (7)$$

$$Q_{STR}^{t} = Q_{STR}^{t-1} + (q_{C2}^{t} - q_{STR}^{t}) \cdot \Delta t \quad (8)$$

*2.3.4. Hydrogen dispatch.* The hydrogen delivery from the offshore wind hydrogen systems in the two MERRA squares is dispatched to meet the total onshore hydrogen demands subject to the availability of hydrogen production and storage. Specifically, the supply $q_{PIPE}^{t}$ of the system is first contributed by the direct hydrogen production, followed by the hydrogen discharge from the storage. Furthermore, to maintain similar SOC levels between multiple systems, the systems having higher relative availability (i.e., the sum of hydrogen production $q_{ELY}^{t} \cdot \Delta t$ and present hydrogen storage $Q_{STR}^{t-1}$ in percentage of the storage capacity) are first used for hydrogen supply until the onshore demand is fully provided or their relative availability declines to the level of other systems; if the onshore hydrogen demand is not fully met, then the remaining demand requirement will be split among all the systems in proportion to their storage capacities. In addition, the hydrogen delivery to shore is limited by the capacity of the 12 inch pipeline that is determined by its diameter and acceptable operational velocity. The latter is dominated by the outlet pressure of the pipeline [27] which is set to 68 bar in this work to facilitate the integration with onshore gas network. When the hydrogen transportation to shore is constrained, the systems with headroom in pipeline capacity will be used to fill in the shortage of hydrogen supply regardless of the resulting differences in SOC levels between systems.

## 3. Techno-economic optimisation of offshore wind hydrogen system

### *3.1. Optimisation variables*

Since the offshore wind hydrogen systems experiencing the same wind resources in a MERRA square are configured and operated in the same way, the optimsiation of a representative system is applicable to the other 29 systems within the same square. The optimsiation variables specified here comprise the electrolyser capacity of the representative system in each square, the storage capacity of the system in MERRA-S1 and the capacity ratio $r_C$ between the two compressors, as shown in Figure 5, which are used to size all the hydrogen system components based on their capacity dependencies described by equations (2)-(6). Furthermore, it is assumed here that the storage asset capacity is proportional to the electrolyser capacity and the central platform size (in MW) is determined by the converter capacity.

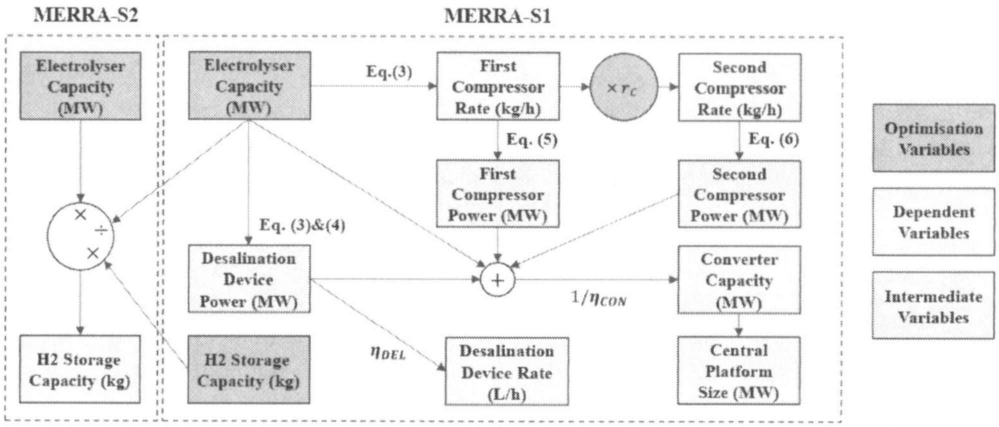

**Figure 5.** The hydrogen system components that are directly or indirectly optimised.

## 3.2. *PSO implementation*

The optimisation variables specified in Figure 5 are estimated here by the PSO algorithm [28], aiming to minimise the average LCOH of offshore wind hydrogen systems in the two MERRA squares given an annual return of 8%:

$$LCOH = \left(CAPEX_{FLOW} + CAPEX_{HYS} + \sum_{m=1}^{240} \frac{OPEX_{FLOW}^{m} + OPEX_{HYS}^{m} + REPEX_{PEM}^{m}}{(1+8\%)^{m/12}}\right) \Big/ \sum_{m=1}^{240} \frac{Q_{PIPE}^{m}}{(1+8\%)^{m/12}} \quad (9)$$

where $m$ is the month index starting from 1 to 240 (i.e., 20 years); $CAPEX_{FLOW}$ and $CAPEX_{HYS}$ are the overall capital expenditures of FLOW farms and hydrogen systems respectively; $OPEX_{FLOW}^{m}$ and $OPEX_{HYS}^{m}$ are the monthly operating expenses of FLOW farms and hydrogen systems; $REPEX_{PEM}^{m}$ is the replacement expenditure of PEM electrolysers occurring in the month $m$; and $Q_{PIPE}^{m}$ represents the total hydrogen demand (kg) supplied in the month $m$. The PSO process will be implemented here by using the techno-economic parameters of semi-submersible FLOW farms and PEM-based hydrogen systems projected for 2030 and 2050 respectively, as listed in in Table 2, in order to assess the impacts of techno-economic improvement on the optimisation results. It is noted that the economics estimated by the references for past years or different currency units have been converted to 2019 values in GBP (British Pound Sterling).

# 4. Optimisation and simulation results

The techno-economic simulation of offshore wind hydrogen systems and the PSO implementation are accomplished here using MATLAB/Simulink [37]. This section first discusses the hydrogen system sizing results obtained based on the techno-economic input parameters for 2030 and 2050, followed by presenting the optimisation-based system operation and cost-benefit analysis to illustrate the model effectiveness and the prospect of offshore wind hydrogen projects in the Milford Haven case study.

## 4.1. *Optimisation results*

The optimal capacities of the hydrogen system components co-located with a representative 600 MW FLOW farm in each MERRA square are tabulated in Table 3. The optimisation results are very similar between the two squares, though the hydrogen systems in MERRA-S2 have greater capacities than those in MERRA-S1 due to the higher load factor of FLOW farms in MERRA-S2. With further improvements in hydrogen technologies in 2050, the hydrogen systems optimised with higher nominal production rates require larger capacities of desalination devices and compressors along with greater storage capacities so as to deliver more hydrogen to shore. However, the electrolyser capacity which dominates the capacities of converter and offshore central platform is reduced in the 2050 scenario due to the increased electrolyser efficiency. It is evaluated that the best electrolyser capacities are around 71%-72% and 67%-68% of the FLOW capacity in 2030 and 2050 scenarios respectively.

**Table 2.** Techno-economic parameters of offshore wind hydrogen systems in 2030 and 2050 scenarios.

| Component | Variable | Unit | 2030 | 2050 | Ref. |
|---|---|---|---|---|---|
| Semi-submersible FLOW Turbines & Platform | Unit CAPEX | £/MW | 2204.4 | 1764.2 | [29], [30] |
| | Unit OPEX | £/MW/yr | 55.1 | 44.1 | [29], [30] |
| 66 kV, 630 mm$^2$ Inter-array AC Cable | AC Resistance | Ω/km | 0.0274 | 0.0274 | [31] |
| | Unit CAPEX | £/m | 398.6 | 398.6 | [31] |
| | Unit OPEX | £/m/yr | 12.0 | 12.0 | [31] |
| Offshore Central Platform | Unit CAPEX | £/MW | 264.0 | 264.0 | [8] |
| | Unit OPEX | £/MW/yr | 2.9 | 2.9 | [8] |
| AC/DC Converter | $\eta_{CON}$ | % | 95.0 | 95.0 | [17] |
| | Unit CAPEX | £/MW | 75.0 | 75.0 | [17] |
| | Unit OPEX | £/MW/yr | 1.5 | 1.5 | [17] |
| Reverse Osmosis Desalination Device | $\eta_{DEL}$ | MWh/L | 5 x $10^{-6}$ | 5 x $10^{-6}$ | [32] |
| | Unit CAPEX | £/(L/h) | 32.1 | 20.5 | [33] |
| | Unit OPEX | £/(L/h)/yr | 1.0 | 1.0 | [13] |
| PEM Electrolyser | $\eta_{ELY}^{P2H}$ | kg/MWh | 20.4 | 22.2 | [34] |
| | $\eta_{ELY}^{W2H}$ | kg/L | 0.0756 | 0.0822 | [34] |
| | $b_{ELY}$ | bar | 50 | 70 | [34] |
| | Stack Lifetime | OP Hours | 90,000 | 120,000 | [34] |
| | Unit CAPEX | £/MW | 838.5 | 429.0 | [34] |
| | Unit OPEX | £/MW/yr | 16.8 | 8.6 | [34] |
| | Unit REPEX | £/MW | 251.6 | 128.7 | [35] |
| 50 kg/hr, 30 bar-200 bar Reference Compressor [a] | Unit CAPEX | £ | 281,388.6 | 281,388.6 | [35] |
| | Unit OPEX | £/yr | 11,255.5 | 11,255.5 | [13] |
| Hydrogen Storage Tank | $b_{STR}$ | bar | 350 | 350 | [35] |
| | Unit CAPEX | £/kg | 440.8 | 440.8 | [35] |
| | Unit OPEX | £/kg/yr | 8.8 | 8.8 | [35] |
| 12 Inch Hydrogen Pipeline | $b_{PIPE}$ | bar | 73~75 acc. pressure drop | | [27] |
| | Unit CAPEX | £/m | 267.6 | 267.6 | [36] |
| | Unit OPEX | £/m/yr | 8.0 | 8.0 | [36] |
| System Integration Test | Unit CAPEX | £/site | 10,263.8 | 10,263.8 | [36] |

[a] Please refer to [17] for the cost calculation of compressors based on a reference compressor system.

**Table 3.** The hydrogen system capacities optimised for a representative 600 MW FLOW farm in each MERRA square based on techno-economic input parameters in 2030 and 2050 scenarios.

| Hydrogen System Component | MERRA Square | 2030 | 2050 |
|---|---|---|---|
| PEM Electrolyser (MW) | MERRA-S1 | 426.1 | 405.4 |
| | MERRA-S2 | 429.6 | 408.1 |
| Desalination Device (L/h) | MERRA-S1 | 130,388.6 | 135,001.7 |
| | MERRA-S2 | 131,459.9 | 135,880.5 |
| First Compressor (kg/h) | MERRA-S1 | 8,692.6 | 9,000.1 |
| | MERRA-S2 | 8,764.0 | 9,058.7 |
| Second Compressor (kg/h) | MERRA-S1 | 2,792.7 | 2,984.7 |
| | MERRA-S2 | 2,815.7 | 3,004.2 |
| Converter (MW) | MERRA-S1 | 451.7 | 430.2 |
| | MERRA-S2 | 455.5 | 433.0 |
| Storage Asset (kg) | MERRA-S1 | 97,882.4 | 102,670.7 |
| | MERRA-S2 | 98,686.7 | 103,339.1 |

### *4.2. Optimisation-based system operation*

Figure 6(a) shows the aggregate available power output of a 600 MW FLOW farm in MERRA-S1, the power available at the central platform after slight inter-array cable losses, the power available for the hydrogen system subject to the conversion capacity and efficiency, and the power eventually absorbed by the electrolyser, desalination device and compressors during a particular simulation day in 2050 scenario. The hydrogen flow rates and resulting SOC levels of a single storage asset and the overall hydrogen supply of the systems in each square over the same day are shown in Figure 6(b) and 7(a) respectively. In the first six hours of the day, the hydrogen systems consume only part of the available power (see Figure 6(a)) for hydrogen production which fully meets onshore demands (see Figure 7(a)), keeping SOC levels at 100% (see Figure 6(b)). When the available FLOW generation decreases over 126-134 h, the hydrogen produced from the remaining power (after losses in cables and converters, see Figure 6(a)) meets only part of onshore demands, which requires additional supply from storage assets and reduces their SOC levels, as shown in Figures 7(a) and 6(b). When it comes back to the high wind period over 134-144 h, the power available for the hydrogen system is fully used to produce hydrogen (see Figure 6(a)), part of which is transported to shore (see Figure 7(a)) while the other part is pressurised further through the second compressor and stored in storage assets (see Figure 6(b)). In addition, Figure 6(b) shows that the SOC levels of the systems in the two MERRA squares are almost the same, illustrating the effectiveness of the specific hydrogen dispatch strategy designed in this work. The distribution of hydrogen supply across different offtake options during the same day is shown in Figure 7(b) where all the hydrogen demands are met, though the options having higher offtake priority form the base of the hydrogen supply.

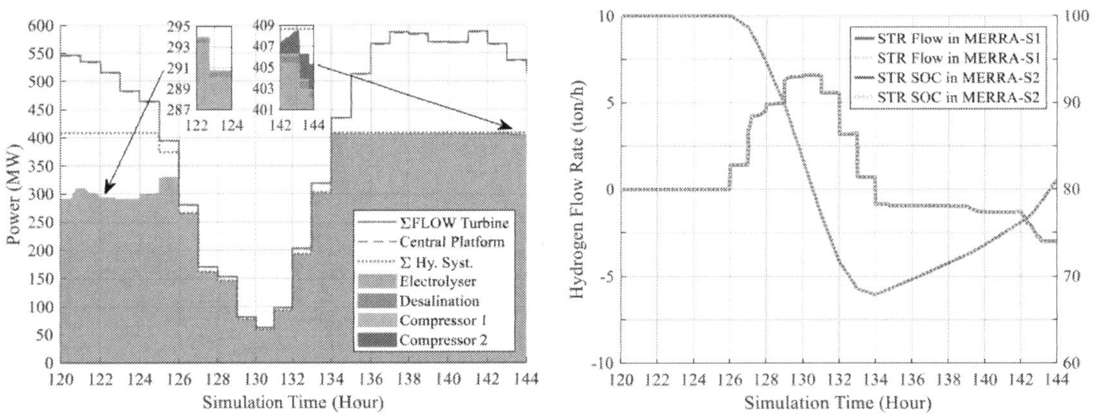


(a) (b)

**Figure 6**. (a) The power (MW) available at the FLOW farm, central platform and hydrogen system and absorbed by the electrolyser, desalination and compressors of a 600 MW system in MERRA-S1, and (b) the hydrogen flow rates (ton/h) and SOC levels (%) of a single storage asset in MERRA-S1 or MERRA-S2 during a particular simulation day over 120-144 h.

### *4.3. Cost-benefit analysis and hydrogen supply*

The cumulative present revenue and costs of the representative offshore wind hydrogen system in each MERRA square are shown in Figure 8(a) respectively. The total system costs mainly come from the CAPEX of FLOW turbines, PEM electrolyser and central platform, followed by the overall OPEX of the FLOW farm and the hydrogen system. Furthermore, the REPEX of electrolyser stacks occurring at the 11$^{th}$ (or 14$^{th}$) year in the 2030 (or 2050) scenario contributes only a small part to the total system costs. Although greater hydrogen production capabilities are used to supply more hydrogen to shore in the 2050 scenario (see Figure 8(b)), the total system costs are largely reduced in the 2050 scenario due to the price drops of wind turbines, electrolysers, etc. The decreases of total system costs together with the growths of hydrogen supply not only lead to the LCOH reduction, but also increase the net present value of the system. It is evaluated that the LCOH and net present value of the representative system in MERRA-S1 (or MERRA-S2) are around £5.35/kg and £0.29bn (or £5.32/kg and £0.31bn) in the 2030 scenario, or £3.88/kg and £1bn (or £3.87/kg and £1.02bn) in the 2050 scenario respectively.

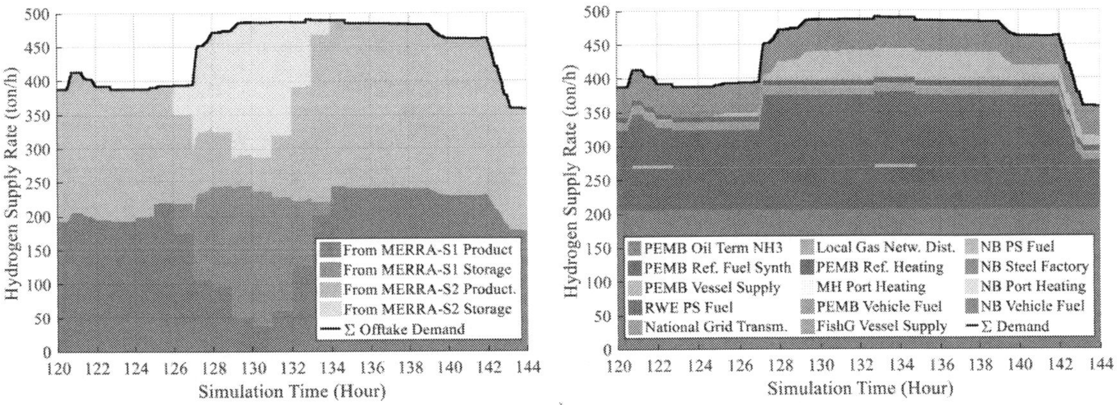


(a) (b)

**Figure 7.** (a) The overall hydrogen supply rates (ton/h) by direct production and storage release in the two MERRA squares, and (b) the distribution of hydrogen supply (ton/h) across offtake options during a particular simulation day over 120-144 h.

As shown in Figure 8(b), the annual hydrogen demand of the offtake options within Pembrokeshire and neighbouring regions is evaluated to be around 3.84 million tons in total, 73% or 76.6% of which would be met on average by the systems in the two squares in the 2030 or 2050 scenario respectively. Most of the hydrogen production is shown to be used by Pembroke Oil Terminal for $NH_3$ production, Pembroke Refinery for low-carbon fuel synthesis, and RWE power station due to their higher offtake priority and large demands for hydrogen. Figure 9 shows the percentage of the annual demand of each offtake option that would be supplied by the FLOW hydrogen production in the 2030 or 2050 scenario, which generally declines with the decreasing offtake priority. The systems in the two MERRA squares would supply about 85%-90% of the demand of the highest-priority Pembroke Oil Terminal and 55%-75% of the demands for most of the other offtake options.

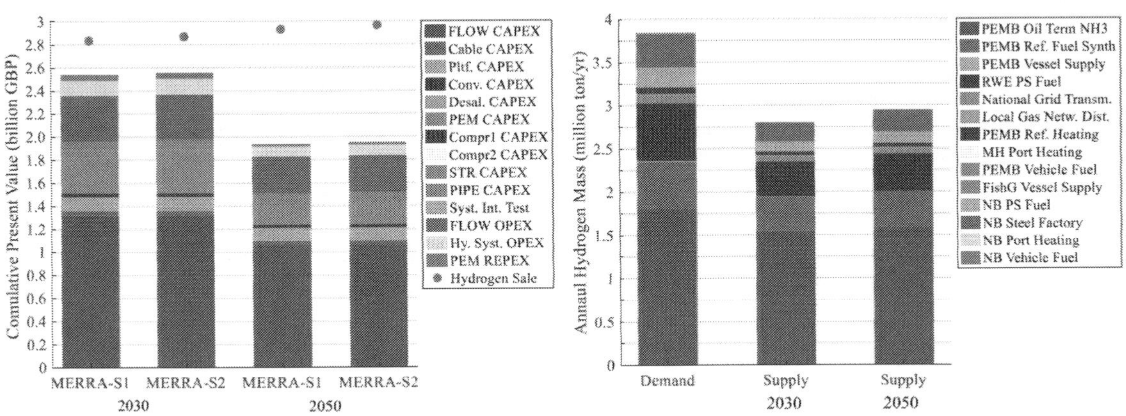


(a) (b)

**Figure 8.** (a) Cumulative present values (billion GBP) of hydrogen sale and costs of the representative offshore wind hydrogen system in each MERRA square, and (b) the annual hydrogen demands (ton/yr) supplied by the systems to different offtake options on average in 2030 and 2050 scenarios.

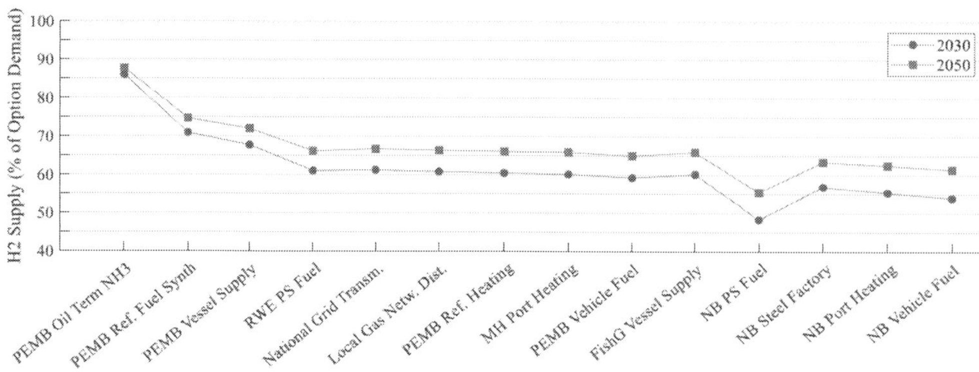


**Figure 9.** The percentages of hydrogen demands of different offtake options met by the offshore wind hydrogen systems in the two MERRA squares in 2030 and 2050 scenarios.

## 5. Conclusion and future work

With the development of electrolyser technologies, dedicated offshore wind farms for green hydrogen production is considered a cost-effective approach to exploiting deep offshore wind resources which can be carried to different energy sectors in the form of hydrogen. To facilitate the co-development of offshore wind and hydrogen systems, this paper has proposed a modelling framework to optimise the capacities of the centralised hydrogen systems that are co-located with offshore wind farms to produce, pressurise, store and transport hydrogen to shore. The power transfer from floating wind turbines to an offshore central platform and the power distribution among hydrogen system components have been simulated by considering the losses in power transmission and conversion and the dependent operation of hydrogen system components respectively. Furthermore, the hydrogen production and storage of multiple systems have been dispatched to meet onshore demands while keeping similar state of charge levels between systems, based on which the hydrogen system power consumptions were determined subject to their own power capacities and available wind power outputs. Then the present values of the hydrogen supply and total system costs were translated into the levelised cost of hydrogen (LCOH) of the system, which was minimised by the particle swarm optimsiation algorithm to estimate the optimal hydrogen system capacities. The proposed modelling framework has been validated in the context of Milford Haven in South Wales, with the associated hydrogen demands and offshore wind resources available for hydrogen production being estimated. The techno-economic parameters of the system components (e.g., semi-submersible wind turbines and polymer electrolyte membrane electrolysers) projected for 2030 and 2050 scenarios have been used in the optimisation process separately to assess the effects of techno-economic improvements in relevant technologies on the hydrogen system sizing.

For an offshore wind hydrogen system comprising 600 MW wind turbines, it has been suggested to deploy an electrolyser with capacity equalling 71%-72% or 67%-68% of the wind farm capacity in the 2030 or 2050 scenario respectively. Although the electrolyser size was reduced in the 2050 scenario, the system achieved a higher nominal hydrogen production rate due to the improvement in electrolyser efficiency. The higher production rate has increased the sizes of desalination devices and compressors and required greater storage capability to deal with the imbalance between hydrogen production and demands. With the system component prices falling in the 2050 scenario, the offshore wind hydrogen systems with greater production capacities would cost less than those in the 2030 scenario. The system cost reduction together with the growth of hydrogen supply resulted in a LCOH of around £3.9/kg in the 2050 scenario which was smaller than the LCOH of around £5.3/kg in the 2030 scenario. Given 60 offshore wind hydrogen systems being installed (i.e., 36 GW wind power capacity in total), their total hydrogen supply would meet about 73% or 76.6% of onshore demands (i.e., totaling 3.84 million tons per year) in the 2030 or 2050 scenario respectively.

The proposed modelling framework will be further developed to not only incorporate the objective function of net present value maximisation, but also enable the optimisation of decentralised offshore wind hydrogen systems. This will assist in understanding the effects of objective functions and system configurations on the hydrogen system optimisation. Furthermore, the hydrogen pipeline diameter will be modelled as an additional optimisation variable. Future work will also simulate wind resources at a higher spatial resolution. The increased diversity of wind resources across wind turbines will incur in the need of a more complicated strategy for hydrogen dispatch between multiple systems.

**Acknowledgments**
This work was conducted as part of the research programme of the Electrical Infrastructure Research Hub in collaboration with the Offshore Renewable Energy Catapult.

**References**

[1] HM Government 2020 *The Ten Point Plan for a Green Industrial Revolution* (London UK)
[2] International Renewable Energy Agency 2019 *Hydrogen: A Renewable Energy Respective* (Abu Dhabi United Arab Emirates)
[3] HM Government 2021 *UK Hydrogen Strategy* (London UK)
[4] Department for Business, Energy and Industrial Strategy 2022 *British Energy Security Strategy* (London UK)
[5] Department for International Trade 2022 *Hydrogen Invstor Roadmap – Leading the Way to Net Zero* (London UK)
[6] HM Government 2022 *Hydrogen Strategy Update to the Market: July 2022* (London UK)
[7] International Renewable Energy Agency 2018 *Hydrogen from Renewable Power – Technology Outlook for the Energy Transition* (Abu Dhabi United Arab Emirates)
[8] Spyroudi A, Wallace D, Smart G, Stefaniak K, Mann S and Kurban Z 2020 *Offshore Wind and Hydrogen – Solving the Integration Challenge* (Glasgow UK: Offshore Renewable Energy Catapult)
[9] Committee on Climate Change 2019 *Net Zero: The UK's Contribution to Stopping Global Warming* (London UK)
[10] Wu Y, Liu F, Wu J, He J, Xu M and Zhou J 2022 Barrier identification and analysis framework to the development of offshore wind-to-hydrogen projects *Energy* **239 B** 122077
[11] Ibrahim O S, Singlitico A, Proskovics R, McDonagh S, Desmond C and Murphy J D 2022 Dedicated large-scale floating offshore wind to hydrogen: Assessing design variables in proposed typologies *Renewable Sustainable Energy Rev.* **160** 112310
[12] Caine D, Wahyuni W, Pizii B, Iliffe M, Whitlock Z, Ryan B and Bond L 2021 *ERM Dolphyn Hydorgen: Phase 2 – Final Report* (Manchester UK: ERM)
[13] Singlitico A, Østergaard J and Chatzivasileiadis 2021 Onshore, offshoe or in-turbine electrolysis? Techno-economic overivew of alternative integration designs for green hydrogen production into offshore wind power hubs *Renewable Sustainable Energy Transition* **1** 100005
[14] Fan F, Zorzi G, Campos-Gaona D and Nwobu J 2022 Wind-plus-battery system optimisation for frequency resposne service: the UK perspective *Electr. Power Syst. Res.* **211** 108300
[15] Baldi F, Coraddu A, Kaliktzarakis M, Jeleňová D, Collu M, Race J and Maréchal F 2022 Optimisation-based system designs for deep offshore wind farms including power to gas technologies *Appl. Energy* **310** 118540
[16] Scolaro M and Kittner N 2022 Optimizing hybrid offshore wind farms for cost-competitive hydrogen production in Germany *Int. J. Hydrogen Energy* **47** 6478-93
[17] Fan F, Skellern S, Campos-Gaona D and Nwobu J 2023 Wind farm and hydrogen storage co-location system optimisation for dynamic frequency response in the UK *Clean Energy*
[18] Hóu P, Enevoldsen P, Eichman J, Hu W, Jacobson M Z and Chen Z 2017 Optimizing investments in coupled offshore wind-electrolytic hydrogen storage systems in Denmark *J. Power Sources* **359** 186-97
[19] Mee D, Elks S, Szczepanski M, Ageyman-Buahin P and Bridge F 2021 *Milford Haven: Energy Kingdom – System Architecture Report* (Birmingham UK: Energy Systems Catapult)

[20] Knight M, Smith L, Bawn G and Gibson T 2020 *Floating Offshore Wind Constraint Mapping in the Celtic Sea* (Glasgow UK: Offshore Renewable Energy Catapult)
[21] 4C Offshore 2023 *Global Offshore Renewable Map* (Lowestoft UK)
[22] Gelaro R, McCarty W, Suárez M J, Todling R, Molod A, Takacs L, et al 2017 The Modern-Era Retrospective Analysis for Research and Applications, Version 2 (MERRA-2) *J. Climate* **30** (14) 5419-54
[23] Vestas 2023 *V236-15.0 MW™* (Aarhus Denmark)
[24] Staffell I and Pfenninger S 2016 Using bias-corrected reanalysis to simulate current and future wind power output *Energy* **114** 1224-39
[25] Robak S and Raczkowski R M 2018 Substations of offshore wind farms: a review from the perspective of the needs of the Polish wind energy sector *Bulletin Polish Academy Sci. Tech. Sci.* **66** (4) 517-28
[26] Nexant, Inc. 2008 *H2A Hydorgen Delivery Infrastructure Analysis Models and Conventional Pathway Options Analysis Results* (Colorado USA)
[27] Menon E S 2011 *Pipeline Planning and Construction Field Manual* (Oxford UK: Gulf Professional Publishing, Elsevier Inc.)
[28] Kennedy J and Eberhar R 1995 Partile swarm optimization. *Proc. ICNN'95 – Int. Conf. Neural Networks* **4** 1942-48
[29] Stehly T, Beiter P and Duffy P 2020 *2019 Cost of Wind Energy Review* (Colorado USA: National Renewable Energy Laboratory)
[30] National Renewable Energy Laboraty 2022 *Annual Technology Baseline* (Colorado USA)
[31] TenneT 2015 *66 kV Systems for Offshore Wind Farms* (Arnhem Netherlands)
[32] Baldinelli A, Barelli L, Bidini G, Cinti G, Di Michele A and Mondi F 2020 How to power the energy-water nexus: coupling desalination and hydrogen energy storage in mini-grids with reversible solid oxide cells *Processes* **8** (11) 1494
[33] Caldera U and Breyer C 2017 Learning curve for seawater reverse osmosis desalination plants: capital cost trend of the past, present, and future *Water Resources Research* **53** (10) 523-38
[34] International Energy Agency 2019 *The Future of Hydrogen* (Paris France)
[35] Fuel Cells and Hydrogen 2 Joint Undertaking 2017 *Study on Early Business Cases for $H_2$ in Energy Storage and More Broadly Power to $H_2$ Applications* (Brussels Belgium)
[36] Bai Y and Bai Qiang 2010 Chapter 6 Subsea cost estimation *Subsea Engineering Handbook* 159-92 (Massachusetts USA: Gulf Professional Publishing)
[37] The MathWorks Inc. 2018 *MATLAB Release 2018b* (Massachusetts USA)

# Economic impact assessment of Hydrogen generated from Offshore Wind: A case study for Belgium

**Maëlig Gaborieau[1], Ozlem Ceyhan Yilmaz[2] and Katherine Dykes[3]**

[1] Offshore Wind Energy Data Analyst at Spinergie, Paris, France
[2] Senior Engineer/Researcher at Sirris/Owi-lab, Belgium.
[3] Head of Section Systems Engineering and Optimization at DTU Wind Energy, Denmark

E-mail: gaborieau.maelig@gmail.com

**Abstract.** Green hydrogen is increasingly cited as a solution to the decarbonisation of industry. Its large-scale production is still a recent topic with uncertainties. In this paper, an economic impact assessment (EIA) method is explained. A modular and flexible cost model is generated, which estimates the LCOE (Levelized Cost of Energy) of an offshore wind farm and the LCOH (Levelized Cost of Hydrogen) of a hydrogen generation plant either as a hybrid renewable energy system (HRES) or independent from each other. The costs are estimated using a schedule-based approach, which considers the reliability, maintenance operations as well as production of both the offshore wind farm and the hydrogen generation plant. Developed EIA is demonstrated for Belgium using Mermaid Offshore Wind Farm.

## 1. Introduction

Green hydrogen, which is generated by using electricity from renewable energy sources, is being investigated as a potential energy source to reach the decarbonisation goals of the EU. Green hydrogen is normally produced by water electrolysis using electrolysers, and the electrolyser capacity needs to grow to 350GW by 2030 according to [1]. Although currently, blue hydrogen (a combination of fossil fuels and carbon capture and storage) is still cheaper than green hydrogen, with both the cost reductions of renewable energy, especially offshore wind and the development of electrolyser technologies, it is predicted that the green hydrogen will become cost competitive by 2030 [2] and further reduction is expected beyond [3], [4], [5], [6], [7]. The understanding of costs involved in hydrogen production needs to be properly studied to ensure financial profitability in comparison to other means of production to realize these goals.

LCOH, together with other economic metrics such as net present value (NPV), is commonly used for the economical assessment of different technologies. There are various models and approaches used to estimate LCOH in the literature. Although most methods focus on the assessment of a specific hydrogen generation technology, other methods also exist, comparing different technologies to find the optimum. Here, we provide an overview of the most recent literature on these methods to cover this rapidly developing landscape of studies analysing hydrogen generation with its LCOH implications.

[8] and [9] reviewed techno-economic analysis approaches to evaluate different hydrogen generation methods. [10] assessed hydrogen storage in combination with renewable energy sources by analysing 15 different projects. [11] proposed integrated systems for the use of

large-scale floating wind farms dedicated to hydrogen generation. [12] developed an eco-techno-economical analysis approach to evaluate hydrogen generation using solid oxide electrolysis cells (SOECs), including their long-term degradation. They showed that LCOH from SOECs are in the range \$2.78/kg to \$11.67/kg compared to grey hydrogen, where LCOH varies between \$1.03/kg and \$2.16/kg, and they furthermore concluded that the electricity price was more dominant than the capital costs in these results. Similarly, [13], [14], [15] looked at Polymer Electrolyte Membrane (PEM) electrolysis, including degradation of efficiency, system modelling, optimisation and economical evaluation. [4] proposed a model to investigate integrated offshore wind and hydrogen generation infrastructure comparing onshore, offshore or in-turbine electrolysis with the goal of reducing LCOH. This study estimated an LCOH value of 2€/kg for green hydrogen generated offshore. [5] modelled and compared green hydrogen generation systems via electrolysis from offshore wind power, taking the hourly wind speeds into account. They found that LCOH from offshore wind electrolysis could drop to \$2.09/kg compared to the conventional way of obtaining offshore wind-generated electricity from the grid, which ends up at \$3.86/kg. A parametric model is proposed by [16] to compare the LCOH from Photovoltaic solar energy (PV), onshore and offshore wind energy. A range from €2.1/kg to €5.05/kg for LCOH for different scenarios was predicted. Other available models [17], [18], [19], [20] and [21] provided detailed modelling frameworks to assess several hydrogen generation options with usage of renewables or other sources. In [18], there is also a multi-criteria analysis (MCA) tool included to help with the decision-making process, which is elaborated in [17]. In most of the tools found in the literature, a significant effort has been put into the hydrogen generation system modelling however offshore wind farm modelling part has been included with less fidelity by focusing on the hourly power based on the wind speeds in the most detailed ones or grid infrastructure.

The EIA approach proposed in this paper models both the hydrogen and the electricity generation with similar fidelity to provide the same developmental and operational flexibility for both hydrogen and electricity generation plants assessing both LCOH and LCOE. This is done by using the existing models available to estimate LCOE of offshore wind farms in [23] and extend these models with the hydrogen generation capability with PEM electrolysis located onshore as this is the most commonly implemented technology currently [22], [9]. As a case study, an offshore wind farm is used to generate electricity and a part of this electricity is used to produce hydrogen in an onshore plant. Most of the costs involved are taken into account using a schedule-based cost model applied to this Hybrid Renewable Energy System (HRES) (Figure 1).

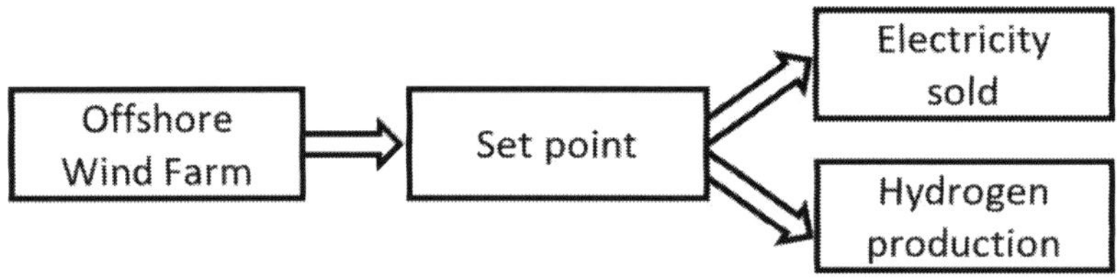


**Figure 1.** HRES model

## 2. Cost Model

The Economic Impact Assessment of the HRES is executed using a cost model which consists of two different modules to cover most of the involved costs of setting up and operating an offshore wind farm and an onshore hydrogen generation plant. These modules include the construction part of the systems, called the CAPEX Module, and a schedule-based module assessing the operational costs as well as the production of the representative systems, called the OPEX and Revenue Module.

### *2.1. CAPEX Module*

First, the cost of setting up both systems, the wind farm and the hydrogen plant, is assessed in a CAPEX module. This part only involves the pre-operational period of both systems and is therefore not time-dependent.

The CAPEX of an offshore wind farm can be divided into two parts: the Balance of Plant (BoP) and the cost of installation. The cost of the BoP is the cost of procuring the equipment and the necessary material to build the wind farm, while the installation costs deal with the cost of constructing the wind farm.
CAPEX installation costs and the BoP of the offshore wind farm are mainly based on the ORBIT model of NREL [24]. Based on ORBIT, different stages of the installation activities are modelled by taking the vessel spread, the vessel rates, and the necessary timing into account. BoP is modelled by summing the cost of monopiles, cables, wind turbines, and other miscellaneous costs.
The cost of monopiles is calculated by entering the dimensions of the monopile, the cost of steel, and the cost of manufacturing using the ORBIT [24]. The cable costs are estimated using the cost of the cables per length and the total length of the cables. The cost of wind turbines is estimated using the empirical formula provided by the Romeo project [26]:

$$Cost_{Turbines} = ((3 * 10^6)ln(MW) - 662400) * 1.16 \tag{1}$$

Where MW is the rating of the turbine in Megawatt, and 1.16 is used to convert from pounds to euros.

Concerning the hydrogen generation plant, the approach to calculating the CAPEX is similar. CAPEX costs are divided into three main parts: the BoP cost, the electrolyser cost, and the installation cost. BoP of the hydrogen generation plant is estimated by summing up the costs of compression, rectifier, gas holder, and ancillary, which are individually obtained or modelled using the approaches in [4] and [20]. The cost of the electrolyser (PEM-electrolysis) is estimated as in [4].

$$Cost_{Electrolyser} = P_{elec}RC_{elec}(\frac{P_{elec} \cdot 10^3}{RP_{elec}})^{SF_{elec}} \tag{2}$$

Where $P_{elec}$ is the electrolyser capacity, $RC_{elec}$ is the reference cost for PEM electrolysis assumed to be 600€/kW, $RP_{elec}$ is the reference power, and $SF_{elec}$ is the scale factor assumed to be -0.14. Since there is not yet much data on the installation costs, it is used as 20% of the CAPEX as recommended in [21].

### *2.2. OPEX and Revenue Module*

In this part, the OPEX and Revenue module is described. This schedule-based module simulates every hour of the HRES operational life to calculate the operational costs and the production of both the offshore wind farm and the hydrogen generation plant. The basic principle of the model can be described in Figure 2.

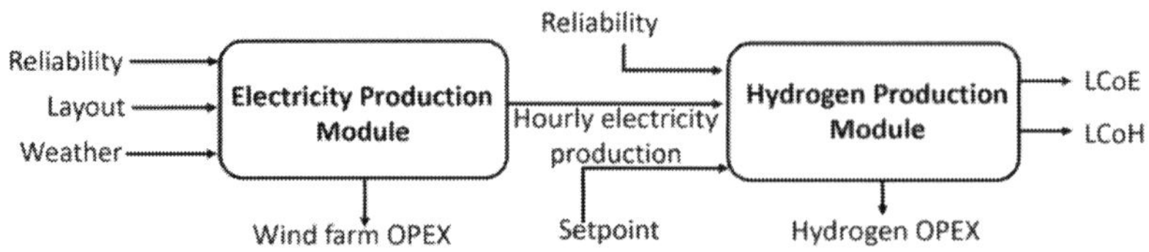


**Figure 2.** OPEX and Revenue Module principle

OPEX costs of the wind farm are estimated by modelling the failures of 21 subsystems composing a wind turbine. Five damage categories based on their estimated severity are implemented. Each of these failure possibilities leads to repair costs and an associated downtime where the turbine involved is not available and can therefore not produce any electricity. To evaluate when these failures happen, a Monte Carlo loop is used following the principles of the NOWIcob model in [25] where a homogeneous Poisson's process (HPP) is used to randomize the component failures for each hour of the offshore wind farm's lifetime. The principle of the failure analysis and the associated downtime for a turbine is summarized in Figure 3.

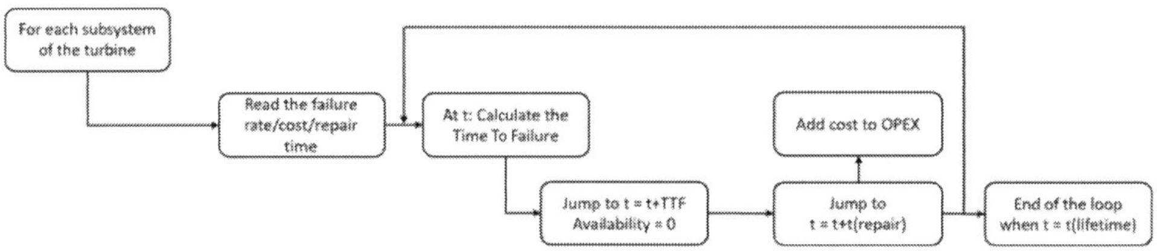


**Figure 3.** Failure and downtime principle

The OPEX cost of every failure is summed to obtain the total OPEX cost of the wind farm over the entire lifetime. Furthermore, the hourly availability of one turbine is calculated and summarized in a matrix where the black tiles represent an unavailability period. This matrix is represented in Figure 4. Once the availability of every turbine is obtained, electricity production of the wind farm is calculated using the historical wind speed, and wind rose information at the wind farm location. The wake losses have also been implemented as a percentage of production.

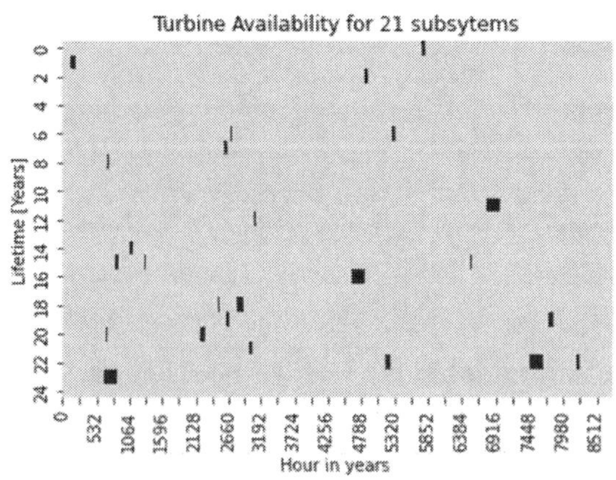


**Figure 4.** Availability matrix of a wind turbine

A percentage of the electricity produced is used to generate green hydrogen, while the other part is sold to the grid. This percentage is chosen based on a set point between 0 and 100%.

Concerning the hydrogen generation plant, a similar approach is used to calculate the failure cost and estimate the availability throughout the lifetime of the plant. Furthermore, part of the electricity sent to this system is used for the compression and for the demineralization of the water used for the electrolysis. The formula 3 is used where the stack efficiency is time-dependent because of the linear degradation of the stack. Additionally, the Lower Heating Value (LHV = 33.3 kWh/kg) of the hydrogen is taken into account to convert the energy into the mass of hydrogen produced [20].

$$m_{H_2}(t) = \frac{(SetPoint * E_{WF}(t) - E_{comp}(t) - E_{demin}(t))\eta_{stack}(t)}{LHV} \tag{3}$$

The cost of replacing the stack every 85000 operating hours is evaluated, as well as the cost of buying the water needed for the electrolysis at the local market price. Furthermore, 14 Liters of water are necessary to produce 1kg of hydrogen.

Finally, the value obtained using this cost model is compared to a case where the electricity is now bought from the local grid at the market price. The LCoE of the offshore wind farm, the LCoH of the hybrid system, and the LCoH considering the grid electricity as input are evaluated with the formulas in Table 1:

**Table 1.** LCoE and LCoH formulas

| **LCoE** | **LCoH1 (from HRES)** | **LCoH2 (from grid electricity)** |
|---|---|---|
| $\frac{\sum_{t=0}^{Lifetime} \frac{(I_{WF,t}+O_{WF,t})}{(1+r)^t}}{\sum_{t=0}^{Lifetime} \frac{AEP_t}{(1+r)^t}}$ | $\frac{\sum_{t=0}^{Lifetime} \frac{(I_{WF,t}+O_{WF,t}+I_{H_2,t}+O_{H_2,t})}{(1+r)^t}}{\sum_{t=0}^{Lifetime} \frac{M_{H_2,t}}{(1+r)^t}}$ | $\frac{\sum_{t=0}^{Lifetime} \frac{(MarketPrice*E_{used}+I_{H_2,t}+O_{H_2,t})}{(1+r)^t}}{\sum_{t=0}^{Lifetime} \frac{M_{H_2,t}}{(1+r)^t}}$ |

Where r is the discount rate considered as 6%, I is the CAPEX costs, O is the OPEX costs of the different systems, and AEP is the annual energy production of the offshore wind farm.

## 3. Study Case

The economic impact of hydrogen generation is mainly quantified by estimating the LCOH of the hydrogen generation plant using the electricity generated by an offshore wind farm. In order to have precise and representative values for the different costs involved, the Mermaid Offshore Wind Farm in Belgium developed and operated by Otary, is chosen in this study, with the following parameters:

**Table 2.** Representative Offshore Wind Farm parameters

| **Parameters** | |
|---|---|
| Number of Turbines | 28 |
| Turbines Type | SG 8.0-167 |
| Farm Capacity | 235MW |
| Foundation Type | Monopile |
| Hub Height | 107.5 meters |
| Distance to Shore | 54km |
| Operator | Otary RS N.V. |

The representative hydrogen generation plant for this study is a virtual plant located in the Belgian city of Zeebrugge, with the following characteristics:

**Table 3.** Representative onshore hydrogen plant parameters

| **Parameters** | |
|---|---|
| Location | Zeebrugge |
| Electrolyzer Capacity | 235MW |
| Type of Electrolysis | PEM |
| Distance to Wind Farm | 54km |
| Compression | 700 kW |
| Lifetime | 25 years |

Several technology types can be used to perform water electrolysis, such as the AEL-electrolysis, the PEM-electrolysis, or the SOEC-electrolysis. All these technologies have different advantages (efficiency, operating time, dynamic response). For this study, the technology used is the Polymer Electrolyte Membrane electrolysis (PEM), as it is appropriate for renewable energy sources such as offshore wind. The stack, which is the component converting the electricity into hydrogen, is supposed to need a replacement every 85,000 working hours. Furthermore, an initial efficiency of 62% is considered with a linear degradation of 0.1% every 1,000 operating hours. The operating temperature is 85°C, and the pressure is 55 bar. Finally, a demineralizer is implemented with an electricity consumption of 1.5 kWh/$m^3$ to ensure that the water bought from the Belgian network is pure.

The values obtained by using the cost model in this study case are also compared with an LCoH estimation when the electricity is coming from the Belgian grid using the 2022 market prices as in [29]. In this case, the studied hydrogen generation plant is considered as decoupled from the offshore wind farm.

## 4. Results and discussion

CAPEX share of different components for wind farm and the hydrogen plant in Figures 5 and 6 shows that the largest costs are the wind turbines and the electrolyser. A CAPEX cost of 619 k€/MW is found for the hydrogen generation plant, which is within the expectation for such a project based on [31].

Journal of Physics: Conference Series 2507 (2023) 012012 doi:10.1088/1742-6596/2507/1/012012

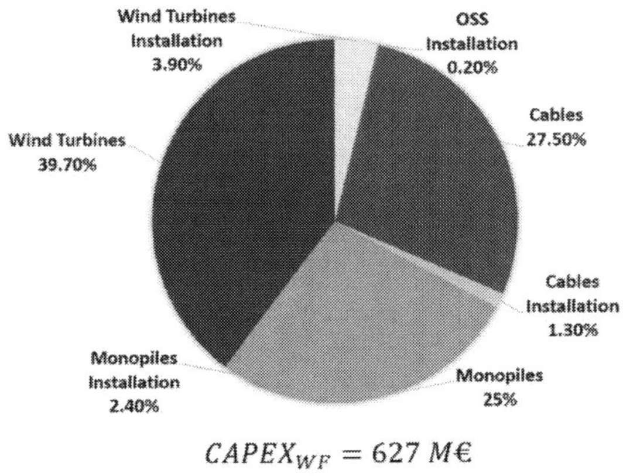


**Figure 5.** Breakdown of the wind farm CAPEX

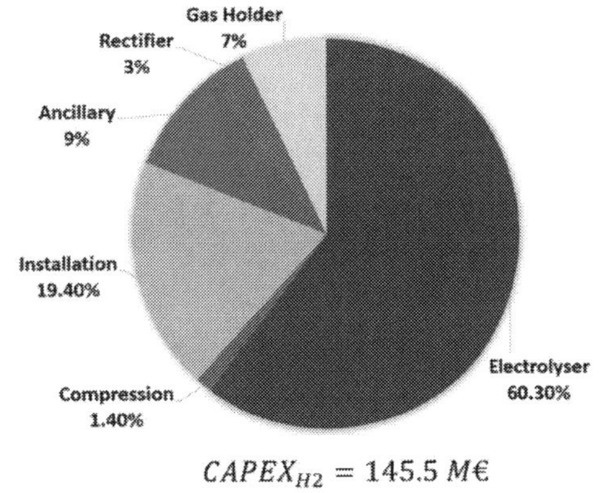


**Figure 6.** Breakdown of the hydrogen plant CAPEX

An OPEX cost of 1,300k€/Turbine/year is found for the wind farm (910.16M€ over the lifetime of Mermaid Wind Farm) with a time availability of 96%. Although the actual availability of this wind farm is not published to our knowledge, [32] estimates an average of 95% for an offshore wind farm which is close to this prediction. The hydrogen generation plant has a lower OPEX cost with 2,921k€/year (73.1M€ over the lifetime). Two different versions of OPEX costs are shown for the hydrogen generation; in Figure 7 using the electricity from the offshore wind farm and in Figure 8 from the grid (bought at Belgian market price) as input.

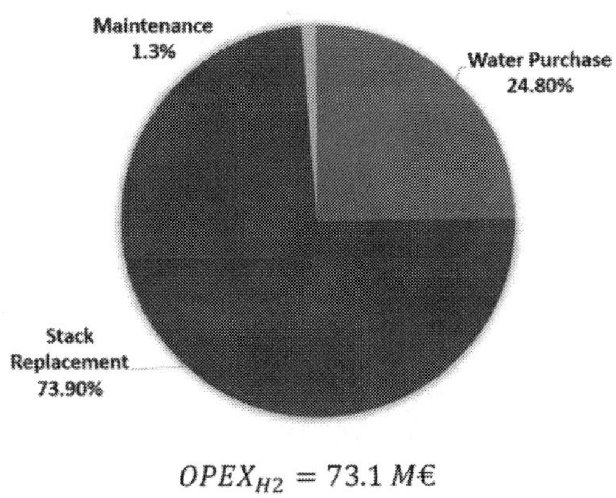


**Figure 7.** Breakdown of the hydrogen generation OPEX (wind farm electricity)

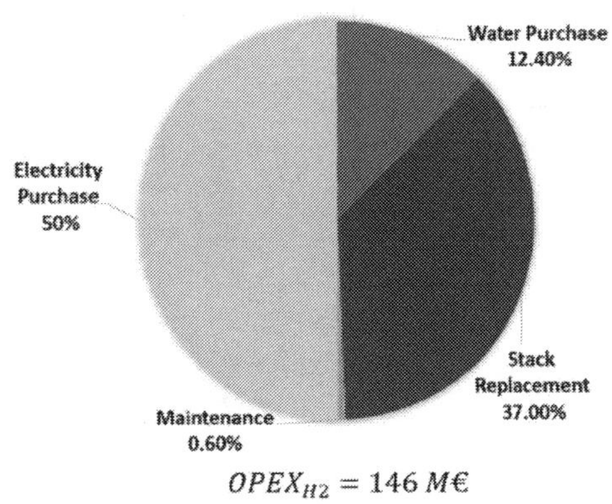


**Figure 8.** Breakdown of the hydrogen generation OPEX (grid electricity)

When the entire HRES is studied, the most significant cost is the stack replacement which happens two times in the entire lifetime of the plant that is modelled in this study (every 85,000 operating hours, which is taken from [4]). Replacing the stack is a very expensive action due to the cost of the stack which is composed of several rare materials such as titanium, platinium, iridium, as explained in [27]. 14L of water is necessary to produce 1kg of hydrogen, and as a result, purchasing the water has a significant share in OPEX. The maintenance costs are less than 2% of the whole OPEX, which is expected due to the fact that the hydrogen plant is located onshore and no delay in repair actions of failures is modelled. When the electricity is bought from the grid, a massive OPEX cost for hydrogen generation is seen, representing half of the OPEX cost.

Finally, the production of both systems is also evaluated. Average hourly electricity production of 96.3 MWh is found for Mermaid wind farm over its lifetime and, when 100% of the electricity is used for hydrogen production, 1555 kg per hour of hydrogen is generated on average.

**Table 4.** LCoE and LCoH results

| LCoE | LCoH1 (from HRES) | LCoH2 (from grid electricity) |
|---|---|---|
| 101.3 €/MWh | 6.76 €/kg | 9.26 €/kg |

The values of LCoE and LCoH obtained are summarized in Table 4. The LCoE found is higher than the published value of 79€/MWh [33]. The difference can be explained by the uncertainty of some assumptions (different turbines, failure rates, wake loss). Government subsidies are also not taken into account in this model. The LCoH1, representing the cost of producing hydrogen from the HRES, is in the range of what was found in [15], which is significantly more expansive than the current cost of grey hydrogen found in [15] (between 0.97€/kg and 2.04€/kg). [30] found a value of approximately 6€/kg which is close to our prediction. However, [28] shows an average LCOH value of 5.3€/kg for Belgium in 2022 for green hydrogen which is lower than our prediction. Since this reference value was obtained for an AEL-electrolysis with better efficiency, a lower LCOH value is expected. LCoH2, when electricity is bought from the grid at market price with the same amount of hydrogen, is also included here for comparison.

To better understand the different cash flows at stake during the lifetime of the HRES, Figure 9 illustrates that the OPEX of the hydrogen plant is most of the time minor. However, every 85,000 operating hours, the stack replacement makes this visible since it leads to a significant operational cost.

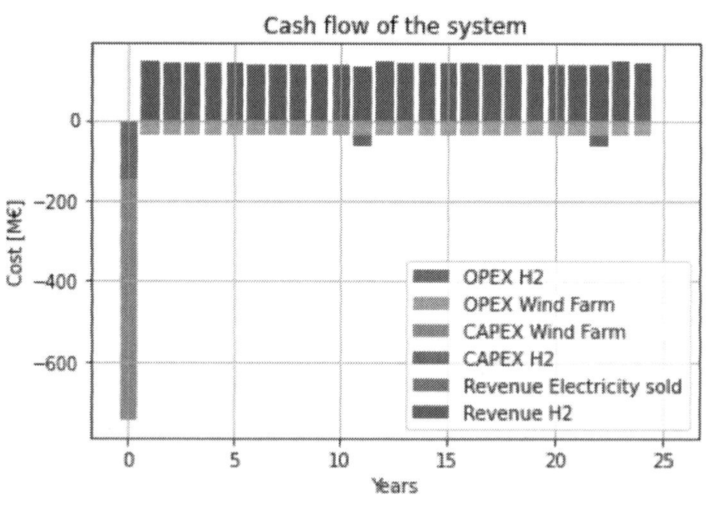


**Figure 9.** Cash flow of the HRES

Linear degradation of the stack efficiency is seen with a decrease in the hydrogen production, and therefore revenue, before a stack replacement. Additionally, the annual OPEX of the wind farm remains regular throughout the lifetime of the system. If the hydrogen is sold at a higher price than the LCoH, the system becomes profitable. Here, a value of 10€/kg is used, which is the hydrogen sale price of the fuel stations in Belgium [34]. With these values, the NPV of the system is 565M€. On the other hand, if all of the wind farm's electricity is sold to the grid at 25c/kWh [29], NPV is calculated to be around 1.5B€. This comparison shows that, for this study, hydrogen generation is less profitable compared to selling electricity to the grid.

As explained before, a setpoint was implemented regulating the quantity of electricity sent from the offshore wind farm to the hydrogen generation plant. By varying the value of this setpoint, the two different LCoH also vary, and Figure 10 illustrates these variations.

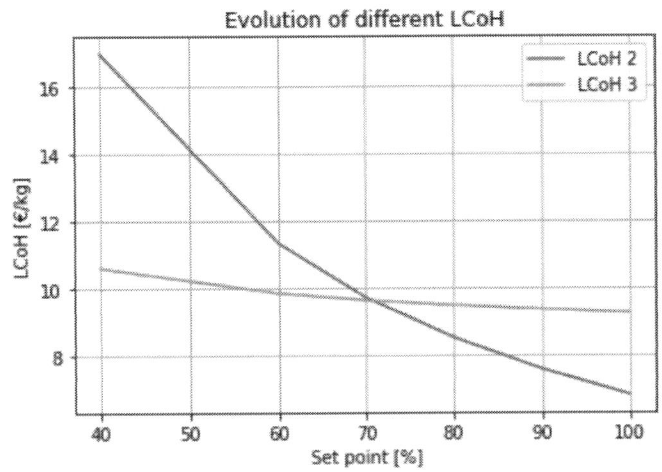


**Figure 10.** Effect of the setpoint on LCoH

LCoH1 corresponds to the LCoH of the total system with electricity from the offshore wind farm production, while LCoH2 is when electricity is bought from the grid at market price with the same amount of hydrogen generated. Figure 10 shows that using more than 71% of the wind farm electricity for hydrogen production is needed to produce cheaper hydrogen than with a grid electricity electrolysis for the study case.

A sensitivity analysis has also been realised to assess the impact of the different assumptions and to estimate the main parameters that can optimize the cost of the hydrogen generated from an offshore wind farm. This analysis is shown in Table 5.

This analysis shows that the stack efficiency and discount rate have the highest impact on the LCoH, whereas water cost seems to have the least impact. Furthermore, a change of 10% of the total CAPEX leads to a change of 6% in the final LCoH. With improved electrolysis technology for better efficiency, the cost of producing green hydrogen could be significantly reduced in the future.

| Criterion | Base Case | New Scenario | Effect on LCoH1 | New LCoH1 [€/kg] |
|---|---|---|---|---|
| Basic LCoH | | | | 6.76 |
| Discount rate | 6% | 3% | -14.35% | 5.79 |
| Discount rate | 6% | 9% | +15.5% | 7.81 |
| Total CAPEX | 772.5M | 695.25M | -6.1% | 6.35 |
| Total CAPEX | 772.5M | 849.75M | +6.1% | 7.17 |
| Stack Efficiency | 62% | 52% | +19.1% | 8.05 |
| Stack Efficiency | 62% | 72% | -13.8% | 5.83 |
| Stack Degradation | 0.1%/1000h | 0.05%/1000h | -1.8% | 6.64 |
| Stack Degradation | 0.1%/1000h | 0.2%/1000h | +3.55% | 7.00 |
| Water Cost | 3.7 €/$m^3$ | 3.4 €/$m^3$ | -0.15% | 6.75 |
| Water Cost | 3.7 €/$m^3$ | 4 €/$m^3$ | +0.15% | 6.77 |
| Failure Rate H2 | Base Case | Base Case * 10 | +5.3% | 7.12 |

**Table 5.** Sensitivity analysis results

## 5. Conclusions

An economic impact assessment method for an HRES, which consist of an offshore wind farm and a hydrogen generation plant, is developed. This method has been demonstrated using the Mermaid offshore wind farm in Belgium and a virtual onshore hydrogen generation facility. From the study, the following conclusions can be drawn:

- Developed approach can be used to compare hydrogen generation strategies coupled or decoupled with an offshore wind farm
- Both offshore wind farm and the hydrogen generation plants are modelled with similar detail including failure rates of various components, hourly wind speeds, weather availability, downtimes, etc. This allows the evaluation and optimisation of many options on the LCOH and LCOE or both at the same time.
- If electricity purchase is not included, the stack replacement is the major cost for the OPEX of the modelled onshore hydrogen plant.
- Estimated LCOH values are slightly higher than the values found in the literature.
- LCOH is shown to be dependent on the electricity source.
- Set point approach makes it possible to identify the amount of electricity from an offshore wind more profitable compared to obtaining it from the grid.

The methodology developed here is quite flexible, allowing various parametrisation possibilities for optimizing LCoH and LCoE values at the same time. However, it also has limitations. The main ones are listed below:

- Hydrogen generation plant is located onshore so the assessments cannot include distance to shore for the hydrogen plant.
- The electrolyser is assumed to respond to the variable energy generation perfectly. And the size of the electrolyser is not evaluated as a parameter in this study although it is possible.
- Variable electricity price is not taken into account.

Although the predicted LCOH values are close to the values found in the literature, the model will need validation when more data from a similar real HRES will be available.

## References

[1] World Energy Transitions Outlook 2022: 1.5°C Pathway, International Renewable Energy Agency, Abu Dhabi. Available for download: www.irena.org/publications
[2] Smart Electrification with Renewables: Driving the transformation of energy services, International Renewable Energy Agency, Abu Dhabi, Available for download: https://www.irena.org/publications
[3] Working paper: Hydrogen demands and cost dynamics, Wind Energy Council, September 2021, Available to download: https://www.worldenergy.org/publications
[4] Singlitico, A., Østergaard, J., Chatzivasileiadis, S. (2021). Onshore, offshore or in-turbine electrolysis? Techno-economic overview of alternative integration designs for green hydrogen production into Offshore Wind Power Hubs. Renewable and Sustainable Energy Transition, 1, [100005]. https://doi.org/10.1016/j.rset.2021.100005
[5] Hugo Groenemans, Genevieve Saur, Cortney Mittelsteadt, Judith Lattimer, Hui Xu, Techno-economic analysis of offshore wind PEM water electrolysis for H2 production, Current Opinion in Chemical Engineering, Volume 37, 2022, 100828, https://doi.org/10.1016/j.coche.2022.100828
[6] Alex Badgett, Mark Ruth, Brian James, Bryan Pivovar, Methods identifying cost reduction potential for water electrolysis systems, Current Opinion in Chemical Engineering, Volume 33, 2021, 100714 https://doi.org/10.1016/j.coche.2021.100714
[7] Hans Böhm, Sebastian Goers, Andreas Zauner, Estimating future costs of power-to-gas – a component-based approach for technological learning, International Journal of Hydrogen Energy, Volume 44, Issue 59, 2019, Pages 30789-30805 https://doi.org/10.1016/j.ijhydene.2019.09.230
[8] R. Yukesh Kannah, S. Kavitha, Preethi, O. Parthiba Karthikeyan, Gopalakrishnan Kumar, N. Vo. Dai-Viet, J. Rajesh Banu, Techno-economic assessment of various hydrogen production methods – A review, Bioresource Technology, Volume 319, 2021, 124175, ISSN 0960-8524, https://doi.org/10.1016/j.biortech.2020.124175
[9] Zulfhazli , Keeley Alexander Ryota, Takeda Shutaro, Managi Shunsuke, A systematic review of the techno-economic assessment of various hydrogen production methods of power generation, Frontiers in Sustainability, Vol.3, 2022.
[10] Torbjørn Egeland-Eriksen, Amin Hajizadeh, Sabrina Sartori, Hydrogen-based systems for Integration of renewable energy in power systems: Achievements and perspectives, International Journal of Hydrogen Energy, Volume 46, Issue 63, 2021, Pages 31963-31983, ISSN 0360-3199, https://doi.org/10.1016/j.ijhydene.2021.06.218
[11] Ibrahim, O. S., Singlitico, A., Proskovics, R., McDonagh, S., Desmond, C., Murphy, J. D. (2022). Dedicated large-scale floating offshore wind to hydrogen: Assessing design variables in proposed typologies. Renewable and Sustainable Energy Reviews, 160, [112310]. https://doi.org/10.1016/j.rser.2022.112310
[12] Naeini Mina, Cotton James S., Adams Thomas A. An eco-technoeconomic analysis of hydrogen production using solid oxide electrolysis cells that accounts for long-term degradation, Frontiers in Energy Research, vol.10, 2022, https://doi.org/10.3389/fenrg.2022.1015465
[13] Escobar-Yonoff R., Maestre-Cambronel D., Charry S., Rincón-Montenegro A., Portnoy A., Performance assessment and economic perspectives of integrated PEM fuel cell and PEM electrolyzer for electric power generation, Heliyon, vol. 7, issue 3, E06506, March 2021, https://doi.org/10.1016/j.heliyon.2021.e06506
[14] Hong Zhang, Tiejiang Yuan, Optimization and economic evaluation of a PEM electrolysis system considering its degradation in variable-power operations, Applied Energy, Volume 324, 2022, 119760, ISSN 0306-2619, https://doi.org/10.1016/j.apenergy.2022.119760
[15] Siracusano, S. van Dijk, Nick Backhouse, R. Merlo, L. Baglio, Vincenzo Arico, A.S.. (2018). Degradation issues of PEM electrolysis MEAs. Renewable Energy. https://doi.org/10.1016/j.renene.2018.02.024
[16] Gregor Brändle, Max Schönfisch, Simon Schulte, Estimating Long-Term Global Supply Costs for Low-Carbon Hydrogen, EWI Working Paper, No 20/04 November 2020, https://www.ewi.uni-koeln.de/cms/wp-content/uploads/2021/03/EWI_WP_2004_Estimating_longterm_global_supply_costs_for_low-carbon_Schoenfisch_Braendle_Schulte1.pdf, accessed on 09-03-2023.
[17] Khan, M.H.A., Heywood, P., Kuswara, A. et al. An integrated framework of open-source tools for designing and evaluating green hydrogen production opportunities. Commun Earth Environ 3, 309 (2022). https://doi.org/10.1038/s43247-022-00640-1
[18] HySupply Cost Tool, available in https://www.globh2e.org.au/hysupplycosttool, accessed on 09-03-2023
[19] Khzouz, Martin Gkanas, Evangelos Shao, Jia Sher, Farooq Beherskyi, Dmytro El-kharouf, Ahmad Al Qubeissi, Mansour. (2020). Life Cycle Costing Analysis: Tools and Applications for Determining Hydrogen Production Cost for Fuel Cell Vehicle Technology. Energies. 13. 3783. https://doi.org/10.3390/en13153783
[20] https://h2tools.org/, accessed on 09-03-2023
[21] https://www.nrel.gov/hydrogen/h2aproductionmodels.html, accessed on 09-03-2023
[22] IRENA (2020), Green Hydrogen Cost Reduction: Scaling up Electrolysers to Meet the 1.5C Climate Goal, International Renewable Energy Agency, Abu Dhabi. Available for download: www.irena.org/publications

[23] Potchara Sumetha-Aksorn, Katherine Dykes and Ozlem Ceyhan Yilmaz, 2022 J. Phys.: Conf. Ser. 2265 042036, https://doi.org/10.1088/1742-6596/2265/4/042036

[24] Nunemaker, Jake, Matt Shields, Robert Hammond, and Patrick Duffy, 2020, ORBIT: Offshore Renewables Balance-of-System and Installation Tool. Golden, CO: National Renewable Energy Laboratory. NREL/TP-5000-77081. https://www.nrel.gov/docs/fy20osti/77081.pdf

[25] Iver Bakken Sperstad et al, 2017, Technical documentation of version 3.3 of the nowicob. https://sintef.brage.unit.no/sintef-xmlui/handle/11250/2478168

[26] ROMEO Wind, Athanasios Kolios and Feargal Brennan, 2018 Review of existing cost and om models, and development of a high-fidelity cost/revenue model for impact assessment. https://romeoproject.eu/wp-content/uploads/2018/12/D8.1$_{R}OMEO_{R}eport - reviewing - exsiting - cost - and - OM - support - models.pdf$

[27] FinH2, https://www.finh2.fi/electrolyser-technologies/

[28] Hydrogen Europe, Clean Hydrogen Monitor, 2022, https://hydrogeneurope.eu/wp-content/uploads/2022/10/Clean$_{H}ydrogen_{M}onitor_{1}0 - 2022_{D}IGITAL.pdf$

[29] Eurostat, Electricity Price Statistics, 2022. https://ec.europa.eu/eurostat/statistics-explained/index.php?title=Electricity$_{p}rice_{s}tatistics : \quad : text = For$

[30] Yuanrong Zhou and Stephanie Searle, 2022, Cost of renewable hydrogen produced onsite at hydrogen refueling station in Europe. https://theicct.org/wp-content/uploads/2022/02/fuels-eu-cost-renew-H-produced-onsite-H-refueling-stations-europe-feb22.pdf

[31] IEA, Electrolysers, 2022. https://www.iea.org/reports/electrolysers

[32] James Carroll, Alasdair McDonald, Iain Dinwoodie, David McMillan, Matthew Revie and Iraklis Lazakis, Availability, operation and maintenance costs of offshore wind turbines with different drive train configurations, 2016. https://docs.wind-watch.org/offshore-availability-costs.pdf

[33] Enerdata, Belgium agrees on a €79/MWh LCOE for three offshore wind parks, 2017. https://www.enerdata.net/publications/daily-energy-news/belgium-agrees-eu79mwh-lcoe-three-offshore-wind-parks.html

[34] Roman Frey, Stations-service d'hydrogène en belgique à Mars 2023, 2023, https://www.glpautogas.info/fr/stations-hydrogene-belgique.html

# Effect of curtailment scenarios on the loads and lifetime of offshore wind turbine generator support structures

**Koen Robbelein[a,b], P.J. Daems[a], T. Verstraeten[a], N. Noppe[a,b], W. Weijtjens[a], J. Helsen[a], C. Devriendt[a,b]**
[a] Vrije Universiteit Brussel, OWI-Lab, AVRG, Pleinlaan 2, BE-1050 Brussels, Belgium
[b] 24SEA, Drukpersstraat 4, 1000 Brussels, Belgium

koen.robbelein@vub.be

**Abstract.** Curtailment is a known phenomenon for wind turbine operators of both onshore and offshore wind turbine generators (WTG). Curtailment refers to the situation in which the power output of all WTG's within a windfarm is forced below the expected power output at the occurring environmental conditions. A direct consequence of curtailment is the loss of power production. In the present contribution further consequences of curtailment of an offshore wind farm (OWF) are studied from the perspective of the support structure, in specific the foundation. In relation to curtailment a couple of potentially critical operational conditions impacting the fatigue consumption of the support structure can be identified. Besides the standstill during operational windspeed conditions, in specific damaging for the +7MW generation WTG's, curtailment introduces repeated transitions between operational conditions. Since transitions between operational conditions of a WTG are known to be a cause of high fatigue loads in the structural components of the WTG, their increased occurrence due to curtailment might also have an impact on the fatigue consumption of the support structure. With the growing interest of the industry to quantify and potentially optimize the structural lifetime consumption in view of potential lifetime extension of OWF assets, any potential fatigue damaging operational condition is to be investigated. The present work focusses on the investigation of the impact these transitional load cycles may have on the structural lifetime of the WTG foundation. To assess the impact on lifetime, the assessment of the damage equivalent loads (DEL) derived from structural health monitoring (SHM) data are used as a data-driven alternative for model-based load simulations. In the present work such data-driven lifetime assessment studies the impact of curtailment regimes with different frequency of stop and start cycles on the structural lifetime. The study is performed based on 1 year of SHM data collected from two OWF's. The assessment demonstrates that the impact of additional transitional load cycles on the structural fatigue life consumption is to be considered when defining a long-term curtailment strategy for an OWF.

## 1. Introduction and motivation

Curtailment is a known phenomenon for wind turbine operators of both onshore and offshore wind turbine generators (WTG). In the present contribution curtailment of an offshore wind farm (OWF) refers to the situation in which the power output of all its wind turbine generators (WTG) is forced below the expected power output at the occurring environmental conditions. The OWF is curtailed by the Balance Responsible Party (BRP). There may be various reasons for which the BRP forces an OWF in curtailment, by example to balance the demand and production of energy (grid congestion) or commercial reasons. With a growing variability in supply and demand curtailment of OWF's is expected to rise in the foreseeable future. Besides the loss of power production - which is the (desired) direct consequence of curtailment - the imposed curtailment regime introduces more standstill periods and transitions between operational conditions of the WTG which will influence the entire structure. Since load cycles due to transitions between operational conditions of a WTG are known to be a potential cause of high fatigue loads in the WTG's structural components, their increased occurrence due to curtailment might also have a detrimental impact on the fatigue life consumption of the support structure. In the present contribution these consequences of curtailment of an offshore wind farm (OWF) are studied from the perspective of the impact on the lifetime of the WTG's support structure.

A curtailment assessment from this perspective ties in with the growing interest from the industry in the quantification of consumed and remaining useful lifetime in view of potential lifetime extension of the offshore wind support structures, which are typically designed for 20 – 30 year service lifetime. To support decision making towards lifetime extension, it is important to investigate any potential fatigue damaging operational condition. An earlier investigation towards the influence of OWF curtailment indicated a reduction of damage equivalent loads (DEL) at tower bottom and thus beneficial effect on lifetime consumption of a Vestas V-52 (850kW) support structure [1].

The evolution to larger, +7MW, WTG's resulted in new insights in the structure's dynamic behavior influencing the fatigue design. For these larger WTG's the introduction of curtailment regimes leads to a couple of potentially critical operational conditions in relation to fatigue life consumption of the support structures. Besides the additional periods of standstill during operational windspeed conditions, which is a known critical fatigue design load case in the design of support structures of large WTG's [2], curtailment introduces repeated transitional load cycles (event load cycles due to WTG stop and start cycles). The increased number of events introduced due to more frequent transitions between the operational regimes, and more standstill, might result in exceeding the provisions taken in design for the event loads, and standstill period. The present work focusses on the investigation of the impact the amount of events may have on the WTG foundation its structural lifetime. This impact of additional event load cycles has to the authors' knowledge not yet been investigated in this context.

The industry's current recommended practices in relation to lifetime assessments (DNVGL-ST-0262, 2016) require to base this assessment on a combination of practical assessments (i.e. offshore inspections) and analytical assessments (i.e. updated fatigue assessments for updated environmental conditions and using an updated design model for the load simulations). This updated model-driven simulations have been subject of research and industrial applications [3][4]. While the use of monitoring data is also recommended in current guidelines, the actual use-cases of data-driven fatigue assessments with load monitoring data are mainly found in a research context [5][15]. The present work aims to investigate the potential of using load monitoring data in data-driven fatigue assessments methodology to evaluate the impact of curtailment scenarios on structural lifetime.

To assess the impact on lifetime, the evaluation of fatigue damage (D) or damage equivalent loads (DEL) derived from structural health monitoring (SHM) data may be used as an alternative for model-based load simulations. The use of D is particularly in favor when changing corrosion models. For purpose of this work DEL is the most suitable parameter to assess the impact on lifetime. The DEL is a commonly known fatigue load parameter used in design of foundations, other structural components and subject of ongoing research for farm wide predictions as disclosed in [5][10]. The present work particularly investigates the role of curtailment regimes with different frequency of stop and start cycles on the consumed lifetime. The study is performed based on 1 year of SHM data collected from four WTG's on two OWF's.

The motivation of this work lies in (i) the growing interest of the industry towards the use of monitoring data for structural assessments of the assets in operation, (ii) the importance to understand the long-term impact curtailment scenarios may have in view of the interest in lifetime extension and (iii) the opportunity to provide data-driven support in asset management decisions towards sustainable curtailment strategies supporting the flexible use of wind energy assets.

## 2. Available data

For this work, data collected over a period of 1 year on four WTG's across two OWF's in the Belgian North Sea has been utilized. The available data consists out of 10-minute environmental and operational condition parameters available through the SCADA system and load monitoring data collected through an SHM system. In view of using data for fatigue predictions over time, it has been demonstrated in earlier research that data collected over a consecutive period of 1 year is recommended in view of including seasonal variations [6]. A recommendation which has been confirmed in various other research on this topic, e.g. [10][13][15].

All four foundations, type monopile with transition piece, are equipped with 6 strain gauges, with a sensor for temperature compensation, equally positioned every 60 degrees along the circumference. The sensors are placed close to the transition piece – tower interface at a distance of 500mm from the nearby primary steel weld to avoid monitoring stress concentrations due to this weld. From the 6 strain measurements the stresses and bending moments are calculated. In accordance with IEC61400-13, the loads measurements are processed in a fore-aft (FA) – side-side (SS) reference determined by the WTG's yaw angle. The load monitoring signals are processed in 10-minute intervals such the SHM and SCADA databases are complementary for further analysis. The derived SHM data is stored in a 10-minute subset database as explained in various earlier publications [7-10][15].

The derived load monitoring metric of interest for further fatigue analysis in the present work is the 10-minute damage equivalent load (DEL). This metric can be derived from the FA and SS stress timeseries. By cycle counting the 10-minute stress signals and evaluation of the cycle counts (stress ranges and corresponding number of cycles) over the Basquin's law for a chosen SN curve with single slope ($m = 5$) and number of equivalent cycles ($N_{eq} = 1e7$), the 10-minute DEL can be calculated. The 10-minute DEL is stored in the SHM database as damage equivalent moment (DEM) [7].

## 3. Methodology

Three domains are to be addressed in the description of the methodology. (i) The annotation of data to allow a binning approach per operational conditions which can be used to simulate curtailment scenarios is explained in 3.1. (ii) The defined operational scenarios to study the impact of various curtailment strategies is described in 3.2. (iii) The methodology to derive a lifetime metric by performing an assessment of the loads (DEM) is explained in 3.3.

### *3.1. Database annotations*

In view of performing a lifetime assessment, a technique to allow for extrapolations over time based on the available monitoring data is found in a binning approach. The 10-minute timeseries database with SCADA and SHM parameters is supplemented with annotation labels to allow binning the data (e.g. based on windspeed). The binned data allows to perform an assessment of the loads per bin and assign a probability of occurrence of each bin. There is various research ongoing towards the most suitable binning approaches in view of lifetime predictions based on limited data. [6][12]

For the purpose of this impact assessment the use of a binning approach based on operational conditions only, a so called 1-dimensional (1D) -binning, is found most suitable. The operational conditions used for binning are limited to: operational, standstill and events. This 1D-binning approach allows to assign probabilities to each of the bins in normal and curtailed operating regimes when defining the curtailment scenarios (see 3.2).

With the available data for both OWF's the decision was made to annotate the data for this initial impact assessment based on 10-minute mean SCADA metrics and SHM load monitoring data. The boundaries of the operational condition bins for the two OWF's are based on 10-minute mean metrics (e.g. RPM, power, pitch, windspeed and damage equivalent moment). Each timestamp of the considered data is evaluated against the boundary conditions of a bin, and assigned to the appropriate bin. To assure the binning was in accordance with the expected behaviour a visual inspection of randomly sampled data was performed. The quantity of data that passed through the classification (due to missing metrics used for classification) and did not get assigned to a bin is neglectable, approximately 0.6%. Inspecting this data confirmed it did not contain a disproportional amount of one of the three operational bins and it can safely be disregarded for further assessments.

More advanced annotation methods based on a detailed analysis of 1-second SCADA are under development by Daems et al. [14]. The applied annotations with the simplified binning approach have been found to be plausible in relation to the initial results from said advanced annotations. The initial integration of the advanced annotation insights in the present work is limited to making use of the probability of curtailment in the assessed curtailment scenarios.

For the purpose of the present work, the applied simplified annotations have been found sufficient to demonstrate the impact of the frequency of events on lifetime. When assessing the entire operational spectrum in future works the advanced curtailment annotation methods will be of added value to perform a refinement (with i.e. de-rated operational conditions during curtailment, further refinement of operational cases in normal or curtailed conditions or including the influence of longer standstill).

Another future refinement of the binning may be to bin the data in each bin according to windspeed, resulting in a 2D-binning. To not overload the work, the 2D-binning has not been assessed in detail.

### *3.2. Operational scenarios with curtailment regimes*

The priority objective of this work is to study the impact of the number of events initiated by curtailments on the support structure's lifetime. In view of this, four operational scenarios with variable curtailment regimes are defined. To allow a realistic assessment with focus on the impact of increased amount of events due to curtailment, the operational scenarios are to be comparable to the real world situation within each OWF, but differ in amount of events due to differences in curtailment regimes. The amount of events has been determined based the power set-point time. The power set-point time is the period which the BRP needs to respect when curtailing an OWF. In consultation with one of the involved OWF operators three set-point times have been defined for the analysis: 30 minutes, 10 minutes and 5 minutes.

The two OWF's have been operated differently. This difference has been reflected in the probabilities assigned to the investigated operational scenarios in each of the OWF's.

Similarly, the two WTG's in each OWF have not been operated identically. The operational scenario per OWF is an intermediate scenario applicable to both WTG's to meet the general operational condition on the OWF but not an asset specific scenario.

By assigning a probability of occurrence to each operational condition (see 3.1) in normal and curtailed regime, the following scenarios are defined for investigation:

- An approximated as-operated scenario: aligned with the initial insights in curtailment windows resulting from the advanced annotation methodology [14].
- Curtailment regime with 30-minute set-point time
- Curtailment regime with 15-minute set-point time
- Curtailment regime with 5-minute set-point time

With wind energy being a flexible energy asset, the real world case is expected to be a combination of various curtailment regimes. As matter of example, an assessment of the lifetime impact when combining the above scenarios has been performed. This combination scenario could be a basis for a long-term curtailment strategy, with the flexibility for short-term variations in curtailment regimes.

Given the approximation of the real world situation, the probabilities of operating conditions under the different scenarios may not be mentioned for reasons of confidentiality.

For a future integral study on the impact of curtailment on structural lifetime, more parameters amongst these scenarios could be varied. Examples of possible extensions to the variations in scenarios could be the period of curtailment, the time in standstill during curtailment, possible stable de-rated operational levels during curtailment and 2D-bin refinements by e.g. new probabilities of occurrences of windspeed.

Journal of Physics: Conference Series **2507** (2023) 012013 doi:10.1088/1742-6596/2507/1/012013

### *3.3. Load and lifetime assessment*

The load monitoring signals from 6 strain gauges are processed on a 10-minute basis into damage equivalent moments (DEM) in fore-aft and side-side direction according the heading of the turbine. The two turbines in each OWF are very similar in terms of loads. With the objective to investigate the impact of curtailment scenarios with variable number of events on loads and lifetime, the DEM in FA direction is the most suitable metric. This is illustrated in Figure 1 in which a curtailment window at OWF1 is visualized. The DEM's in FA (dots) at the initiation and termination of the curtailment window (see red circles) are clearly exceeding the FA DEM's in operational conditions while the SS DEM's (crosses) do not show similar behaviour. To illustrate the origin of the high FA DEM, the timeseries of the bending moments from which these DEMs are derived are shown in Figure 2. The large load cycles in FA direction (orange) both during a WTG stop and start event are the main contributors to the high DEMs in FA direction. The windspeeds shown in Figure 2 illustrate it concerns events within the operational windspeeds and not nearby cut-in or cut-out conditions. In the further description of the load assessments and results, we refer to the DEM in FA direction as DEM.

In future extensions of the analysis, in which also the detrimental effect of standstill of larger WTG's on the support structure's fatigue life consumption will be investigated or when a comparison to the as-designed DEM is required, the DEM in SS direction will need to be considered as well for a more refined directional assessment similar to earlier data-driven lifetime case studies [12].

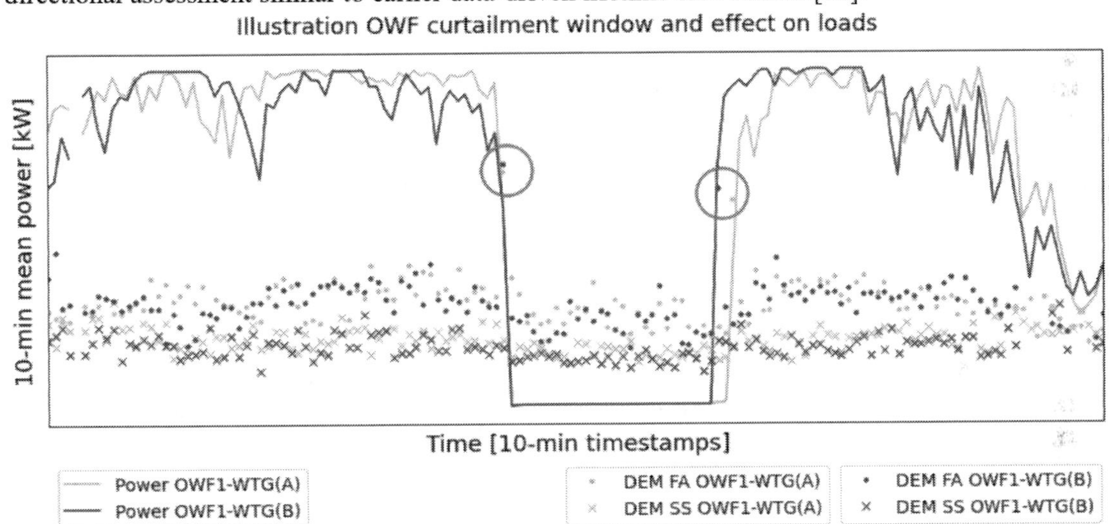


*Figure 1: Illustration of OWF1 curtailment windows and effect on DEM FA and DEM SS*

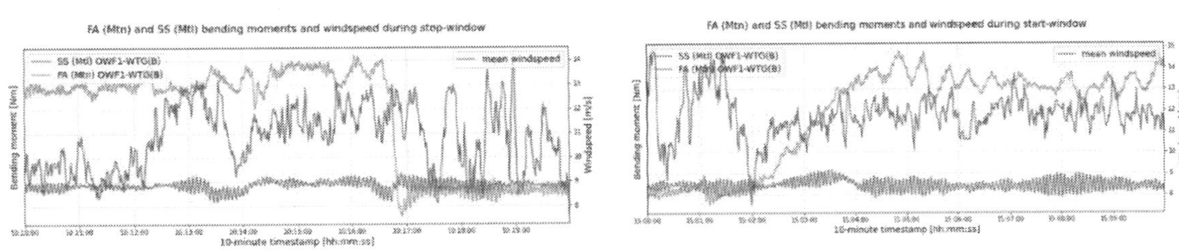

*Figure 2: FA and SS bending moment time signal at WTG stop (left) and start (right)*

The chosen binning approach allows to assess the DEM's per operational condition as described in Section 3.1. A representative value of the DEM per bin in normal and curtailed conditions needs to be chosen. The statistical distribution of the 10-minute DEM's per bin is verified to define a representative

DEM for each bin. A detailed statistical analysis of the distributions within each bin is expected to be an extension of the present study when 2D-binning is being applied, an aspect which was not assessed in detail (ref. section 3.1). A commonly applied representative value per bin in a research context is the mean value [15]. For the purpose of the present work, an engineering judgement based on the quantile values per bin was performed. A sensitivity study to assess the impact of selecting different percentiles (varying between P25 and P90) as representative DEM per bin showed similar – yet amplified - trends as the outcome with a uniform P50-approach. To not overload this impact assessment, the uniform use of P50 as representative DEM per bin was chosen for this work.

Combination of the representative DEM's with the probability of occurrences of the bins per scenario using (1), results in a total DEM for that respective scenario. The factor $m$ in (1) represents the Wöhler coefficient for which the DEM has been derived (in this assessment m=5).

$$DEM_{tot,scen} = \sqrt[m]{\sum_{bin,0}^{Number\ of\ bins} probability\ of\ occurance_{\ bin,i} \cdot DEM_{rep,bin,i}^{m}} \quad (1)$$

From the total DEM per scenario the impact on lifetime of the operational conditions of that respective scenario can be determined by comparison to a reference DEM. The impact on lifetime is based on the ratio of both DEM's (2). In lifetime assessments based on DEM, the reference DEM is typically the as-designed DEM. Given our focus on events and FA DEM only, the comparison with design is not the most relevant for the purpose of this work. Instead of using the as-designed DEM as reference, the fictive operational scenario with a curtailment regime and 30-minute set-point time is used as reference. This scenario is chosen as reference since it may be the consensus between interests of BRP's, grid operators and wind farm operators when developing a curtailment strategy and allows to evaluate the approximated as-operated scenario of the OWF's.

$$Lifetime\ Factor\ (LF) = \left(\frac{DEM_{reference}}{DEM_{total,scenario}}\right)^{m} = \left(\frac{DEM_{total,scenario\ 30-\min set\ point\ time}}{DEM_{total,scenario}}\right)^{m} \quad (2)$$

In case the reference DEM is higher than the total DEM in a scenario, the fatigue consumption according the operational conditions in the scenario is less than expected in the reference case. In the above a Lifetime Factor (LF) greater than 1 indicates a potential extension to the reference lifetime. The LF can be used to quantify the lifetime prediction based on the lifetime related to the reference DEM according (3).

$$LF \cdot Reference\ lifetime = data\ driven\ lifetime\ prediction \quad (3)$$

For publication of the results indicating the positive or negative impact on lifetime under each curtailment regime, the LF is converted to a Lifetime Impact Factor (LIF) according (4).

$$LIF = LF - 1 \quad (4)$$

A LIF of zero corresponds with no impact on lifetime compared to the reference scenario. A negative LIF indicates the evaluated scenario has a lower lifetime compared to the reference scenario. A positive LIF greater than zero indicates a lifetime reserve compared to the reference scenario.

## 4. Results and discussion

While the exact operating conditions may not be mentioned for reasons of confidentiality, we can share that the probabilities of events in curtailment regimes included in the calculations are as follows:

- Curtailment with 30-minute set-point time: 0.33 %
- Curtailment with 15-minute set-point time: 0.67 %
- Curtailment with 5-minute set-point time: 2%

As explained in 3.3, the results in this publication are based on the load assessment with the 50$^{th}$ percentile (P50) DEM in each of the bins in normal and curtailed conditions as representative DEM used in (1).

Below the resulting Lifetime Impact Factors for various scenarios relative to the reference scenario are visualized. Figure 3 is the bar chart with LIF per turbine for the various scenarios. The resulting lifetime impact of the investigated scenarios allows to discuss a couple of observations:

1. The difference between current operational conditions (red) at OWF1 and OWF2. The LIF at OWF1 is greater than the LIF at OWF2. This indicates that the current operational conditions at OWF1 are more favourable compared to the reference curtailment regime opposed to the operational conditions of OWF2. This observation matches with the insight that OWF2 has been more frequently subjected to curtailment regimes during the assessed period. OWF2 has an operational regime closer to the reference scenario, thus subjected to more event load cycles, compared to OWF1.
2. The more frequently curtailment of OWF2 can also be observed from the lower effect of the more flexible evaluated curtailment regimes with 15- and 5-minute set-point times (yellow and blue) opposed to the impact on the lifetime in OWF1.
3. The difference between WTG(A) and WTG(B) of OWF1 in the approximated as-operated scenario (red) is minor, which is corresponding with the very similar operational conditions of both turbines. The minor difference can be explained by the fact that WTG(B) has been subjected to a slightly larger portion of events.
4. Similar, but more significantly the difference between WTG(A) and WTG(B) of OWF2 in the approximated as-operated scenario (red) can be explained. WTG(A) in OWF2 has been subjected to approximately 18% more events relative to the number of events at WTG(B). This is visualised in Figure 4 in which the LIF is shown in function of the number of events per evaluated scenario.
5. The impact of curtailment regimes with shorter set point times, allowing a more frequent possibility to stop and start the WTG, has a detrimental impact on the lifetime. The impact for a 15-minute set-point time (yellow) varies from a 20% to 30% reduction of lifetime, while the impact of a 5-minute set-point time (blue) ranges between 50% and 75% reduction of lifetime.
6. The evaluation of the combination scenario (grey) indicates that by combining the different regimes the detrimental effect of flexible curtailment regimes on lifetime consumption can be mitigated while still allowing flexible curtailment for a certain period of time.

At first sight the results indicate the detrimental effect of flexible curtailment regimes on the support structures' fatigue lifetime. Prior to drawing conclusions, it is however important to mention that it is not the intention of this work to advocate against the flexible curtailment of OWF assets, since this flexibility is one of the great advantages of wind energy.

The first objective of this work is to highlight the importance to take the long-term detrimental effect from transitional load cycles, due to frequent curtailment instructions, on the consumed fatigue life of a WTG support structure into consideration. Based on the rather theoretical curtailment regimes we believe this awareness is created.

The second objective is to provide data-driven support in asset management decisions towards curtailment strategies supporting the flexible use of wind energy assets. In view of this, we made an interpretation of the research findings towards an industry context. The real world operational scenario will be likely a combination of various curtailment regimes. The resulting lifetime impact factor plots below include this combination scenario (grey). The combination scenario is an arbitrary combination of the evaluated scenarios. In the example below we assessed the lifetime impact of a combination scenario based on a curtailment strategy in which the BRP's and grid operators can influence the operation of the turbines within following boundary conditions:

- For at least 40% of the time as per the current operational conditions
- Up to 20% of the time as per a curtailment regime with min. 30-minute set-point time
- Up to 25% of the time as per a curtailment regime with min. 15-minute set-point time
- Up to 15% of the time as per a curtailment regime with min. 5-minute set-point time

The resulting LIF > 0 in the combination scenario indicates the feasibility to operate an OWF with a very flexible curtailment regime, without critical long-term detrimental effect on lifetime. With the above combination of scenarios the LIF at OWF2-WTG(A) indicates a minor detrimental impact on lifetime. As mentioned before, this matches with the insights in the operational condition of this asset.

In the present case study the comparison is made against a reference scenario, in integral lifetime assessments this reference would be the design which would allow to identify a critical condition in relation to the as-designed structural capacity.

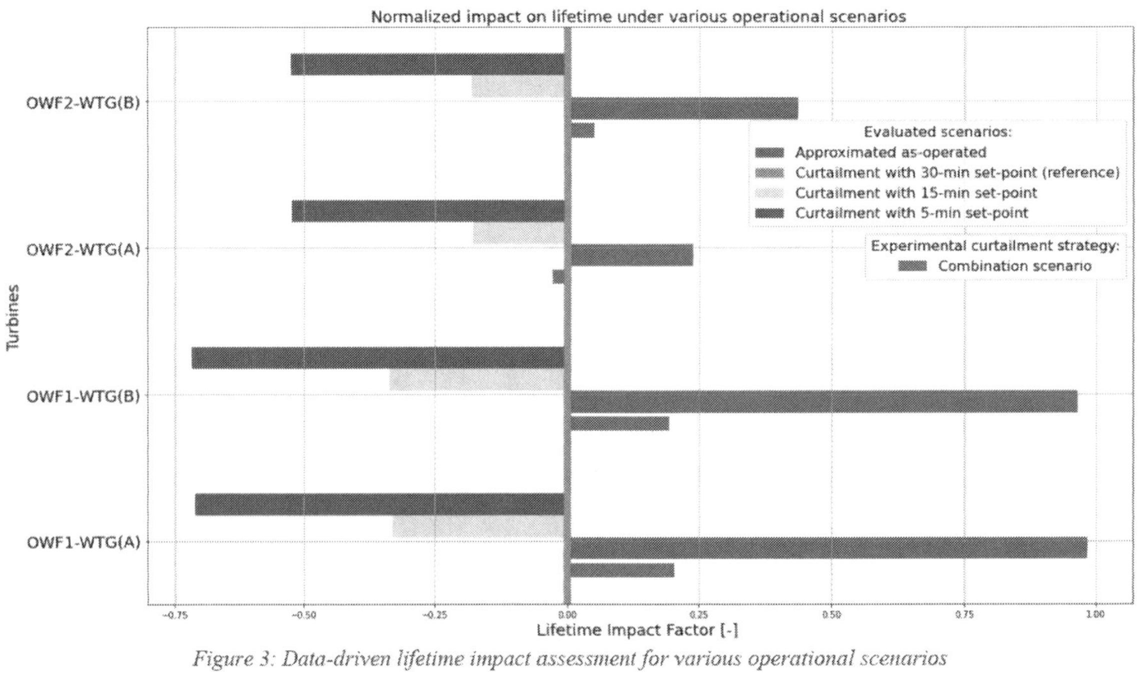


*Figure 3: Data-driven lifetime impact assessment for various operational scenarios*

Figure 4 shows the LIF in function of the amount of events in each scenario.

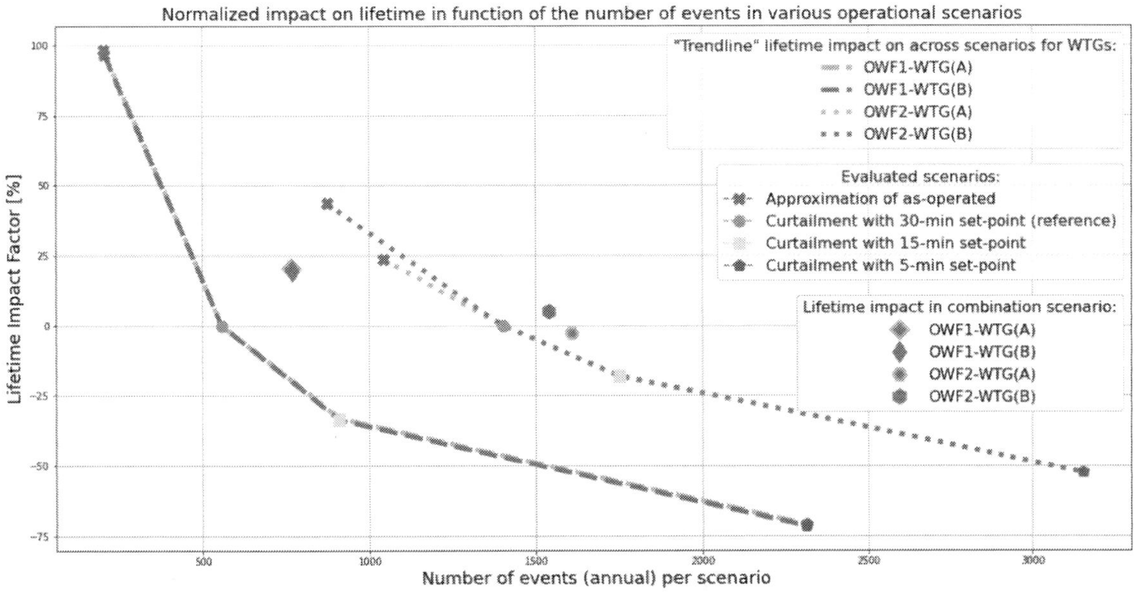


*Figure 4: Data-driven lifetime impact assessment in function of number of events in the investigated operational scenarios*

## 5. Conclusion

One of the advantages of having wind energy assets in the grid is their flexibility. In today's energy management, the use of curtailment is an essential tool to balance production and demand on short-term. The long-term impact on the support structure's lifetime from the consequences curtailment has on structural load cases has been discussed and studied in this work.

While there is the general awareness on the criticality of standstill of larger WTG's, the present work focussed on the impact on the foundation's fatigue life when additional event load cycles are introduced by curtailment regimes. We demonstrated that the impact of additional event cycles under various curtailment regimes on the fatigue life of the WTG's support structure cannot be neglected and can be quantified with data-driven lifetime assessment methods using real-world load measurements. To safeguard the flexible use of wind energy assets on short-term and continuous reliable energy asset on the long-term with the ambition of lifetime extension a long-term curtailment strategy may thus be advised.

The structural integrity may not be the priority concern when discussing short-term curtailment regimes. However in view of the general interest to explore lifetime extension of OWF's, we cannot lose sight on the detrimental long-term effects of curtailment to the structural lifetime. To address this, there might be the need for a discussion between the BRP, the grid and turbine operators for a long-term, but still flexible, curtailment strategy. A strategy which may potentially be defined similarly to the arbitrary combination scenario presented in this work. With designs becoming less conservative, such alignment might be needed at an early stage of the operational phase of the OWF or during the design phase if feasible.

Within an OWF this type of assessments may also highlight critical assets, like the OWF2-WTG(A) in the above example.

In the broader picture, these curtailment strategies may be synchronized between different OWF's to ensure a balanced curtailment, taking into account the structural reserves as one of the parameters.

## 6. Outlook

The limitations mentioned in this work lead to the future works.

Following this initial impact analysis, the ambition is to perform an integral assessment addressing both detrimental consequences curtailment regimes have on the support structure's fatigue lifetime: increased standstill time and additional transitional load cycles.

Besides broadening the view to the entire load spectrum, refinements to the currently applied methodology are to be investigated. Examples of such refinements are the further implementation of advanced annotations [14] to serve in the binning approach, more refined curtailment regime definitions with e.g. a de-rated power production regime instead of going to standstill, extending to a 2D-binning approach by including the windspeed as binning parameter.

In addition to the current deterministic approach, a probabilistic assessment by means of statistical methodologies to perform analysis with resampled datasets, e.g. by means of bootstrapping may be of interest to quantify the uncertainty [13].

The present analysis has been performed on a WTG support structure which is instrumented with a load monitoring setup. Future work will be to assess the influence of curtailment on loads and lifetime farm wide by implementation of the research towards farm wide DEL predictions [10].

## References


[1] Natarajan A and Friis Pedersen T 2018 Remaining Life Assessment of Offshore Wind Turbines subject to Curtailment, *In Proceedings of the Twenty-eighth (2018) International Ocean and Polar Engineering Conference* pp 527-532.

[2] Gengenbach J, Mikkelsen K, Rüdinger F, Brommundt M, Gretlund J 2020 Design challenges of XL monopiles, WindEurope 2020 conference.

[3] Ziegler L and Muskulus M 2016 Fatigue reassessment for lifetime extension of offshore wind monopile substructures, *J. Phys.-Conf. Ser.*, 753, 092010, https://doi.org/10.1088/1742- 6596/753/9/092010.

[4] Augustyn D, Ulriksen MD and Sørensen JD 2021 Reliability Updating of Offshore Wind Substructures by Use of Digital Twin Information, *Energies 2021*; 14(18):5859. https://doi.org/10.3390/en14185859.

[5] De Nolasco Santos F, Robbelein K, D'Antuono P, Noppe N, Weijtjens W and Devriendt C 2022 Towards a fleetwide data-driven lifetime assessment methodology of offshore wind support structures based on SCADA and SHM data, *EWSHM Palermo 2022* https://doi.org/10.1007/978-3-031-07254-3_13.

[6] Hübler C, Weijtjens W, Rolfes R, and Devriendt C 2018 Reliability analysis of fatigue damage extrapolations of wind turbines using offshore strain measurements, *J. Phys.-Conf.* Ser., 1037, 032035, https://doi.org/10.1088/1742-6596/1037/3/03203.

[7] Weijtjens W, Iliopoulos A, Helsen J and Devriendt C 2015 Monitoring the consumed fatigue life of wind turbines on monopile foundations *EWEA Offshore 2015 Copenhagen*, doi: 10.13140/RG.2.1.1614.6162.

[8] Weijtjens W, Verbelen T, De Sitter G and Devriendt C 2015 Foundation structural health monitoring of an offshore wind turbine – a full scale case study, *SAGE Structural Health Monitoring* May 2015, doi: 10.1177/1475921715586624.

[9] Weijtjens W, Noppe N, Verbelen T, Devriendt C and Iliopoulos A 2016 Fatigue life assessment of three offshore wind turbines. *In Life-Cycle of Engineering Systems: Emphasis on Sustainable Civil Infrastructure* CRC Press pp 742-747.

[10] De Nolasco Santos F, D'Antuono P, Robbelein K, Noppe N, Weijtjens W and Devriendt C 2023 Long-term fatigue estimation on offshore wind turbines interface loads through loss function physics-guided learning of neural networks. *Renewable Energy*, 205, 461-474 https://doi.org/10.1016/j.renene.2023.01.093.

[11] Robbelein K, D'Antuono P, Noppe N, Weijtjens W and Devriendt C 2021 Early perspectives on the development of a certifiable data-driven lifetime assessment methodology *Electric City 2021*, poster SP004.

[12] Robbelein K, D'Antuono P, Noppe N, Weijtjens W and Devriendt C 2023 A real-world data-driven lifetime assessment of a WTG support structure *WindEurope's annual on-and offshore wind energy event*, poster PO254.

[13] Hübler C and Rolfes R 2022 Probabilistic temporal extrapolation of fatigue damage of offshore wind turbine substructures based on strain measurements. *Wind Energy Science* 7(5) pp 1919-1940 https://doi.org/10.5194/wes-7-1919-2022.

[14] Daems PJ, Peeters C, Matthys J, Verstraeten T, Helsen J 2023, Fleet-wide analytics on field data targetting condition and lifetime aspects of wind turbine drivetrains Forschung im Ingenieurwesen, Springer Berlin Heidelberg

[15] Pacheco J, Pimenta F, Pereira S, Cunha Á and Magalhães F 2022 Fatigue Assessment of Wind Turbine Towers: Review of Processing Strategies with Illustrative Case Study. *Energies. 2022*; 15(13):4782. https://doi.org/10.3390/en15134782.

# Assessment of turbulence intensity estimates from floating lidar systems

**Felix Kelberlau**[1], **Vegar Neshaug**[1], **Anish Venu**[2]
[1]Fugro Norway AS, Havnegata 9, 7462 Trondheim, Norway
[2]DNV

E-mail: f.kelberlau@fugro.com

**Abstract.** In the pre-construction phase of offshore wind energy projects floating lidar systems (FLS) are used for wind site assessment. Their measurements of mean wind speed and direction have proven to be accurate according to existing standards. But for the assessment of turbulence intensity (TI), a widely-accepted procedure and acceptance criteria are missing. This study investigates different evaluation methods, namely linear regression analysis and the key performance indicators (KPIs) presented by the Consortium for Advancing Remote Sensing (CFARS). The assessment is based on data from an offshore trial of the Fugro SEAWATCH Wind Lidar Buoy (SWLB) against the meteorological mast and a collocated fixed profiling wind lidar at Blyth, UK. The results show that the accuracy of TI estimates from FLS can be evaluated well, when the KPIs mean bias error (MBE) and representative TI error suggested by CFARS are used. We propose best-practice acceptance thresholds of ±1% for MBE and ±1.5% for the representative TI error. The motion-compensation approach of the SWLB works well and after compensation, its TI data are similar to the data from the fixed reference lidar. The impact of lidar-specific effects is minor in the analyzed data set and near-to-zero biases are found for all measurement elevations and wind speed bins in comparison to mast data.

## 1. Introduction

Floating lidar systems (FLS) are frequently used for measuring wind conditions in the pre-construction phase of offshore wind energy projects. They usually offer the most cost-effective method for acquiring high quality wind data. Stage-3 rated FLSs like the Fugro SEAWATCH Wind LiDAR Buoy (SWLB) have demonstrated a great track record of measuring primary wind data like mean wind speeds and directions accurately [1].

However, for estimates of second-order statistics like turbulence intensity (TI), it is known that the influence of lidar motion leads to an overestimation of TI values from FLS compared to what fixed lidar systems would measure [2, 3, 4]. Fugro has developed a motion-compensation algorithm that effectively takes the motion out of floating lidar and hence solves the issue of motion-induced TI [3]. In addition, it is known that profiling wind lidars measure TI differently from in-situ anemometry and measurement deviations can occur [5].

What remains unsolved is the question of how to validate TI estimates from FLS. Annex L of IEC standard 61400-12-1 prescribes a comprehensive methodology for FLS classification and validation of primary wind data, but it does not account for TI data [6]. The upcoming IEC standard 61400-50-4 on the use of floating lidars for wind measurements will have an informative annex on TI that does not prescribe a validation procedure either.

**Figure 1.** SEAWATCH Wind Lidar Buoy (SWLB) deployed offshore

The Carbon Trust Offshore Wind Accelerator Roadmap (Roadmap) is a widely accepted guidance document on FLS performance. It recommends to conduct linear regression analyses for comparisons of TI from FLS and trusted reference sources, but it does not provide acceptance criteria [7]. The Consortium for Advancing Remote Sensing (CFARS) issued a white paper that introduces a benchmarking framework for the assessment of TI estimates from remote sensing devices against reference values from in-situ anemometry [8]. The methodology appears well-suited also for judging the performance of a motion-compensation approach for FLS.

This study applies linear regression as recommended in the Roadmap and the CFARS evaluation scheme to data from a pre-deployment validation trial of a SWLB and reference data from the meteorological mast at Blyth. The next Section 2 describes the SWLB, the sea trial, and the methods used for the assessment of data. Section 3 thereafter presents the results of the scatter analysis and the application of the CFARS benchmark and is followed by the conclusions of the study in Section 4.

## 2. Methods

### *2.1. SEAWATCH Wind Lidar Buoy*

The Stage-3 rated SEAWATCH Wind Lidar Buoy by Fugro is a FLS based on the original SEAWATCH Wavescan Buoy design (see Fig. 1). The profiling wind lidar used is the marinized version of the ZX 300 VAD-scanning continuous-wave profiling wind lidar type by ZX Lidars. For the purpose of estimating motion-compensated TI values, the buoy is equipped with a motion reference unit. Furthermore, accurate heading data is acquired by a Dual GPS system. An embedded system onboard the SWLB records the lidar line-of-sight data and calculates the required motion data in all six degrees-of-freedom. The motion-compensation algorithm is a refined version of the one previously described [3].

### *2.2. Blyth Test Site*

The National Offshore Anemometry Hub (NOAH) at Blyth, UK, serves as reference site for the results presented here. The test site offers pairs of cup anemometers along a meteorological mast at elevations of 35m, 52m, 69m, 86m, and 103m above mean sea level. In addition, a fixed ZX300 reference lidar is collocated to the mast and measures vertical profiles of wind speeds up to 191m above mean sea level. Comparisons of FLS and reference lidar allow for benchmarking the performance of the motion compensation of the FLS. And comparisons of lidar data against cup measurements can reveal lidar-specific effects. The measurement campaign took place from Jul 23rd until Sep 9th, 2022. Flow disturbances caused by the mast are accounted for by using data from the anemometer in upwind direction only when the wind blows in boom direction (± 30 degrees). Data from the wind sector between 30 and 150 degrees are filtered because wind turbine wakes are expected. Furthermore, wind speeds below $2\text{ms}^{-1}$ are excluded from the assessment.

### 2.3. Offshore Wind Accelerator Roadmap

The Roadmap is a document that prescribes a path for FLS from the first unit built to commercial maturity. For reaching the different maturity stages, mean wind speed and direction measurements must be assessed in comparison to measurements from trusted reference sources and pass fixed acceptance criteria. TI from FLS is considered a parameter of secondary importance and the Roadmap recommends to compare TI data with values from trusted reference sources. The slope and correlation coefficient of linear regression forced through the origin are defined as the key performance indicators (KPIs) for the assessment of TI data but no acceptance criteria are given.

### 2.4. CFARS Benchmarking

The CFARS Site Suitability Initiative document is a guidance for the assessment of TI estimates from remote sensing devices. It suggests using the Mean Bias Error (MBE) for each $1\text{ms}^{-1}$-wide wind speed bin $i$

$$MBE_i = \frac{1}{N_i}\sum_{n=1}^{N_i} TI_{comp,n,i} - TI_{ref,n,i} \tag{1}$$

where $TI_{comp}$ is the comparison quantity (e.g., $TI_{Lidar}$), $TI_{ref}$ is the reference quantity (e.g., $TI_{Mast}$), $N_i$ is the number of values in wind speed bin $i$, and $n$ is the individual data point. In addition, CFARS suggests to use the representative TI ($\text{TI}_{\text{Rep}}$) error in comparisons. Representative TI is defined as the $90^{\text{th}}$ percentile of a TI distribution. Its inclusion ensures that not only the mean of all TI values but also TI variance within each wind speed bin is considered. It is calculated from $TI_{mean,i}$, the mean of all TI values in a bin and $TI_{std,i}$, its standard deviation by

$$TI_{Rep,i} = TI_{mean,i} + 1.28 TI_{std,i}. \tag{2}$$

Furthermore, the Root Mean Square Error (RMSE) shall be used to measure the TI precision. It accounts

$$RMSE_i = \sqrt{\frac{1}{N_i}\sum_{n=1}^{N_i}(TI_{comp,n,i} - TI_{ref,n,i})^2}. \tag{3}$$

## 3. Results

### 3.1. Linear regression analysis

Figure 2 shall demonstrate challenges in using ordinary linear regression for the analysis of highly scattered data. It shows TI data from the reference mast on the x-axis plotted against the same data on the y-axis. The only difference is that a temporal offset of 10 minutes is introduced, i.e., each data point consists of one TI value and its subsequent value in the time series. The resulting point cloud shows large scatter but no systematic bias. In addition to the horizontal and vertical grid lines in the background, the plot also shows diagonal grid lines that connect TI values on the y-axis with corresponding TI values on the x-axis. The x and y-values of all data pairs between two of these diagonal grid lines are averaged and plotted as red circle markers. The perpendicular distance of these diagonally-binned averages from the 1:1 line is

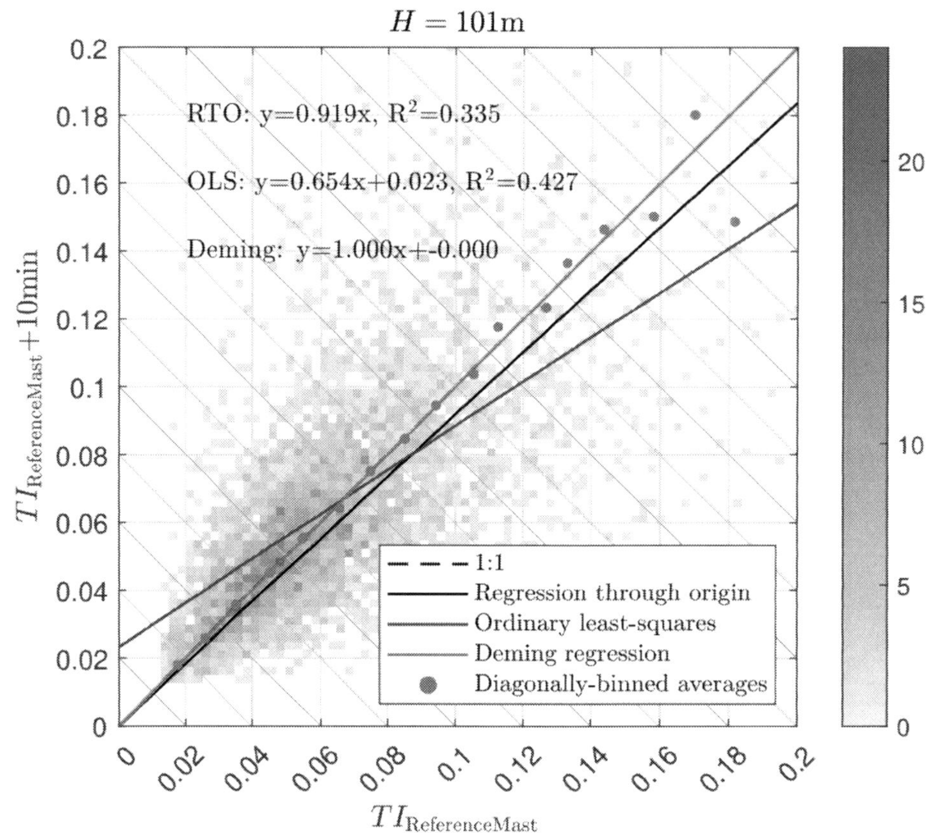


**Figure 2.** Scatter plot of data from reference mast on both axes with 10 minutes offset. Regression lines from linear regression through origin (black), unforced ordinary least-squares regression (blue), and Deming regression (red).

representative for the systematic bias in the data. Since the plotted data contains no bias, the diagonally-binned averages lie close to the 1:1 line for all sufficiently populated bins.

The black line in the figure is the regression line resulting from linear regression forced through the origin (RTO). This single-variant regression is often used for mean wind speed validations according to the Roadmap and is therein also recommended for TI assessments. The given example of scattered but unbiased data, shows an $R^2$ value below one and also the slope of the regression line is well below unity. It is important to not interpret the slope below one as a signal for bias in the data but rather as a symptom of random error or uncertainty. The result of unforced ordinary least-squares (OLS) regression shown as blue line makes this effect clearer because its slope is even lower and it has a positive offset where it meets the y-axis.

If linear regression shall be used for the analysis of systematic trends in TI scatter plots, Deming regression can be applied. The resulting regression line is shown in red and does not show any bias with a slope of one and zero offset. Deming regression assumes identical non-zero uncertainties for values on both axes and minimizes the quadratic sum of perpendicular distances of the data points from the regression line [9].

Figure 3 shows actual data from the validation trial at Blyth. Subplots (*a*) and (*b*) display motion-compensated TI data from the floating lidar system against mast reference data from 67m and 101m respectively. Subplots (*c*) and (*d*) show the floating lidar system data against the

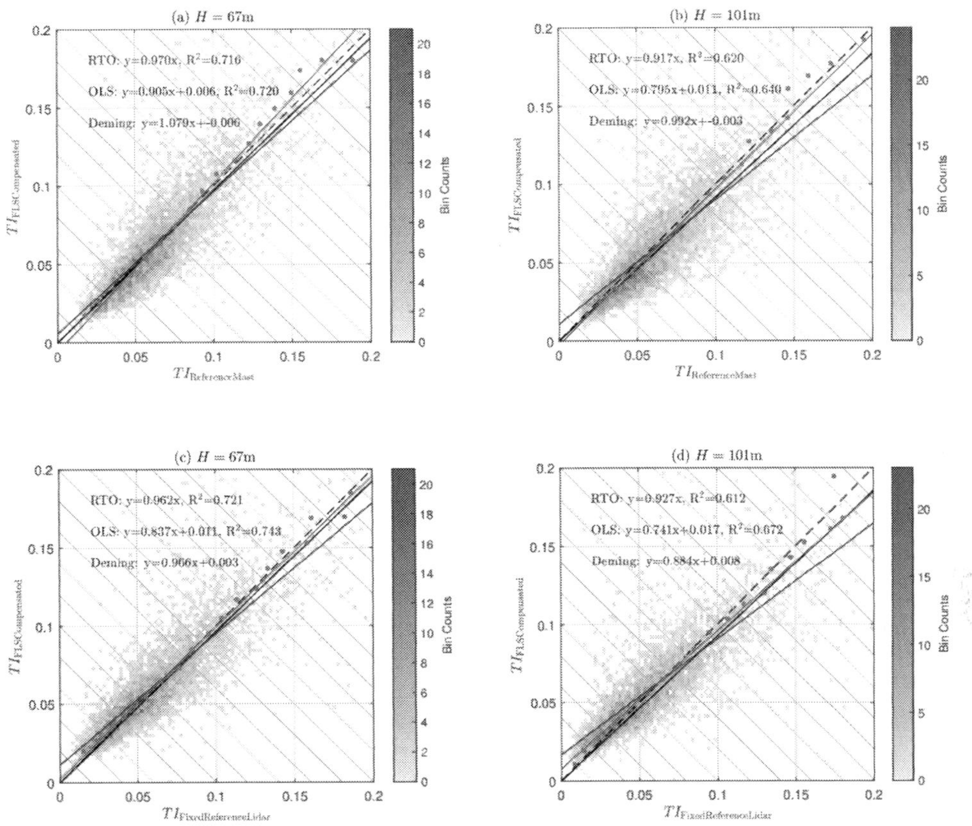


**Figure 3.** Scatter plot of data from floating lidar vs. reference mast (top) and fixed reference lidar (bottom) for elevations 67m (left) and 101m (right). Regression lines from linear regression through origin (black), unforced ordinary least-squares regression (blue), and Deming regression (red). Legend as in Fig. 2

fixed reference lidar for the same measurement elevations. In all four examples RTO and OLS regression shows slopes below unity and the offsets of OLS are positive like in the example of pure scatter shown in Fig. 2. Deming regression lines show slopes between 0.884 and 1.079 and offsets between -0.006 and +0.008. The diagonally-binned averages allow a more nuanced interpretation of the measurement accuracy relative to the reference TI. At 67m the FLS overestimates high TI values above 9% slightly when compared to mast data (*a*). But when compared to the fixed lidar this effect cannot be confirmed (*c*). So, this could be a lidar-specific effect. The same accounts for a small underestimation of low TI values at the same height level.

At 101m the FLS slightly underestimates medium TI values when compared to mast data (*b*), while it overestimates them in comparison to the fixed reference lidar (*d*). Systematic measurement differences between the floating lidar system and the fixed reference lidar can be caused by insufficient motion compensation. Another possible cause are the different elevations of both lidar systems above the sea. At Blyth, the fixed lidar is mounted 18m above mean sea level. When both systems scan at the same elevation above the sea, the measurement volumes and the measurement cone diameter are smaller for the fixed reference lidar. This can

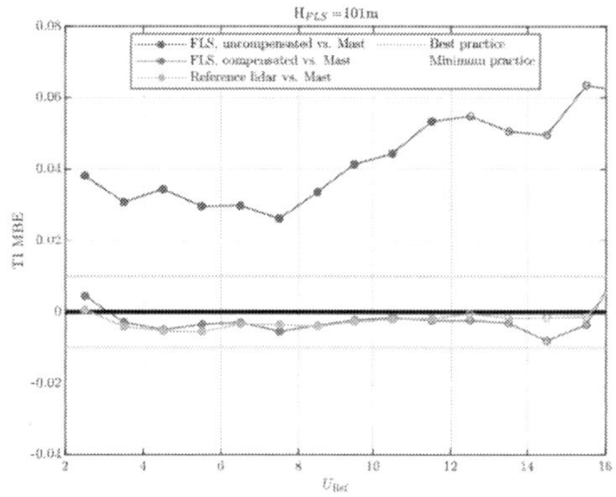


**Figure 4.** Mean bias error for floating lidar without (blue) and with (red) motion compensation as well as fixed reference lidar (orange) against reference mast at 101m elevation.

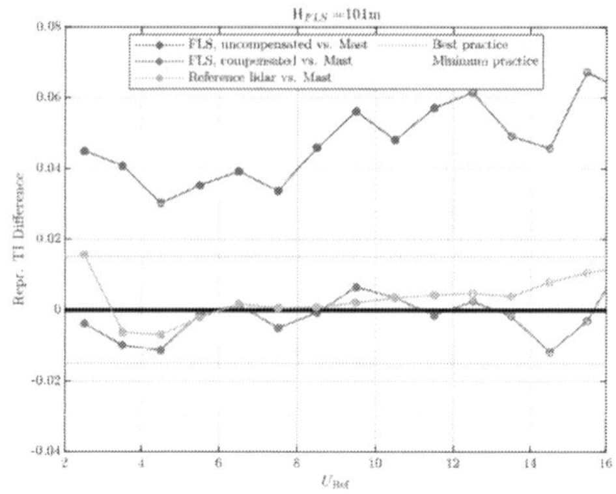


**Figure 5.** Representative TI error for floating lidar without (blue) and with (red) motion compensation as well as for fixed reference lidar (orange) against reference mast at 101m elevation.

introduce small measurement deviations that might influence the results presented here. Overall, systematic deviations of the SWLB data and data from the reference sources are small.

### *3.2. CFARS Benchmarking*

An alternative to the interpretation of scatter plots, which show the measurement deviation in dependence of the reference TI, is offered in the CFARS benchmarking document. Figure 4 shows the velocity-binned mean bias errors of the uncompensated and compensated floating lidar system in blue and red respectively as well as the fixed reference lidar in orange. In all three cases mast data from 101m is the reference. The uncompensated TI data from the FLS are way too high. Especially at higher wind speeds, where they are more than 4% higher than the mast data. Uncompensated TI data from FLS should not be considered valid.

Motion-compensated TI data and the data from the fixed reference lidar show very similar MBE results for all wind speeds. The similarity of both curves shows that the motion compensation algorithm works very well in all wind speed conditions. Significant deviations are only visible for very high wind speeds above $14\text{ms}^{-1}$. These high wind speed bins are sparsely populated, which is indicated by unfilled markers in the plot.

Only at very low wind speeds the lidar-measured TI is slightly higher than the corresponding values from the mast. At all other wind speeds, both lidar systems underestimate the mast TI slightly. It appears from this visualization that lidar-specific effects are small but larger than the effects of motion after compensation. All MBE values are within an error interval of $\pm 1\%$ marked as green horizontal lines in the plot.

The second suggested KPI is the representative TI error. It is shown in Fig. 5 for the same data as before. The curves for floating and fixed lidar show more variation than for MBE but the trends are the same for both. The representative TI error is close to zero and most values are within an error interval of $\pm 1.5\%$ marked as green horizontal lines. The only value outside of these bounds is the lowest wind speed bin for the fixed reference lidar. While the MBE value for this bin is close to zero, its standard deviation is too large.

The last KPI considered in this study is the RMSE shown in Fig. 6. The plot shows that the RMSE of the motion-compensated FLS is higher than the RMSE of the fixed lidar system. This is not surprising because of the larger spatial separation between the floating lidar system and the mast than between the fixed lidar and the mast. The fixed lidar might sample turbulent structures that are correlated with the turbulence measured by the mast, while the wind field sampled by the floating lidar is likely independent from what the mast samples. At least while the floating lidar and mast are not in line with the mean wind direction. Furthermore, RMSE values are higher for low wind speeds than for high wind speeds. Therefore, it appears not useful to include RMSE as a performance indicator for the assessment of TI estimates from floating lidar systems. However, it can be helpful for the comparison and evaluation of different motion compensation methodologies.

Figure 7 shows the results for $MBE$ and $TI_{Rep}$ error of the FLS against the reference mast for all five comparable measurement elevations. It can be seen that TI measurements from the SEAWATCH Wind Lidar Buoy after motion compensation are comparable to mast values at all heights and all wind speeds. The only elevated values are found for very low wind speeds that are not relevant for load and energy yield assessment and at very high wind speeds that were not frequent enough for statistically relevant conclusions. In many cases mast data are not available for floating lidar validation trials. Instead, fixed reference lidars are used to validate or verify the performance of floating lidar systems. Furthermore, meteorological masts offshore are often not high enough to enable comparisons of measurements taken at hub height of modern wind turbines. In these cases, the fixed lidar can be used as reference data source for TI assessments. Such comparisons allow for an assessment of the performance of the motion compensation approach but they do not discover lidar-specific effects that would be found in both, floating and fixed lidar data. Figure 8 shows the performance in terms of $MBE$ and $TI_{Rep}$ error of the FLS against the fixed lidar for all ten comparable measurement elevations up to 191m. For $MBE$, like in the comparisons against mast data, larger deviations are only found for the lowest and the highest wind speed bins. For $TI_{Rep}$ error, a couple of outliers are found at 173m that should be investigated. The value of -2.2% at wind speeds of 8-9ms$^{-1}$ is caused by the contribution of standard deviation of TI because its MBE is zero. The negative sign of the representative TI error means in this case that the standard deviation of the fixed lidar is higher than the standard deviation of the floating lidar. Therefore, we assume that measurement error is caused rather by the reference lidar than by the floating lidar. Finding the definite cause of this outlier requires a more detailed analysis of the underlying data. In any case, it is unlikely that the motion-compensation works worse at one particular elevation. This is supported by the averaged values in the last column of the table that show similar averaged KPI values for all elevations.

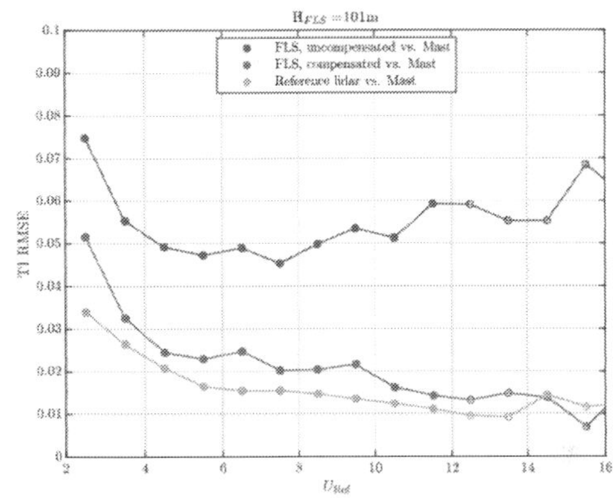


**Figure 6.** Root mean square error for floating lidar without (blue) and with (red) motion compensation as well as for fixed reference lidar (orange) against reference mast at 101m.

## 4. Conclusions

Scatter analysis can help to identify systematic trends in TI data from FLS. But we discourage from using slope and offset information from ordinary linear regression as performance indicators for measurement accuracy because both are influenced by random errors which are not entirely attributable to the FLS. Deming regression can be an alternative but should only be used if linear trends are present in the data. Non-linear correlations cannot be captured.

Adopting the CFARS TI benchmark scheme for the performance assessment of a motion-compensation approach for floating lidar systems works well and is the better option. We can demonstrate that motion-compensated TI estimates of the Fugro SEAWATCH Wind LiDAR Buoy show close-to-zero bias when compared to reference values from a meteorological mast. This accounts for both TI and representative TI values and all measurement elevations. Wind speed bins included in the assessment should be limited to the ones that are statistically and practically relevant. The random error (RMSE) is reduced to an acceptable level. Based on the measurement data presented here, we suggest the constant MBE and representative TI error thresholds listed in Table 1 for the performance assessment of FLS. For RMSE, we do not recommend to use constant thresholds for all velocity bins because comparability of RMSE values from different measurement setups is not given. Further studies of a similar kind are required to gain experience with the applied methods and to confirm that the suggested best and minimum practice criteria are suitable.

**Table 1.** Suggested acceptance thresholds for mean bias and representative TI benchmark

| KPI | Best practice | Minimum practice |
|---|---|---|
| Mean bias error (MBE) | 1.0% | 2.0% |
| Representative TI error | 1.5% | 3.0% |

## Acknowledgments

We acknowledge EDF Renewables who funded the validation trial and kindly authorized publication of the results presented here.

| Aggregated TI data | | | | | | | | | | | | | | | |
|---|---|---|---|---|---|---|---|---|---|---|---|---|---|---|---|
| | Mean bias error (MBE) | | | | | | | | | | | | | | |
| Height | Velocity bin [m/s] | | | | | | | | | | | | | | |
| [m] | 2...3 | 3...4 | 4...5 | 5...6 | 6...7 | 7...8 | 8...9 | 9...10 | 10...11 | 11...12 | 12...13 | 13...14 | 14...15 | 15...16 | ***4...16*** |
| 33 | 0.8 % | -0.1 % | 0.0 % | -0.3 % | 0.0 % | -0.2 % | -0.1 % | 0.2 % | 0.1 % | 0.2 % | 0.4 % | 0.2 % | 1.8 % | 0.2 % | **0.2 %** |
| 50 | 0.8 % | -0.2 % | -0.2 % | -0.2 % | -0.3 % | -0.2 % | -0.2 % | 0.0 % | 0.1 % | 0.2 % | 0.3 % | 0.0 % | -0.4 % | -0.9 % | **-0.1 %** |
| 67 | 1.3 % | 0.0 % | -0.3 % | -0.3 % | -0.3 % | -0.3 % | -0.3 % | 0.0 % | 0.1 % | 0.1 % | 0.1 % | -0.1 % | -0.7 % | 0.3 % | **-0.1 %** |
| 84 | 1.2 % | -0.3 % | -0.4 % | -0.3 % | -0.2 % | -0.5 % | -0.3 % | 0.0 % | 0.0 % | -0.2 % | 0.0 % | -0.2 % | -0.9 % | 0.8 % | **-0.2 %** |
| 101 | 0.4 % | -0.3 % | -0.5 % | -0.3 % | -0.3 % | -0.5 % | -0.4 % | -0.2 % | -0.2 % | -0.2 % | -0.2 % | -0.3 % | -0.8 % | -0.4 % | **-0.4 %** |
| ***33...101*** | **0.9 %** | **-0.2 %** | **-0.3 %** | **-0.3 %** | **-0.2 %** | **-0.3 %** | **-0.3 %** | **0.0 %** | **0.0 %** | **0.0 %** | **0.1 %** | **-0.1 %** | **-0.2 %** | **0.0 %** | **-0.1 %** |

| | Representative TI error | | | | | | | | | | | | | | |
|---|---|---|---|---|---|---|---|---|---|---|---|---|---|---|---|
| Height | Velocity bin [m/s] | | | | | | | | | | | | | | |
| [m] | 2...3 | 3...4 | 4...5 | 5...6 | 6...7 | 7...8 | 8...9 | 9...10 | 10...11 | 11...12 | 12...13 | 13...14 | 14...15 | 15...16 | ***4...16*** |
| 33 | 0.8 % | -0.6 % | 0.3 % | -0.3 % | 0.2 % | -0.2 % | 0.2 % | 0.5 % | 1.0 % | 0.6 % | 1.1 % | 0.2 % | 1.8 % | 0.2 % | **0.5 %** |
| 50 | 0.6 % | -0.4 % | -0.2 % | 0.0 % | -0.2 % | 0.1 % | 0.0 % | 0.4 % | 0.6 % | 0.8 % | 0.7 % | 0.5 % | -1.0 % | -0.9 % | **0.1 %** |
| 67 | 1.0 % | -0.1 % | -0.3 % | -0.2 % | -0.1 % | -0.1 % | 0.2 % | 0.3 % | 0.6 % | 0.4 % | 0.7 % | 0.4 % | -1.0 % | 0.3 % | **0.1 %** |
| 84 | 1.7 % | -0.8 % | -0.8 % | -0.2 % | 0.1 % | -0.3 % | 0.0 % | 1.0 % | 0.5 % | 0.1 % | 0.6 % | 0.0 % | -1.0 % | 0.8 % | **0.1 %** |
| 101 | -0.4 % | -1.0 % | -1.1 % | -0.1 % | 0.2 % | -0.5 % | -0.1 % | 0.7 % | 0.4 % | -0.1 % | 0.3 % | -0.2 % | -1.2 % | -0.3 % | **-0.2 %** |
| ***33...101*** | **0.8 %** | **-0.6 %** | **-0.4 %** | **-0.2 %** | **0.0 %** | **-0.2 %** | **0.0 %** | **0.6 %** | **0.6 %** | **0.3 %** | **0.7 %** | **0.2 %** | **-0.5 %** | **0.0 %** | **0.1 %** |

**Figure 7.** Aggregated TI data for $MBE$ and $TI_{Rep}$ error from the FLS with mast data as reference. Color-coding according to acceptance thresholds suggested in Table 1

| Height [m] | Aggregated TI data – Mean bias error (MBE) – Velocity bin [m/s] | | | | | | | | | | | | | | |
|---|---|---|---|---|---|---|---|---|---|---|---|---|---|---|---|
| | 2...3 | 3...4 | 4...5 | 5...6 | 6...7 | 7...8 | 8...9 | 9...10 | 10...11 | 11...12 | 12...13 | 13...14 | 14...15 | 15...16 | ***4...16*** |
| 33 | -0.9 % | -0.6 % | -0.4 % | -0.7 % | -0.6 % | -0.4 % | -0.4 % | -0.2 % | -0.2 % | -0.1 % | -0.4 % | 0.3 % | 0.4 % | -0.9 % | **-0.3 %** |
| 50 | 0.1 % | -0.2 % | -0.2 % | -0.2 % | -0.3 % | -0.3 % | -0.2 % | -0.1 % | -0.2 % | -0.1 % | 0.0 % | -0.2 % | 0.3 % | -2.1 % | **-0.3 %** |
| 67 | 1.2 % | 0.2 % | 0.1 % | -0.1 % | -0.2 % | -0.2 % | -0.1 % | 0.1 % | 0.0 % | -0.1 % | 0.1 % | -0.1 % | -0.5 % | 1.4 % | **0.0 %** |
| 84 | 0.8 % | 0.2 % | 0.1 % | 0.0 % | -0.1 % | -0.2 % | 0.0 % | 0.1 % | 0.0 % | 0.0 % | -0.1 % | -0.1 % | -0.5 % | -0.4 % | **-0.1 %** |
| 101 | 0.2 % | 0.4 % | 0.1 % | 0.0 % | 0.0 % | -0.2 % | 0.1 % | 0.0 % | 0.0 % | 0.1 % | -0.1 % | -0.1 % | -0.6 % | 0.0 % | **-0.1 %** |
| 119 | 0.9 % | 0.1 % | 0.2 % | 0.2 % | 0.0 % | -0.2 % | 0.1 % | 0.0 % | 0.0 % | 0.0 % | 0.0 % | 0.3 % | -0.5 % | -0.3 % | **0.0 %** |
| 137 | 1.1 % | 0.3 % | 0.4 % | 0.2 % | 0.1 % | -0.2 % | 0.1 % | 0.2 % | 0.2 % | 0.2 % | 0.0 % | 0.0 % | -0.1 % | 0.0 % | **0.1 %** |
| 155 | 0.8 % | 0.2 % | 0.5 % | 0.2 % | 0.1 % | 0.0 % | 0.0 % | 0.2 % | 0.4 % | 0.2 % | 0.3 % | 0.1 % | -0.2 % | -0.3 % | **0.1 %** |
| 173 | 0.7 % | 1.1 % | 0.3 % | 0.4 % | 0.1 % | -0.1 % | 0.0 % | 0.0 % | 0.4 % | 0.3 % | 0.4 % | 0.1 % | -0.3 % | -0.7 % | **0.1 %** |
| 191 | 1.0 % | 0.3 % | 0.5 % | 0.4 % | 0.2 % | 0.0 % | -0.2 % | 0.0 % | 0.2 % | 0.2 % | -0.1 % | -0.3 % | -0.6 % | 0.3 % | **0.0 %** |
| ***33...191*** | **0.6 %** | **0.2 %** | **0.1 %** | **0.0 %** | **-0.1 %** | **-0.2 %** | **-0.1 %** | **0.0 %** | **0.1 %** | **0.1 %** | **0.0 %** | **0.0 %** | **-0.3 %** | **-0.3 %** | **0.0 %** |

| Height [m] | Representative TI error – Velocity bin [m/s] | | | | | | | | | | | | | | |
|---|---|---|---|---|---|---|---|---|---|---|---|---|---|---|---|
| | 2...3 | 3...4 | 4...5 | 5...6 | 6...7 | 7...8 | 8...9 | 9...10 | 10...11 | 11...12 | 12...13 | 13...14 | 14...15 | 15...16 | ***4...16*** |
| 33 | -2.9 % | -1.8 % | -1.0 % | -1.3 % | -0.8 % | -0.6 % | -0.4 % | -0.3 % | -0.3 % | 0.5 % | -0.3 % | 1.0 % | 0.4 % | -0.9 % | **-0.3 %** |
| 50 | -1.6 % | -1.0 % | -0.7 % | -0.5 % | -0.8 % | -0.5 % | -0.2 % | -0.1 % | -0.2 % | -0.3 % | 0.6 % | 0.1 % | -2.6 % | -3.2 % | **-0.7 %** |
| 67 | -1.3 % | -0.4 % | -0.2 % | -0.5 % | -0.4 % | -0.6 % | 0.0 % | 0.1 % | -0.2 % | -0.1 % | 0.1 % | -0.2 % | -0.9 % | 1.4 % | **-0.1 %** |
| 84 | -2.3 % | -1.0 % | -0.8 % | -0.2 % | -0.7 % | -0.6 % | -0.1 % | 0.9 % | -0.1 % | -0.1 % | -0.1 % | -0.7 % | -1.0 % | -0.8 % | **-0.4 %** |
| 101 | -3.7 % | -1.3 % | -0.5 % | -0.4 % | -0.3 % | -0.8 % | 0.3 % | 0.2 % | -0.1 % | 0.0 % | -0.3 % | -0.6 % | -1.4 % | -0.8 % | **-0.4 %** |
| 119 | -2.3 % | -2.1 % | -0.8 % | 0.0 % | -0.5 % | -0.7 % | 0.2 % | 0.1 % | -0.3 % | -0.1 % | -0.2 % | 0.2 % | -1.6 % | -0.8 % | **-0.4 %** |
| 137 | -2.6 % | -0.5 % | -0.5 % | -0.8 % | -0.5 % | -0.9 % | 0.0 % | 0.1 % | 0.2 % | 0.4 % | -0.4 % | -0.2 % | -0.6 % | -0.4 % | **-0.3 %** |
| 155 | -2.9 % | -3.5 % | -0.7 % | -1.1 % | -0.5 % | -0.4 % | -0.3 % | -0.1 % | 0.6 % | 0.0 % | 0.3 % | -0.3 % | -0.8 % | -1.3 % | **-0.4 %** |
| 173 | -1.6 % | 0.6 % | -2.1 % | -0.1 % | -0.5 % | -0.7 % | -2.2 % | -1.2 % | 0.6 % | 0.4 % | 0.9 % | -0.4 % | -1.0 % | -1.8 % | **-0.7 %** |
| 191 | -1.4 % | -1.8 % | -1.0 % | -0.5 % | -0.7 % | -0.1 % | -0.5 % | -0.6 % | 0.1 % | -0.4 % | -0.4 % | -2.0 % | -1.8 % | 0.2 % | **-0.7 %** |
| ***33...191*** | **-2.3 %** | **-1.3 %** | **-0.8 %** | **-0.5 %** | **-0.6 %** | **-0.6 %** | **-0.3 %** | **-0.1 %** | **0.0 %** | **0.0 %** | **0.0 %** | **-0.3 %** | **-1.1 %** | **-0.8 %** | **-0.4 %** |

**Figure 8.** Aggregated TI data for $MBE$ and $TI_{Rep}$ error. Color-coding according to acceptance thresholds suggested in Table 1

## References

[1] DNV GL 2021 WS181: Independent performance verification of Seawatch Wind Lidar Buoy at Frøya, Norway Tech. rep. DNV GL
[2] Gottschall J, Wolken-Möhlmann G, Viergutz T and Lange B 2014 *Energy Procedia* **53**
[3] Kelberlau F, Neshaug V, Lønseth L, Bracchi T and Mann J 2020 *Remote Sensing* **12**
[4] Salcedo-Bosch A, Farré-Guarné J, da Silva M P A and Rocadenbosch F 2023 *Remote Sensing* **15**
[5] Sathe A, Mann J, Gottschall J and Courtney M S 2011 *Journal of Atmospheric and Oceanic Technology* **28** 853–868
[6] 2017 61400-12-1:2017 edition 2.0 wind energy generation systems – power performance measurements of electricity producing wind turbines Standard International Electrotechnical Commission Geneva, CH
[7] Carbon Trust 2018 Offshore wind accelerator roadmap for the commercial acceptance of floating lidar technology Tech. rep. Carbon Trust
[8] Alexandra St Pé *et al* 2021 Site suitability initiative: An open source approach to evaluate the performance of remote sensing device (rsd) turbulence intensity measurements & accelerate industry adoption of rsds for turbine suitability assessment Tech. rep. CFARS
[9] Adcock R J 1878 *The Analyst* **5** 53–54

# Wind resource modelling of entire sites using Large Eddy Simulation

**Jahnavi Kantharaju[1], Rupert Storey[2], Anatole Julian[3], Francois Delaunay[3] and Daniel Michaud[4]**

**GE Renewable Energy**

[1]Garching, Germany, [2]Berlin, Germany, [3]Barcelona, Spain, [4]Schenectady, NY, USA

Email: jahnavi.kantharaju@ge.com

**Abstract**. Accurate wind speed, direction, shear and turbulence information are key inputs for wind farm energy yield and turbine suitability assessment. Met-mast measurements offer limited coverage both in horizontal and vertical directions, with few locations on the site and heights typically limited to below turbine hub-height. Simulation becomes an increasingly appealing option to mitigate these shortcomings. Current flow models used in wind resource assessment (WRA) rely heavily on assumptions to simplify complex atmospheric physics and reduce computing expense. As a result, they cannot resolve turbulence, and output average or annualized statistics. A new generation of models utilizing high-performance-computing now allows for high-fidelity simulation of sites with fewer modelling assumptions. In this work, we demonstrate and validate a computationally feasible large eddy simulation (LES) approach to generate high-fidelity time series of relevant quantities for WRA - including resolved turbulence - at sites in the order of 1000 square kilometres. The capability of the LES to produce insights in complex terrain is presented. A validation of the approach is performed by comparison of raw model results against met-mast measurements in a wide range of sites with varied complexities. Results show good agreement with measurements, with further error reduction expected through downstream adjustment of the model results with met-mast data on sites. Overall, the approach enables high-fidelity time-series based modelling for wind resource characterization and value addition to the WRA tool chain.

## 1. Introduction

Traditionally, wind resource assessment (WRA) for wind energy is performed with a combination of met-mast measurements and simplified flow models. These models do not resolve turbulence – a key piece of information for turbine load and lifetime estimation. With the ever-increasing turbine hub-heights and siting in complex terrain, an emphasis on improved modelling and analysis is required to ensure reliable and performant turbine operation.

Met-masts typically measure up to a height of 100m and are limited in numbers on a given site due to the economic cost and complication involved in their installation. These constraints result in a limited picture of the spatial and temporal variation of wind conditions across the site [1]. Remote sensing devices like lidars can help mitigate some of these challenges by measuring wind speeds across the rotor plane and are being continuously developed to work in complex terrain.

For large modern turbines, classical assumptions about the wind resource are becoming less valid. A neutrally-stratified flow with constant power-law shear occurs only rarely in practice. Complex flow phenomena due to complex terrain, atmospheric stability, mountains waves [2] are common on real sites and remain poorly understood in wind turbine suitability assessments. Another key topic that emerges from this discussion is the variation of flow conditions over the course of the day. Classical resource assessment tends to rely heavily on average statistics where the time correlation between flow properties is lost. Flow modeling techniques that preserve this information are required for accurate load prediction and siting.

Looking to literature, modeling atmospheric turbulence has been identified as one of the grand challenges in wind energy research [3]. Large eddy simulation (LES), a high-fidelity simulation approach, resolves key physical phenomena to accurately characterize the wind and offers a solution to better understand wind characteristics at potential turbine sites. A limitation of this approach in a traditional simulation setting is the high computational cost required to capture the large range of length and time scales in the atmospheric boundary layer [4]. In most cases, this limitation means LES is not feasible for use in a commercial setting. In recent years, GPU powered simulation technique has advanced significantly to address these issues. Numerical simulation codes developed specifically for GPU are able to harness the power and parallelization of GPUs to speed up simulations by orders of magnitude, thereby making high fidelity simulation a realistic option.

Furthermore, the application of LES for WRA is not limited to modeling freestream atmospheric conditions. The high-fidelity approach, where physical assumptions are minimized, makes the simulation framework extendable to include the effects of wind turbines and other obstacles directly through actuator methods. This enables the investigation of phenomena such as blockage effects [5], wake losses [6] and aeroelastic loads [7].

In the current work, we present the application of GPU powered LES to model and characterize the wind resource at prospective wind turbine sites in high-fidelity. We demonstrate the capability to resolve turbulence and deliver time-dependent results in a range of terrain types and climates. The validation presented enables the quantification of error and uncertainty, as well as the continuous testing and improvement of the modelling technique.

The paper is organized as follows: We present the details of the methodology and its validation procedure in section 2. The results are included in section 3 showing the overall capability of the LES model and then the validation results in comparison to measurements. We conclude in section 3 the outlook on the use of LES for wind resource assessment.

## 2. Methodology

The LES software, ASPIRE, based on the DALES code [8,9], was developed by Whiffle in the Netherlands. The framework has evolved from a meteorological background with an anelastic formulation for buoyancy effects and the inclusion of transport for temperature and humidity. The ground topology is represented by an immersed boundary technique, with the land-air interface modelled in detail to include heat and moisture fluxes. This allows the model to resolve atmospheric phenomena such as stability, convection and cloud formation - key to the accurate representation of the wind. Further details about the model can be found in [6]. Figure 1 illustrates a typical simulation at a mountainous site with complex flow.

The solver itself is GPU resident, meaning computationally expensive routines are highly parallelized and handled efficiently by avoiding CPU to GPU communication overhead as much as possible. The performance of the software on a single GPU is equivalent to parallelization across hundreds of CPUs in more classical approaches, in line with speed-ups recently reported by [10]. This performance is a key enabler for the temporal and spatial scales able to be resolved in the simulations and makes LES simulation of entire wind farms feasible for resource assessment.

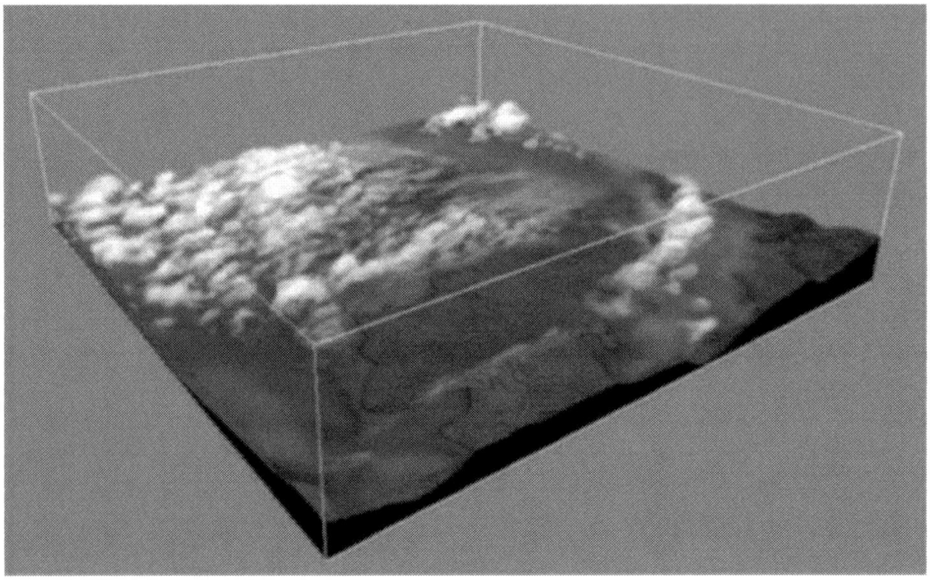

*Figure 1 - LES at a complex site - A horizontal slice shows velocity magnitude around topology, yellow shows high velocity regions, blue indicates low velocities. Terrain is shown in dark green. Cloud formation is also visualized in white.*

### 2.1. *Simulation for WRA*

For a typical WRA use-case, the model is run in a 'hind-casting' mode, where boundary conditions are derived from historical large-scale data from ECMWFs ERA5 reanalysis dataset [11]. These conditions are downscaled and fed to the simulation via an intermediate domain with the final simulation domain size typically set at approximately 30x30km horizontally and at least 2.5km high.

The simulation setup is automated in a pre-processing step with a set of rules to generate the domain and down-scaled boundary conditions. The surface characteristics of the site are automatically obtained from land-use databases such as the ESA worldwide landcover database [12]. A global recipe of simulation parameters is applied to all sites, thereby requiring minimal intervention from the user. This global recipe is validated over a large range of diverse sites as described in the next section.

For converged statistics, at least a 1-year period is simulated, with 10-min statistics of horizontal wind speed (*vel*), its standard deviation (*std*) and wind direction (*dir*) recorded over the lower portion of the domain. To evaluate turbulence resolved by the model, we also compute turbulence intensity as $TI = std/vel$. Other variables such as density, temperature, pressure and specific humidity are also recorded for a complete site suitability assessment. The 10-min statistics collected from the simulations are analogous to those collected directly from met-masts, allowing direct comparison and post-simulation processing.

The resolution of the simulation is 80m the horizontal direction and 20m in the vertical direction allowing the model to resolve turbulence length-scales in the order of a turbine rotor diameter. Grid sensitivity studies for a range of resolutions were performed to investigate the convergence of results. LES is by definition grid dependent due to spatial filtering of the Navier-Stokes equations, however, at the 10 minute statistics level only small changes in key metrics, in the order of 1%, were observed for higher resolutions. For the given resolution, the computational time for 1 simulated day is approximately 4 hours on a mid-range GPU, although this depends heavily on the hardware used and the average wind-speed.

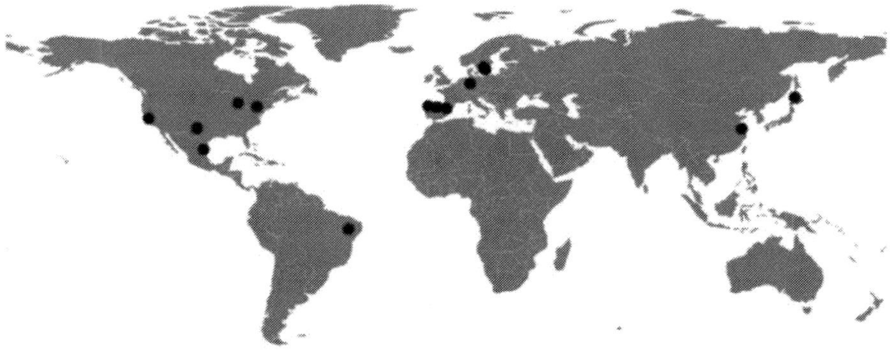

*Figure 2: Location of the validation sites in different parts of the world with varied terrain complexity and local climate*

### 2.2. Validation methodology

The modelling approach is validated over 13 diverse sites shown in figure 2 with various terrain complexities and local climates. Results are compared against multiple met-mast measurements at multiple heights. Overall, more than 50 cumulative years of met-mast data are included in the validation.

To improve the cycle time for validation, comparisons are performed for a set of 10 representative days chosen from the met-mast time-period, rather than a full year. The days are selected using a clustering algorithm to cover a range of variations in wind-speed and TI.

Validation is then conducted in a blind comparison and focusses on both statistical distributions, as well as direct comparison of 10-minute statistics from concurrent simulations and met-mast measurements. We compute aggregated metrics based on errors per timestamp and consider mean bias and absolute errors on *vel*, *std* and wind rose distribution of *dir*. The error metrics are weighted by the fraction of representative days in their respective clusters to give representative absolute errors. The convention for presenting errors is *(measurement data – simulation data)* meaning positive errors indicate under-prediction of a given quantity.

## 3. Results

This section is presented in two parts: 1) General output from the LES model that demonstrate the capability of the model to capture key quantities such as turbulence and wind shear, and to generate time-series data on a 4-D grid. 2) Validation results of WRA quantities in comparison to met-mast measurements on a wide range of sites.

### 3.1. Output from the LES model

A sample of the time-series output of the LES at a Swedish site is shown in figure 3. The data are recorded at an elevation of 128m and are presented with concurrent measurement data as a function of local time. The model is seen to accurately capture the trend in the conditions over the course of a day through the downscaling of large scale forcing conditions. This behaviour can be further confirmed in figure 4 by examining the variation in conditions over the day, averaged over a one-year period. A good representation of the diurnal patterns in *vel* and TI is obtained from the model, with higher wind speeds during the night due to stable atmospheric conditions, and higher turbulence during the day from buoyancy induced vertical mixing. Some differences in wind speed are observed for a few hours both during day and night times. In this particular case, we attribute this to seasonal variations in the diurnal patterns, as the frequency distribution of *vel* in the simulation results matched well with the measurements.

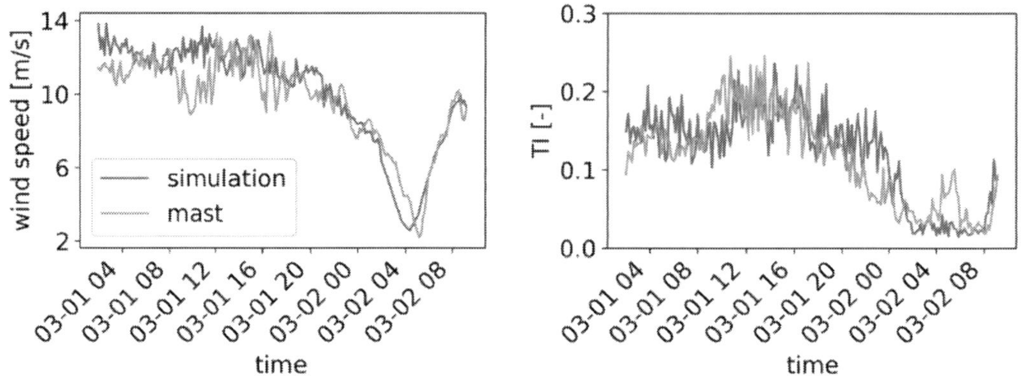


*Figure 3: Sample 10-min timeseries output from the flow model of wind speed (left), turbulence intensity (middle) and vertical shear exponent (right) for a Swedish site*

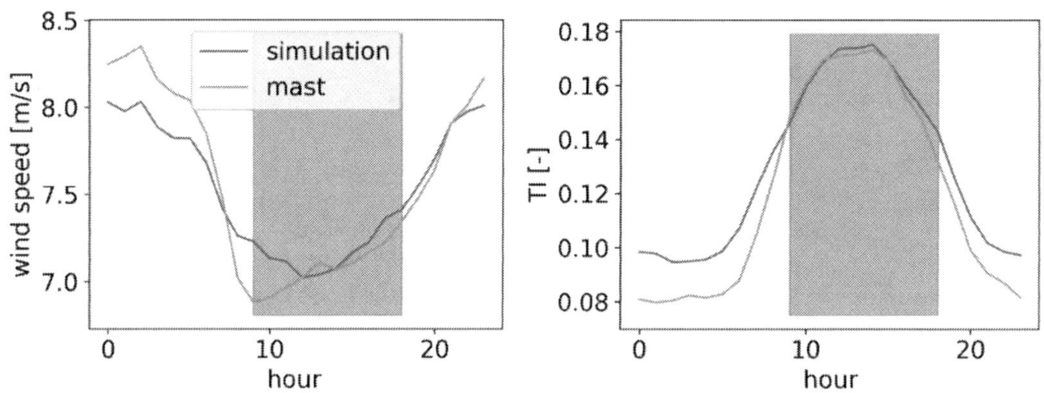


*Figure 4: Diurnal averages of the year-long dataset from the flow model: wind speed (left), turbulence intensity (middle) and vertical shear exponent (right) for the same Swedish site as in above figure. Shaded part denotes daytime period.*

Another important quantity of interest in WRA is the vertical variation of wind speed, or shear. A sample of this in shown in figure 5, which includes the timeseries of the vertical wind shear exponent and its diurnal average for a US site that experiences low-level jet phenomena [13]. The vertical shear is typically characterized in terms of the exponent of a power law fit over wind speeds at multiple heights. The diurnal trends in shear are seen to be well captured by the model i.e. higher shear values occur during stably-stratified conditions in the night. Some under-prediction of shear is noted during the early hours of the morning, however this could partly be due to a poor power law fit of the vertical profile influenced by the low-level jet occurrence.

Overall, the above figures demonstrate the capability of the model to capture key physical process in the atmosphere. Results also show the ability to generate time-series at any location and height on the site, emulating met-mast data. This information is a step change from that provided by more classical simulation approaches where conditions are simulated in a sector-wise steady-state fashion.

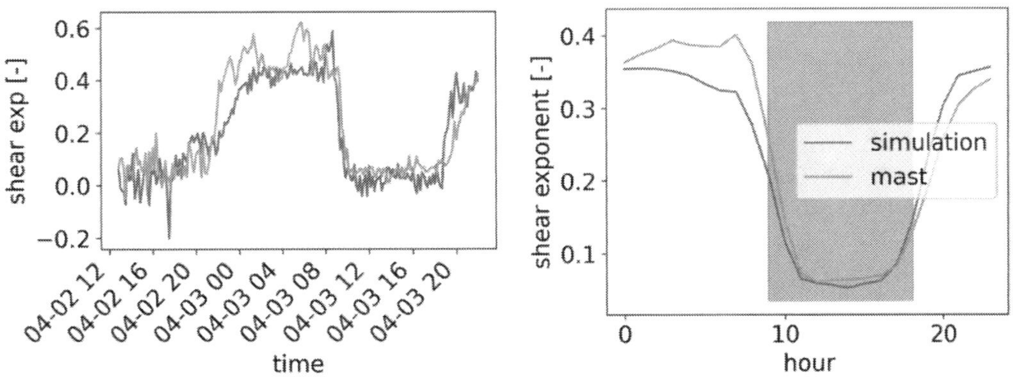


*Figure 5: 10-min time series (left) and its diurnal average (right) of the year-long dataset of vertical wind shear exponent from the flow model, for a flat terrain site in the US with low-level jet occurrence. Shaded part denotes the daytime period.*

In addition to 10-min statistics from points withing the domain, specific horizontal and vertical slices can also be collected during the simulation to illustrate the spatial distribution of wind conditions and the underlying atmospheric phenomena. A sample of such an insight is shown in figure 6 for a complex site in the US during a night-time period. Characteristic down-slope or katabatic winds can be observed, with high wind speeds at low elevations and complex vertical shear profiles, with a wind speed maximum near the surface. This type of condition is potentially problematic for wind turbines and is a key finding for long term site suitability.

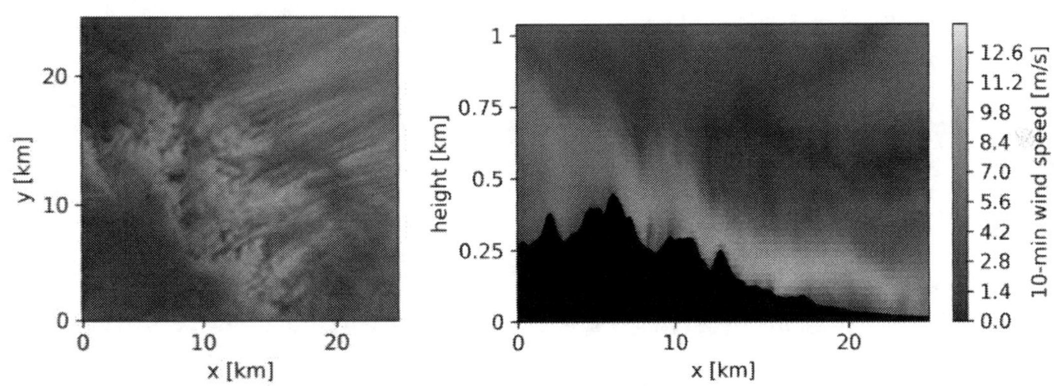


*Figure 6 – Heatmaps of horizontal wind speed on a complex terrain site in the US during a night-time period: a terrain following horizontal slice at 80m height (left) and a vertical slice with terrain shaded in black (right).*

### *3.2. Validation results*

Next, we present validation of the model performance for key WRA quantities, i.e. *vel, std* and *dir,* and their distributions. Figure 7 shows frequency distributions of *vel* and a TI curve comparing simulations with the measurements for one of the validation sites in the US. Good agreement is shown overall for both velocity and turbulence. Some under-prediction of TI in the lowest velocity bins from 3m/s to 6m/s is noted for the model, however these are not load driving conditions. Figure 8 includes wind direction distributions aggregated over all met-masts on the site. Again, good agreement is observed demonstrating the ability of the model to predict conditions across the site. The modelled wind rose is seen to capture well the distribution of wind speeds in different sectors, with small differences in frequencies in certain sectors. Similar observations were made for other validation sites.

Similarly, figure 9 shows the distribution of vertical shear exponent with TI for the same US site as in figure 5, along with the average values from TI bins. Some underprediction of shear is observed for the lowest TI bins, most likely linked to stable atmospheric conditions where the turbulence length-scales become small. Overall, the average results show the relationship between shear and TI is well captured – a result of the physics-based modelling approach.

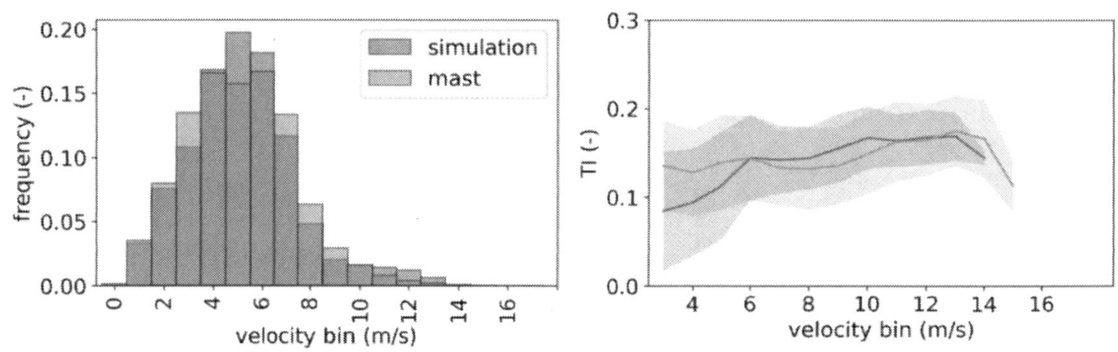


*Figure 7 - Velocity and TI distributions for 1 m/s velocity bins (left and right respectively), for a low complexity validation site in the US. The TI curve shows both the mean (solid line) and std. of TI (shaded) for each velocity bin.*

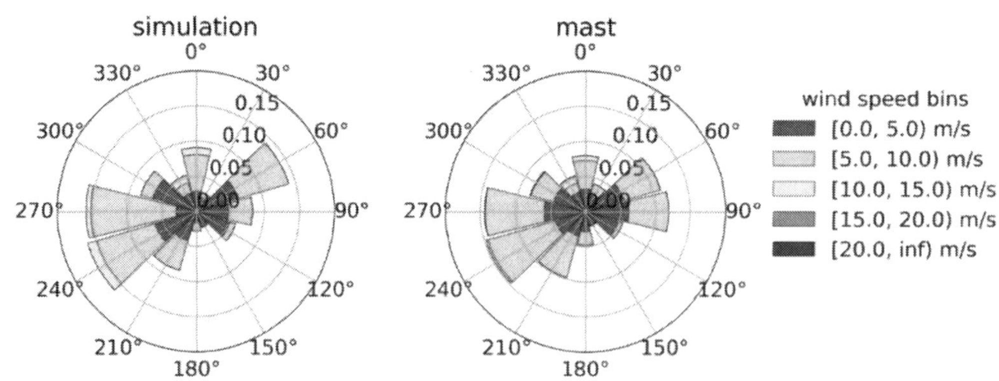


*Figure 8 - Wind rose comparison between simulated and measured results for the same validation site as Figure 2.*

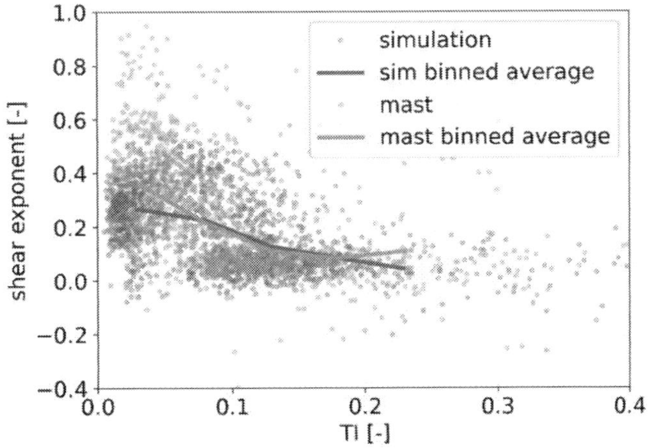


*Figure 9 - Distribution of vertical shear exponent and TI for the US site as in figure 5.*

In terms of quantitative assessment of the modeling uncertainties, we present the mean bias of *vel* and *std* in figures 10 and 11 respectively. These boxplots capture the variation of uncertainties within (multiple masts and heights) and across the validation sites. A positive value indicates underprediction and a negative value indicates overprediction by the flow model.

We see mostly underprediction of wind speed and *std* by the model except for a few sites. On average, the model underestimates wind speed by 0.4 m/s and *std* by 0.004 m/s at most locations. The extrema in bias values are seen for complex sites where the atmospheric flows were driven primarily by either mesoscale effects or presence of small-scale forestry which are difficult to capture in the model.

Differences in the distributions in velocity, TI and direction (shown in figures 7 and 8 for example) are presented in figure 12 in terms of mean absolute errors in the frequency of occurrence. Overall, errors 2-3% are seen for the distribution of wind speed, mean TI values as well as the wind rose.

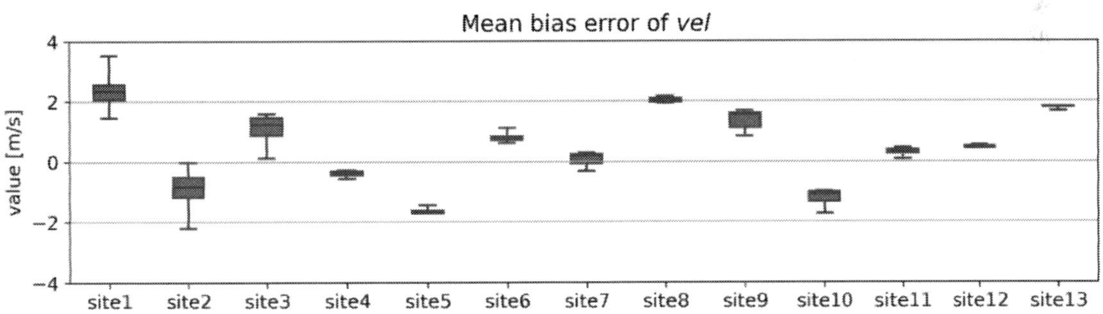


*Figure 10 – Box plot showing mean bias errors on vel for all masts and heights on a site. The center and edges of the box represent median, the first and third quartiles where each point is the value at a single mast location and height.*

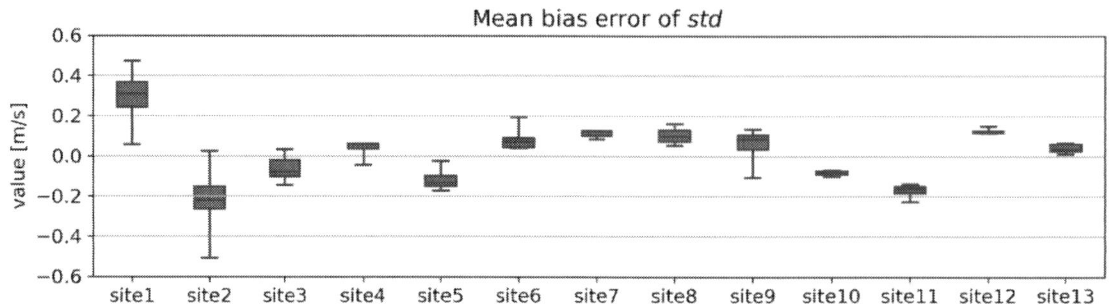


*Figure 11 – Box plot (as in figure 10) showing mean bias errors on std for all masts and heights on a site.*

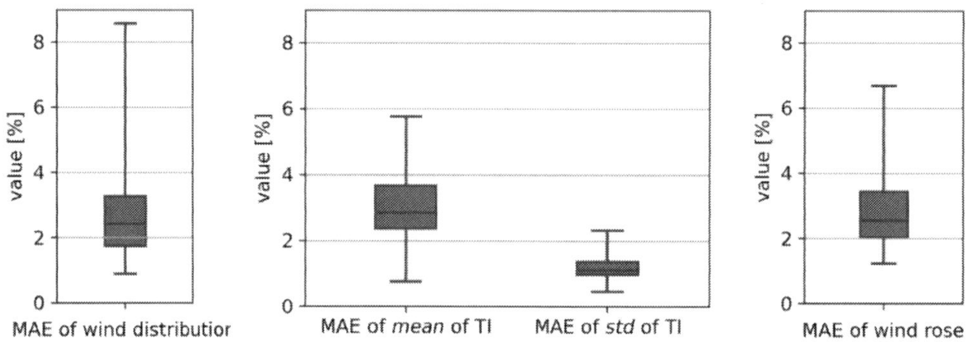


*Figure 12 – Mean absolute error on the frequency distribution of vel (leftmost) and dir (rightmost) shown in figures 7 and 8. On the center is the MAE on the* TI *curves for mean and std of* TI

## 4. Discussion

The results presented above illustrate the capability of LES in a WRA context. Some of the results, such as wind speed distributions and wind roses are standard outputs, available from much simpler models. What is not typical, is the ability of the model to deliver accurate turbulence information across the site, and key time-dependent phenomena such as shear during the diurnal cycle. These are key data for improved turbine suitability and lifetime analysis.

In general, the validation results above demonstrate very good agreement with measured data. Some conditions and sites are notably more difficult to simulate, such as stable night-time periods with low TI and high shear. Resolving turbulence in stable boundary layers is still challenging given the presence of smaller turbulent scales that need higher horizontal resolution. Also, some of the highest biases in wind speed and *std* were seen to come from sites with large mesoscale effects and heavily forested areas. The downscaling of boundary conditions is an ongoing topic of research where spanning the correct ranges of turbulence length-scales in the modelling chain are key to success. Several improvements to the modelling setup are already planned, which target improvement in the handling of meso-scale information. Improvement to the canopy modelling is also planned to improve model predictions at low elevations.

It should be emphasized that the results presented in this work are raw outputs from the model without any input from measurements. Calibration of flow model outputs with measured time-series data as anchors is standard practice in WRA and will remove most systematic biases in the model. The intention in this work was to present a transparent view of the model capability and its potential to improve standard industry practices.

## 5. Conclusions

A flow modelling approach based on LES for wind resource characterization has been presented. The approach is shown to generate met-mast like time-series at any location and height of interest on large sites for reasonable computational expense. The validation results demonstrate the capability of the model to accurately predict key conditions on sites by capturing the underlying atmospheric physics and thereby the spatio-temporal correlations on sites.

The ability of the model to explicitly resolve turbulence is demonstrated which is significant for turbine suitability analysis. The temporal nature of the results also provides key information to correlate flow quantities as shown in the accurate representation of site-specific diurnal cycles. Additionally, site-wide visualisation is shown to give insights into atmospheric events occurring on sites, especially with complex terrain.

Overall, the results offer new perspectives on wind resource modelling and will contribute to improved turbine siting with better reliability and reduced costs of energy. The presented LES model is also capable of simulating turbines to capture the effect of wakes and farm blockage. One of the immediate next steps of the current work is to include this capability in the proposed wind resource modelling framework.

## References

[1] Clifton, A. B. (2022). Research challenges and needs for the deployment of wind energy in hilly and mountainous regions. *Wind Energ. Sci.,* **7**, 2231–2254.

[2] Durran, D. (1990). Mountain Waves and Downslope Winds. *Blumen, W. (eds) Atmospheric Processes over Complex Terrain. Meteorological Monographs, vol* **23**. *American Meteorological Society, Boston, MA*.

[3] Veers, P. D. (2022). Grand Challenges: wind energy research needs for a global energy transition. *Wind Energ. Sci.,* **7**, *2491–2496.*

[4] Alfredo Peña, J. D. (2022). A one-year long turbulence simulation using a WRF-LES based modeling system at Østerild. J. Phys.: Conf. Ser. 2265 022011.

[5] Jessica M.I. Strickland, R. J. (2022). Investigating wind farm blockage in a neutral boundary layer using large-eddy simulations. European Journal of Mechanics - B/Fluids, Vol 95, 303-314,.

[6] Baas, P. V. (2022). Investigating energy production and wake losses of multi-gigawatt offshore wind farms with atmospheric large-eddy simulation. Wind Energ. Sci. Discuss. [preprint].

[7] Schepers, G. v. (2021). Aeroelastic loads on a 10 MW turbine exposed to extreme events selected from a year-long large-eddy simulation over the North Sea. Wind Energ. Sci., 6, 983–996,.

[8] Heus, T. v.-G. (2010). Formulation of the Dutch Atmospheric Large-Eddy Simulation (DALES) and Overview of Its Applications. Geosci. Model Dev., 3, 415–444.

[9] Schalkwijk, J. H. (2015). A Year-Long Large-Eddy Simulation of the Weather over Cabauw: An Overview. Monthly Weather Review 143 (3): 828–44. .

[10] Sauer, J. A.-E. (2020 ). The FastEddy® resident-GPU Accelerated Large-eddy Simulation Framework: Model Formulation, Dynamical-core Validation and Performance Benchmarks. Journal of Advances in Modeling Earth Systems 12 , 11.

[11] Hersbach, H. B.-S. (2020). The ERA5 Global Reanalysis. Quarterly Journal of the Royal Meteorological Society 146, 730.

[12] Zanaga, D. V. (2021). ESA WorldCover 10 m 2020 v100.

[13] Smith, E. N. (2019). The Great Plains Low-Level Jet during PECAN: Observed and Simulated Characteristics. . Mon. Wea. Rev., 147, 1845–1869.

# Analysis of the systematic errors of energy yield assessment in the context of wind farm repowering

**P Mazoyer[1,2], T Duc[2], A Bechmann[3] and G Kariniotakis[1]**

[1] Mines Paris, PSL University, Centre for processes, renewable energy and energy systems (PERSEE),1 rue Claude Daunesse, Sophia Antipolis 06904, France
[2] Engie Green, 6 Rue Alexander Fleming, Lyon 69007, France
[3] DTU Wind and Energy Systems, Frederiksborgvej 399, Roskilde 4000, Denmark

E-mail: paul.mazoyer@minesparis.psl.eu

**Abstract.** The repowering of wind farms is a rapidly developing area of research and is expected to represent 40 GW of wind projects by 2030 in the European Union. This has led to the emergence of energy yield assessment methods that incorporate operational data from existing farms with the aim of surpassing traditional methods that rely solely on physical modelling and onsite measurements. The current literature on repowering relies upon the assumption that learning from operational farm data applies to the future farm. Indeed, calibration and adjustment methods assume that physics-driven models (PDMs) have spatially and temporally correlated errors. This study investigates this assumption by analysing PDM errors for 25 pairs of nearby wind projects. A statistically significant correlation is observed. We discuss whether it is reasonable to utilise operational data from existing farms, which possess different characteristics, to improve the long-term production prediction of a repowered farm.

## 1. Introduction

The outcomes of energy yield assessment (EYA) are critical in the decision process of financial investment in new wind farm projects. In particular, reducing the uncertainty in predicting long-term annual energy production (AEP) is a lever to improve a project's economic yield [1]. Greenfield wind farm projects have motivated the development of well-established EYA models. These models are based on a sequence of equations that solve the physics, from wind flow modelling to wind turbine power conversion [2]. We refer to them as "Physics-Driven Models" (PDM). These models can have up to 12% uncertainty in the long-term AEP in simple terrains [3].

In Europe, 80 GW of wind power will reach its end of life by 2030. This opens the door for an alternative to greenfield development: repowering. The latter involves replacing an existing farm with new wind turbines and infrastructure. Repowering projects avoid the hurdles of greenfield projects as they benefit from existing permits, better local acceptance, and installed grid connexion. The paradigm of EYA differs for repowering projects since long-term historical measurements from the operating farm are available. This data can be integrated into the EYA process to estimate the annual yield contributing to the otherwise limited history of wind campaigns used in greenfield projects.

In the literature, this is done through either adjusting models' outputs [4], calibrating the flow models [5, 6], or replacing the PDM with a surrogate machine learning model [7]. The author are also aware that a common industry practice consists in calibrating the long- term mean wind speed at a site to the power production of an existing nearby farm, as done in [8] and in commercial softwares [9]. The surrogate machine learning models suffer from poor generalization performance [7], and the calibration models still face challenges due to the multicollinearity of parameters [6]. The adjustment models are promising as they quantify the uncertainty associated with the prediction, thus capturing the generalization skills of a model. They are single-parameter models, thus avoiding issues of multicollinearity.

Adjustment models assume that the data from an existing farm can be used to train a predictive model. Specifically, the training set comprises a predictor variable, which is the long-term AEP of the existing farm predicted using a PDM, and a response variable, which is the observed AEP of the same farm from operational data. An adjustment model learns a PDM error at one existing farm and then corrects the PDM prediction at the future farm using this learned error, either employing a linear model [4] or more sophisticated methods [10].

The error learned at the existing farm applies to the planned farm (to a certain extent) because both farms are similar: they are located on the same site. Some site-specific PDM errors are known to correlate: (1) the historical weather data, used to capture inter-annual variability of wind, have a spatially correlated error that allows for correction using the Kriging method [11, 12, 13], and (2) the local wind flow models, used to model the impact of obstacles, roughness, and topography, have a spatially correlated error in simple terrains [14]. On the other side, the farms have different operation periods, wind turbines, layouts, and hub heights, so that the same PDM applied with the two different farm characteristics over the two different periods may not make the exact same error.

To use the existing farm data, the PDM error correlation should be non-negligible; in other words, the farm-specific errors should not prevail over the site-specific errors. However, this correlation structure has not yet been quantified or observed. This paper bridges this research gap by providing experimental values of the correlation of PDM errors. The methodology involves the application of a PDM to pairs of nearby wind farms. The PDM errors are obtained by comparing the predictions to the actual power production data.

The rest of this paper is organized as follows. In section 2, the datasets used for the study are described, along with the methodology applied for assessing the PDM errors. The correlation results are shown and discussed in section 3. Finally, section 4 concludes the paper and offers some perspectives about future work in this domain.

## 2. Methodology and datasets

We had no access to datasets of repowered wind farms; instead, we had access to datasets from 18 wind farms located within a maximum distance of 7.50 km from at least one other wind farm. We applied the same PDM to both wind farm characteristics for each pair over two distinct periods of similar duration. We then compared the PDM results to production data to evaluate the PDM error for each pair: we obtained two values of errors that we also compared. We expected these values to be statistically correlated, but with a different level of correlation for each pair. Indeed, the correlation values depend on the degree of similarities between the two farms. The latter depends on the distance between the farms, the layout, the hub height, and the wind turbine type similarities.

### *2.1. Wind farms*

The 18 selected wind farms are all located in the north of France, as shown in Figure 1. They were divided into six groups, each labelled with a letter, and are located within a 7.5-kilometre radius of each other. Within each group, the wind farms were labelled with a number. Table 1 describes the selected wind farms' characteristics, including the wind turbine generator (WTG) specifications. Each group comprises wind farms that feature different types of WTG, and

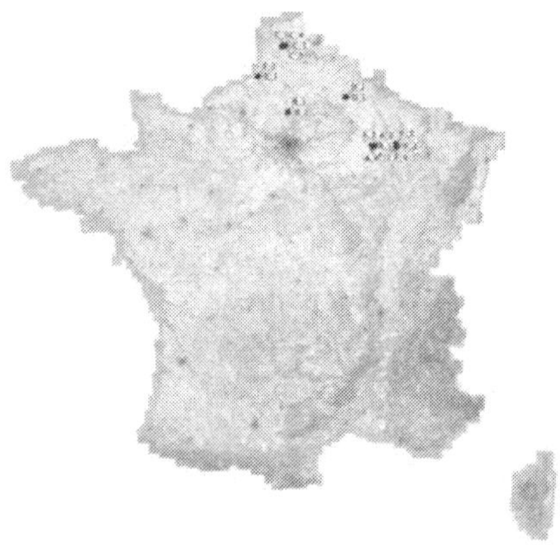

Figure 1: Location of the selected wind farms

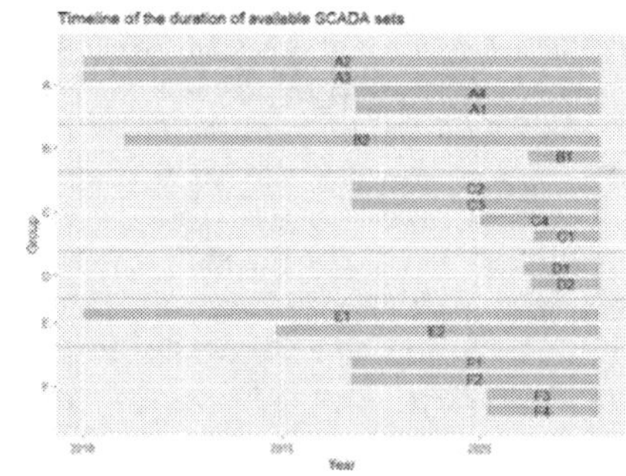


Figure 2: Timeline of available datasets

| Group | Wind farm | Average distance to closest farm [m] | WTG type and number | Rotor diameter [m] | Hub height [m] | Rated power [MW] | Reanalysis dataset |
|---|---|---|---|---|---|---|---|
| A | $A_1$ | 660 | 3 Senvion MM92 | 92 | 80 | 2.05 | ERA5 |
| | $A_2$ | | 14 Gamesa G58 | 58 | 65 | 0.85 | |
| | $A_3$ | | 5 Gamesa G58 | 58 | 65 | 0.85 | |
| | $A_4$ | | 4 Vestas V90 | 90 | 80 | 2.05 | |
| B | $B_1$ | 1860 | 3 Vestas V110 | 110 | 80 | 2.2 | EMD-WRF Europe+ |
| | $B_2$ | | 14 Senvion MM92 | 80 | 80 | 2.20 | |
| C | $C_1$ | 592 | 25 GE X 77 | 80 | 65 | 1.5 | EMD-WRF Europe+ |
| | $C_2$ | | 4 Senvion MM82 | 80 | 59 | 2.05 | |
| | $C_3$ | | 4 Senvion MM82 | 80 | 59 | 2.05 | |
| | $C_4$ | | 3 Vestas V105 | 105 | 80 | 3.45 | |
| D | $D_1$ | 2265 | 6 Enercon E-92 | 92 | 98 | 2.35 | EMD-WRF Europe+ |
| | $D_2$ | | 4 Senvion MM92 | 92 | 80 | 2.05 | |
| E | $E_1$ | 706 | 5 Gamesa G52 | 52 | 55 | 0.85 | EMD-WRF Europe+ |
| | $E_2$ | | 3 Enercon E70 | 87 | 57 | 2.30 | |
| F | $F_1$ | 2540 | 7 Senvion MM82 | 80 | 80 | 2.05 | EMD-WRF Europe+ |
| | $F_2$ | | 6 Senvion MM82 | 80 | 80 | 2.05 | |
| | $F_3$ | | 6 Gamesa G90 | 80 | 78 | 2.00 | |
| | $F_4$ | | 3 Gamesa G90 | 80 | 78 | 2.00 | |

Table 1: Description of the 18 selected wind farms.

simulated a typical repowering project for which the existing farm WTGs are generally no longer available. The repowered farm is equipped with a newer type of WTG. Groups A and E represented a repowering project with significantly improved rated power. In contrast, the other groups represented projects with significantly improved capacity factors, which is common in repowering projects [15]. Groups A, C, and D have WTGs with significantly different hub heights, enabling them to harvest a higher, and thus better, wind resource. These groups simulated repowering projects where the WTG tip height is increased. However, in cases where regulations impose a maximum height, the hub height remains constant, as simulated by projects B, E and F. Group B represented a scenario where the rotor diameter increases, resulting in an improved capacity factor. Group F corresponded to a repowering scenario with WTGs of identical characteristics.

### *2.2. Wind farm data*

The operational datasets utilized in this study were collected from SCADA systems at a 10-minute resolution and include various turbine-specific parameters. The data were obtained from different SCADA systems, providing a diverse range of parameters such as wind speed measurements using a nacelle anemometer, active power readings, and corresponding timestamps. Additional parameters such as rotor speed, average blade angle, turbine heading, and wind direction were also available in some datasets. The duration of the datasets varied, as depicted in Figure 2. For instance, Group A provided an opportunity to investigate the correlation of PDM errors for long-term AEPs, with wind farm $A_2$ and $A_3$ covering the period from early 2010 to mid-2016, and with wind farm $A_1$ and $A_4$ covering the period from mid-2016 to early 2023. This allowed for the simulation of an ideal case of repowering, where the wind power farm is repowered after 6.5 years. Group E also permitted similar simulations. Similarly, Group C and F simulated periods of approximately three years, Group B represented a simulated farm repowered after two years, and Group D evaluated a short period of approximately two years.

### *2.3. Evaluation of power production from operational data*

To evaluate power production using operational data, removing points unrelated to nominal farm performance, known as "anomalies", is necessary. According to ref. [16], anomalies can be classified into three categories: (1) type 1 anomalies correspond to turbine parking/idling while wind speed is above the cut-in wind speed due to external constraints such as a request from the grid operator, (2) type 2 anomalies correspond to production significantly below the power curve values, which are generally due to curtailments such as noise reduction at night for farms close to inhabited areas, and (3) type 3 anomalies correspond to isolated power production readings, which can be due to sensor failures or turbine starts and stops. Although anomalies represent only a small portion of points in a dataset, they must be filtered out to obtain meaningful results. Data treatment is essential for a WTG with many anomalies, as no treatment can result in a 5.2% difference in estimated AEP compared to treated data [17]. We processed data in three steps, running analysis on each WTG independently :

- Contextual filtering: we filtered points corresponding to power production close to zero while measured wind speed is above cut-in values. We also filtered when the wind speed or power production values were obvious outliers or were identical six times consecutively (frozen data).
- Statistical filtering: we used an isolation forest method to identify isolated points. We identified that the optimal parameters are 100 trees with two dimensions and a threshold of 0.55. The isolation forest tends to produce false positives at the tails of skewed distribution. We manually selected a maximum wind speed for outlier searching (typically 11 m/s) to avoid this effect for high wind speed points. The isolation forest method showed better results than the four other methods (not shown here) suggested in [16].
- Visual analysis: we identified the noise and grid operator curtailments with a visual inspection of the power curves with wind speed, rotor speed, and mean blades angles. We delimited the points corresponding to curtailment manually. We also manually filtered points that appeared as outliers on power curves.

Figure 3 shows the observed power curve before and after all these filtering steps for one example turbine in the dataset. Finally, the data are averaged to an hourly resolution to be compared to the PDM time series.

### *2.4. PDMs*

To use the errors learned at the existing farm for the repowered farm, the PDM for the existing and repowered farm must use as much similar information as possible. Consequently, we used the same reanalysis dataset for a given group of farms as input for the wind flow modelling and

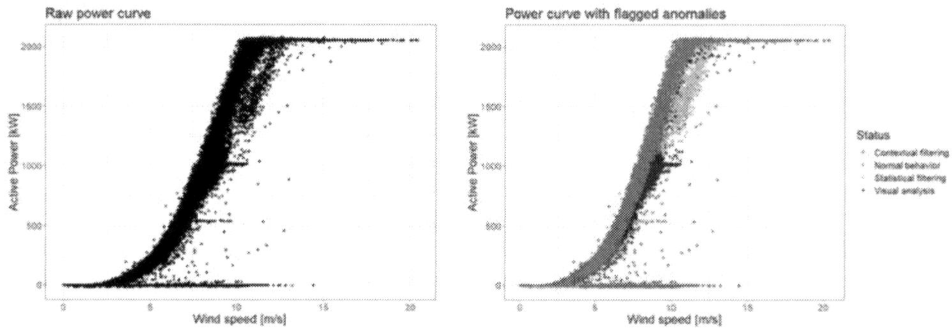


(a) Initial scatter plot. (b) Post-processed scatter plot.

Figure 3: Example of power curve filtering for one WTG of wind farm $D_1$. The points corresponding to the turbine's nominal behaviour are shown in green, while the others emphasise the effect of each data processing step.

kept the same flow and wake model parameters. The reanalysis datasets considered in this study were either ERA5 or EMD-WRF Europe+, depending on the wind farm (see Table 1). The grid point closest to the wind farms was used, and a logarithmic wind profile calibrated on reanalysis data was used to model wind speed at hub heights [9]. An hourly time series of power production data was generated for each turbine on the farms. We used the softwares WindPRO 3.6 and WAsP 12 and the warranted power curves provided by the turbine manufacturer for each WTG. We disregarded the simulation of technical losses such as curtailment, unavailability, or environmental losses since those anomalies are filtered in the operational data.

### *2.5. Comparison of PDM results and operational data*

The errors of the PDM are assessed at hourly intervals by comparing the PDM time series with the power production time series from operational data. These errors were then summed and normalized by the total power production. In backcast studies, the operational data is often reconstructed using historical weather data, as described in studies [18, 19, 20], to calculate the AEP and facilitate comparison with the PDM predictions. However, to improve the accuracy of the error analysis and avoid the confounding effect of long-term extrapolation in the PDM, we only considered valid operational data for comparison. This avoided the use of historical weather data and ensured that, for the operational data, the synthetic power production points generated from such data were not conflated with the PDM predictions. On the other side, using only filtered points prevented us from evaluating the PDM error for certain circumstances, such as wind sectors and the time of the day. Indeed, we filtered noise curtailment in the datasets that generally correspond to a wind sector at night time. We plotted wind roses (not shown here) and compared the wind conditions before and after filtering. We verified that the remaining data points were representative of the long-term climate.

## 3. Results

Figure 4 depicts the X-Y plot of the PDM errors for the first and second periods: these correspond to the distinct periods, so that the first periods simulate the existing farm and the second periods simulate the repowered farm. The periods depend on the available operational data for each farm. In the first periods, the PDM error ranges from -14% to 55% and the standard deviation is 16%. In the second period, it ranges from -11% to 53% and the standard deviation is 17%.

The PDM error sets have a good amplitude to evaluate the correlation. The PDM error sample correlation coefficient is 89%, evaluated on 25 points. The p-value of the correlation coefficient test is $1*10^{-7}$%, implying that the correlation is statistically nonnull.

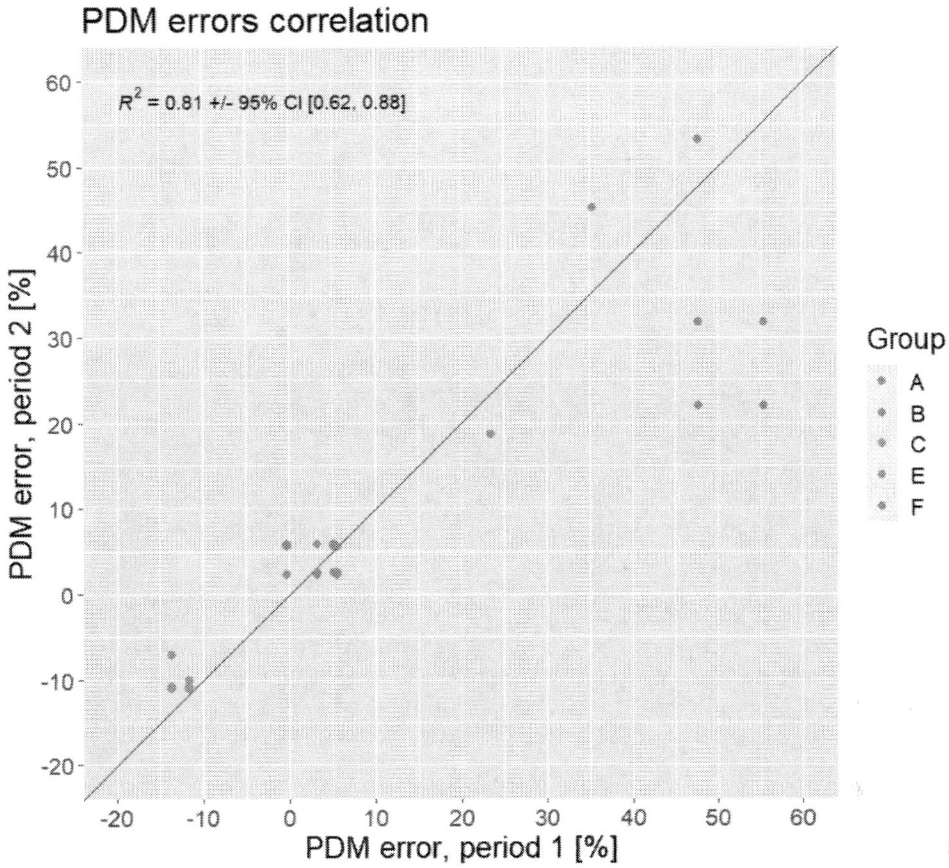


Figure 4: Comparison of PDM errors for each possible pair in each group. A pair is composed of two farms over two distinct periods. The first and second periods correspond to the selected distinct periods. For example, $A_2$ from 2010 to mid-2016 corresponds to the first period, and $A_1$ from mid-2016 to early 2023 corresponds to the second period. Therefore, one point corresponds to the PDM errors for the farm $A_2$ from 2010 to mid-2016 (x-axis) and for the farm $A_1$ from mid-2016 to early 2023 (y-axis).

PDM errors extracted from group F show little consistency. The PDM error evaluated on farm $F_2$ from 2016 to 2019 is 33% higher than the PDM error evaluated on farm $F_4$ from 2019 to 2023. We could not determine if this point is a statistical outlier or whether it could be explained by the farm and site characteristics. Farms $F_2$ and $F_4$ have very similar hub heights (78 vs 80 metres) and the same rotor diameter (80 meters). The centre of the farms are 2.8 kilometres apart. However, we did not identify a significant decrease in the error differences with distance, as seen in Figure 5. Farms $F_2$ and $F_4$ are located on two sides of a small valley with up to 15% slopes; this is likely to disrupt the similarities of site conditions and results in poor error correlations. This issue is left for further investigation.

With pairs corresponding to two sides of the valley removed in group $F$, the distribution of the error difference has a mean of 1.6%(+/- 0.8%) and a standard deviation of 7.7%. Besides,

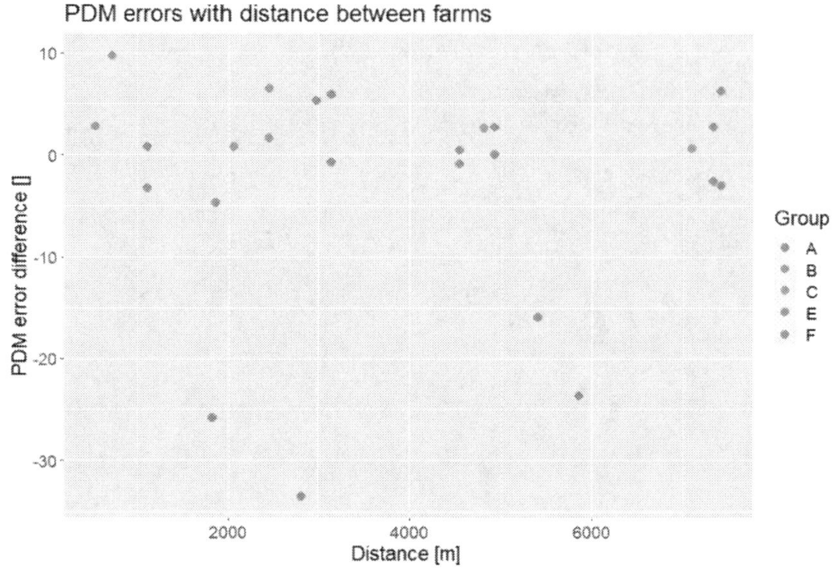


Figure 5: PDM errors difference with the distance between the two farms of the corresponding pairs.

the sample passes a Shapiro normality test with p-scores higher than 50%. This infers that correcting the PDM for the second period using the observed PDM errors for the first period would result in a 7.7% prediction uncertainty of long-term AEP (as long as we consider that bias is negligible). This is a significant reduction compared to the uncertainty of PDM, which is 17% when calculated on observed errors.

## 4. Conclusion

In the present investigation, our findings indicate that PDM leads to comparable long-term AEP assessment errors for two wind power farms in close proximity, despite being assessed on two separate periods. To assess the existence of a statistically significant correlation structure, we analysed the PDM errors for 25 pairs of wind farms over different periods. The correlation coefficient of long-term AEP assessment error is 89%. This implies that the AEP prediction uncertainty reduces by more than 9% when incorporating the observed errors at nearby farms. It should be noted that the quality of observation impacts the correlation evaluation, especially for older datasets that can be difficult to analyse. Ref [10] presents an EYA repowering method that includes the uncertainty of operational assessment in evaluating repowered farm AEP.

In the context of repowering or wind farm extension, using operational data from existing farms to calibrate or adjust a PDM approach is common practice. This practice assumes that PDM errors exhibit spatial and temporal correlation. We observed a statistically significant correlation between PDM errors calculated over distinct periods. However, the correlation appears to drop to zero in certain complex conditions. To generalize these findings and avoid the potential pitfalls of relying on nearby operational data when no correlation exists, a model of PDM error correlation should be developed. This model should consider variables such as distance, time difference, and terrain complexity, among other farm characteristics. Ongoing research is currently being conducted on this topic. Finally, it is important to note that while operational data improves AEP prediction for the studied wind farms, these represent a degraded case compared to repowering due to their non-negligible distance from each other. Consequently, a greater reduction in uncertainty is expected when operational data are used for repowering purposes.

**Acknowledgments**
The authors would like to thank Leo Pereniguez and Anthony Cottard for their help in producing the simulation results despite the ambitious timing. Their contributions were essential to the success of this project, and we are truly thankful for their expertise and dedication.

## References

[1] Bailey B H 2014 The financial implications of resource assessment Tech. rep. AWS Truepower LLC URL https://www.sewind.org/presentations/2014/2014-07-24$_S$*ECWC*$_W$ *orkshop*$_P$ *resentation–Bruce*$_B$*ailey.pdf*
[2] Clifton A, Smith A and Fields M 2016 Wind plant preconstruction energy estimates. current practice and opportunities Tech. rep. National Renewable Energy Lab. (NREL) URL https://www.osti.gov/biblio/1248798
[3] Lee J C Y and Fields M J 2021 An overview of wind-energy-production prediction bias, losses, and uncertainties *Wind Energy Science* **6** 311–365 URL https://wes.copernicus.org/articles/6/311/2021/
[4] Bullard M H 2019 Getting back in the game, uncertainty in wind speed dating in the repower world Presentation at the annual conference of American Wind Energy Association, Seattle, USA
[5] Schreiber J, Bottasso C L, Salbert B and Campagnolo F 2020 Improving wind farm flow models by learning from operational data *Wind Energy Science* **5** 647–673 URL https://wes.copernicus.org/articles/5/647/2020/
[6] Braunbehrens R, Vad A and Bottasso C L 2022 The wind farm as a sensor: learning and explaining orographic and plant-induced flow heterogeneities from operational data *Wind Energy Science Discussions* **2022** 1–50 URL https://wes.copernicus.org/preprints/wes-2022-67/
[7] Park J and Park J 2019 Physics-induced graph neural network: An application to wind-farm power estimation *Energy* **187** ISSN 03605442
[8] Bezbradica M, Kerkvliet H, Borbolla I M and Lehtimaki P 2016 Introducing multi-criteria decision analysis for wind farm repowering: A case study on gotland *2016 International Conference Multidisciplinary Engineering Design Optimization (MEDO)* (IEEE) pp 1–8 ISBN 9781509021116
[9] EMD International 2022 WindPro User Manual, September 2022 Tech. rep. https://www.emd-international.com/windpro/downloads/
[10] Mazoyer P, Duc T, Bechmann A and Kariniotakis G 2022 CONWEY – A new method for assessing the energy yield of repowered wind farms with quantified reduced uncertainty *preprint*
[11] Luo W, Taylor M C and Parker S R 2008 A comparison of spatial interpolation methods to estimate continuous wind speed surfaces using irregularly distributed data from England and Wales *International Journal of Climatology* **28** 947–959 URL https://rmets.onlinelibrary.wiley.com/doi/abs/10.1002/joc.1583
[12] Cellura M, Cirrincione G, Marvuglia A and Miraoui A 2008 Wind speed spatial estimation for energy planning in Sicily: A neural kriging application *Renewable Energy* **33** 1251–1266 ISSN 0960-1481 URL https://www.sciencedirect.com/science/article/pii/S0960148107002649
[13] Hu H, Hu Z, Zhong K, Xu J, Wu P, Zhao Y and Zhang F 2020 Long-term offshore wind power prediction using spatiotemporal kriging: A case study in China's Guangdong Province *Energy Exploration & Exploitation* **38** 703–722 URL https://doi.org/10.1177/0144598719889368
[14] Clerc A, Anderson M, Stuart P and Habenicht G 2012 A systematic method for quantifying wind flow modelling uncertainty in wind resource assessment *Journal of Wind Engineering and Industrial Aerodynamics* **111** 85–94 ISSN 01676105
[15] Lacal-Arantegui R, Uihlein A and Yusta J M 2020 Technology effects in repowering wind turbines *Wind Energy* **23**(3) 660–675 ISSN 10991824
[16] Morrison R, Liu X and Lin Z 2022 Anomaly detection in wind turbine SCADA data for power curve cleaning *Renewable Energy* **184** 473–486 ISSN 0960-1481 URL https://www.sciencedirect.com/science/article/pii/S0960148121017134
[17] Craig A, Optis M, Fields M J and Moriarty P 2018 Uncertainty quantification in the analyses of operational wind power plant performance *Journal of Physics: Conference Series* **1037**(5) ISSN 17426596
[18] Lunacek M, Fields M J, Craig A, Lee J C Y, Meissner J, Philips C, Sheng S and King R 2018 Understanding biases in pre-construction estimates *Journal of Physics: Conference Series* **1037** 062009 URL https://doi.org/10.1088/1742-6596/1037/6/062009
[19] Vidal J, Ziesler C and Monnich K 2020 Wind energy yield methods update a white paper on validation and update of methods for performing pre-construction wind energy yield assessments in the

european context Tech. rep. UL
[20] Papadopoulos I, Beckford T and Ribeiro C 2019 Dnv gl energy production assessment validation whitepaper 2019 Tech. rep. DNV GL URL https://issuu.com/dnvgl/docs/7bc75c58ca7643d9b94be2d957a9b9c0

# Wind fields from atmospheric turbulence measurements

**Jan Friedrich and Joachim Peinke**

ForWind, Institute of Physics, University of Oldenburg, Küpkersweg 70, D-26129 Oldenburg, Germany

E-mail: jan.friedrich@uni-oldenburg.de

**Abstract.** We present recent advances in the modeling of wind fields and their reconstruction from real-world atmospheric turbulence measurements. The proposed wind field model provides a statistically coherent framework for modeling the empirically observed occurrence of extreme atmospheric events. Furthermore, we demonstrate that the model is general enough to enmesh real-world measurement points, e.g., from meteorological masts or LIDAR, and thus provides a rather convenient method for the reconstruction of highly resolved, three-dimensional wind fields. Our methodology is based on the so-called superstatistics of Gaussian-distributed (or Mann-type) velocity fields with fluctuating covariances and exactly reproduces higher-order statistics due to extreme small-scale wind fluctuations. Therefore, it could lead to more realistic inflow conditions and might potentially enhance the current design standard of wind turbines. We further discuss potential applications of the wind field model in the context of LIDAR measurements as well as for wake situations.

## 1. Introduction

The ever-increasing size of wind turbines, which might eventually exceed the height of the atmospheric surface layer, leads to new challenges for the design process and operation of modern wind turbines [1, 2]. Therefore, wind energy applications are in strong need of novel methods such as the use of reduced-order surrogate models or new ground-based systems, e.g., advanced LIDAR or SODAR, as well as aerial measurement campaigns with drones or airplanes. Contrary to the relatively steady and controllable power output of nuclear or combustion plants, the operating conditions and power output of wind farms are heavily influenced by extreme wind fluctuations [2, 3, 4]. Latter may only be detectable on time scales that are smaller than one second but can nevertheless affect the power output of the entire wind plant, sometimes even leading to a power increase of more than eighty percent.

Empirically, the occurrence of such extreme wind gusts is closely related to the phenomenon of small-scale intermittency and manifests itself by strong deviations from Gaussian statistics of wind fluctuations. Current design standards [5], however, do not capture the non-Gaussianity, non-stationarity, and non-homogeneity of turbulent inflow conditions. This inevitably leads to maintenance issues or material fatigue due to unpredictable loads, for example on the rotor or the blades. The cost of such "unexpected failures" and subsequent maintenance over the typical 20-year lifespan of a wind turbine is hard to estimate but is sometimes assumed to lie in between 65 and 95 percent of the initial cost of the turbine [6].

Inflow turbulence models such as the Mann, Kaimal, or Veers model [7, 8] are based on Gaussian random fields that can be efficiently sampled by prescribing certain spectral tensorial forms. Therefore, the latter models are frequently used on an industrial level in order to achieve a certain standard of product reliability [1]. Nonetheless, non-Gaussian statistics of such stochastic wind field models have only been incorporated in a temporal sense [9, 10], i.e., without accounting for spatial coherence in the rotor plane. Recently, a "superstatistical" wind field model was proposed where intermittency of a fully three-dimensional wind field is exactly controllable and where real-world measurement data can be integrated in the sense of a "constrained" wind field [11, 12].

In this contribution, we discuss current and potential future applications of this wind field model at the example of meteorological mast array measurements [13, 14], LIDAR measurements, and the modeling of turbine wakes. The paper is organized as follows, Section 2 and 3 give an account of the modeling framework, Section 4 describes potential future applications, whereas concluding remarks are given in Section 5.

## 2. Superstatistical wind field model

This section reviews the superstatistical wind field model proposed in refs. [13, 15]. To this end, we first present the statistical description of current wind field models covered by standards of the International Electrotechnical Commission (IEC) [5]. Characteristics of the atmospheric turbulence in such Gaussian wind field models such as the Mann, Veers, or Kaimal model enter through the covariance tensor of the random field $\mathbf{u}(\mathbf{x})$, i.e.,

$$\sigma_{i\alpha,j\beta} = \langle u_\alpha(\mathbf{x}_i) u_\beta(\mathbf{x}_j) \rangle \ , \tag{1}$$

where brackets denote a suitable averaging procedure (e.g., ensemble averaging or temporal averaging). In the homogeneous and isotropic wind field models of the IEC standard, the Fourier transform of the covariance tensor (1) is entirely defined by the energy spectrum $E(k)$ according to

$$\langle \hat{u}_\alpha(\mathbf{k}) \hat{u}_\beta(\mathbf{k}') \rangle = \frac{1}{(2\pi)^6} \int \mathrm{d}\mathbf{x}_i \int \mathrm{d}\mathbf{x}_j e^{-i\mathbf{k}\cdot\mathbf{x}_i - i\mathbf{k}'\cdot\mathbf{x}_j} \langle u_\alpha(\mathbf{x}_i) u_\beta(\mathbf{x}_j) \rangle = \delta(\mathbf{k}+\mathbf{k}') \left( \delta_{\alpha\beta} - \frac{k_\alpha k_\beta}{k^2} \right) \frac{E(k)}{4\pi k^2}, \tag{2}$$

where $\delta(\mathbf{k} + \mathbf{k}')$ denotes the Dirac delta distribution and $\delta_{\alpha\beta}$ the Kronecker delta. For intermediate wavenumbers the energy spectrum possesses the universal form $E(k) \sim k^{-5/3}$, whereas additional features of atmospheric turbulence such as shear lead to slightly different tensorial forms [5]. Fixing the mean $\mathbf{U} = \langle \mathbf{u} \rangle$ and the covariances (1) in a Gaussian model fully determines the statistics of the wind field characterized by the so-called joint multipoint probability density function

$$f_n(\mathbf{u}_1, \mathbf{x}_1; \ldots; \mathbf{u}_n, \mathbf{x}_n) = \frac{1}{\sqrt{(2\pi)^{3n} \det \sigma}} e^{-\frac{1}{2}(u_{i,\alpha} - U_\alpha)\sigma^{-1}_{i\alpha;j\beta}(u_{j,\beta} - U_\beta)} \ . \tag{3}$$

Such Gaussian random fields can be sampled efficiently in Fourier space. Nonetheless, as already highlighted in Section 1, they do not account for a crucial feature of atmospheric turbulence, i.e., the occurrence of extreme wind fluctuations. Figure 1(a) shows the probability distribution $h(v, r)$ of wind field fluctuations $v(r) = u(x+r) - u(x)$ at a fixed scale $r = 0.0044L$ ($L$ denotes the so-called integral length scale or correlation length of the wind) determined from the GROWIAN measurement data consisting of 16 propeller anemometers distributed on two meteorological masts [16, 17]. Current wind field models in the IEC standard predict a Gaussian distribution for $h(v, r)$, which is represented by the turquoise curve in Figure 1(a) and has the same standard deviation as the measurement data (orange). Hence, IEC standard models underestimate the

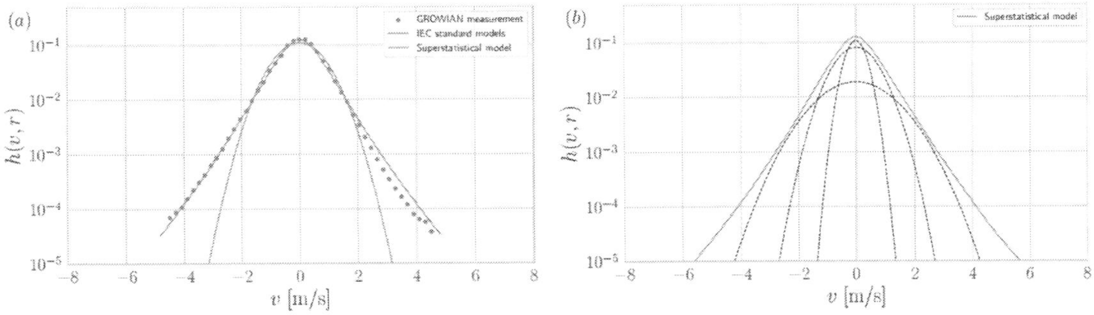


**Figure 1.** (a) Probability distribution of wind field fluctuations $h(v, r)$. Temporal increments have been converted based on Taylor's hypothesis (see ref. [13] for further details).

occurrence of extreme wind fluctuations (e.g., those belonging to $|v| > 4$ m/s, i.e., tails of the probability distributions).

The main idea of the superstatistical approach [13, 15, 18] consists in considering a superposition of the multivariate Gaussian distributions (3) according to

$$f_n(\mathbf{u}_1, \mathbf{x}_1; \ldots; \mathbf{u}_n, \mathbf{x}_n) = \int_0^\infty \mathrm{d}\xi g(\xi) \frac{1}{\sqrt{(2\pi)^{3n} \det \sigma_\xi}} e^{-\frac{1}{2}(u_{i,\alpha}-U_\alpha)\sigma^{-1}_{\xi,i\alpha;j\beta}(u_{j,\beta}-U_\beta)} \,. \quad (4)$$

Here, the covariances $\sigma_{i\alpha;j\beta}$ in Eq. (3) have been re-parameterized as $\sigma_{\xi,i\alpha;j\beta}$ by introducing fluctuations between two spatial points

$$r_{ij} = |\mathbf{x}_i - \mathbf{x}_j| \to \rho_\xi(r_{ij}) = \xi^{\sqrt{A+\mu \ln_+ \frac{x^\succ}{r_{ij}+x^\prec}}} \left(\frac{r_{ij}+x^\prec}{x^\succ}\right)^{\frac{\mu}{2}} r_{ij} \,, \quad (5)$$

where $x^\prec$ is a small-scale cut-off whereas $x^\succ$ and $A$ represent large-scale flow characteristics. Deviations from Gaussianity are characterized by the intermittency coefficient $\mu$ in combination with fluctuations $\xi$ that follow a lognormal distribution $g(\xi)$, which mimics the influence of fluctuations of the local energy dissipation rate in the turbulent flow [19]. The superstatistics (4) is illustrated by the probability distributions of wind field fluctuations in Figure 1(b). Here, the orange curve represents a superposition of Gaussian distributions with fluctuating variances (indicated by the three dashed black curves). As in Figure 1(a), the latter parametrization can precisely control the occurrence of small-scale extremes $u(x + r) - u(x)$ by the so-called intermittency coefficient $\mu$. In other words, the superstatistical approach can formally extend *any* standard model of the IEC norm (represented by the covariances $\sigma_{i\alpha;j\beta}$) in order to account for heavy-tail behavior due to the occurrence of small-scale extremes. The additional model parameter $\mu$ has to be determined from real-world measurements (e.g., $\mu = 0.243$ for the GROWIAN data set [13]) and could be strongly site-dependent. Furthermore, as the superstatistics forms a so-called *Gaussian scale mixture*, wind fields can be sampled in a relatively efficient way that consists of generating multiple Gaussian random fields (e.g., of Mann-type but with re-parameterized covariances) $\mathbf{u}(\xi, \mathbf{x})$ with the same noise realization and subsequent scale mixing (see ref. [13] for further details on the sampling algorithm). The following section describes how the proposed framework can reconstruct wind fields from sparse real-world measurements.

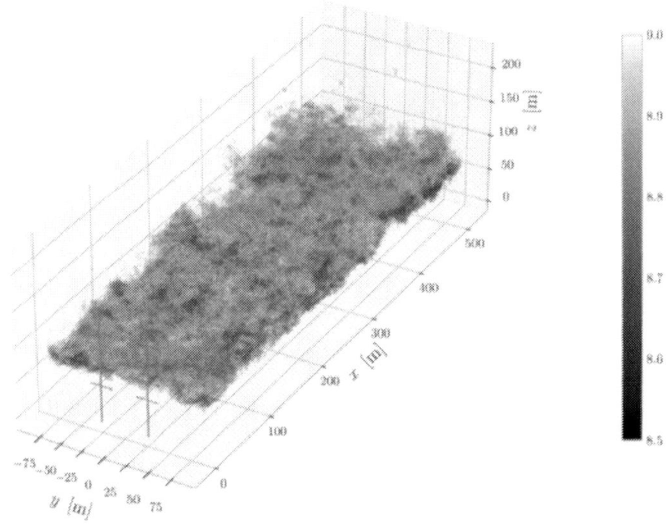


**Figure 2.** Reconstructed wind field from the GROWIAN measurement array that consisted of 16 propeller anemometers mounted on two meteorological masts (grey).

## 3. Reconstruction of turbulent wind fields from atmospheric turbulence measurements

The wind field model proposed in the previous section can be apprehended as an extension of the standard IEC models by an additional parameter, the so-called intermittency coefficient $\mu$, which characterizes heavy-tailed behavior of the PDF of wind field fluctuations at small scales as demonstrated in Figure 1. The advantage of sampling the wind fields from such a Gaussian scale mixture is that methods that are valid for Gaussian statistics (3), such as the conditioning of the stochastic process on measurement points [11, 12], can also be applied to the superstatistical wind field. As it has been shown for the GROWIAN data set consisting of time series of 16 propeller anemometers arranged in a meteorological mast array [13], the framework can constrain the stochastic wind field $\mathbf{u}(\mathbf{x})$ on measurement $\mathbf{U}_i$ measured at points ($\mathbf{x}_i$ by a so-called bridge construction

$$\mathbf{u}^B(\xi,\mathbf{x}) = \mathbf{u}(\xi,\mathbf{x}) - \left[u_\alpha(\xi,\mathbf{x}_i) - U_{\alpha,i}\right] \sigma^{-1}_{\xi,i\alpha;j\beta} \left\langle u_\beta(\xi,\mathbf{x}_j)\mathbf{u}(\xi,\mathbf{x})\right\rangle \ . \tag{6}$$

A reconstructed wind field is shown in Figure 2. Thereby the bridge construction (6) is an exact interpolation of the pointwise GROWIAN measurements as it fulfills $\mathbf{u}^B(\xi,\mathbf{x}_i) = \mathbf{U}_i$. Nonetheless, we emphasize that the proposed framework is general enough to "constrain" the wind field on any observable, which will be discussed in the following section.

## 4. Potential future applications and further validation of the superstatistical model

In this section, we describe future applications and potential validations of the wind field model from LIDAR measurements of turbulent inflow and in wake situations.

### *4.1. Reconstruction of spatiotemporal wind fields from line-of-sight LIDAR measurements*

The superstatistical model has only been validated based on the GROWIAN data. Hence, it would be desirable to perform further validations on the basis of more finely resolved wind fields, e.g., from LIDAR or SpinnerLIDAR [20, 21, 22]. The framework (4) can be extended to account for the spatiotemporality of wind field measurements $\mathbf{u}(\mathbf{x},t)$ by introducing the covariances

$$\sigma_{i\alpha,j\beta} = \left\langle u_\alpha(\mathbf{x}_i,t_i)u_\beta(\mathbf{x}_j,t_j)\right\rangle \ , \tag{7}$$

measured at two distinct points in space *and* time. Under the assumption of Taylor's hypothesis, the latter covariances can be simplified according to [19]

$$\sigma_{i\alpha,j\beta} = \langle u_\alpha(\mathbf{x}_i - \mathbf{U}(t_i - t_j), t_i) u_\beta(\mathbf{x}_j, t_i) \rangle \ , \tag{8}$$

where $\mathbf{U}$ denotes a mean velocity field. Hence, assuming that the mean flow merely advects the turbulence allows for modeling a spatiotemporal field by the joint statistics (4). Furthermore, the bridge construction (6) can be reformulated to only constrain the wind field on the instantaneous radial component of the wind field available from the line-of-sight measurements from LIDAR. Therefore, a systematic reconstruction of the wind field,e .g., from SpinnerLIDAR trajectories as outlined in [23], should offer further possibilities for validating the superstatistical model.

### *4.2. Modeling of turbine wakes*

As demonstrated in the previous sections, the wind field model proposed in Section 2 can be considered a somewhat realistic model of an atmospheric flow. Nonetheless, it relies on certain assumptions, such as the homogeneity or isotropy of the turbulent flow. Vertical velocity profiles due to shear are only taken into account by adding an external shear field and - as of now- do not enter the covariance tensors in the superstatistics (4), as it is for instance the case in the Mann model [8], which uses rapid distortion theory. Hence, we implicitly assume that the small-scale statistics of atmospheric turbulent wind fields are somehow unaffected by large-scale anisotropies, which might be valid for turbulent inflow. Nevertheless, wind energy converters are usually clustered in wind farms implying that downstream turbines operate in the wake of the upstream turbines. Therefore, wind velocities in the wake are typically lower than inflow, whereas turbulence intensities are more pronounced [24]. Accurately predicting extreme wind fluctuations thus plays a crucial role in subsequent turbine load calculations or load-surrogate models [25]. Due to the Gaussian scale mixture described in Section 2, it could be possible to model different regions by an adaptive superposition of Gaussian statistics and thus mixing flows composed of sub-flows with different turbulent levels. Ultimately, results obtained from such refined dynamic wake wind field models (taking into account the effects of wake meandering or tip-vortex instabilities [26]) could lead to potential improvements of current engineering models [27].

## 5. Conclusions

We have presented an extension of current Gaussian wind field models in the IEC norm by including an additional parameter, the so-called intermittency coefficient $\mu$, which characterizes the statistical significance of the occurrence of extreme wind fluctuations. It will be a task for future research to further assess the implications of this additional parameter, which characterizes the statistical significance of extreme wind gusts. Next to more elaborate aerolastic simulations, a first assessment of the different behavior of IEC models and extended (i.e., non-Gaussian) models could be the wind speed averaged over the rotor plane. Consequently, the wind field model could be relevant for a broad range of applications ranging from the enhancement of incomplete measurements to the improvement of load calculations and ultimately improved design standards.

**Acknowledgments**

This work is partly funded by the German Federal Ministry for Economic Affairs and Energy in the scope of the projects EMUwind (03EE2031A/C) and by the European Commission in the realm of the FLOW project.

## References

[1] Veers P *et al.* 2022 *Wind Energy Science Discussions* **2022** 1–102 URL `https://wes.copernicus.org/preprints/wes-2022-32/`
[2] Veers P *et al.* 2019 *Science* **366**
[3] Boettcher F, Renner C, Waldl H P and Peinke J 2003 *Bound.-Layer Meteorol.* **108** 163–173
[4] Peinke J, Barth S, Böttcher F, Heinemann D and Lange B 2004 *Physica A* **338** 187 – 193
[5] Commission I E 2005 *International Electrotechnical Commission*
[6] Walford C A 2006 Wind turbine reliability: understanding and minimizing wind turbine operation and maintenance costs. Tech. rep. Sandia National Laboratories
[7] Veers P 1984 *25th Structures, Structural Dynamics and Materials Conference* p 910
[8] Mann J 1998 *Probabilistic Eng. Mech.* **13** 269–282
[9] Mücke T, Kleinhans D and Peinke J 2011 *Wind Energy* **14** 301–316
[10] Kleinhans D, Friedrich R, Schaffarczyk A P and Peinke J 2009 *Progress in Turbulence III* (Springer) pp 111–114
[11] Dimitrov N and Natarajan A 2017 *Wind Energy* **20** 79–95
[12] Friedrich J, Gallon S, Pumir A and Grauer R 2020 *Phys. Rev. Lett.* **125** 170602
[13] Friedrich J, Moreno D, Sinhuber M, Wächter M and Peinke J 2022 *PRX Energy* **1** 023006
[14] Friedrich J, Moreno D, Sinhuber M, Wächter M and Peinke J 2022 *Journal of Physics: Conference Series* **2265** 022026
[15] Friedrich J, Peinke J, Pumir A and Grauer R 2021 *J. Phys. Complexity* **2** 045006
[16] Günther H and Hennemuth B 1998 *Deutscher Wetter Dienst* **BMBF-Projekt** 0329372A
[17] Koerber F, Besel G and Reinhold H 1988
[18] Beck C 2004 *Physica D* **193** 195–207
[19] Monin A S and Yaglom A M 2007 *Statistical Fluid Mechanics: Mechanics of Turbulence* (Courier Dover Publications)
[20] Kapp S and Kühn M 2016 *J. Phys. Conf. Ser.* **555** 012112
[21] Kapp S 2017 *Lidar-based reconstruction of wind fields and application for wind turbine control* Ph.D. thesis Universität Oldenburg
[22] Mikkelsen T 2014 *J. Phys. Conf. Ser.* **524** 012007
[23] Fu W, Sebastiani A, Peña A and Mann J 2022
[24] Neunaber I, Hölling M, Stevens R J A M, Schepers G and Peinke J 2020 *Energies* **13** 5392
[25] Rinker J *et al.* 2020 *J. Phys. Conf. Ser.* **1618** 052052
[26] Meyers J *et al.* 2022 *Wind Energy Science Discussions* 1–56
[27] Göçmen T *et al.* 2016 *Renewable and Sustainable Energy Reviews* **60** 752–769

# A workflow for including atmospheric stability effects in wind resource and yield assessment and its evaluation against wind measurements and SCADA

**Diallo M., Kwak G., Tüzünoglu S, Abiven C., Rol E., Vermeir J., Frère A.**

Corresponding author: mouhamet.diallo@tractebel.engie.com

**Abstract.** Atmospheric stability conditions are known to impact the wind resource and yield assessments. However, they are too barely or not correctly taken into account in the industry due to several reasons such as limitations of commercial software or the relative inertia in updating industrial processes. This paper proposes a simplistic approach to improve wind resource and yield assessment certainty while keeping very similar software and industry processes. Two test cases are considered. First, the wind speed estimates made using a CFD software (Meteodyn 5.3) for different stability classes are compared to measurements obtained on a site with four met masts. Second, the wake losses obtained with a commercial yield assessment solver (WindPRO 3.5) considering different wake decay constant definitions are compared to SCADA data. In both cases, it appears that dividing the timeseries in "stability classes" and using corresponding stability parameters in the CFD and in the wake model parameters enable a reduction of the uncertainty. In the case of the energy estimation compared to SCADA, an improvement of 1.25% is obtained compared to the conventional approach.

## 1. Introduction

According to WindEurope's Central Scenario, 323 GW of cumulative wind energy capacity would be installed in the EU by 2030. With this capacity, wind energy would produce 888 TWh of electricity, equivalent to 30% of the EU's power demand [1].

However, the locations with high wind potential and meeting environmental and technological constraints, and where profitability can be maximized are limited. Consequently, the number of wind turbine (WT) within a wind farm (WF) are often maximized. Thus, downstream WT are exposed to lower incoming wind velocities than those operating upstream. This reduction of wind speed (WS), which is hereafter referred to as wake effects, are responsible for significant power losses in WF. Recently, the Dutch approved plans to double the amount of wind power in their part of the North Sea by 2030. Studies carried out concluded that to increase the energy yield of a WF by 50% required doubling the amount of WT within the allocated space [2]. However, associated wake losses are expected to increase by 30%.

Thermal stratification in the atmospheric boundary layer (ABL), hereafter referred to as Atmospheric Stability (AS) influence on WS, wake growth and decay has already been investigated in several reports [3], [4]. Studies quantifying the AS impact on wake interactions between WTs or WFs were carried out by using computational fluid dynamics (CFD) based on large-eddy simulation (LES) or Reynold-averaged Navier-Stokes (RANS) calculations coupled with a rotor actuator disk model of the WT [3], [4]. However, these models and approaches are still computationally expensive for engineering purposes as pointed out in the previous study of Branlard et al. [7].

Schmidt et al. [8] initially attempted to evaluate the AEP of a WF and model the AS impact on its output. They utilized one year of mesoscale model simulations as initial and boundary conditions for CFD calculations. These CFD calculations were performed for four distinct AS classes, each weighted according to their frequency of occurrence derived from the mesoscale model. Wind turbine wakes were modeled using two different methods: the first approach involved uniformly loaded actuator disks, while the second used simple engineering models. In the latter method, the AS impact on wakes were taken into account by fitting parameterized curves to the central wind speed deficit results from previously conducted CFD actuator disk simulations. Although this approach considers AS impact on wind speed and turbine wakes, it is not well-suited for engineering applications due to its significant computational demand. First, a mesoscale model must be executed to drive the CFD calculations, and then even more computationally intensive rotor actuator disk simulations are required to evaluate wakes and or calibrate engineering models.

Later, Martin et al. [9] investigated the AS impact on power curves and annual energy production (AEP) by utilizing upwind and nacelle-based measurements. The AS conditions were primarily characterized using the Bulk Richardson (BR) number and Turbulence Intensity (TI). The results demonstrated that the classification method plays a crucial role in the conclusions drawn. It was discovered that TI and BR agreed on stable conditions at 15% and unstable conditions at 17%. By employing tower data and TI classification, Martin et al. [9] determined that the AEP could fluctuate between -15% and -32% under various AS conditions when compared to AEP under neutral conditions. Meanwhile, using tower data and BR classification, they found that the AEP could range between +16% and -28% under different AS conditions compared to AEP under neutral conditions.

In their research, Bahamonde and al. [3] modelled the atmospheric SI on the AEP considering a single turbine WF. Only measurements were used and no CFD calculations were carried out. Wind speed profile were computed using the Monin-Obukhov (MO) similarity theory and considering a non-neutral empirical AS correction function. This approach suffers from the limitation of the MO limitations at higher heights [10]. Additional, having only one wind turbine do not allows to study the AS impact on the wakes. Furthermore, no validation against yield based on Supervisory Control and Data Acquisition (SCADA) data was performed.

More recently, Kim and al [11] analyzed changes in wind turbine power characteristics and annual energy production due to AS. The Wind farm studied have 15 turbines each having a 2 MW rated capacity. Similarly to Martin et al. [9], the AS conditions were primarily characterized using the Bulk Richardson (BR) number and Turbulence Intensity (TI). Additionally, no CFD was carried out, the power curve analysis were carried out using cup and nacelle anemometers mounted at the hub height of a meteorological mast. Kim and al [11] found the unstable regime generally showed a high AEP, and the highest AEP appeared in the moderately unstable condition. Kim and al [11] also found that the moderately unstable condition showed an AEP difference of approximately 4.0%, with the neutral condition at the average wind speed of the study site.

The aim of this work is to propose an approach suitable for engineering purposes and able to quantify the AS impact on the Annual Energy Production (AEP) of a WF. The novelty of our approach is to propose a workflow accounting for AS impact when assessing WS as well as wake effects while limiting computing efforts and using available engineering software. In order to evaluate the uncertainty of our approach, SCADA measurements from an undisclosed onshore WF were collected and the production from a selected subset of turbines was used. To the best of our knowledge, a similar approach to the one proposed in this study has not been carried out yet.

## 2. Data and models

First, this section presents the datasets used in this study, which includes meteorological measurements (hereafter simply referred to as "Mast data"), SCADA measurements, and Reanalysis data. Each dataset was inspected to ensure its quality and error-free for the study. The subsections below describe the specific characteristics of each dataset and the steps taken during the quality control process. Second, the different models used to derive WS, wind direction (WD) and turbulence intensity (TI) estimates are shortly introduced.

### *2.1. Mast data*

WS, WD, and TI were measured at four masts located within the wind farm: they are referred to as Mast A, Mast B, Mast C, and Mast D. For confidentiality reasons, the specific locations and measurement periods are not provided.

In this study, Mast A was set to the primary mast and used for horizontal extrapolation of WS, WD, and TI at every 10 minutes to the three other masts. Measurements were taken at 32m, 50m, and 59m above ground level (AGL). The anemometers used in the measurement campaign have been calibrated before installation and class I anemometers were used. Each mast has the same configuration and uses the same sensor types. For Mast A, a total of 1666 days of measurements were available. Out of these measurement durations, 784 days were free from turbine wake. Mast B, C, and D were solely used for validation purposes. **Table 1** shows the inter-distance between Mast A and Mast B, Mast A and Mast C, and Mast A and Mast D, as well as their overlapping measurement periods.

**Table 1**:Inter-distance and overlapping periods between masts. The overlapping period considers days that are free from turbine wake. It was estimated up to the day of the 1$^{st}$ turbine installation

| | **Predictand** | | |
|---|---|---|---|
| **Predictor** | Mast B | Mast C | Mast D |
| | distances | | |
| Mast A | 17.5 km | 21.2 km | 17.5 km |
| | Overlapping measurement periods | | |
| | 391 days | 441 days | 314 days |

A quality check of the measurement data has been carried out according to standard practice [12]. Therefore, the following steps were carried out:

1. range test to ensure that measured data lies within operational range of sensors
2. constant value test: repetitions of consecutive data with the same value,
3. visual inspection of the data to detect invalid data such as spikes or sudden drops,
4. filtering out icing events,
5. correlation test to assess whether the correlation between different sensors at two heights is plausible,
6. correction the mast shading effects.

After conducting the quality checks described above, the availability at 59m for Mast A, B, C and D were 91.8%, 84.2%, 90.5% and 63.9%, respectively.

Journal of Physics: Conference Series **2507** (2023) 012018 doi:10.1088/1742-6596/2507/1/012018

### 2.2. *SCADA data*

For this study, one year of data were collected from a wind farm of approximately two hundreds of MW installed capacity. The data on turbine-level is available as 10-minute statistics. The production data, nacelle WS, WD, estimated turbulence, alarms code and alarms estimated power loss were also available. Only the power production alarms code and alarms estimated power loss were used in this study.
About 20 thousand alarms were collected from SCADA system from all WTs during the considered period. Prior to using SCADA data for power production evaluation, data representing curtailment, downtime, and other anomalies were filtered out. It is worth noting that time stamps with alarm code raised and with positive estimated power loss were filtered out. When comparing the estimated power production to SCADA measurement, only the concurrent time stamps are considered.

In this study we focus on a single wind direction, the main direction and one row in order to reduce the uncertainty that could appear while taking a large number of turbines which might not operate simultaneously.

### 2.3. *Reanalysis data*

To assess the AS conditions at the study site, MO lengths derived from the ECMWF Atmospheric Reanalysis 5 (ERA5) [13] output at a height of 2m were used. The ERA5 outputs were freely available but in this study, the data were downloaded from WindPro on a rectangular geographical grid with a resolution of 0.25 x 0.25 degrees.

The MO length was estimated using the following parameters: 2m friction velocity, 2m instantaneous surface sensible heat flux, 2m temperature, surface pressure, and humidity. As temperature measurements were not available at two different heights at masts, it was not possible to compute the stability at hub height. A benefit of using reanalysis for assessing the AS are their availability worldwide and free of charge. Besides, they dispense the need for running a in house mesoscale model. Drawbacks of using reanalysis for assessing the AS are their horizontal and vertical resolution.

The different AS classes used in this study were defined as follows:

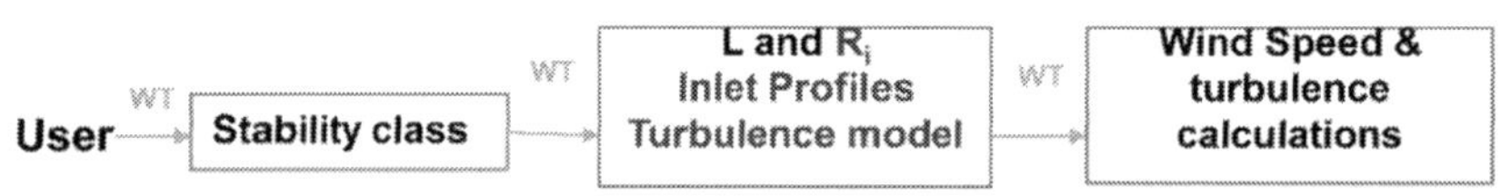


| WT Stability Class | Stability | Monin-Obukhov length (m) | Corresponding M-O length interval |
|---|---|---|---|
| 0 | Very unstable | -80 | -140 < L < 0 |
| 1 | Unstable | -500 | -1000 < L < -140 |
| 2 | Neutral | 10000 | L < -1000 or L > 2500 |
| 3 | Slightly stable | 1500 | 1000 < L < 2500 |
| 4 | Stable | 800 | 600 < L < 1000 |
| 5 | Stable | 500 | 380 < L < 600 |
| 6 | Stable | 300 | 220 < L < 380 |
| 7 | Very stable | 200 | 140 < L < 220 |
| 8 | Very stable | 130 | 60 < L < 140 |
| 9 | Strongly stable | 60 | L < 60 |

Figure 1: Atmospheric stability classes as defined in the Meteodyn CFD software [14].

### *2.4. CFD Model*

Meteodyn WT 5.3 [14], hereafter Meteodyn, is a software that solves steady, incompressible, isothermal, and turbulent flow problems using the Reynolds-Averaged Navier-Stokes (RANS) equations. Turbulent fluxes are modeled using a one-equation k-L turbulence closure scheme [15].

The software numerically solves the state variable on a finite-volume grid, which is set up over a selected area using site-independent vertical wind profiles at the inlet boundaries of the computational domain. To obtain site-specific WS from these profiles, measurements heights at masts are required as an anchor point.

Meteodyn accounts for the AS by adjusting the turbulent length scale and viscosity based on a user-defined AS classification **Figure 1**. **Table 2** presents the mesh setting in Meteodyn CFD used in this study, while other parameters remained unchanged and followed the standard options in Meteodyn. The mesh consisted of approximately 2 million points, with 850 points in the x-direction, 697 in the y-direction, and 35 in the z-direction. The computational time per sector was about 160 minutes, and each sector was run on a single core.

Table 2:Meteodyn mesh setting

| | Mesh option |
|---|---|
| Minimal horizontal resolution | 25m |
| Minimal vertical resolution | 4m |
| Horizontal expansion coefficient | 1.04 |
| Vertical expansion coefficient | 1.2 |
| Verticality | 0.5 |
| Radius | 14 km |
| No. wind directions | 36 |

### *2.5. WindPro and WAsP*

The Wind Atlas Analysis and Applications Program (WAsP) [16] is a linearized flow model that has been widely applied in wind energy industry for flow modeling and site assessment over the past 30 years. The WAsP methodology estimates the wind climate at a particular point by extrapolating horizontally and vertically from a measured wind climate at a nearby point. To do this, the model removes topographic effects, such as orographic, roughness, and obstacles, from the known wind climate estimated by the linearized flow model using the topographical maps of the surrounding area. The model then applies drag law relations for vertical extrapolation and adds the estimated topographic effects at the target point to the wind climate. WAsP is applicable for the locations where the geostrophic forcing remains constant [17][18].

WindPRO 3.5 [19], hereafter referred as WindPro, is used for two purposes:

1. To compute the AEP using the WS estimated with Meteodyn and user provided wakes. In this case the WAsP model is not used;

2. To compute a WindPro classical AEP that is used solely as a benchmark to assess the benefit of accounting for the AS. In this case WAsP is used and no correction for AS were made in these runs; neutral conditions were assumed.

In this study, WAsP 11.6 is used as an internal calculation engine within the WindPro software [19] to produce WS estimates. This version do not include the AS model option introduced in WAsP 12.8.

When performing the WAsP calculation, the Copernicus Global Land [21] and NASADEM [22] databases were used as input for roughness and orography, respectively. The WS, WD, and TI are obtained from Mast A. In this study, wakes were computed using N.O Jensen Park 2 [23]. The associated wake decay constant (WDC) was computed as a fraction of turbulence intensity, as detailed below.

## 3. Proposed methodology and evaluation approach

This section describes the methodology and the procedure carried out for its evaluation. First, the stability dependent method and how it compares to classical AEP is discussed. Second, the validation steps are described including the statistical metrics chosen. Third, a summary of the conducted experiment is provided.

### *3.1. A method accounting for stability in the AEP*

#### *3.1.1. Classical AEP workflow*

The typical workflow for the estimation of the AEP in the wind industry consists in [24]:

1. Computing speed-up factors (SF) between measurement location(s) and wind turbine location(s) for each WD sector for every 10-min averaged time stamps. These SF can be obtained using a linear model (WAsP [16]) or a CFD model (Openfoam [25], Meteodyn [26] , WindSim [27]) using the RANS equations. Both linear and CFD models are typically used assuming neutral AS [20], [28]–[30]. Having the SF enables to compute free-stream WS at each wind turbine location.

2. WS measurements durations is lower than 7 - 8 years in most cases, they are often correlated with hourly mesoscale model outputs to obtain long-term and representative periods, i.e. 10- or 20-year WS estimates. In our study we did not carry out any long term extrapolation.

3. Computing for each WT the single wake model and aggregate all individual wakes using a mathematical or an empirical combination rule to account for multiple turbine wakes. The diurnal variation of the wake expansion due to the AS is not accounted for by engineering models at this stage [6], [7], [31].

4. Interpolating linearly the power curve provided by the manufacturer to obtain the expected power production for every WS data at the WT location(s).

5. Summing the estimation for each turbine and each timestamp to get a yearly MWh figure.

### *3.1.2. A workflow including stability in the AEP*

The novelty of our approach is to propose a workflow accounting for the AS impact on AEP while limiting computing efforts and using available engineering software. Usually stability condition is either assumed neutral or chosen based on yearly mean stability on the site. This approach does not account for the AS variability with time. One solution to include the time dependence would be to run 10 CFD computations corresponding to the stability classes available in Meteodyn (**Figure 1**) and use results every 10 minutes according to the stability per 10 min. Yet, this approach require intensive computing power. We propose to use only a small representative subset of the 10 CFD possibility depending on the AS pattern analysis.

Our aim is to include the AS impact when assessing WS as well as wake effects, as described in the first and second steps of the workflow. Therefore, the following procedure is carried out to obtain the AEP considering AS:

1. First, a set of 10 CFD computations were run with Meteodyn CFD accounting for all AS classes ranging from very unstable to strongly stable. In our approach, only two CFD computations for two AS classes are used. The remaining eight computations are used only to validate our approach and quantify the impact of selecting a subset of these 10 computations representing all AS conditions. This approach allows being computationally affordable and describing day and night diurnal AS variations that were observed from mesoscale models estimates. Time series from the two selected classes are combined as follows: stable during nighttime and unstable during daytime. Consequently, the AS which is often neglected is accounted for in the first step of the workflow (section 3.1.1. ).

2. Second, the atmospheric AS is also accounted for when assessing wakes. For this purpose, the N.O Jensen Park 2 model is first used with the free-stream WS obtained at the previous step. The coupling with atmospheric strategies is obtained using turbulence intensities (TI) from measurements as a proxy. As described by [32], for simple and homogeneous terrain TI may be expressed as a function of AS as follows:

$$TI = \frac{A \times \kappa}{\ln\left(\frac{z}{z_0}\right) - \psi\left(\frac{z}{L}\right)}; \quad (1)$$

where $\kappa$ is the Kármán constant; A, a parameter depending on AS and ABL height; $z_0$ the roughness length and $\psi$ the AS correction function that depends on the height z above ground and the Monin-Obukhov length L. Therefore, having time-varying TI values accounts for time-varying AS. TI can either be obtained from mast measurements or from mesoscale model. To model wakes, a time dependent wake decay constant (WDC) for the N.O Jensen Park 2 model is again used; it is obtained by multiplying the TI by a fixed coefficient as suggested in [31], [32].

$$WDC = \mathrm{a} \times TI \quad (2)$$

Where, a is a constant that is selected based on the wake model. N.O Jensen Park 2 model that is equivalent to 0.48 [23]. Consequently, the AS is accounted for in the third step of the workflow (section 3.1.1. ).

### *3.2. Methodology validation*

To validate our approach, we proceeded by a comparison against masts for the WS and against SCADA for the AEP.

#### *3.2.1 Comparison against mast data*

First, the WS estimates obtained using Meteodyn including AS are compared against measurements from four masts. Second, the impact of selecting a subset, i.e. two stability classes instead of the entirety (10 stability classes defined in Meteodyn) is evaluated. For this validation purpose, a single time-series of WS is constructed considering the 10 time-series for all stability conditions. This construction is done as follows:

$$WS(t) = \sum_{i=0}^{N} f_{ci} \times WS_{ci}(t). \quad (3)$$

where, ($f_i$) is the frequency of occurrence for each stability class ($c_i$) ; it is computed based on ERA 5; ($WS_i$) is the 10 min wind speed time series generated from CFD computations and N+1 stability classes considered.

#### *3.2.2 Comparison against SCADA*

AEP accounting for AS, hereafter referred to as stability dependent AEP, is compared against production data extracted from SCADA measurements. The approach proposed here is also compared against AEP calculated using WAsP and WindPro [9] [17] based on WS time series at the turbine locations from neutral stability. No SF are computed by WindPro itself; it is used for assessing wakes, blockage and AEP figures considering a single averaged TI value and WDC. This result is used as a reference and hereafter referred to as non-stability dependent AEP.

#### *3.2.3 Statistical metrics used for comparison*

Statistical metrics such as the mean bias error (MBE), mean absolute error (MAE) and standard deviation (StD) of the error of the bias are evaluated. The definition of these metrics are found in [33].

The rationale for choosing these metrics are as follows: the MBE gives an information on whether there is an overestimation or underestimation. Yet, for the MBE, positive biases can compensate negative biases; therefore a bias close to 0 might not reflect accurately a model performance. To alleviate this drawback, the MAE was also used. This metric is not susceptible to outliers; besides errors cumulate and do not cancel each other out. Finally, the StD allows analyzing the spread of the MBE; it gives an indication of how biases between a model and measurements at given times are distributed compared to the mean bias value, the MBE.

### *3.3. Experiments summary*

A total of four experiments are carried in this study. The first and second experiments assess the accuracy of the WS estimates whereas experiment 3 and 4 assess the accuracy of the AEP estimates.

The first experiment analyses the WS estimates from Meteodyn's 10 stability classes to assess the wind resource (section 2.3). The second experiment combines a subset of Meteodyn stability 10 classes following Equation (3). WS from both experiments 1 and 2 are compared against mast measurements.

The third experiment uses the WS estimates from experiment two that is computed at each turbine location and a stability dependent WDC to compute a stability dependent AEP (section 3.1.2. ). The fourth experiment computes an AEP using WindPro and WAsP. WS are horizontally extrapolated from mast A to each turbines and a single yearly averaged wake for 12 wind directions is used. AEP from both experiment 3 and 4 are compared against SCADA measurements.

## 4. Results and discussion

The first subsection analyzes the diurnal and monthly variations in different atmospheric stabilities. The second subsection compares the WS estimates from Meteodyn stability classes with measurements at masts. In the third and fourth subsections, the WS estimates from each stability class are weighted, combined, and used as input for assessing the AEP. Finally, AEP derived from our proposed methodology were compared with the SCADA measurements.

### *4.1. Diurnal and monthly variation of the atmospheric stability*

**Figure 2** displays the frequency of occurrence for each stability class (as defined in **Figure 1**) on an hourly and monthly basis at 2m AGL. **Figure 2** illustrates that class 0 (very unstable) and 9 (strongly stable) are the most frequent stability classes. Additionally, there appears to be a pattern of stability during night-time and instability during daytime. This result is in line with what we would expect because night-time temperatures tend to be more homogenized, which hinders mixing and favours stability.

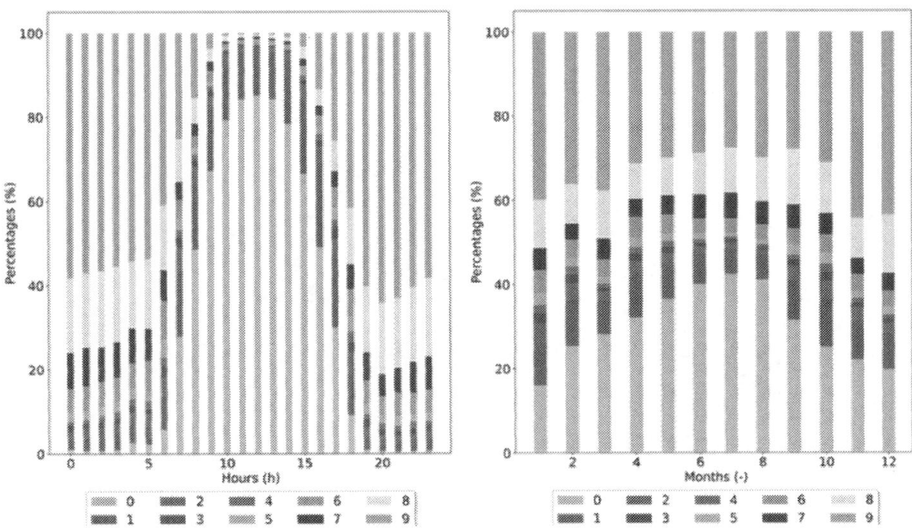


**Figure 2**: Monthly and diurnal variation in different atmospheric stability at 2m high AGL derived from ERA5 estimates.

As temperature measurements were not available at two different heights at masts, it was not possible to compute the stability at hub height. Therefore, it was assumed that while the frequency of occurrence of each stability class may change, the pattern of stability during nighttime and instability during daytime will still hold at higher heights. Based on this assumption, we derived a stability-dependent TI and, therefore, a TI dependent WDC. **Figure 3** shows a static TI, while **Figure 4** shows time- and stability-dependent TI. Higher values of TI during daytime will lead to a faster wake recovery rate due to enhanced mixing, whereas lower TI will lead to a slower wake recovery rate [4]. defining two TI, rather than one mean, enables to describe the diurnal variation of wakes.

As a result, this time- and stability-dependent TI will lead to lower wind speed in the turbine wake during nightime and higher wind speed during daytime compared to the static TI.

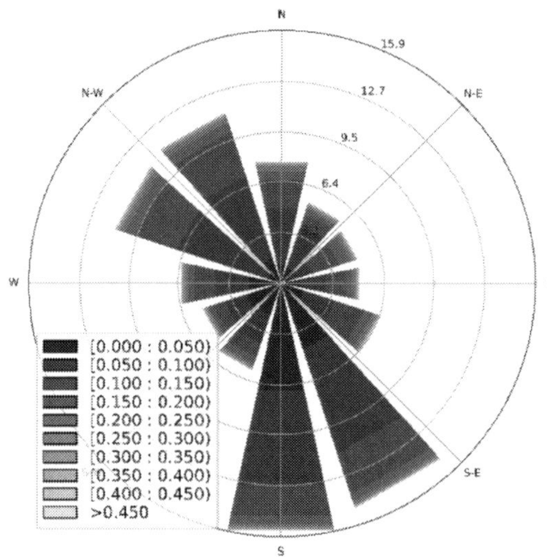


**Figure 3**: TI rose at Mast A. This TI rose does not vary with time and account for atmospheric stability to calculate diurnal variations. The main wind direction is 150 ±15°

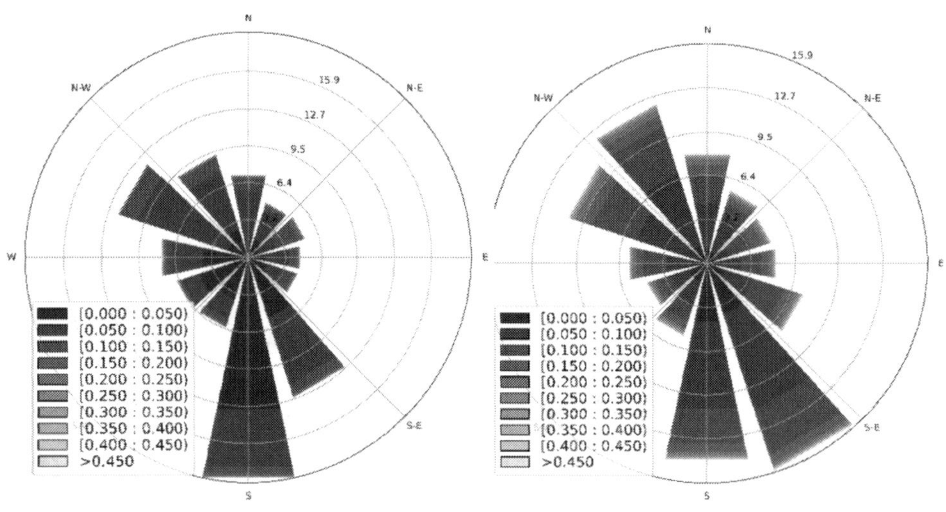


**Figure 4**: Time dependent TI rose at Mast A. This TI varies with time: the figure on the left-side shows values during nightime (stable) whereas the figure on the right-side shows values during daytime (unstable)

### *4.2. Evaluating the error and the sensitivity in wind speed when using different stability classes as inputs for the CFD model*

In this section, the accuracy of Meteodyn WS estimates extrapolated for each stability classes from Mast A to Mast B, C, and D is evaluated.

**Figure 5**, **Figure 7** and **Figure 9** compare the wind speed estimates for each stability class calculated by Meteodyn against measurements from Mast B, C, and D at a height of 32m AGL. **Figure 6**, **Figure 8** and **Figure 10** shows the same comparison at a height of 59m.

**Figure 5**, **Figure 7** and **Figure 9** reveal that the wind speed estimates with stability class 9 at a height of 32m AGL, have the worst performance: with the highest MBE and MAE. However, wind speed estimates with stability class 9 at a height of 59m, have the best performance: with the lowest MBE except for Mast B. Therefore, the accuracy of each stability class appears to be height dependent. A good compromise for both heights were able to find at stability class 6.

Moreover, at 32m AGL, the difference between the model with the lowest MBE and the model with the highest MBE is greater than at 59m AGL. At Mast D, this difference reaches approximately 25% for 32m, while for Mast B and C, it ranges between 23% and 29%. In contrast, at 59m, the difference reaches 2% at Mast D, while for Mast B and C, it ranges between 1% and 3%. A similar pattern were observed with the MAE.

To further analyze the strengths and weaknesses of each stability class, the diurnal patterns of errors is examined from **Figure 11** to **Figure 13**. These figures display the percentage bias of wind speed estimates between calculated by Meteodyn and measurement at Mast C at a height of 32m for the very unstable, neutral, and strongly stable stability classes. They also illustrate how the accuracy of each model can be divided into three distinctive time bins that follow clear patterns: the first bin (B1) ranges from 00:00 to 08:00, the second bin (B2) ranges from 08:00 to 18:00, and the third bin ranges from 18:00 to 00:00 (B3). B1 and B3 represent nighttime, while B2 represents daytime.

Additionally, **Figure 14** illustrates that between 08:00 and 18:00, the bias distribution for stability class 2 is centered around 0, while it is skewed to the left for stability classes 8 and 9. In contrast, during nighttime, the bias distribution for stability class 2 is skewed to the right, while the distributions for stability classes 8 and 9 are centered around 0. As a result, the accuracy of unstable models (classes 8 and 9) decreases during daytime and increases during nighttime.

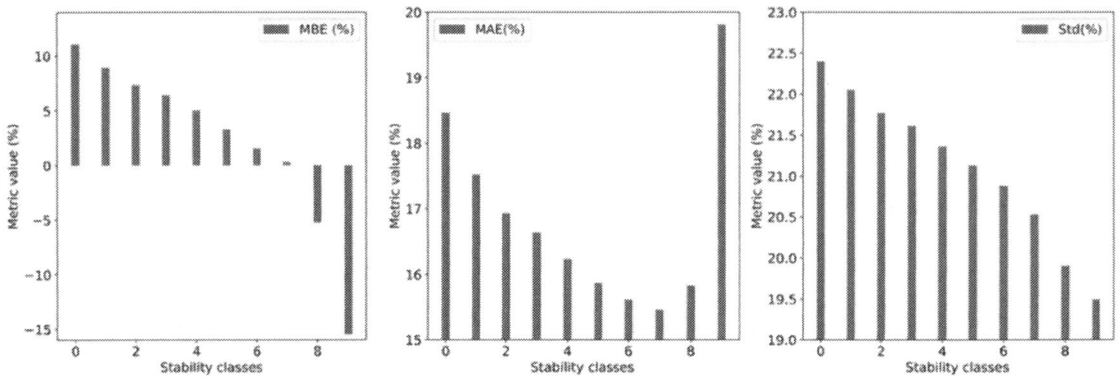


**Figure 5**: Comparisons of wind speed estimates by Meteodyn for each class against measurements at 32m AGL at Mast D.

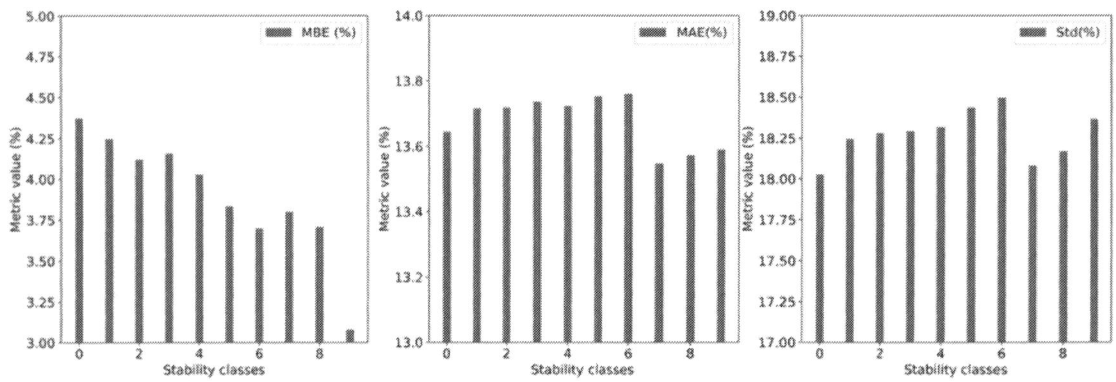


**Figure 6:** Comparisons of wind speed estimates by Meteodyn for each class against measurements at 59m AGL at Mast D.

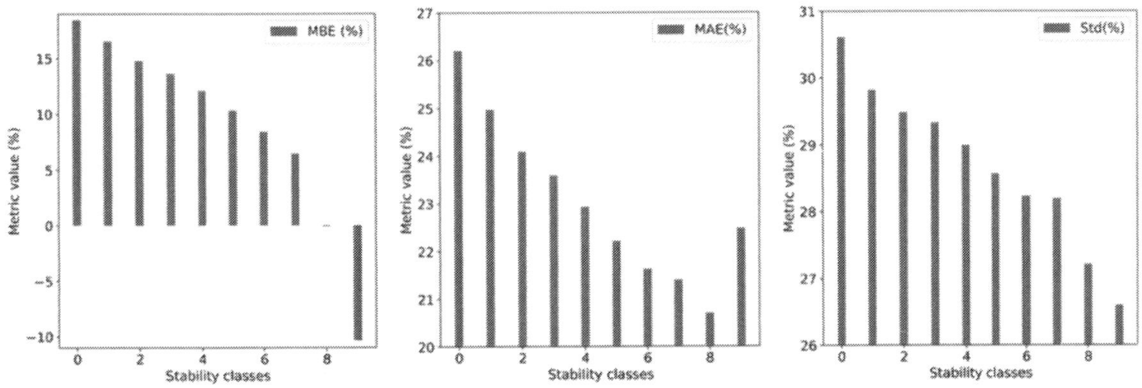


**Figure 7**: Comparisons of wind speed estimates by Meteodyn for each class against measurements at 32m AGL at Mast C

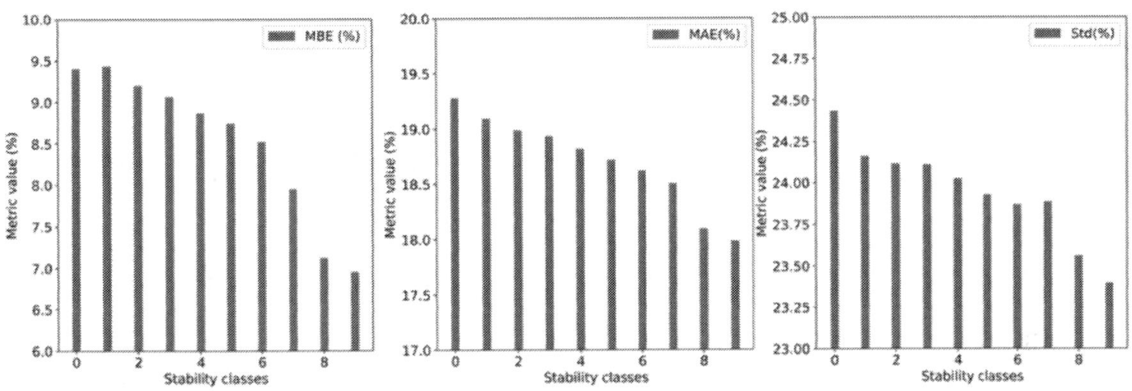


**Figure 8:** Comparisons of wind speed estimates by Meteodyn for each class against measurements at 59m AGL at Mast C

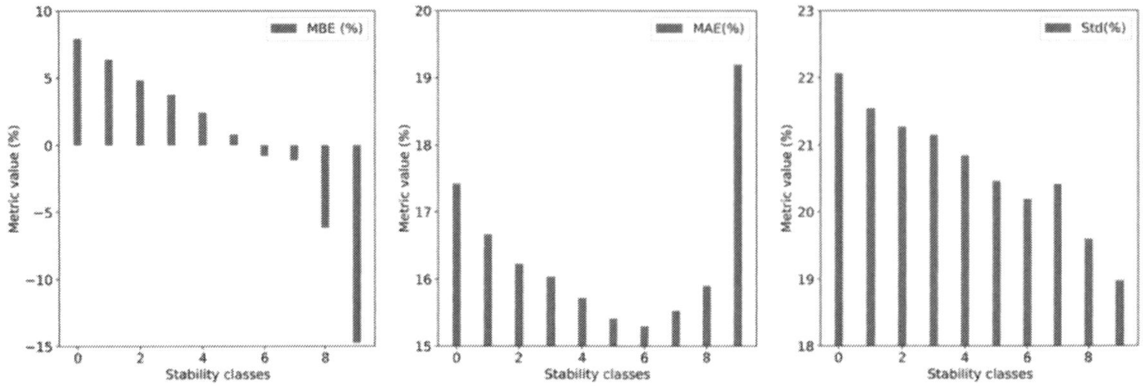


**Figure 9**: Comparisons of wind speed estimates by Meteodyn for each class against measurements at 32m AGL at Mast B

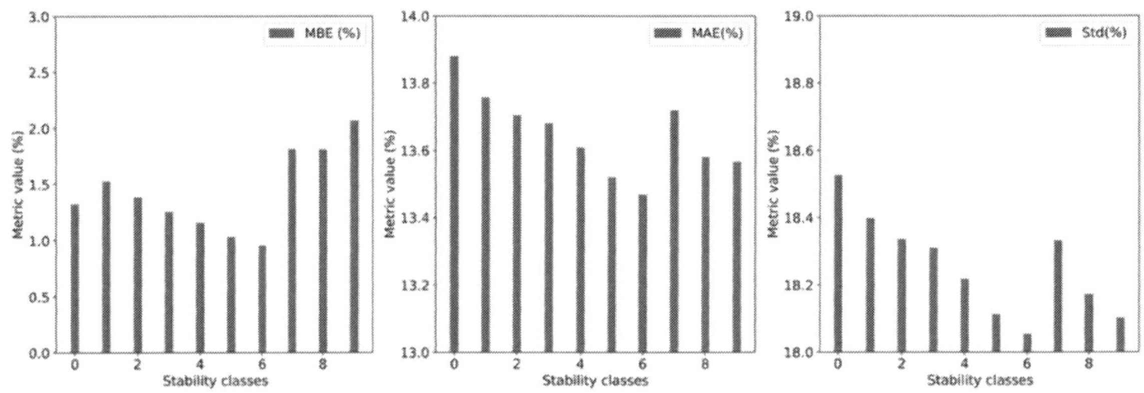


**Figure 10:** Comparisons of wind speed estimates by Meteodyn for each class against measurements at 59m AGL at Mast B

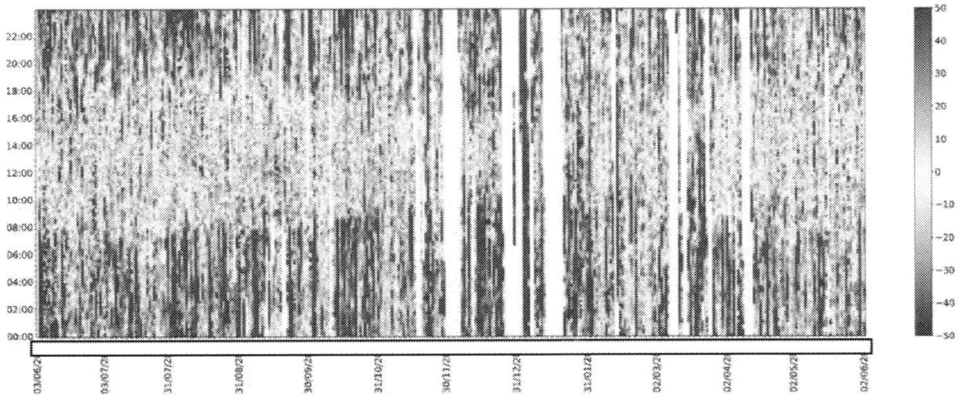


**Figure 11**: Comparisons of WS estimate for stability class 2 (neutral) at 32m AGL between Meteodyn vs Mast C. The color bar represents the bias in (%) for each time stamp. Data range from 03/06/2xxx to 02/06/2xxx, they were normalized using Mast C yearly mean value of wind speed at 32m.

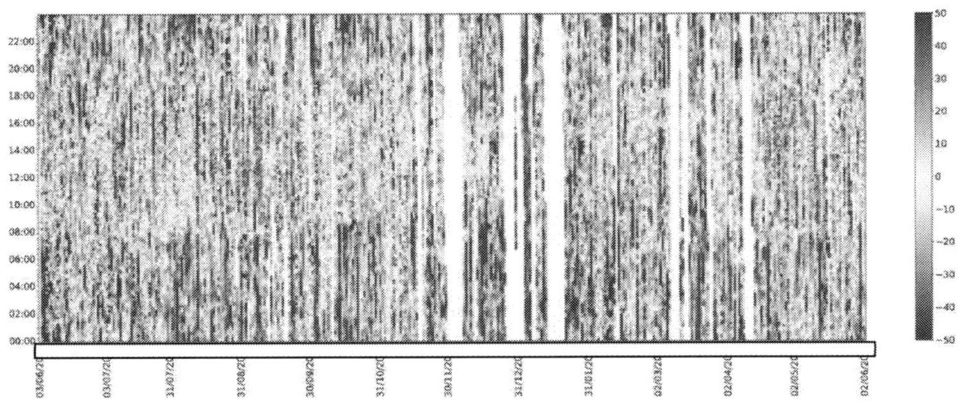


**Figure 12:** : Comparisons of WS estimate for class 8 (very stable) at 32m AGL between Meteodyn vs Mast C. The color bar represents the bias in (%) for each time stamp. Data range from 03/06/2xxx to 02/06/2xxx, they were normalized using Mast C yearly mean value of wind speed at 32m.

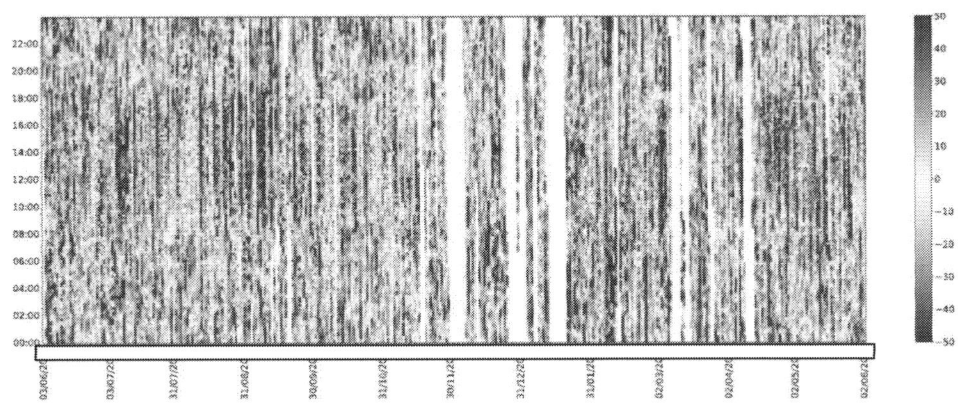


**Figure 13:** : Comparisons of WS estimate for class 9 (strongly stable) at 32m AGL between Meteodyn vs Mast C. The color bar represents the bias in (%) for each time stamp. White coloured data represent missing and or filtered data after quality check. Data range from 03/06/2xxx to 02/06/2xxx, they were normalized using Mast C yearly mean value of wind speed at 32m.

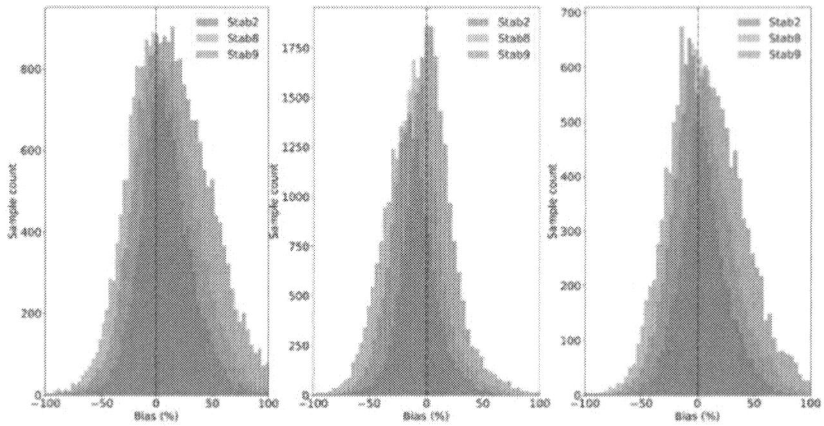


**Figure 14:** : Comparisons of WS estimate bias (%) for class 2, 8 and 9 at 32m AGL, respectively between Meteodyn vs Mast C. Left chart contains samples between 00:00 to 08:00, middle chart contains samples from 08:00 to 18:00, right chart contains samples from 18:00 to 00:00.

### *4.3. Combining Meteodyn WS estimates from different stability classes*

To combine WS estimates from Meteodyn for different stability classes, Equation (3) described in the previous chapter methodology was used. Two combination strategies are considered here: the first strategy uses all ten stability classes (referred to as "frequency"), while the second strategy uses only stability classes 0 and 9, which are the most frequent classes (referred to as "day-night").

**Figure 15** to **Figure 17** compare the results from the Meteodyn stability class with the lowest MAE presented in **Figure 6**, **Figure 8** and **Figure 10** against the frequency and day-night strategies for Masts B, C, and D. The results show that the frequency strategy yields the poorest results, which is attributed to the ERA5 derived stability at 2m AGL being unable to accurately reproduce the stability at turbine hub height. In contrast, the day-night strategy achieves an accuracy similar to the results of the Meteodyn stability classes with the lowest MAE. MAE, StD are within a 1% difference for all masts at 59m AGL.

Based on these findings, we conclude that for the studied site, instead of computing all ten stability classes, only two classes (0 and 9) are sufficient for accurate AEP estimation using WS estimates by Meteodyn CFD.

Journal of Physics: Conference Series **2507** (2023) 012018 doi:10.1088/1742-6596/2507/1/012018

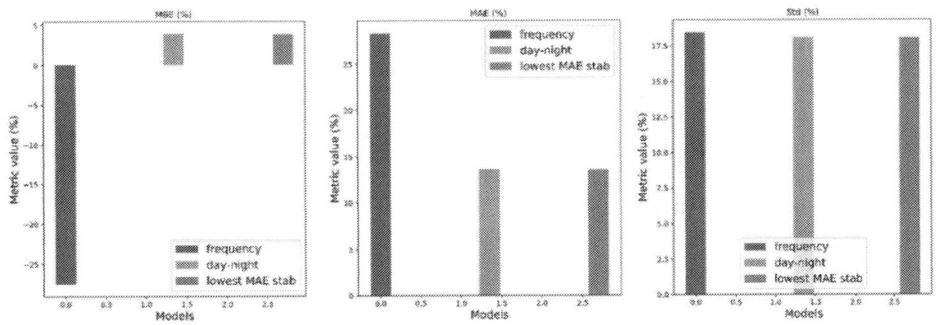


**Figure 15**: Comparisons of Meteodyn stability class with the lowest MAE against the frequency and day-night strategy at 59m AGL for mast D

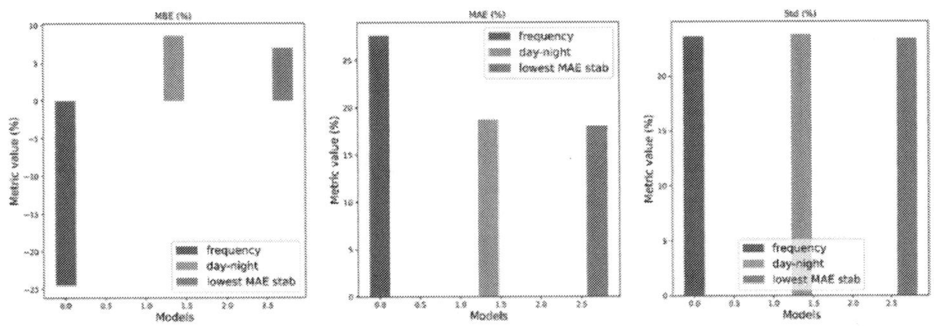


**Figure 16:** : Comparisons of Meteodyn stability class with the lowest MAE against the frequency and day-night strategy at 59m AGL for mast C

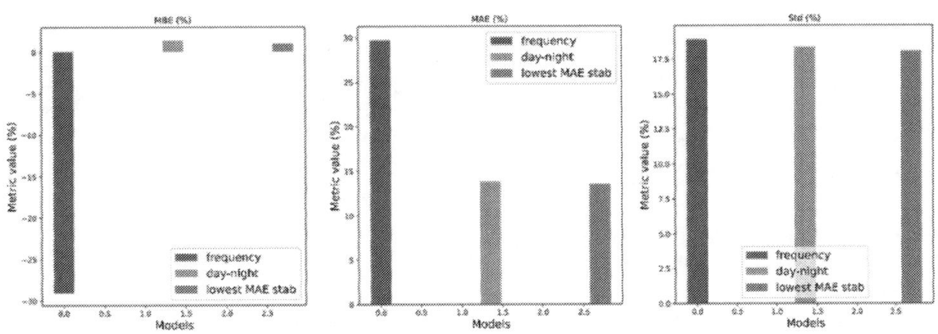


**Figure 17:** : Comparisons of Meteodyn stability class with the lowest MAE against the frequency and day-night strategy at 59m AGL for mast B

### *4.4. Comparison of AEP calculated based on SCADA against modelled ones*

**Table 3** presents a comparison between Windpro classical AEP, called "WindPRO with WDC" (see section 2.5. ) and the stability dependent AEP introduced in this study. For the stability dependent AEP, we distinguish a case with a stability dependent wake "Day-night with WDC(t)" and non-stability dependent wake "Day-night with WDC". Each modelled AEP are benchmarked against SCADA measurements, see section 0. The comparisons consider a row of 4 turbines following the main wind direction that is 150 ±15° (**Figure 3**).

To minimize the effect of extrapolation, a model-dependent correction factor is applied to set the bias at the first turbine to zero. This correction factor is then successively applied to the second, third, and fourth turbines, following the primary wind direction. This method enables a focus along the turbines row. Consequently, the MBE were updated and are shown Table 3.

Overall, Table 3 indicates that the method proposed here result in an improvement ranging between 1.24% and 1.27% of production for the selected row of turbines and for the main wind direction.

Table 3:MBE of each model

| | MBE (%) |
|---|---|
| WindPRO with WDC | 2.09 |
| Day-night with WDC(t) | 0.85 |
| Day-night with WDC | 0.82 |

## 5. Summary and conclusions

The objective of this study is to develop an engineering approach to quantify the impact of Atmospheric Stability (AS) on the net production of a large wind farm (WF), while minimizing computational effort and utilizing available engineering software. Our innovative method accounts for AS when evaluating wind speed (WS) and wake effects on Annual Energy Production (AEP).

To incorporate AS into wind speed estimates, we employed a two-stage process. First, diurnal and monthly variations in different atmospheric stability conditions were derived from ERA5 reanalysis data. By identifying the dominant atmospheric stability classes, we were able to reduce the effort associated with WS estimates limiting the amount of distinct stability classes (calculated using Meteodyn 5.3 WT) considered from ten to two classes. These two classes represent the observed diurnal variations in stabilities: stable during nighttime and unstable during daytime. We concluded that although the frequency of occurrence of each stability class may change, the pattern of nighttime stability and daytime instability persists at higher elevations. Second, we constructed time series of WS using very unstable stability for daytime and strongly stable stability for nighttime, referred to as the day-night strategy. This approach allowed us to obtain wind speeds that vary with AS.

The accuracy of the day-night strategy's WS was assessed through a comparison with WS measurements from three masts. The discrepancy was within 1% of Mean Bias Error, Mean Absolute Error, and Standard deviation of the bias when compared to the WS estimates of the Meteodyn 5.3 model with the lowest Mean Absolute Error. For other sites, this discrepancy value might be different depending on the diurnal on monthly variability of the AS pattern.

To account for AS in the wake effects, we defined two mean wake decay constants, one derived from daytime mean turbulence intensity (TI) and the other from nighttime mean TI. This enabled us to describe the diurnal variation of wakes and establish a time-dependent wake.

By combining the WS and wakes obtained using the day-night strategy, we calculated a stability-dependent AEP. This stability-dependent AEP was compared to SCADA measurements and was also benchmarked against a classical neutral AEP based on WAsP. For this analysis, a single row of turbines following the main wind direction, rather than the entire wind farm for all wind directions, was used. The production from the day-night strategy was found to be closer to measured production from SCADA than the production modelled using neutral calculations, demonstrating an improvement in production estimates by approximately 1.25%. To conclude, having a stability dependent AEP is of prime importance for site with stabilities that are predominantly non neutral.

**References**

[1] Aloys Nghiem and al., "Wind energy in Europe: Outlook to 2020." WindEurope, 2017.
[2] B. Mark, "EU offshore wind: A trade off between density and efficiency," *Windpower monthly*, 2022.
[3] M. I. Bahamonde and S. P. Litrán, "Study of the energy production of a wind turbine in the open sea considering the continuous variations of the atmospheric stability and the sea surface roughness," *Renew. Energy*, vol. 135, pp. 163–175, May 2019, doi: 10.1016/j.renene.2018.11.075.
[4] F. Porté-Agel, M. Bastankhah, and S. Shamsoddin, "Wind-Turbine and Wind-Farm Flows: A Review," *Bound.-Layer Meteorol.*, vol. 174, no. 1, pp. 1–59, Jan. 2020, doi: 10.1007/s10546-019-00473-0.
[5] A. M. Forsting *et al.*, "Verification of induction zone models for wind farm annual energy production estimation," *J. Phys. Conf. Ser.*, vol. 1934, no. 1, p. 012023, May 2021, doi: 10.1088/1742-6596/1934/1/012023.
[6] M. Abkar and F. Porté-Agel, "Influence of atmospheric stability on wind-turbine wakes: A large-eddy simulation study," *Phys. Fluids*, vol. 27, no. 3, p. 035104, Mar. 2015, doi: 10.1063/1.4913695.
[7] E. Branlard, E. Quon, A. R. Meyer Forsting, J. King, and P. Moriarty, "Wind farm blockage effects: comparison of different engineering models," *J. Phys. Conf. Ser.*, vol. 1618, no. 6, p. 062036, Sep. 2020, doi: 10.1088/1742-6596/1618/6/062036.
[8] J. Schmidt, C.-Y. Chang, M. Dörenkämper, M. Salimi, T. Teichmann, and B. Stoevesandt, "The consideration of atmospheric stability within wind farm AEP calculations," *J. Phys. Conf. Ser.*, vol. 749, p. 012002, Sep. 2016, doi: 10.1088/1742-6596/749/1/012002.
[9] C. M. St. Martin, J. K. Lundquist, A. Clifton, G. S. Poulos, and S. J. Schreck, "Wind turbine power production and annual energy production depend on atmospheric stability and turbulence," *Wind Energy Sci.*, vol. 1, no. 2, pp. 221–236, Nov. 2016, doi: 10.5194/wes-1-221-2016.
[10] A. Peña, S.-E. Gryning, and C. B. Hasager, "Comparing mixing-length models of the diabatic wind profile over homogeneous terrain," *Theor. Appl. Climatol.*, vol. 100, no. 3–4, pp. 325–335, May 2010, doi: 10.1007/s00704-009-0196-8.
[11] D.-Y. Kim, Y.-H. Kim, and B.-S. Kim, "Changes in wind turbine power characteristics and annual energy production due to atmospheric stability, turbulence intensity, and wind shear," *Energy*, vol. 214, p. 119051, Jan. 2021, doi: 10.1016/j.energy.2020.119051.
[12] MEASNET, "MEASNET: Evaluation of site specific wind conditions." Measurement network of wind energy institutes, 2016. [Online]. Available: https://www.measnet.com/wp-content/uploads/2016/05/Measnet_SiteAssessment_V2.0.pdf

[13]EMD, "ERA5(T) Rectangular Grid," 2022. https://help.emd.dk/mediawiki/index.php?title=ERA5(T)_Rectangular_Grid
[14]Meteodyn, "Meteodyn WT Help Facility and On-line Documentation." METEODYN MANUEL TEST, 2023.
[15]D. L. Martindale and T. L. Acker, "Distributed wind resource assessment: Comparing measured annual energy production with predictions from computational fluid dynamics," *Wind Eng.*, vol. 43, no. 6, pp. 657–672, Dec. 2019, doi: 10.1177/0309524X19846515.
[16]Troen, I., & Lundtang Petersen, E, *European Wind Atlas*, Risø National Laboratory. 1989.
[17]M. Dörenkämper *et al.*, "The Making of the New European Wind Atlas – Part 2: Production and evaluation," *Geosci. Model Dev.*, vol. 13, no. 10, pp. 5079–5102, Oct. 2020, doi: 10.5194/gmd-13-5079-2020.
[18]L. Landberg, N. G. Mortensen, O. Rathmann, and L. Myllerup, "The similarity principle - on using models correctly," in *Proceedings CD-ROM. CD 2*, European Wind Energy Association (EWEA), 2003.
[19]WindPro, EMD International A/S, "windPRO 3.5," *https://www.emd-international.com/windpro/downloads/*, Nov. 2022.
[20]G. Giebel, S.-E. Gryning, and G. Giebel, "Shear and stability in high met masts, and how WAsP treats it," p. 8, 2007.
[21]M. Buchhorn *et al.*, "Copernicus Global Land Service: Land Cover 100m: collection 3: epoch 2019: Globe." Zenodo, Sep. 08, 2020. doi: 10.5281/ZENODO.3939050.
[22]OpenTopography, "NASADEM Global 1 arc-second Digital Elevation Model," 2021, doi: 10.5069/G93T9FD9.
[23]O. S. Rathmann, B. O. Hansen, K. S. Hansen, N. G. Mortensen, and J. P. M. Leon, "The Park2 Wake Model - Documentation and Validation".
[24]S. Barber *et al.*, "The wide range of factors contributing to wind resource assessment accuracy in complex terrain," *Wind Energy Sci.*, vol. 7, no. 4, pp. 1503–1525, Jul. 2022, doi: 10.5194/wes-7-1503-2022.
[25]H. G. Weller, G. Tabor, H. Jasak, and C. Fureby, "A tensorial approach to computational continuum mechanics using object-oriented techniques," *Comput. Phys.*, vol. 12, no. 6, p. 620, 1998, doi: 10.1063/1.168744.
[26]Meteodyn, "Meteodyn a CLS group company," *meteodyn.com*, 2022. https://meteodyn.com/business-sectors/renewable-energy/meteodyn-universe/meteodyn-wt/
[27]Windsim, "Windsim CFD based modeling," *windsim.com*, 2022. https://windsim.com/
[28]B. Lange and J. Højstrup, "Evaluation of the wind-resource estimation program WAsP for offshore applications," *J. Wind Eng. Ind. Aerodyn.*, vol. 89, no. 3–4, pp. 271–291, Mar. 2001, doi: 10.1016/S0167-6105(00)00082-9.
[29]José L Maza and al, "Atmospheric Stability Influence on Wind Resource - WindSim," Windeurope, 2017.
[30]J. Barcons, M. Avila, and A. Folch, "Diurnal cycle RANS simulations applied to wind resource assessment," *Wind Energy*, vol. 22, no. 2, pp. 269–282, Feb. 2019, doi: 10.1002/we.2283.
[31]EMD, "Introduction to Wind Turbine Wake Modelling and Wake Generated Turbulence." Windpro, 2021.
[32]A. Peña, P. Réthoré, and M. P. Laan, "On the application of the Jensen wake model using a turbulence-dependent wake decay coefficient: the Sexbierum case," *Wind Energy*, vol. 19, no. 4, pp. 763–776, Apr. 2016, doi: 10.1002/we.1863.
[33]P. Piotrowski, I. Rutyna, D. Baczyński, and M. Kopyt, "Evaluation Metrics for Wind Power Forecasts: A Comprehensive Review and Statistical Analysis of Errors," *Energies*, vol. 15, no. 24, p. 9657, Dec. 2022, doi: 10.3390/en15249657.

# Data-driven characterization of performance trends in ageing wind turbines

**Alessandro Murgia[1], Henrique Cabral[1], Elena Tsiporkova[1], Davide Astolfi[2], Ludovico Terzi[3]**

[1] EluciDATA Lab of Sirris, Bd A. Reyerslaan 80, 1030 Brussels, Belgium
[2] Department of Engineering - University of Perugia, Via G.Duranti 93, 06125, Perugia, Italy
[3] ENGIE Italia, Via Chiese 72, Milano, 20126, Italy

E-mail: alessandro.murgia@sirris.be, Presenting Author

**Abstract.** The precise quantification of wind turbine long- and short-term performance is crucial to assess the health state of ageing turbines and to evaluate the benefit of maintenance activities. Indeed, during its lifetime, wind turbines can experience a decay in terms of performance (e.g. due to wear) or improvement (e.g. due to technology optimizations). For this reason, we developed an integrated data-driven methodology to characterize the long- and short-term performance trends and performance variability in turbines. The methodology is validated on a synthetic dataset with imposed decay and then tested on a real wind farm operated by Engie Italy and composed of seven turbines for which ten years of SCADA data are collected. We show how this methodology accurately captures the evolution of a turbine's performance and how it is capable of quantifying the impact of the controller update.

## 1. Introduction

A remarkably increasing number of industrial wind turbines are reaching their end of expected design lifetime. For example, it is estimated that more than 50% of wind turbines sited in Germany, Denmark and Spain are aged more than fifteen years [1], with an average lifetime of 20-25 years. A reliable estimation of long-term wind turbine performance is therefore fundamental for end-of-life evaluation as well as for the project design phase [2, 3].

In literature, empirical studies are commonly used to evaluate the performance evolution of ageing wind turbines [4, 5, 6]. Originally, the estimation of long-term wind turbine performance trends has been performed by using cumulative data. For example, in [4], the data of 282 wind turbines sited in the UK are analyzed and a regression modelling is attempted between age and average capacity factor. It is estimated that the load factor decays by 1.57% per year. Over a 20-year lifetime, this corresponds to a 12% reduction and a 9% increase of the electricity cost. In [5], smaller decay rates are identified for wind turbines sited in Sweden, namely a 0.15% capacity factor decay per year, corresponding to a lifetime energy loss of 6%. More recent studies, like [6] and [7], formulate a distinction between older and newer wind turbines. In [7] it is reported that older plants, installed before 2008, are characterized by an average production decay with age in the order of -0.5% per year. For newer plants, online after 2008, a lower capacity factor decay rate (-0.17% per year) is observed. The evidence collected in [8] indicates that the performance decay accelerates as the facilities get older. As a consequence, it is not completely clear if the results regarding the newer plants in [7] constitute a trend which is to be expected for the whole wind farm lifetime or if there will be a sudden decay.

Recently, the estimation of wind turbine performance decay with age, based on SCADA data analysis, has attracted a certain attention in the literature. Previous works by the fourth author [9] has supported the hypothesis that a noticeable decline regards a certain percentage of wind turbines with hydraulic blade pitch control, for which the loss manifests mainly as diminished extracted power for given rotational speed [10, 11]. An instructive test case is discussed in [10], which is a Vestas V52 wind turbine installed in 2005. It is observed that the decay with age is quite limited up to the eleventh year (not more than -1% with respect to the first years of operation), but the decay accelerates at the twelfth year of age, reaching the order of -5% with respect to the optimal performance. In [12] and [13], two fleets of operating similar types of wind turbines are analyzed in order to estimate the variability of the ageing effects and it is observed that trends severe as in [10] regard a minority of the turbines. Further relevant studies about SCADA-based estimations of wind turbine performance decline are [14, 15, 16].

The reported literature studies present two main shortcomings. Firstly, studies on SCADA analysis are mainly focused on issues related to the functioning of the asset and do not fully account for the influence of environmental conditions on turbine production. Although some studies handle the effect of environmental conditions on power curve models by considering the air density correction, as in [17], there are still several other environmental factors such as humidity, pressure and icing, which are neglected, despite their influence on the turbine production. Secondly, these studies do not explicitly handle the confounding factor associated with the presence of multiple operating modes, which can strongly influence turbine production, such as curtailment and downtime periods.

In this work, we propose an integrated data-driven methodology to characterize the performance evolution of ageing turbines which can overcome the shortcomings present in the literature. Its main advantage is the fact that the methodology is designed to cope with the presence of confounding factors, such as operative modes and environmental conditions, even when they are not tracked by the SCADA system. As such, the methodology is suitable for ageing wind turbines in order to characterize the long-term performance and also to evaluate the effect of maintenance activities in the short-term. For this reason, the methodology can be adopted during the various phases of a wind farm project, from the design time, i.e. when it is required to estimate reliable Annual Energy Production [18], to the end-of-life, i.e. when the decommissioning is considered.

The first three authors originally envisioned the methodology in a position paper [19]. This study extends the previous one by (i) providing the implementation details of methodology, (ii) validating it in a realistic scenario and finally by (iii) testing it on a real use case. For validation, a realistic synthetic dataset which simulates over 20 years a power decay on a power curve is used. Here, the methodology proves to be able to correctly capture the simulated decay. For testing, ten years of data gathered from a wind farm owned by ENGIE Italia is investigated. In this case, the methodology is used to characterize the impact of the control optimization in the long- and short-term performance of the turbines.

The structure of the paper is the following. The methodology is outlined in Section 2; the experimental setup is described in Section 3; the results are collected and discussed in Section 4 and, finally, the conclusions are drawn in Section 5.

## 2. Methodology

Figure 1 depicts our overall methodology, composed of four steps (blocks). The rationale behind the proposed workflow is to arrive at turbine performance characterisation by factoring out confounding effects such as operative mode, the environmental factors and seasonal effects.

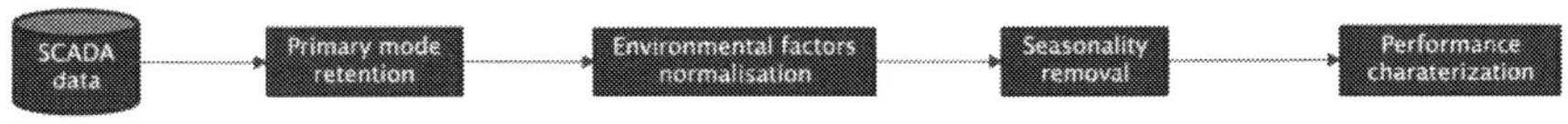


**Figure 1.** The building blocks of the methodology.

### *2.1. Primary mode retention*

The operating mode influences the power production of a wind turbine. In primary mode, the turbine extracts the maximum possible energy from the wind while ensuring the structural integrity of the turbine. In secondary modes, energy output of a turbine is limited, e.g. to reduce the noise emitted according to environmental constraints. During its lifetime, the turbine can switch from one mode to another. As a consequence, not filtering out secondary modes from analysis might lead to a perceived reduction in performance (since the production is capped) which is, however, not related to failure or wear of the turbine. This highlights the fact that the operative modes are confounding factors. It is therefore essential to benchmark against a fixed operating mode in order to correctly identify the long-term performance trend. In our methodological workflow, only the primary mode will be considered during the benchmarking. The latter is composed of the following steps:

(i) *Binning*: the wind speed is uniformly binned with 0.5 m/s resolution. For each bin, the the active power distribution is modelled by a Gaussian kernel density estimator. Figure 2a reports an example of a wind speed bin and its associated active power distribution.

(ii) *Filtering*: the active power distribution is used to define the expected power range during primary mode operation. Data points that do not belong to this range, such as noise and secondary modes, are filtered out. This is done by identifying the main peak in the distribution and excluding all points that have a distribution density below 1% of the peak's height. Figure 2b reports the final results of the filtering.

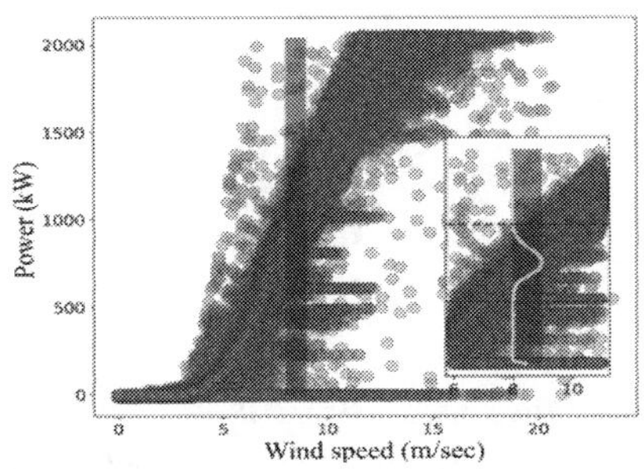


(a) The grey area represents a wind speed bin. On the bottom right is reported as a yellow line the distribution of the active power within the bin.

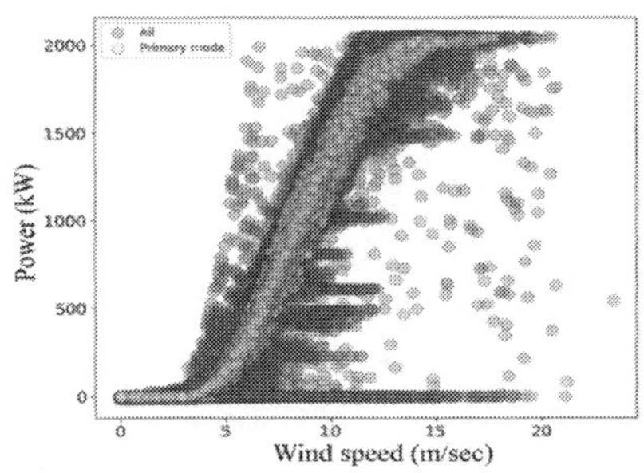


(b) The yellow points describe the retained points after the filtering. Secondary modes are filtered out.

**Figure 2.** Power curve before and after the filtering.

### *2.2. Environmental factors normalisation*

The environmental conditions in which the turbine operates influence the power production. To factor out this effect we compute the ratio between actual active power production ($P_{actual}$) and expected active power production ($P_{expected}$) in the same environmental conditions. We call this ratio *efficiency*:

$$efficiency = \frac{P_{actual}}{P_{expected}}. \tag{1}$$

To determine the expected production based on the environmental conditions we use a data-driven model, which computes the expected power production based on the environmental conditions (e.g. wind speed, wind direction) in which the turbine operates. Then, the time series of the actual and expected power production are re-sampled based on a certain frequency (e.g. week) and aggregation function (e.g. median). The former is decided in order to cope with the possible presence of periods of time with missing data. For the latter, the median is generally advised to cope with the possible presence of outliers. Finally, the efficiency is computed.

### *2.3. Seasonality removal*
There are seasonal effects/factors which are not tracked by the SCADA system, such as icing, air density and humidity, and which can interfere with the normal power production of a turbine. These variables are not recorded and subsequently, they cannot be used to train the data-driven model (see section 2.2) but they can still affect the evolution of the efficiency. Thus, it is necessary to develop a dedicated solution which factors out the influence of these variables from the evolution of the efficiency. We consider two alternative state-of-the-art methods: Seasonal and Trend decomposition using Loess (STL) [20] and Year-over-Year degradation detection (YoY) [21]. Both techniques are selected since they are well-known statistical approaches for performance decay detection in the solar energy domain [22].

The STL method decomposes the efficiency time series in three components: seasonality, trend, and residuals. The seasonality contains the seasonal patterns. The trend component contains the long-term evolution of the efficiency, namely it describes how the performance trend evolves with the turbine age. The residual component contains the noise, i.e. the signal once the seasonal and trend components are removed.

The YoY computes the difference, called residual, between the efficiency achieved in the same day for two subsequent years. This procedure is repeated for all data points in the time series. These residuals describe the distribution of the changes in efficiency of the turbine. The rationale behind this method is that, broadly speaking, for the same days during the year, the turbine should experience similar environmental conditions. Consequently, comparing the difference in efficiency will remove or at least mitigate the effect of the seasonality.

### *2.4. Performance characterization*
The aim here is to derive actionable information related to the health of the turbine in terms of performance trend and performance variability on a yearly basis (refer to Figure 6 for an example):

- The *performance trend* is computed by leveraging on the information extracted by the STL and YoY methods. For the STL, the performance trend is computed as the slope of the linear fit of the trend component extracted by the STL. For YoY, the performance trend is computed as the median of the residual distribution. A negative median value indicates the decrease in turbine efficiency on an annual basis. In both cases, the performance trend is reported as the yearly percentage change of the efficiency.
- The *performance variability* is expressed by a confidence interval consisting in a standard deviation above and below the mean of the residual distribution. Such variability is computed to better understand the common range of variability of the performance.

## 3. Experimental Setup
This section describes the dataset and how the methodology is instantiated for the analysis.

### *3.1. Dataset*
**Synthetic data**

A synthetic dataset with imposed performance decay is used for validation. This dataset is created by combining SCADA data of a real turbine with ERA5 reanalysis data. These two dataset are combined as follows:

(i) The SCADA wind speed is uniformly binned using a resolution of 0.5 m/s.
(ii) For each bin, the distribution of active power is modelled using a Gaussian distribution and its mean and standard deviation are determined.
(iii) The ERA5 wind speed is multiplied by a Gaussian noise to simulate the wind stochasticity. This represents the simulated wind speed.
(iv) Each ERA5 wind speed sample (from step 3) is mapped to one wind speed bins (step 1) and its associated active power is inferred from that bin's Gaussian distribution (step 2).

At the end of this process, 20 years of simulated wind speed and active power are generated. To the latter are added the wind direction and air density reported in ERA5. After the third year, to simulate a performance decay, the mean active power per wind speed bin (from the inferred distribution in step 2 above) is progressively decreased over time as can be seen in Figure 3 (red curve). In the remainder of the paper, we will refer to the progressively decreased active power as *degraded active power*.

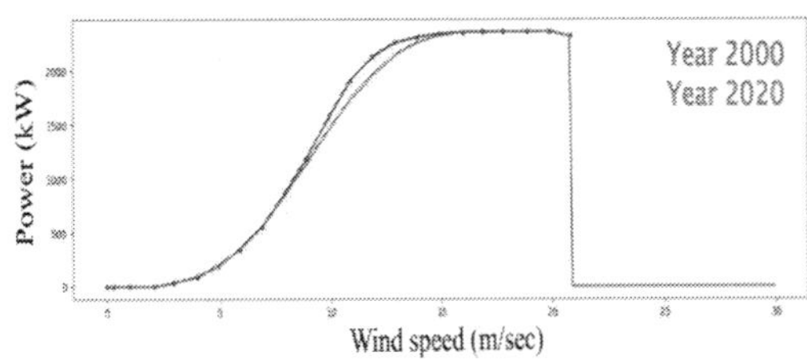


**Figure 3.** Power curve. The blue curve represents the power curve without decay. The red curve represents the power curve with the imposed decay.

### Real-world data

The dataset is provided by ENGIE Italy and consists of the time series of wind speed, wind direction, active power and rotor speed recorded by the SCADA system from 2011 to 2021. The analyzed wind farm consists of 7 Vestas V90 wind turbines, located in southern Italy.

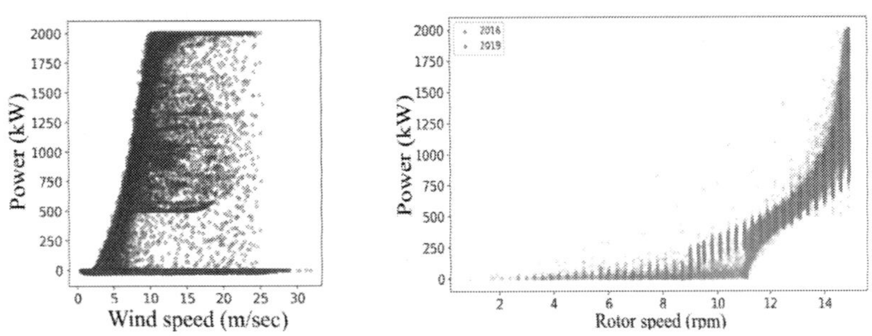


(a) A sample power curve (b) Rotor speed - power curve

**Figure 4.** Features of the dataset

Figure 4a reports the power curve of a turbine where multiple curtailment modes are visible. Figure 4b shows the rotor curve of the turbine. This figure highlights how the change of the control optimization (applied to all turbines during 2018) influenced the rotor curve. This is an interesting case to highlight the influence of the control system in the performance decay of the turbine. For both datasets, the values of wind speed and direction are combined to compute the eastward and northward wind component variables U and V. This transformation is done to better model the circularity of the wind direction.

### *3.2. Methodology instantiated*
For the synthetic dataset, the methodology is instantiated as follow:

- Regression algorithm selection: the XGBoost algorithm is chosen for its execution speed and high accuracy. The algorithm uses as input parameters: air density and the eastward and northward wind components. The target variable of the regression is the active power.
- Model training: the XGBoost model is trained on the first three years of data, i.e. the years where there is no performance decay.
- Efficiency estimation: the efficiency, preceded by the environmental factors normalization, is computed using the expected and observed active power re-sampled with a weekly median.

For the real-world dataset, the methodology is instantiated as reported above with two differences: 1) no air density was used; 2) the entire dataset is used as a training set. The latter setup was chosen since it was not possible to identify a time period for which there is a 100% certainty that the turbine does not under-perform. This does not represent a shortcoming since the methodology can still be used to monitor postmortem the performance trend evolution.

## 4. Results and Discussion
This section reports the validation of methodology on the synthetic data and the insights that can be extracted in a real-world scenario.

### *4.1. Synthetic data*
In this section, the methodology is applied to the synthetic dataset to highlight the most important insights that can be extracted. Then, the methodology is tested to evaluate to what extent the expected decay is aligned with the imposed one.

Figures 5a and 5b report the evolution of the degraded active power and efficiency at the end of the step *environmental factors normalization*. A qualitative comparison of the two signals highlights how, despite the fact that a decay was imposed in the synthetic dataset, no clear trend can be visually observed on the evolution of the degraded active power. On the other hand, the evolution of the efficiency shows a clear downward trend. This illustrative example highlights the need to address environmental conditions as a confounding factors and benchmark within the same environmental conditions to extract the performance trends. Figure 5b shows the presence of yearly peaks (indicated by the arrows) in the evolution of the efficiency. This seasonal variability can represent an obstacle in real-industrial cases. Indeed, in cases where the performance decay is less pronounced, or the available data is too limited, the variability of the efficiency may hinder the possibility of highlighting a performance trend. This example illustrates why the step *seasonality removal* (either using the STL or YoY methods) was introduced to clean the signal. Figure 6 shows the final outcome of the methodology, i.e. the turbine performance characterization. Figure 6a reports the performance decay of 0.36% based on information extracted by the STL method. Figure 6b reports the performance decay of 0.39%, with performance variability generally within 0.45% and 0.29%, based on the information extracted by the YoY method. By comparing the performance decays based on the information extracted by the STL and YoY methods, we can notice that they are similar, but not equal, which can be explained by the different ways in which each method removes seasonality.

As the final step, we evaluate to what extent the extracted performance decays are aligned with the one imposed on the synthetic dataset. For this reason, we compute for each year after 2003, i.e. the year from which the decay is introduced, the real and expected losses:

- the real loss: it represents the difference between the real and degraded active power.
- the expected loss: it represents the difference between the active power expected (by the model) and the active power degraded. The expected active power is expressed as active power degraded divided by the efficiency (see equation 1). The efficiency is computed as the slope of an univariate linear regression:

$$f(x) = m * x + c. \tag{2}$$

where $x$ is time and $m$ is the performance trend. $c$ is the intercept with the y-axis and is set to one, since before the decay starts the efficiency is 1).

Then we compute the R^2 between the real losses and expected losses. The value of R^2 based on performance trends of STL and YoY are 0.94 and 0.99, respectively. This result highlights that the expected losses are very similar to the real ones, i.e. the extracted performance decay is very close to the one imposed in the synthetic dataset. This proves that the methodology can be used to characterize the long-term performance of ageing turbines.

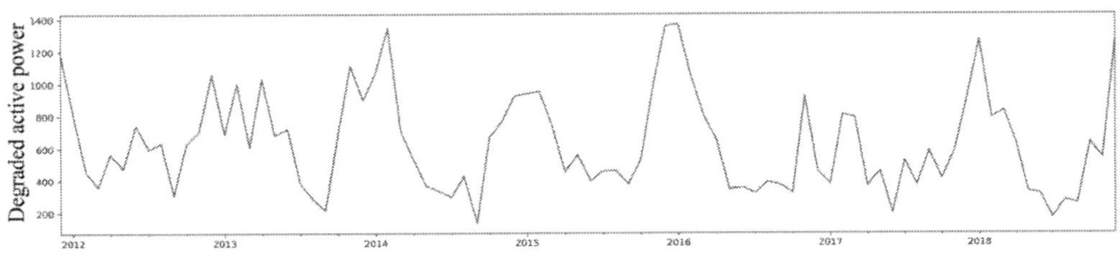


(a) Degraded active power. Peaks in power production are observable each winter

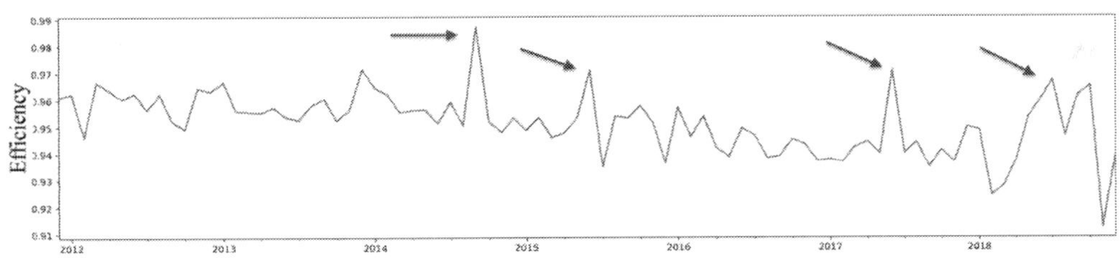


(b) Efficiency. Peaks in power production are observable in some summers indicated by the arrows

**Figure 5.** Monthly median of the degraded active power (top) and effiency (bottom) in the synthetic dataset between 2012 and 2018

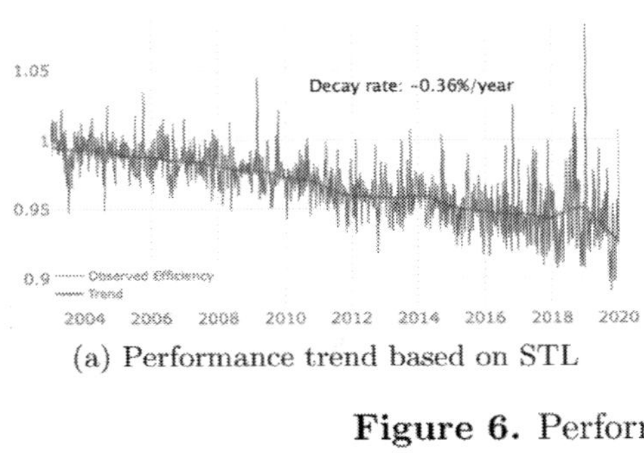


(a) Performance trend based on STL

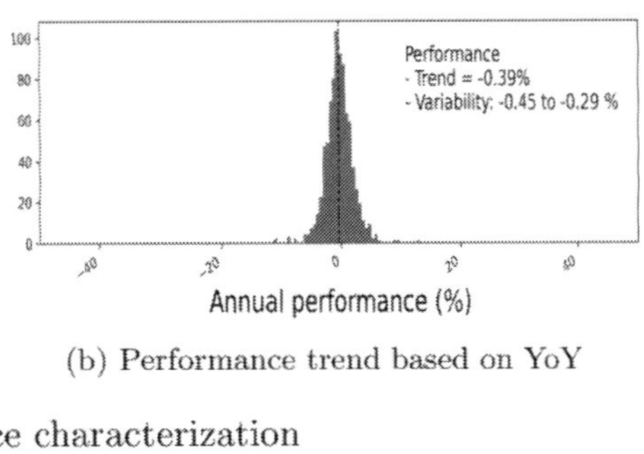


(b) Performance trend based on YoY

**Figure 6.** Performance characterization

### *4.2. Real-world data*

In this section, the methodology is applied to the real-world dataset to characterize the long- and short-term performance of a fleet of wind turbines. The final outcome of the methodology is reported in Table 1 in terms of performance trend and performance variability. In this case too, the results obtained leveraging on the STL and YoY methods are similar but not equal. The majority of the wind turbines present a performance trend around zero as highlighted by the performance variability. The only turbine representing an exception is T07 where a clear positive performance trend and variability is observed both for the YoY- and STL-based methods. These results are in general better than the ones reported in [7] and mainly consistent with those reported for turbines of similar size in [13]. These differences among results present in literature are somehow to be expected considering that even in the same farm each turbine presents a different performance variability.

| Wind Turbine | YoY-based performance trend | YoY-based performance variability | STL-based performance trend |
|---|---|---|---|
| T01 | 0.02 | [-0.26; 0.20] | -0.38 |
| T02 | -0.04 | [-0.53; 0.31] | 0.00 |
| T03 | 0.10 | [-0.30; 0.61] | 0.11 |
| T04 | -0.20 | [-0.52; -0.01] | 0.06 |
| T05 | -0.04 | [-0.53; 0.31] | 0.15 |
| T06 | -0.18 | [-0.43; 0.06] | 0.10 |
| T07 | 0.42 | [0.08; 0.60] | 0.52 |

**Table 1.** Percentages of performance trend and variability for the wind farm.

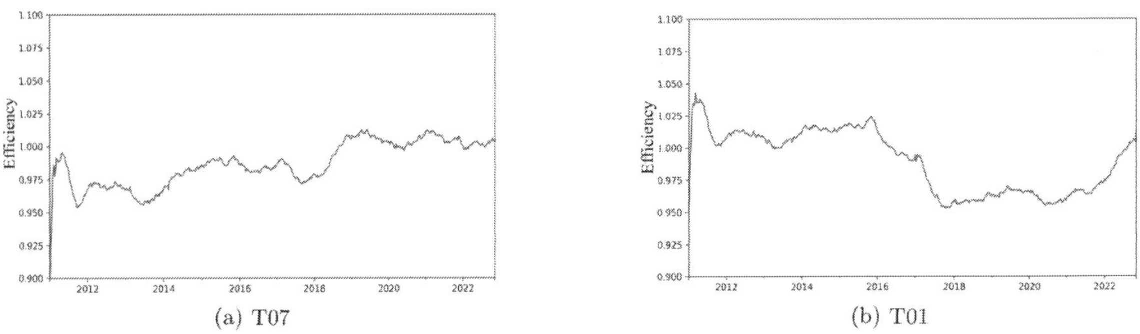


**Figure 7.** Yearly rolling average of the efficiency

The performance results in Table 1 can only provide a synthetic characterization of the long-term performance evolution of the turbine. Therefore, to provide a qualitative description of the performance evolution over the years, we report in Figure 7 the efficiency evolution, computed at the end of the step *environmental factors normalization*, for two representative turbines. Figure 7a shows a clear step increase in efficiency after 2018. This step change is exhibited, although with slight differences, also by the other turbines with the only exception of T01, as shown in Figure 7b. This step change occurs right after the change of control optimization in mid 2018. To prove the convenience of having a methodology to evaluate the effect of maintenance activities in the short-term performance, we quantify the step change introduced by the maintenance activity. For this purpose, the methodology is used to compute the performance trends only using the years 2016 and 2019 assuming that they occurred one after the other chronologically in time. These years are selected since the efficiency is relatively stable before and after the control optimization. The computed performance trends are reported in Table 2. From this table it can be observed that for all the wind turbines there is an improvement in performance, except for T01, as expected from Figure 7b. Moreover, it is also possible to observe a certain difference in the improvement of performance trends for wind turbines T02-T07. On the one hand, this result may appear unexpected since the same control optimization, applied on a fleet of wind turbines of the same model on the same site, should produce equal or similar effects on turbine performance. On the other hand, the different ageing of the wind turbines may justify these results. Indeed, it is possible that different levels of wear in the hydraulic blade pitch system play a direct role in the effectiveness of the control optimization which drives the pitch control algorithm. To the best of the authors' knowledge, this is the first work in literature which documents qualitatively and quantitatively the effect on performance of the same type of control optimization on a whole wind farm.

| Wind Turbine | YoY-based performance trend |
|---|---|
| T01 | -1.92 |
| T02 | 1.44 |
| T03 | 2.74 |
| T04 | -0.05 |
| T05 | 0.45 |
| T06 | 1.01 |
| T07 | 1.07 |

**Table 2.** Change of performance trend between 2016 and 2019

## 5. Conclusions

This work presents a novel integrated methodology which facilitates the characterization of performance degradation, both long- and short-term, associated with wind turbine ageing. It was demonstrated on a synthetic dataset with imposed decay, that the proposed methodology is able to correctly capture the induced performance trend. In a real-case scenario represented by a wind farm with seven turbines monitored for ten years, the methodology proved to be useful for gaining insights into how long-term and short-term performance occur in practice. It elucidated a valuable observation, namely that maintenance activities can usually, but not always, introduce performance improvement. Indeed, in one of the turbines, upon control optimization, the performance trend decayed. Furthermore, for the cases of turbines exhibiting performance improvement, it was established that the technology optimization induces different impact on the performance of the different turbines, suggesting that the improvement may depend on the health status of the wind turbine.

**Acknowledgments**

The authors thanks (1) the support of the Region of Bruxelles-Capitale—Innoviris through the project ReWind and the Flemish Government through the AI Research Program for the fundings, (2) Patrick Hoebeke from 3E for the synthetic data generated for the analysis and (3) Andrea Lombardi from Engie Italia for the technical support.

## Bibliography

[1] Leon Mishnaevsky Jr and Kenneth Thomsen. Costs of repair of wind turbine blades: Influence of technology aspects. *Wind Energy*, 23(12):2247–2255, 2020.

[2] Eduardo Martínez, Félix Sanz, Stefano Pellegrini, Emilio Jiménez, and Julio Blanco. Life cycle assessment of a multi-megawatt wind turbine. *Renewable energy*, 34(3):667–673, 2009.

[3] E Martínez, JI Latorre-Biel, E Jiménez, F Sanz, and J Blanco. Life cycle assessment of a wind farm repowering process. *Renewable and Sustainable Energy Reviews*, 93:260–271, 2018.

[4] Iain Staffell and Richard Green. How does wind farm performance decline with age? *Renewable energy*, 66:775–786, 2014.

[5] Jon Olauson, Per Edström, and Jesper Rydén. Wind turbine performance decline in sweden. *Wind Energy*, 20(12):2049–2053, 2017.

[6] Sonja Germer and Axel Kleidon. Have wind turbines in germany generated electricity as would be expected from the prevailing wind conditions in 2000-2014? *PloS one*, 14(2):e0211028, 2019.

[7] Sofia D Hamilton, Dev Millstein, Mark Bolinger, Ryan Wiser, and Seongeun Jeong. How does wind project performance change with age in the united states? *Joule*, 4(5):1004–1020, 2020.

[8] Timothy Fitzgerald and Michael Giberson. Wind project performance with age: Policy, technology, markets, and the maturing wind power industry. *The Electricity Journal*, 34(10):107047, 2021.

[9] Davide Astolfi, Ravi Pandit, Ludovico Terzi, and Andrea Lombardi. Discussion of wind turbine performance based on scada data and multiple test case analysis. *Energies*, 15(15):5343, 2022.

[10] Raymond Byrne, Davide Astolfi, Francesco Castellani, and Neil J Hewitt. A study of wind turbine performance decline with age through operation data analysis. *Energies*, 13(8):2086, 2020.

[11] Davide Astolfi, Raymond Byrne, and Francesco Castellani. Analysis of wind turbine aging through operation curves. *Energies*, 13(21):5623, 2020.

[12] Davide Astolfi, Raymond Byrne, and Francesco Castellani. Estimation of the performance aging of the vestas v52 wind turbine through comparative test case analysis. *Energies*, 14(4):915, 2021.

[13] Davide Astolfi, Ravi Pandit, Ludovica Celesti, Andrea Lombardi, and Ludovico Terzi. Scada data analysis for long-term wind turbine performance assessment: A case study. *Sustainable Energy Technologies and Assessments*, 52:102357, 2022.

[14] Juchuan Dai, Wenxian Yang, Junwei Cao, Deshun Liu, and Xing Long. Ageing assessment of a wind turbine over time by interpreting wind farm scada data. *Renewable energy*, 116:199–208, 2018.

[15] Hyun-Goo Kim and Jin-Young Kim. Analysis of wind turbine aging through operation data calibrated by lidar measurement. *Energies*, 14(8):2319, 2021.

[16] Manuel S Mathew, Surya Teja Kandukuri, and Christian W Omlin. Estimation of wind turbine performance degradation with deep neural networks. In *PHM Society European Conference*, volume 7, pages 351–359, 2022.

[17] Ravi Kumar Pandit, David Infield, and James Carroll. Incorporating air density into a gaussian process wind turbine power curve model for improving fitting accuracy. *Wind Energy*, 22(2):302–315, 2019.

[18] Erik Möllerström, Sean Gregory, and Aromal Sugathan. Improvement of aep predictions with time for swedish wind farms. *Energies*, 14(12):3475, 2021.

[19] Alessandro Murgia, Henrique Cabral, Christos Droutsas, Tom Tourwé, Mathias Verbeke, Pierre Dagnely, and Elena Tsiporkova. A data-driven methodology for the characterization of performance decay in ageing wind turbines. *Proceedings of the 5th Renewable Energy Sources–Research and Business (RESRB)*, 5, 2020.

[20] Robert B Cleveland, William S Cleveland, Jean E McRae, and Irma Terpenning. Stl: A seasonal-trend decomposition. *J. Off. Stat*, 6(1):3–73, 1990.

[21] Ernest Hasselbrink, Mike Anderson, Zoe Defreitas, Mark Mikofski, Yu-Chen Shen, Sander Caldwell, Akira Terao, David Kavulak, Zach Campeau, and David DeGraaff. Validation of the pvlife model using 3 million module-years of live site data. In *2013 IEEE 39th Photovoltaic Specialists Conference (PVSC)*, pages 0007–0012. IEEE, 2013.

[22] David Moser, D Bertani, AJ Curran, RH French, M Herz, S Lindig, G Makrides, B Muller, M Richter, M Van Iseghem, et al. International collaboration framework for the calculation of performance loss rates: Data quality, benchmarks, and trends. Technical report, National Renewable Energy Lab.(NREL), Golden, CO (United States), 2019.

Journal of Physics: Conference Series **2507** (2023) 012020 doi:10.1088/1742-6596/2507/1/012020

# Development of an aerodynamic measurement system for wind turbines

**Malte Fredebohm*, Johannes N. Theron, Leo Höning, Sanaz Weis, Bernhard Stoevesandt, Anna Wegner, Nora Denecke, Heiko Rosemann, Matthias Leonhard Huhn**

Fraunhofer Institute for Wind Energy Systems IWES, 27572 Bremerhaven, Germany

malte.fredebohm@iwes.fraunhofer.de; anna.wegner@iwes.fraunhofer.de

**Abstract**. In this paper an aerodynamic measurement system is presented that can be installed as a retrofit on virtually any onshore turbine. The aerodynamic measurement system consists of pressure sensors embedded in thin glass-fiber shells, which are glued to the rotor blades. Additionally, an aerodynamic probe is attached to outboard side the shells with a thin flange. In this study the system was installed on an 8 MW offshore prototype turbine located in Bremerhaven. It was mounted at two sections of one of the rotor blades with 72 pressure sensors in total (18 sensors each on the pressure side and suction side, respectively). Additionally, at each section an aerodynamic probe with 5 sensors was installed in front of the leading edge to measure inflow speed and direction. Results were compared to CFD simulations.

## 1. Introduction

The aerodynamic flow around the rotor blade is crucial for wind turbine performance. While several wind tunnel experiments [1] [2] and field tests on smaller wind turbines [3] are available in the literature, a comprehensive set-up including aerodynamic pressure, inflow angle and extensive wind measurements on large wind turbines is unavailable. The data from such a system is crucial to set boundary conditions for model development, for blade design and to validate CFD simulations. Compared to conventional rotor blade design reported in [3], contemporary blades (with blade lengths exceeding 100m) are characterized by a more slender design to reduce relative material and weight. The aerodynamics of these slender, flexible blades have not been thoroughly studied yet, and the accuracy of typical design tools such as BEM codes not yet validated for multi-MW wind turbines.

In the publicly funded project High-RE [4] an aerodynamic measurement system was therefore developed to investigate the aerodynamic conditions of the rotor blade at two distinct radial locations. This provides the basis for CFD simulation validation, to answer the question whether contemporary CFD simulations adequately resolve real-world dynamic effects and serve as a valid basis for a constructive design.

In order to measure the blade aerodynamics at a given the profile / radial location on the blade, the absolute pressure at various chordwise locations was measured and the required values like the dimensionless coefficient of pressure (Cp), the inflow velocity and the angle of attack (AoA) were calculated. These measured results can then be validated against a CFD simulation from which both the Cp curves at a specific radial station as well as field properties from in the computational domain, have been extracted.

Torben Reichstein et al. [5] mounted an aerodynamic glove with embedded sensors to a 2MW wind turbine. However, they focused on short-time measurements with sample frequencies up to 250 Hz to get an impression of the pressure distribution of a real wind turbine during operation and for calculating the laminar-turbulent transition locations. [5]

As part of the research project HighRe [4], this work goes one step further and compares long-term aerodynamic measurements on a large-scale wind turbine of the 8MW class with CFD and BEM simulations. In the framework of the HighRe project an aerodynamic measurement system is installed on two sections (60m and 73m from the rotation center) on one blade of an 8MW offshore prototype wind turbine.

### *1.1. Test site*

The measurements are caried out on a turbine located in Bremerhaven, Germany. The 8MW test turbine has a rotor diameter of 180 meters and is thus representative for modern offshore wind turbines.

The area is classified as a nearshore site with flat terrain, surrounded by an industrial harbour area on the eastern side and a bird protection area as well as the Weser River on the western side. The primary wind direction is south-west – typical conditions for a middle European location. The test area contains an IEC-compliant hub-height metrological mast with cup and sonic anemometers and wind vanes on multiple heights, as well as temperature, humidity and atmospheric pressure sensors.

## 2. Methods

### *2.1. Requirements and solutions*

The system had to fulfill multiple safety, installation and aerodynamic requirements: Firstly, it is crucial to ensure that any additional installations on the rotor do not affect the behaviour of the turbine during operation. This is especially the case when additional masses or aerodynamic changes may lead to aerodynamic or mass imbalances that could influence the safety systems of the turbine. Secondly, the changes on the turbine must not affect the structural properties of the turbine´s construction or lead to weaknesses compared to the original turbine design. Third, the proper functioning of the lightning protection of the turbine and the system had to be ensured.

As the test location is directly in an industrial harbour area, which also is classified as major infrastructure, this adds additional constraints (related to acoustics and loss of the glued-on components) to adding any additional equipment on the outside of a rotating blade.

Besides the safety aspects there were additional constraints of a more pragmatic nature. To measure the aerodynamic on the profile and collect data that are comparable to simulation, any aerodynamic changes to the original profile, like thickness, length or surface properties, had to be known. Moreover, there were limitations for the installation as well. As the blade is one of the largest on the European market, it was a challenge to procure / rent a service-platform that can handle the size of the blade and give enough space to work on, with part of about 3 meters in length. This platform-imposed chord-length limitation dictated the installation location closest to the blade root.

In order to satisfy all the above requirements, the aerodynamic measurement system was designed as a distributed system without any conductive materials. All cabinets and electrical systems were placed inside the hub, where they were connected to the power systems and covered by the lightning protection systems of the wind turbine. All parts inside and on the blade were made of glass fiber and non-conductive materials, where fiber-optical sensors were embedded in a fiber reinforced plastic construction, shown in Figure 1.

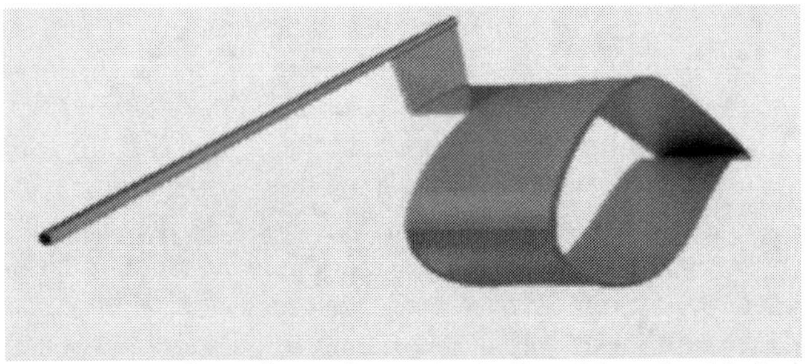

**Figure 1** Design of aerodynamic shells with embedded fiber-optical-pressure-sensors and an aerodynamic probe.

The wind turbine operator additionally required that the shells had to be decoupled from the blade´s movement and structure, without influencing the sensor values at the same time. After several laboratory tests, an adhesive was selected that is flexible enough to avoid an increase in the structure's stiffness and stress concentration in the critical areas, yet strong and tough enough to resist extreme loads e.g. in case of electrical load loss and emergency stops during the turbine operation.

*2.2. Initial calculations and simulations*

To guarantee a safe operation with the planned measurement system, several calculations and simulations were made during the planning and permitting phase.

*2.2.1. FEM-Simulation:* The system had to be installed as a retrofit and should not influence or destroy the turbine´s structure. With the aid of an FEM-Simulation, critical areas on the blade were investigated and the bonding areas were optimized by calculating multiple configurations.

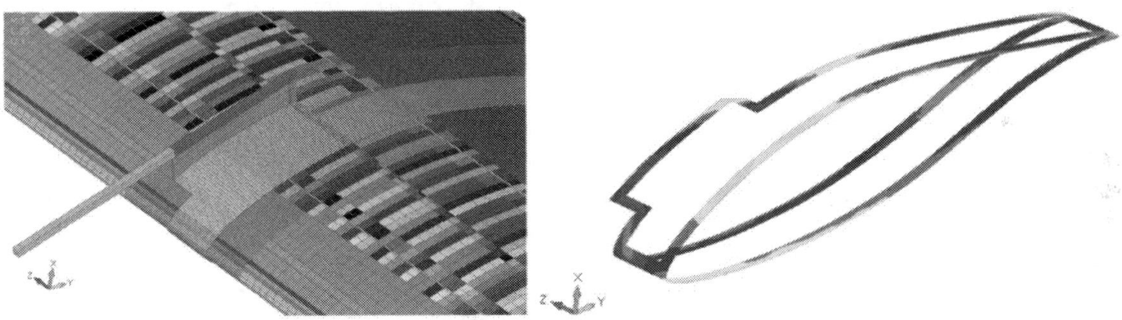

**Figure 2** Left: FEM-Simulation of the sensor shells on a generic blade.
Right: Stress distributions on contact surfaces between shells and blade.

The simulation scenarios were focus on the most critical operation conditions. The bonding calculation included an extreme load case on rated conditions with an unexpected grid loss, followed by an emergency pitch event. As the measurement campaign was planned for six months only, fatigue loads were neglected. The simulation showed that both the bonding and the blade´s laminate would resist the worst-case scenario. It was also shown that the bonding would fail before any major damage on the blade would occur.

*2.2.2. Simulation of rotor imbalances:* Although the mass of the measurement system is significantly smaller than the rotor mass of an 8 MW wind turbine (which has a weight of several hundred metric tonnes), it was important to ensure that the measurement system does not affect the system safety by causing critical changes in the natural frequency of the blade. To check this, the expected rotor imbalance was simulated for several extreme load cases.

The rotor simulations for the certification processes of the test turbine had been conducted with DNV Bladed. However, as Bladed is only able to simulate three identical blades, the Fraunhofer IWES inhouse aero-servo-elastic simulation tool MoWiT [6], was used, which had previously been verified with the Bladed model. MoWiT has the ability to configure each blade individually, both from an aerodynamic- as well as from a structural perspective. The investigation of the influence of the two aerodynamic measurement systems on the loads and dynamic behaviour of the test turbine was carried out by comparing the simulation results of two different models in MoWiT: a baseline model and a model including the aerodynamic measurement systems. Two types of possible unbalance were investigated: a possible mass imbalance and a possible aerodynamic imbalance. For the former, the masses of all already installed sensors and all sensors, which were planned to be installed, were individually added to the blade mass distribution (with mass and position in the blade). To calculate the impact of the aerodynamic measurement equipment on the aerodynamic behaviour, a CFD study was performed to calculate the lift, drag, and moment polars in the presence of the aerodynamic probe. These modified polars were used only for blade 1 at the radial area (measured from blade root) of 57.9 m to 58.2 m and 70.9 m to 71.2 m, thus over a length of 30 cm each. The three blades were parameterized individually.

The extreme load cases DLC 1.1, 2.3, 5.1 and 6.2 according to IEC 61400-1 [7] were considered. For the load case DLC 6.2, the aerodynamic settings had to be adjusted for numerical reasons. The BEM extensions for dynamic stall and dynamic wake had to be deactivated to ensure the stability of the simulations. In the case of a skewed inflow of +/- 90 deg, additionally, the skew inflow correction had to be deactivated.

To investigate if the additional mass of the installed sensors leads to a rotor mass imbalance, the rotor speed and tower top side-side deflection during power production were considered. If a rotor mass imbalance were present, a 1P oscillation in the rotor speed and the tower top side-side deflection would be expected. A potential aerodynamic rotor imbalance would lead to a 1P oscillation of the rotor nodding moment at the hub.

The calculations showed that for all loads at the hub, the maximum difference was less than 1%. At the tower top, loads increased by less than 1.2%. At the tower bottom, side-to-side bending moment increased by 1.05% while other loads increased by less than 0.6%. Blade root bending moments (flapwise and edgewise) as well as blade root torsional moments were elevated by less than 1% for all load cases. Finally, no significant rotor imbalance could be detected.

*2.2.3. Acoustic-Simulations:*

Since the test turbine is located close to residential areas, it was necessary to prove a priori that the five-hole probe did not cause excessive acoustic noise. The aerodynamic gloves were only 10mm thick and the spanwise edges filleted to avoid flow separation and noise. Hence one could assume that the main source of additional noise would be generated by the shaft of the 5-hole probe.

In order to obtain results in a reasonable time, the probe was modeled as a cylinder in crossflow using the aeolian-tone approach where the primary and secondary lift and drag dipoles were rotated with the blades [8].

Although some additional tonality was present between 160Hz and 1kHz, the overall sound pressure level (SPL) was elevated by less than 0.5dB compared to the turbine without 5-hole probes.

*2.3. Construction and manufacturing*

To be able to match the pressure and inflow measurements on the real rotor blade to the outputs of CFD, BEM and other simulations, the location of both the pressure sensors and the inflow probe for measuring air inflow velocity and angle need to be known as precisely as possible, along with the orientation of the inflow probe.

Also, as with every measurement, the aerodynamic influence of the sensors themselves on the airflow needs to be as small as possible. This is true for the overall turbine aerodynamics as well as the blade aerodynamics to avoid imbalance and to ensure the measurements are representative for a clean blade, and also on a smaller scale the upstream sensors (closer to the leading edge of the blade) must not disturb the airflow reaching downstream sensors.

To fulfill these requirements and after identifying the exact locations on the blade, the sensors should be installed – mostly determined by keeping the parts small enough to handle them, i.e. rather closer towards the tip, but not as far out that the pre-bend of the blade would prevent the intended tower-based installation platform from reaching around the blade – half shells to be glued to the rotor blade were designed. The positions of the shells were at two radial positions at 70% and 85% blade length, each requiring two half shells meeting at the leading edge and the trailing edge, with 18 pressure sensors per half shell. Both suction side half shells also included a flange and pipe to hold the five-hole probe in a well-defined position in front of the leading edge.

The shells were designed to be as thick as the pressure sensors themselves, mostly to facilitate the installation, not out of structural reasons, i.e. approximately 4 mm. To allow for some structural decoupling through the adhesive and tolerance for routing the fiber-optic cables, the shells' outsides – the defining surface, which also needed aerodynamic smoothness – were made 1cm offset from the blade. At the inner of the two radii, this still resulted in 3.5m chord length.

For building the shells, the Direct Tooling approach developed by Fraunhofer IWES [9] was adapted to these specific needs, most notably omitting all the fabric layers since the four molds for this project didn't need integrated heating for making thin, structurally irrelevant shells and because for single lots the required surface durability was achieved much easier than for lot sizes in the hundreds or thousands. What was left was milling the outer shape of the half shells into blocks of foam on the BladeMaker 6 axis double gantry milling machine, including flanges and alignment features for the inflow probes on the two suction side half shells. After milling, the foam surface was sealed vacuum-proof with a gelcoat resin and treated with mold release agent.

**Figure 3** Sealed Foammolds after milling.

On top of the CAD models of the mold, draping simulations of glass fiber biax NCFs were run to create the blank shapes to be cut on our CNC fabric cutting table. These blanks also included cutouts for the sensors, and a template for placing the sensors was also cut on the CNC cutting table. See Figure 4 for a screenshot of the draping simulation and the resulting outlines for the CNC cutting table.

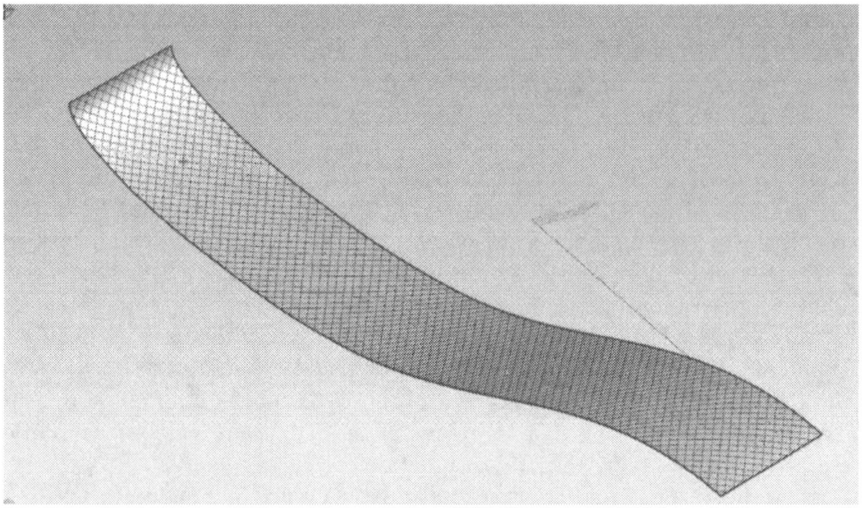

**Figure 4** CAD for NCF fabric cutter with sensor cut-outs in green.

After sensor installation, the laminate was built up using hand lamination techniques with white-tinted epoxy resin. This step required carefully threading the fiber optic cables from the sensors through pre-cut holes in the NCF blanks, and was followed by vacuum compaction of the setup. The fiber optic cables were all routed towards the trailing edge, where a square patch was embedded to accommodate the splices to long multicore fiber optic cables running all the way to the blade root along the trailing edge (Figure 5).

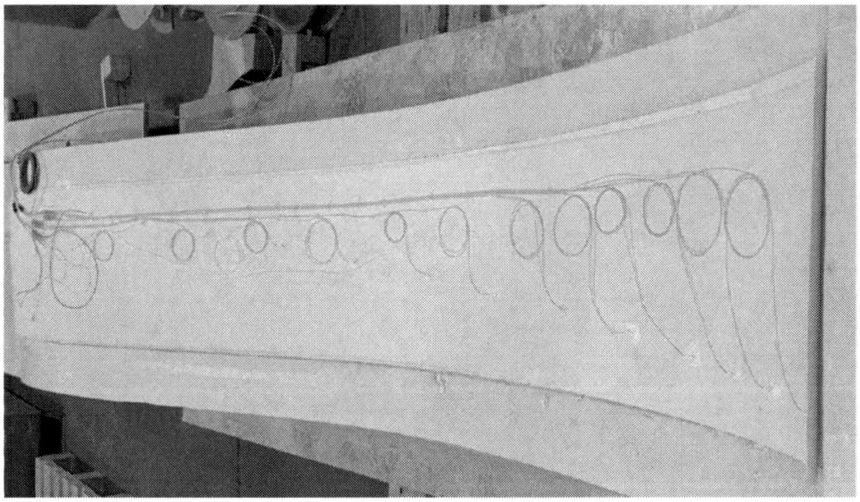

**Figure 5** Cable guiding in the glass fiber shells.

### *2.4. Installation and commissioning*

The installation was limited by the size and availability of the service platform. Thus, one of the biggest platforms available on market was used, as shown in Figure 6.

The interaction between sensor shells and the blade´s laminate was a critical aspect within the planning phase, thus, the results from the FEM analysis (described in Chapter 2.2.1. were used for an optimized bonding of the fiber reinforced plastic structure to the blade surface.

All fiber optical sensor cables were routed on the pressure side of the trailing edge towards the blade root, where they were fed inside of the blade. The cables were covered with a sealer to reduce unwanted aerodynamic turbulence and sound emissions. The electrical components e.g. data acquisition and data storage were installed on the hub site of the blade root, where they were connected to the lightning protection system of the wind turbine.

After installation and curing of the sensor shells, several commissioning tests were conducted, where the turbine was set in test operation mode to mimic parameters like pitch angle and yaw misalignment during production. In this phase the turbine was monitored with additional measuring systems for e.g. bending moments, vibrations and other turbine parameters, and the bonding of the shells were visually inspected. The data were also used to set alarm limits for a continuous blade monitoring system that measured frequencies and vibrations during the entire measurement campaign.

**Figure 6** Installation of the sensor shells with service platform.

*2.5. Measurements*

In addition to the aerodynamic measurement system, the test turbine was also equipped with a complete loads- and power measurement system according to IEC-Standard [10] [11], as well as a comprehensive drive train monitoring system [14] and several wind scanning lidars [12]. In addition, short term measurements for sound emissions and rotor imbalance were made from the ground, to check the previously-made assumptions and calculations.

*2.5.1. Description of the aerodynamic system:* The aerodynamic system consists of four fiber reinforced plastic shells with embedded fiber optical sensors, as well as two fiber optical five-hole-probes. Respectively two shells, one for the pressure side and one for the suction side were installed at each of the two measuring sections of the blade. It was decided to place one section at 60 meters and another at 73 meters away from the centre of rotation (CoR), where aerodynamic baseline models from the blade manufacturer were known. Moreover, measuring on two sections gives the advantage of comparing both sections under the same environmental conditions.

The sample rate was 1kHz continuous and increased to 10kHz in special situations. The data acquisition system (DAS) in the blade root contains a buffer storage for at least two weeks of data. It also manages the time synchronization of all channels, where the time stamp is retrieved from a central time server inside of the turbine, that serves all measurement systems, as well as a meteorological mast over ethernet. With this method it is ensured that all systems and subsystems are synchronized to each other. A data connection between hub and nacelle was used to transfer the data out of the rotating system to a data server in the tower bottom, where the data are backed up and prepared for remote data transfer and long-term storage.

**Figure 7** Measurement sections on the turbine on 60m und 73m from the CoR.

Fraunhofer IWES uses an in-house solution for a measurement database. This database collects measurement data from all decentral systems on the test turbine and homogenize them to configurable set of data.

*2.5.2. Special needs of fiber optical sensors:* Compared to electrical sensors, fiber optical sensors have some advantages and disadvantages. The main reasons why they were used in this project, were that they are not affected by electromagnetism or static charge. As they are completely free of conductive materials, they did not compromise the lightning protection system of the turbine. On the other hand, they have to be handled much more carefully during installation than electrical sensors, and they are significantly affected by the environmental conditions, like changes in temperature or mechanical stress.

To handle these challenges, there was a mechanical decoupling between the sensors and the sensor shell, as well as the sensor shell and the blade surface. By taking the mechanical decoupling into account it was possible to reduce the influence of mechanical stress and the increase of different materials due to temperature changes.

In addition to that, every single sensor was pre-calibrated in a climate chambre before embedding them in the sensor shells. With the sensor specific temperature curves and the distributed temperature sensors in the shells the influence of temperature changes could be reduced even more.

## 3. Results

This chapter gives an overview of the results of the aerodynamic measurements and simulations. As this paper covers a wide range of different work packages, only the most important results are shown.

### *3.1. Calibration*

Fiber optical sensors show some disadvantages compared to electrical sensors (see also Chapter 2.5.2. The measurement campaign showed that there is the need of a multi-step calibration procedure to reduce parasitic influences and physical effects due to the operation of the turbine. As a CFD simulation only shows the fluid behaviour, this also includes a correction of a variable height of the measurement sections, caused by the rotation of the rotor.

*3.1.1. Calibration of probes:* The probes were calibrated in different laboratories. Like all other single sensors, the pressure sensors itself were calibrated in a climate chamber to generate a sensor specific temperature curve and calibration factors. In case of the probes, it was necessary to perform an additional calibration after assembling of the probe head and define a calibration matrix for velocities and angles of attack. A detailed description of the calibration process is presented in *[13]*.

Former researchers concentrated on the use of innovative fiber optical sensors for probes under laboratory conditions. As the probe employed in this project operated under unsteady in-situ conditions, there was a need for more complex post-processing to identify and reduce the influence of an unsteady altitude, temperature, and radiation effects. A further calibration method is included in the following chapter.

*3.1.2. Calibration of profile sensors:* The calibration procedure for in-situ measurements on wind turbines is affected by environmental conditions. For mechanical measurements, the procedure is described in the IEC-Standard *[10]*. Especially the predominant wind conditions have a strong influence on the quality of the calibration and should be less than 4 m/s, to reduce the wind loads on the blade. As there is no standard for aerodynamic measurements, there was no prescribed procedure for the calibration, but the known standards gave some orientation.

The sensors were calibrated in a post process. This allows one to pick certain situations where environmental conditions like temperature and solar irradiation were comparable to each other and reduce effects of external conditions on the calibration to a minimum. Absolute pressure sensors were used in the project. This means that the raw values also include the ambient pressure and the variation of the measurement sections with height and per revolution. As the distance between the centre of rotation and the shell´s position was known from the turbine monitoring system, the measured static pressure was an indicator that was used for function checks of the system.

To compare the measurements to CFD simulations, the aerodynamic pressure was calculated by subtracting the ambient pressure from the static pressure due to height variations. To do so, the pressure measurements during several idling situations, with at least three revolutions were averaged and compared with the pressured measured at a neighboured meteorological mast. In further steps, the measured rotor position was used to calculate the pressure changes by height and subtracted from the sensor values. Furthermore, the temperature compensation factors from the laboratory calibration were applied and another dimension, which represents the sensor location on the shell was added. With this procedure, new calibration factors were generated, that could be applied to measurement sequences under operating conditions.

### *3.2. Comparison of CFD-Simulation and aerodynamic measurements*

Figure 8 shows a comparison of the coefficient of pressure (cp) between measured pressure on the suction side (blue), measured pressure on the pressure side (red), a steady state CFD-Simulation (green dots) and multiple XFoil simulations for different angles of attack (light blue), for one revolution of the rotor. The simulations were adjusted to the original profile of the turbine. However, the profile, shown in the center of the diagrams, is generic. In contrast to the CFD simulation, the XFoil simulation shows static graphs, while the CFD changes with time.

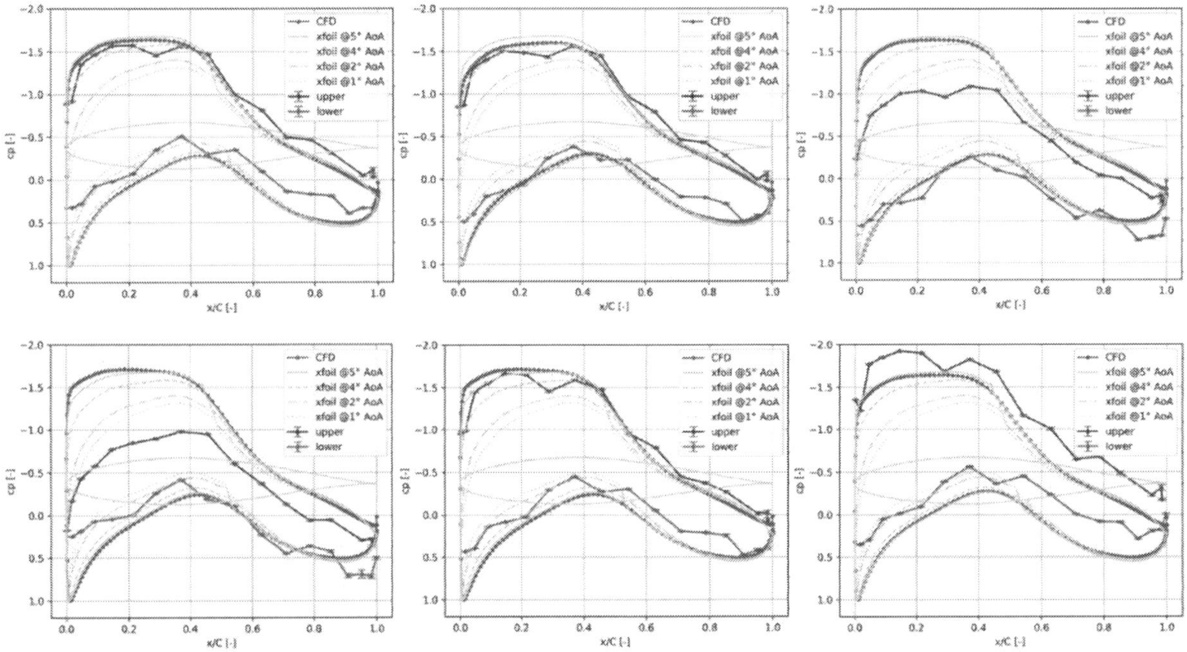


**Figure 8** Comparison of measurements, CFD- and XFoil-Simulation for one rotor revolution on the 8th of January 2022.

Comparing the measured data with the CFD it is apparent that the measurements are in the same range, but show a significantly more dynamic behaviour. Diagram 4 in the lower left, represents a tower pass through, where the differential pressure between pressure and suction side is minimal.

## 4. Conclusions

In this study an aerodynamic measurement system was developed that could be installed on virtually any onshore turbine as a retro-fit. It was possible to fulfil the requirements posed by the operator and manufacturer of the turbine. All add-ons to the turbine could be removed without residue or blade surface damage. According to the previous calculations the turbine did not show any changes in behaviour or rotor imbalance during operation. It was possible to reduce the influence of temperature and environmental influences on the measurement by a continuous calibration process.

The measurement results are plausible. The expected variation of the pressure during the revolution of the rotor could be reproduced. The comparison between aerodynamic measurement and CFD simulation showed that the aerodynamic and the CFD simulation are in the same range, while the fluctuation of the measurements is significantly higher than the fluctuation of the CFD simulation. This leads to the assumption that the CFD simulation underestimates all dynamic effects of the real operation conditions. The detailed evaluation on reasons for this is part of further research.

## 5. Acknowledgments

This research was carried out in the framework of the project HighRe (ref. no. 03EE2001) funded by the German Federal Ministry for Economic Affairs and Energy (BMWi) on the basis of a decision by the German Bundestag. Further to this we used the "Testfeld BHV" infrastructure, funded within the project of the same name (ref. no. 0324148) also by the BMWi.

## References

[1] Hand M M; Simms D A; Fingersh L J; Jager D W Cotrell J R; Schreck S and Larwood S M 2001, Unsteady aerodynamics experiment phase VI: Wind tunnel test configurations and available data campaigns., *United States: N. p.*

[2] Snel H, Schepers JG and Montgomerie B 2007, The MEXICO project (model experiments in controlled conditions): The database and first results of data processing and interpretation," *J. Phys.: Conf. Ser.*

[3] Aagaard Madsen H, Bak C, Schmidt Paulsen U, Gaunaa M, Fuglsang P, Romblad J, Olesen N A, Enevoldsen P, Laursen J and Jensen L 2010, The DAN-AERO MW experiments, *Final report.*

[4] Fraunhofer IWES, HighRe: Aerodynamics with High Reynolds Numbers for the Large Offshore Wind Turbines of the Future, 2019 - 2023. [Online]. Available: https://www.iwes.fraunhofer.de/en/research-projects/current-projects/highre.html. [Accessed 09. 02. 2023].

[5] Reichstein T, Schaffarczyk A, Dollinger C, Balaresque N, Schülein E, Jauch C and Fischer A, 2019, Investigation of laminar–turbulent transition on a rotating wind turbine blade of multimegawatt class with thermography and microphone array *Energies* **12** 2102.

[6] Fraunhofer IWES, The MoWiT (Modelica for Wind Turbines) Library," [Online]. Available: https://www.iwes.fraunhofer.de/en/research-spectrum/entry-oem-supplier/aerodynamics-for-wind-turbines/Load-Calculations.html#1330606953. [Accessed 13. 02. 2023].

[7] International Electrotechnical Commission, 2019, IEC 61400 - 1: Wind turbines Part 1: Design requirements, (VDE Verlag GmbH, Geneva).

[8] Selfridge R, 2018, Real-Time Sound Synthesis of Aeroacoustic Sounds using Physically Derived Models, (Queen Mary University of London).

[9] Gebauer I, Rosemann H and Dörsch C, 2017, Integrated design and manufacturing approach for a faster and easier production of rotor blade molds - direct tooling by BladeMaker, *3. International Symposium on Automated Composites Manufacturing*, Montreal, Canada.

[10] International Electrotechnical Commission, 2015, IEC 61400-13 Wind turbines - measurement of mechanical loads, (VDE Verlag GmbH, Geneva).

[11] International Electrotechnical Commission, 2017, IEC 61400-12-1 Wind energy generation systems - power performance measurements of electricity produciung wind turbines, (VDE Verlag GmbH, Geneva).

[12] Giyanani A, Sjöholm M, Thorsen G R, Schumacher J and Gottschall J, Wind speed reconstruction from three synchronized, *J. Phys: Conf. Ser. (TORQUE 2022),* **2265** 022032.

[13] Heckmeier F M, Iglesias D, Kienitz S and Breitsamter C, 2019, An innovative development of a five-hole pressure probe highly unsteady flow phenomena , *Proceedings of ASME Turbo Expo 2019: Turbomachinery Technical Conference and Exposition,* **GT2019**.

Journal of Physics: Conference Series **2507** (2023) 012021 doi:10.1088/1742-6596/2507/1/012021

# Effect of wind speed distribution and site assessment on pitch bearing loads and life

**Ashkan Rezaei, Amir R. Nejad**

Department of Marine Technology, Norwegian University of Science and Technology (NTNU), NO-7491, Trondheim, Norway

E-mail: ashkan.rezaei@ntnu.no

**Abstract.** In this paper, the wind speed distribution at thirteen onshore and offshore wind sites has been studied. Different probability distributions are used to estimate the wind speed distribution. Several goodness-of-fit indicators were used to assess the suitability of the fitting. The highest results were achieved by Kernel distribution in both onshore and offshore wind sites. Onshore wind sites did not fit well compared to offshore wind sites. Rayleigh distribution results at onshore wind sites were worse than at offshore wind sites. Onshore and offshore wind distributions result in various load duration distributions in pitch bearing. The concept of life ratio was introduced to compare the long-term fatigue life of the pitch bearing in different wind speed conditions. It is observed that the fatigue life of the pitch bearings in some wind sites is less than that of related IEC classes, and the risk of failure of the pitch bearing before the end of its expected designed fatigue life exists.

## 1. Introduction

The wind speed distribution at the site is significant for the wind turbine design because it determines the frequency of occurrence of the individual load components.

In wind energy, many distributions are investigated. Carta et al. [1] studied several probability distribution functions (PDFs) using Canary Island case studies. They investigated various PDFs that had one to three parameters. Despite the fact that the Weibull distribution has advantages over the PDFs under study, it is limited in its ability to capture some of the wind regimes that are common in nature, such as those with substantial proportions of null wind speeds, bimodal distributions, etc. For five wind sites in the east and south-east of Iran, Alavi et al. [2] assessed eight different PDFs. Due to its greater fit at two stations, their analysis demonstrated the Nakagami distribution's effectiveness. Jung et al. [3] reviewed 46 studies published between 2010 and 2018, which compared the goodness-of-fit of different theoretical parametric distributions and were evaluated. It was found that the two-parameter Weibull distribution is by far the most frequently evaluated distribution (in 44 out of 46 studies). Shi et al. [4] reviewed different distributions for wind energy. Additionally to investigate at the single and combination wind speed distributions, they also examined non-parametric distribution models including kernel density estimation and the maximum entropy principle. Ahsan-ul-Haq et al. [5] introduced a new three-parameter probability distribution called "New Alpha Power Transformed Power Lindley Distribution (NAPTPL)". They studied the distribution for five district regions of Pakistan and justified that the NAPTPL distribution has favorable performance for all five regions.

In this study, different offshore and onshore wind fields were studied, and the most suitable wind distribution was fitted to the data to compare the results with standard proposed distributions. According to the standards [6, 7], the Rayleigh distribution shall be taken into account for the load calculations for the standard wind turbine classes. However, it does not truly represent wind distribution at wind sites, and according to results, the Rayleigh distribution underestimates the above-rated wind speed at the onshore site while overestimating it at the offshore site. The uncertainty in the wind speed distribution is studied, and the resulting uncertainty in long-term fatigue life is stated.

Besides the wind speed distribution, the wind sites are studied based on wind energy potential [8, 9]. In this work, the wind sites are based on the loads on the blade's root, which is very important for pitch bearing. The pitch bearing is a component that transfers the loads from the blades to the hub and nacelle. The pitch system is the most critical subassembly in offshore and the fourth critical subassembly in onshore sites based on failure rate and downtime [10]. Failure in the pitch bearing consists of fatigue and wear modes [11]. Fatigue mode is categorized into rolling contact fatigue, core crushing, edge loading, and ring fracture. In this paper, rolling contact fatigue is studied, and hereafter, whenever bearing life is mentioned, it refers to rolling contact fatigue. The bearing fatigue life calculation is documented in the National Renewable Energy Laboratory design guideline (DG03) [12]. Despite the existence of other work done by Woll et al. [13] or Breslau et al. [14] to calculate the slewing bearing fatigue life, the DG03 calculation process is referred in standards [15]. A wind turbine and its components are designed based on standards, such as IEC 61400 [7]. These standards are also used to classify wind sites, and wind turbine manufacturers assign wind turbines based on wind site classifications. The life behavior of wind turbine components at real wind sites has not been investigated extensively. This paper presents a study of pitch bearing loads and life in IEC-designed cases and a comparison with real wind site data.

The rest of the paper is organized as follows: Section 2 describes the methodology for wind distribution and load calculations. Wind speed data is given in Section 3. The wind speed and load analysis and its results are presented in Section 4. Finally, Section 5 presented the conclusions.

## 2. Methodology

The study starts with the different probability distribution functions of wind sites. The wind speeds are projected at different heights. By using the statistical approach, the goodness-of-fit of each distribution function is evaluated, and the result is validated with known data at specific heights.

In the next step, the uncertainty induced on the rotor based on wind speed distribution is compared according to pitch bearing load and life. The main focus is on the blade root loads.

### *2.1. Wind speed distribution*

Different distribution functions are studied. They include generalized extreme value, Gamma, inverse Gaussian, Kernel, lognormal, Nakagami, Rayleigh, Rician, and Weibull. In Table 1, PDFs of the nominated distribution function are presented. More information on the equations and parameters definitions of generalized extreme value, Gamma, Kernel, and Weibull is referred to [4]. The parameters of inverse Gaussian, lognormal, and Nakagami are referred to [2]. Rayleigh and Rician parameters are referred to [16].

Table 1: PDFs of nominated distribution function [2, 4, 16]

| Distribution function | PDF |
|---|---|
| Generalized Extreme Value(GEV) | $f(x) = \frac{1}{\alpha}[1 - \frac{k}{\alpha}(x-\mu)]^{\frac{1}{k}-1} - e^{-[1-\frac{k}{\alpha}(x-\mu)]^{\frac{1}{k}}}$ |
| Gamma(Gam) | $f(x) = \frac{\alpha^k}{\Gamma(k)} x^{k-1} e^{-\alpha x}$ |
| Inverse Gaussian (IG) | $f(x) = \sqrt{\frac{\lambda}{2\pi x^3}} e^{-\frac{\lambda}{2\mu^2 x}(x-\mu^2)}$ |
| Kernel (Ker) | $f(\alpha) = \frac{1}{nh}\sum_{i=1}^{n} K(\alpha), \quad \alpha = \frac{x-x_i}{h}$ |
| Lognormal (LN) | $f(x) = \frac{1}{x\sigma\sqrt{2\pi}} e^{-\frac{1}{2}[\frac{ln(x)-\mu}{\sigma}]^2}$ |
| Nakagami (Nak) | $f(x) = \frac{2m^m}{\Gamma(m)\Omega^m} x^{2m-1} e^{-\frac{m}{\Omega}x^2}$ |
| Rayleigh (Ray) | $f(x) = \frac{x}{\sigma^2} e^{-\frac{x^2}{2\sigma^2}}$ |
| Rician (Ric) | $f(x) = \frac{x}{a^2} e^{-\frac{x^2+b^2}{2a^2}} I_0(\frac{bx}{a^2})$ |
| Weibull (Wbl) | $f(x) = \frac{k}{\alpha}(\frac{x}{\alpha})^{k-1} e^{-(\frac{x}{\alpha})^k}$ |

In this study, the parameters were calculated by maximum likelihood estimator [17] using MATLAB software.

There are different statistical approaches to assessing the performance and goodness-of-fit (GoF) of the parameter estimation method [4, 18, 19, 20]. In this study, the following unbounded and bounded indicators have been applied.

- Chi-square error $\chi^2$
- Root mean square error (RMSE)
- Kolmogorov-Smirnov test (K-S)
- Coefficient of efficiency (CE)
- Coefficient of determination ($R^2$)
- Index of agreement (IA)
- Modified index of agreement (MIA)

The equations related to each indicator are presented in Table 2.

Table 2: Nominated applied goodness-of-fit (GoF) indicators [4, 18, 19, 20]

| Goodness-of-fit function | Equation |
|---|---|
| Chi-square error $\chi^2$ | $\chi^2 = \sum \frac{(Q_i - \hat{Q}_i)^2}{\hat{Q}_i}$ |
| Relative root mean square error (RMSE) | $RMSE = \frac{\sqrt{\frac{1}{n}\sum (Q_i - \hat{Q}_i)^2}}{\frac{1}{n}\sum Q_i} 100$ |
| Kolmogorov-Smirnov test (K-S) | $KS = max\lvert F_i - \hat{F}_i \rvert$ |
| Coefficient of efficiency (CE) | $CE = 1 - \frac{\sum (Q_i - \hat{Q}_i)^2}{\sum (Q_i - \bar{Q})^2}$ |
| Coefficient of determination ($R^2$) | $R^2 = [\frac{\sum (Q_i - \bar{Q})(\hat{Q}_i - \tilde{Q})}{\sqrt{\sum (Q_i - \bar{Q})^2 \sum (\hat{Q}_i - \tilde{Q})^2}}]^2$ |
| Index of agreement (IA) | $IA = 1 - \frac{\sum (Q_i - \hat{Q}_i)^2}{\sum (\lvert \hat{Q}_i - \bar{Q} \rvert + \lvert Q_i - \bar{Q}_i \rvert)^2}$ |
| Modified index of agreement (MIA) | $IA = 1 - \frac{\sum (Q_i - \hat{Q}_i)}{\sum (\lvert \hat{Q}_i - \bar{Q} \rvert + \lvert Q_i - \bar{Q}_i \rvert)}$ |

$Q_i$: Observed data at i-th level
$\hat{Q}_i$: Estimated data at i-th level
$\bar{Q}$: Mean of observed data
$\tilde{Q}$: Mean of estimated data
$F_i$: CDF value of observed data at i-th level
$\hat{F}_i$: CDF value of estimated data at i-th level

The wind speeds are measured at some finite heights, and they need to be projected to different heights. Two mathematical models have been used to model the vertical profile of wind speed: the logarithmic profile (log law) and power law [21]. The power and log laws are presented as follows, respectively:

$$\frac{U(z)}{U(z_r)} = \left(\frac{z}{z_r}\right)^{\alpha} \tag{1}$$

$$\frac{U(z)}{U(z_r)} = \frac{Ln\frac{z}{z_0}}{Ln\frac{z_r}{z_0}} \tag{2}$$

where wind speed ($U$) at the projected height ($z$) is calculated from the reference height ($z_r$), $\alpha$ is the power exponent, and $Z_0$ is the surface roughness length. Power law exponent and surface roughness can be calculated from two sets of known wind speed data at different heights. The power law exponent is calculated in two different ways. In the first one, $U$ is the average annual wind speed, while in the second one, the power law exponent in every 10-minutes simulation is calculated and a series of exponents is created. Afterward, polynomials of order 0 to 2 are fitted.

### *2.2. Wind to bearing life ratio*

In order to calculate the blade roots' loads from wind, the National Renewable Energy Laboratory's (NREL's) 5 MW reference wind turbine was considered [22]. The wind turbine model is considered from the reference model in GitHub/OpenFAST [23]. The pitch bearing model is considered from reference [24]. The blade roots' loads are calculated using OpenFAST [25].

The relation between blade roots' loads and pitch bearing life is described further. The equivalent dynamic thrust load ($P_{ea}$) is a constant centric (uniformly distributed) axial load, under whose influence a rolling bearing would have the same life as it would attain under the actual load conditions [12]. It can be estimated from

$$P_{ea} = 0.75F_r + F_a + \frac{2.5M}{D_{pw}} \tag{3}$$

where $F_r$, $F_a$, and $M$ denote the applied radial, axial, and moment loads, respectively. The pitch diameter of the bearing is denoted by $D_{pw}$ [26]. The moment part of equation 3, $2.5M/D_{pw}$, represents the strongest influence on the basic dynamic axial load rating [27]. The basic rating life, $L_{10}$, expressed in millions of revolutions, is the rating life associated with 90% reliability and given by the following [12].

$$L_{10} = (\frac{C_{a,osc}}{P_{ea}})^p \tag{4}$$

where $C_{a,osc}$ is the basic dynamic axial load rating for oscillation and $p$ denote-s the life exponent, which equals 3 for ball bearings. The formulation of $C_{a,osc}$ depends on a prorated angle of oscillation, $\theta$ , in comparison to the critical angle of oscillation, $\theta_{crit}$.

$$C_{a,osc} = \{ \begin{array}{l} C_a(\frac{180^o}{\theta})^{3/10} Z^{0.033} \text{ for } \theta < \theta_{crit} \\ C_a(\frac{180^o}{\theta})^{1/p} \text{ for } \theta \geq \theta_{crit} \end{array} \tag{5}$$

where $C_a$ is the basic dynamic axial load rating and $Z$ is the number of balls. The prorated angle of oscillation, $\theta$ is

$$\theta = \frac{\sum_{k=1}^{K} N_k t_k \theta_k}{\sum_{k=1}^{K} N_k t_k} \tag{6}$$

where $K$ is the number of load cases. Parameters $t_k$ and $N_k$ denote the decimal fraction of time and speed of oscillation, respectively, for the bearing operated under the condition yielding $\theta_k$.

$L_{10}$ life can also be determined in hours of operation, $L_{10h}$ as follows, where rotational speed $N$ is expressed in oscillations per minute (opm).

$$L_{10h} = \frac{10^6 L_{10}}{60N} \tag{7}$$

When $\theta < \theta_{crit}$, the contact stresses of the individual rolling elements do not overlap, and each rolling element has its own discrete stressed volume. These individual stressed volumes then must be combined statistically to calculate the overall capacity and life [12]. In this case, combining equations 3 to 7 results in the following equations:

$$L_{10h} = C(P_{ea})^{-3}\theta^{-0.3} \tag{8}$$

where $C$ is a function of pitch bearing characteristics and is a constant. $C$ is calculated as

$$C = \frac{10^6}{60N} C_a Z^{0.033} 180^{0.3} \tag{9}$$

The equation 8 shows that the bearing life, $L_{10h}$ is a function of $P_{ea}$ and $\theta$. It is also possible to calculate the rating life from equation 10 [15]

$$L_{10} = \frac{\sum q_i}{\sum \frac{q_i}{L_{10i}}} \tag{10}$$

where $L_{10}$ is the combined rating life of the bearing, $q_i$ is the time share on the i-th load level, and $L_{10i}$ is the rating life of the bearing on the i-th load level. It is assumed that the difference of $\theta$ in different sites is not significant. By combining Equations 10 and 8 relation between the life of the bearing with respect to load and time share is derived. Life ratio $Lr_{a,b}$ concept is introduced to compare the life of the bearing in two different wind sites ($WSa$ and $WSb$) by just knowing the time share of the i-th load level ($P_{ea,i}$) in each wind site. The life ratio, which is the relation between the life of the bearing ($L_{10,WSa}$, $L_{10,WSb}$) in two wind sites (a,b), is calculated as

$$Lr_{a,b} = \frac{L_{10,WSa}}{L_{10,WSb}} = \frac{\sum q_{i,WSb}(P_{ea,i})^3}{\sum q_{i,WSa}(P_{ea,i})^3} \tag{11}$$

where $q_{i,WSa}$ and $q_{i,WSa}$ are the time shares of the i-th load level in wind sites a and b, respectively.

## 3. Wind speed data

In the present study, 13 wind sites in Iran [28], Pakistan [29], Vietnam [30], Ethiopia [31], Denmark [32], and United State of America [33] were studied. The data includes the mean and standard deviation of 10-min wind speed. In order to account for the wind's seasonal effect, data needs to cover an entire year. Nominated wind sites cover a whole year's measurements. In Table 3, in addition to the year of measurement, the geographical location of the wind sites with their longitude and latitude and the measurement height of the wind speed have been shown. The last wind site in the table, Anholt, is offshore, and the others are onshore wind sites.

Table 3: Geographical location of the selected wind sites

| Country | Wind site | Latitude | Longitude | measurement height | year |
|---|---|---|---|---|---|
| Iran | Khaf | 34°29'10.2"N | 60°18'32.1"E | 10, 30, 40 (m) | 2008 |
| Iran | Mil nader | 31°05'11.0"N | 61°09'23.0"E | 10, 30, 40 (m) | 2011 |
| Iran | Shourjeh | 36°04'18.3"N | 49°26'41.2"E | 10, 30, 40 (m) | 2009 |
| Iran | Khalkhal Bafrajerd | 37°32'23.0"N | 48°34'27.0"E | 10, 30, 40 (m) | 2012 |
| Iran | Moaleman | 34°51'57.4"N | 54°34'25.1"E | 10, 30, 40 (m) | 2007 |
| Pakistan | Sujawal | 24°30'56.0"N | 68°11'19.1"E | 40, 60, 80 (m) | 2017 |
| Vietnam | Thanh Hai | 9°53'43.1"N | 106°39'39.6"E | 40, 60, 80 (m) | 2013 |
| Ethiopia | Aysha | 10°49'22.2"N | 42°30'12.1"E | 40, 60, 80 (m) | 2020 |
| Ethiopia | Gode | 5°34'42.1"N | 43°20'22.3"E | 40, 60, 80 (m) | 2020 |
| Ethiopia | Kebribeyah | 8°58'22.6"N | 43°14'58.8"E | 40, 60, 80 (m) | 2020 |
| Ethiopia | Tuluguled | 9°39'07.1"N | 42°43'09.6"E | 40, 60, 80 (m) | 2020 |
| USA | NREL's Flatirons Campus | 39°54'38.3"N | 105°14'05.3"W | 20, 50, 80 (m) | 2021 |
| Denmark | Anholt | 56°35'44.4"N | 11°09'09.8"E | 65.6, 85.6, 101.6 (m) | 2013 |

## 4. Result and discussion

The wind measurement at selected offshore and onshore wind sites was fitted with different PDFs. The results for the selected sites are illustrated in Figure 1.

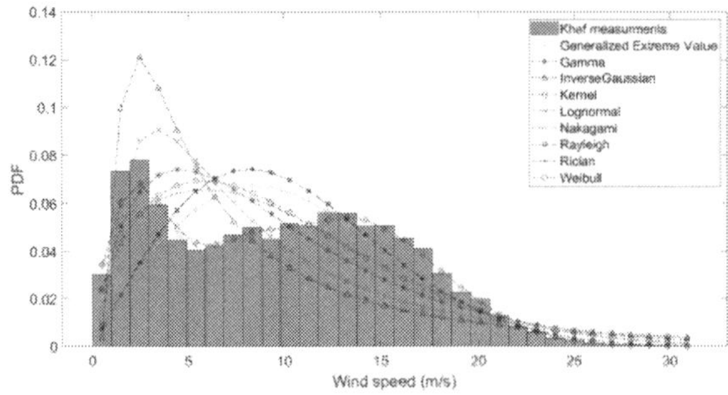


(a) Khaf

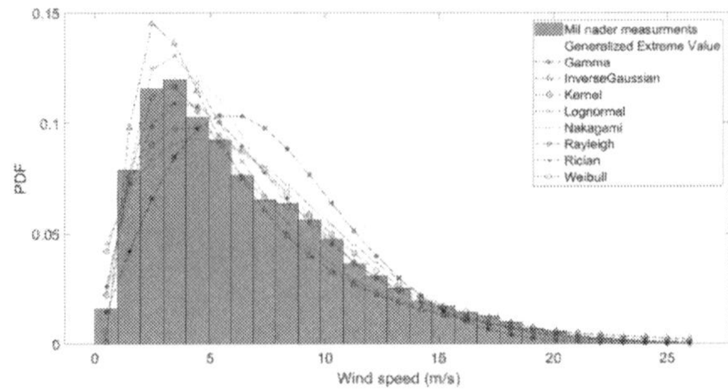


(b) Mil nader

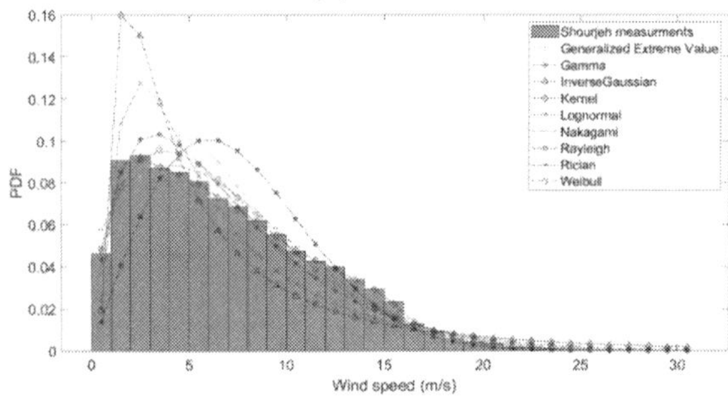


(c) Shourjeh

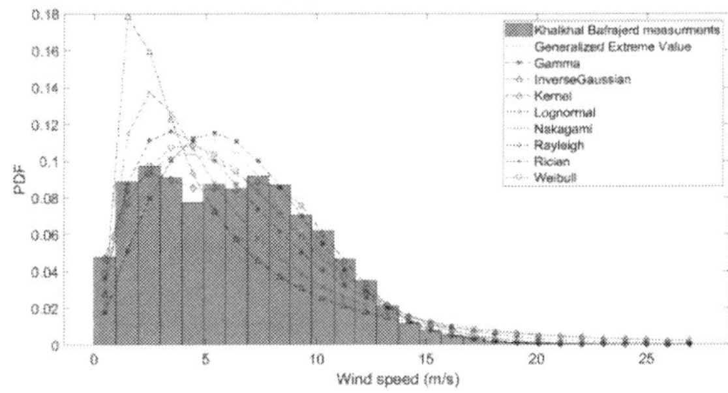


(d) Khalkhal Bafrajerd

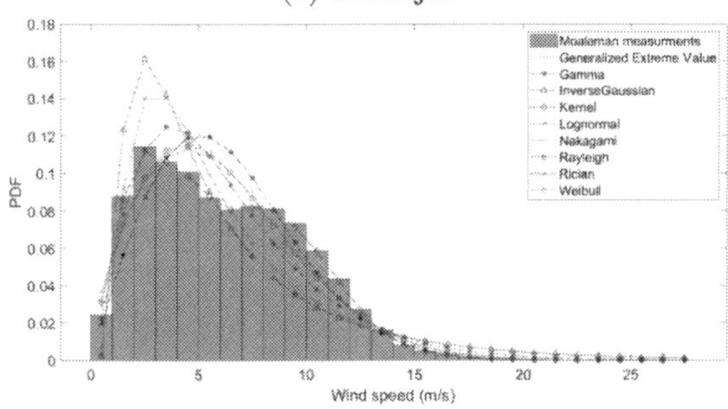


(e) Moaleman

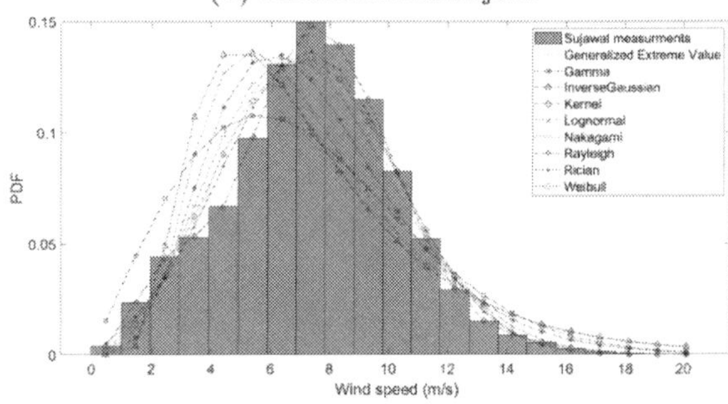


(f) Sujawal

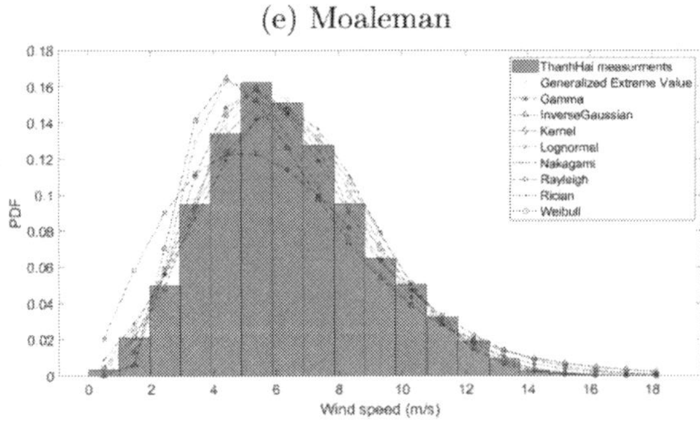


(g) ThanhHai

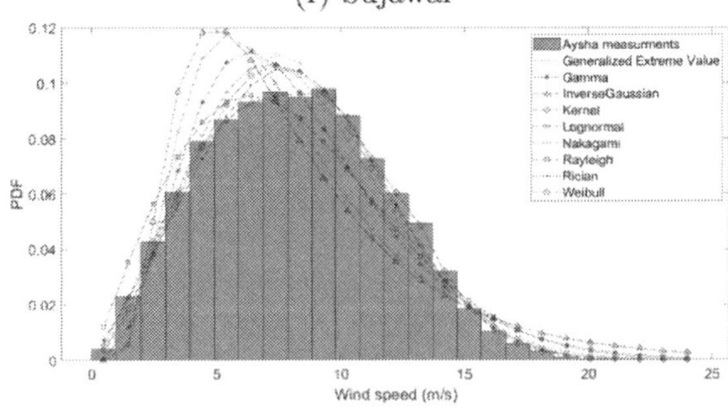


(h) Aysha

Figure 1: PDFs of mean wind speed at (a) Khaf, 40m height, (b) Mil nader, 40m height, (c) Shourjeh, 40m height, (d) Khalkhal Bafrajerd, 40m height, (e) Moaleman, 40m height, (f) Sujawal, 80m height, (g) Thanh Hai, 80m height, (h) Aysha, 80m height, (i) Gode, 80m height, (j) Kebribeyah, 80m height, (k) Tuluguled, 80m height, (l) NREL's Flatirons Campus, 80m height, (m) Anholt, 101.6m height

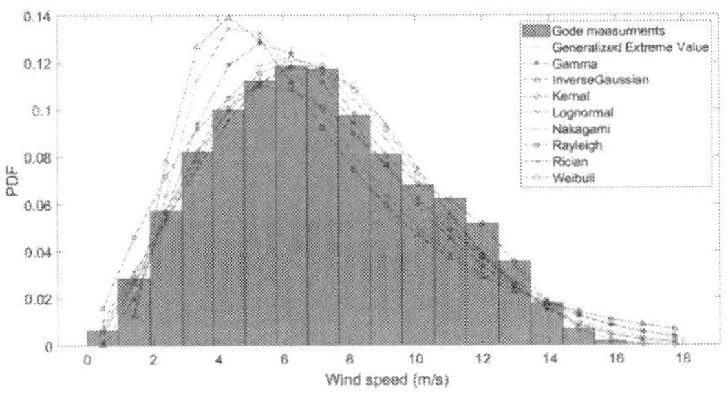


(i) Gode

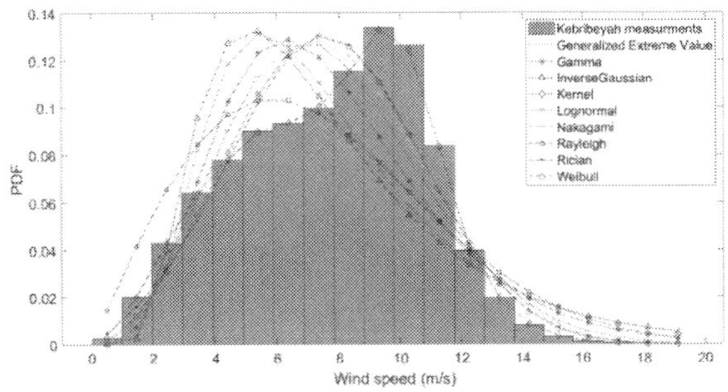


(j) Kebribeyah

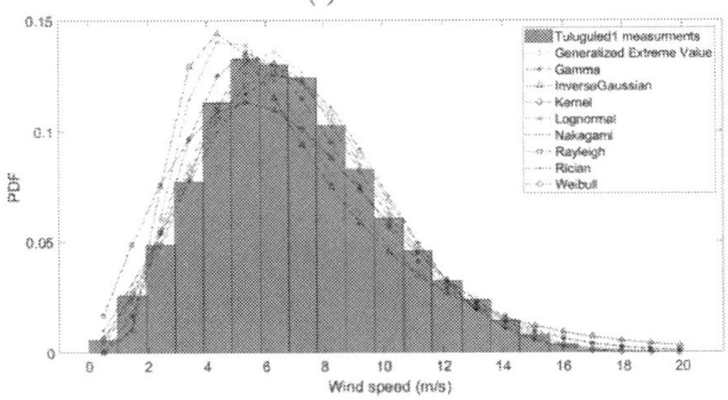


(k) Tuluguled

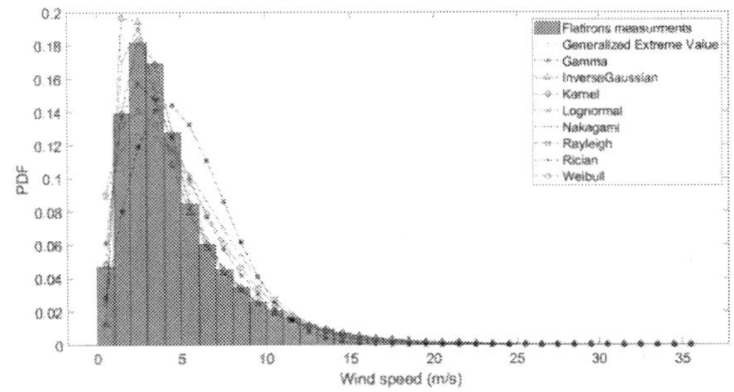


(l) Flatirons Campus

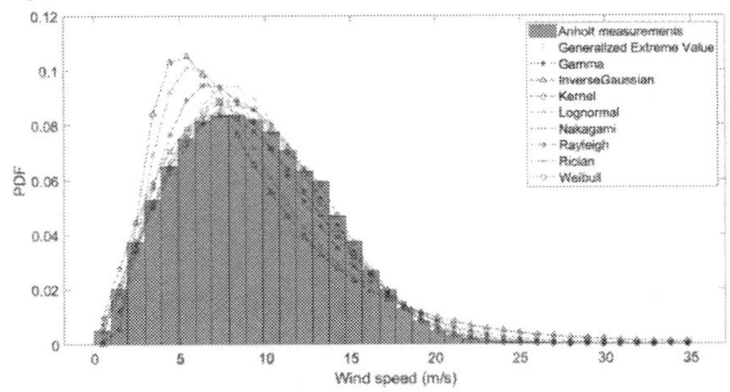


(m) Anholt

Figure 1: PDFs of mean wind speed at (a) Khaf, 40m height, (b) Mil nader, 40m height, (c) Shourjeh, 40m height, (d) Khalkhal Bafrajerd, 40m height, (e) Moaleman, 40m height, (f) Sujawal, 80m height, (g) Thanh Hai, 80m height, (h) Aysha, 80m height, (i) Gode, 80m height, (j) Kebribeyah, 80m height, (k) Tuluguled, 80m height, (l) NREL's Flatirons Campus, 80m height, (m) Anholt, 101.6m height

The results show that the Kernel estimator has the best fit. In some sites, such as Khaf or Kebribeyah, Rayleigh distribution, which is proposed by standards and guidelines [6, 7] doesn't fit well. To show how a theoretical probability function matches with the observation data, the results of the considered goodness-of-fit criteria for wind speed data are presented in Table 4 for all selected stations. Generally, the fewer the errors, the better the fit. In $\chi^2$, $RMSE$ and $K-S$ the lower value indicates a distribution better fitted to observation. In $CE$, $R^2$, $IA$ and $MIA$ a value close to one indicates better fitting.

Table 4: Goodness-of-fit in different PDFs in selected wind sites

| Site | GoF | Distribution functions | | | | | | | | |
|---|---|---|---|---|---|---|---|---|---|---|
| | | GEV | Gam | IG | Ker | LN | Nak | Ray | Ric | Wbl |
| Khaf | $\chi^2$ | 0.187 | 0.184 | 0.716 | 0.007 | 0.376 | 0.111 | 0.328 | 0.328 | 0.143 |
| | RMSE | 0.459 | 0.460 | 0.722 | 0.109 | 0.580 | 0.379 | 0.551 | 0.551 | 0.430 |
| | K-S | 0.095 | 0.076 | 0.174 | 0.040 | 0.106 | 0.073 | 0.151 | 0.151 | 0.087 |
| | CE | 0.618 | 0.615 | 0.052 | 0.978 | 0.389 | 0.739 | 0.448 | 0.448 | 0.664 |
| | $R^2$ | 0.658 | 0.665 | 0.531 | 0.980 | 0.565 | 0.753 | 0.583 | 0.583 | 0.699 |
| | IA | 0.950 | 0.928 | 0.861 | 0.998 | 0.897 | 0.954 | 0.933 | 0.933 | 0.942 |
| | MIA | 0.775 | 0.732 | 0.627 | 0.951 | 0.678 | 0.786 | 0.742 | 0.742 | 0.759 |
| Mil nader | $\chi^2$ | 0.040 | 0.018 | 0.259 | 0.003 | 0.048 | 0.062 | 0.195 | 0.195 | 0.039 |
| | RMSE | 0.235 | 0.161 | 0.273 | 0.050 | 0.178 | 0.304 | 0.476 | 0.476 | 0.241 |
| | K-S | 0.086 | 0.079 | 0.051 | 0.059 | 0.063 | 0.097 | 0.175 | 0.175 | 0.081 |
| | CE | 0.944 | 0.974 | 0.925 | 0.997 | 0.968 | 0.907 | 0.772 | 0.771 | 0.941 |
| | $R^2$ | 0.952 | 0.974 | 0.955 | 0.998 | 0.979 | 0.908 | 0.786 | 0.786 | 0.942 |
| | IA | 0.991 | 0.996 | 0.989 | 1.000 | 0.994 | 0.987 | 0.967 | 0.967 | 0.993 |
| | MIA | 0.906 | 0.939 | 0.893 | 0.982 | 0.922 | 0.886 | 0.819 | 0.819 | 0.917 |
| Shourjeh | $\chi^2$ | 0.069 | 0.039 | 0.280 | 0.001 | 0.148 | 0.015 | 0.221 | 0.221 | 0.021 |
| | RMSE | 0.308 | 0.196 | 0.653 | 0.032 | 0.406 | 0.147 | 0.496 | 0.496 | 0.156 |
| | K-S | 0.080 | 0.057 | 0.105 | 0.042 | 0.064 | 0.058 | 0.160 | 0.161 | 0.062 |
| | CE | 0.909 | 0.963 | 0.588 | 0.999 | 0.841 | 0.979 | 0.763 | 0.763 | 0.977 |
| | $R^2$ | 0.919 | 0.969 | 0.767 | 0.999 | 0.882 | 0.979 | 0.809 | 0.809 | 0.979 |
| | IA | 0.988 | 0.994 | 0.947 | 1.000 | 0.973 | 0.997 | 0.975 | 0.975 | 0.997 |
| | MIA | 0.889 | 0.922 | 0.770 | 0.990 | 0.837 | 0.948 | 0.841 | 0.841 | 0.942 |
| Bafrajerd | $\chi^2$ | 0.065 | 0.086 | 0.419 | 0.002 | 0.246 | 0.028 | 0.115 | 0.115 | 0.041 |
| | RMSE | 0.342 | 0.347 | 0.789 | 0.065 | 0.539 | 0.225 | 0.387 | 0.387 | 0.269 |
| | K-S | 0.086 | 0.061 | 0.143 | 0.048 | 0.085 | 0.063 | 0.126 | 0.126 | 0.072 |
| | CE | 0.892 | 0.888 | 0.422 | 0.996 | 0.730 | 0.953 | 0.861 | 0.861 | 0.933 |
| | $R^2$ | 0.901 | 0.897 | 0.625 | 0.996 | 0.774 | 0.955 | 0.887 | 0.887 | 0.937 |
| | IA | 0.988 | 0.984 | 0.925 | 1.000 | 0.956 | 0.994 | 0.988 | 0.988 | 0.992 |
| | MIA | 0.891 | 0.874 | 0.727 | 0.981 | 0.791 | 0.924 | 0.893 | 0.893 | 0.908 |
| Moaleman | $\chi^2$ | 0.075 | 0.068 | 0.423 | 0.002 | 0.199 | 0.038 | 0.068 | 0.068 | 0.040 |
| | RMSE | 0.376 | 0.303 | 0.546 | 0.042 | 0.431 | 0.258 | 0.363 | 0.363 | 0.268 |
| | K-S | 0.092 | 0.072 | 0.073 | 0.052 | 0.067 | 0.076 | 0.117 | 0.118 | 0.077 |
| | CE | 0.890 | 0.929 | 0.769 | 0.999 | 0.856 | 0.949 | 0.898 | 0.898 | 0.944 |
| | $R^2$ | 0.899 | 0.935 | 0.827 | 0.999 | 0.878 | 0.950 | 0.910 | 0.910 | 0.947 |
| | IA | 0.987 | 0.990 | 0.967 | 1.000 | 0.978 | 0.993 | 0.991 | 0.991 | 0.993 |
| | MIA | 0.886 | 0.902 | 0.818 | 0.991 | 0.853 | 0.919 | 0.904 | 0.904 | 0.915 |
| Sujawal | $\chi^2$ | 0.040 | 0.233 | $> 100$ | 0.001 | 22.30 | 0.057 | 0.175 | 0.018 | 0.029 |
| | RMSE | 21.16 | 38.23 | 61.89 | 0.799 | 53.39 | 26.29 | 49.79 | 14.84 | 18.93 |
| | K-S | 0.062 | 0.061 | 0.083 | 0.073 | 0.083 | 0.055 | 0.085 | 0.065 | 0.062 |
| | CE | 0.958 | 0.862 | 0.637 | 1.000 | 0.730 | 0.935 | 0.765 | 0.979 | 0.966 |
| | $R^2$ | 0.958 | 0.862 | 0.651 | 1.000 | 0.735 | 0.935 | 0.779 | 0.979 | 0.966 |
| | IA | 0.993 | 0.975 | 0.932 | 1.000 | 0.949 | 0.990 | 0.944 | 0.997 | 0.995 |
| | MIA | 0.916 | 0.842 | 0.740 | 0.997 | 0.775 | 0.898 | 0.763 | 0.943 | 0.926 |
| Thanh Hai | $\chi^2$ | 0.004 | 0.072 | $> 100$ | 0.002 | 13.66 | 0.007 | 0.107 | 0.023 | 0.014 |
| | RMSE | 5.197 | 12.35 | 33.73 | 6.013 | 26.66 | 8.072 | 37.58 | 16.14 | 13.67 |
| | K-S | 0.080 | 0.056 | 0.047 | 0.073 | 0.045 | 0.080 | 0.057 | 0.099 | 0.092 |
| | CE | 0.997 | 0.986 | 0.892 | 0.997 | 0.932 | 0.994 | 0.866 | 0.975 | 0.982 |

Continuation of Table 4

| Site | GoF | Distribution functions | | | | | | | | |
|---|---|---|---|---|---|---|---|---|---|---|
| | | GEV | Gam | IG | Ker | LN | Nak | Ray | Ric | Wbl |
| | $R^2$ | 0.998 | 0.986 | 0.895 | 0.997 | 0.934 | 0.994 | 0.884 | 0.976 | 0.983 |
| | IA | 0.999 | 0.997 | 0.980 | 1.000 | 0.987 | 0.999 | 0.974 | 0.996 | 0.997 |
| | MIA | 0.978 | 0.947 | 0.858 | 0.980 | 0.887 | 0.969 | 0.839 | 0.935 | 0.949 |
| Aysha | $\chi^2$ | 0.024 | 0.086 | > 100 | 0.001 | 2.729 | 0.019 | 0.056 | 0.008 | 0.010 |
| | RMSE | 15.05 | 25.44 | 46.85 | 1.567 | 39.57 | 14.32 | 22.64 | 9.532 | 11.19 |
| | K-S | 0.063 | 0.046 | 0.068 | 0.048 | 0.069 | 0.049 | 0.043 | 0.055 | 0.055 |
| | CE | 0.973 | 0.924 | 0.741 | 1.000 | 0.815 | 0.976 | 0.940 | 0.989 | 0.985 |
| | $R^2$ | 0.976 | 0.929 | 0.771 | 1.000 | 0.831 | 0.977 | 0.943 | 0.990 | 0.987 |
| | IA | 0.996 | 0.986 | 0.955 | 1.000 | 0.966 | 0.996 | 0.987 | 0.999 | 0.998 |
| | MIA | 0.936 | 0.881 | 0.787 | 0.994 | 0.815 | 0.936 | 0.888 | 0.961 | 0.952 |
| Gode | $\chi^2$ | 0.028 | 0.076 | > 100 | 0.001 | 2.034 | 0.023 | 0.050 | 0.020 | 0.019 |
| | RMSE | 14.55 | 18.11 | 37.93 | 0.797 | 30.95 | 10.77 | 17.69 | 11.74 | 10.79 |
| | K-S | 0.072 | 0.050 | 0.065 | 0.057 | 0.065 | 0.054 | 0.037 | 0.067 | 0.062 |
| | CE | 0.963 | 0.943 | 0.748 | 1.000 | 0.832 | 0.980 | 0.945 | 0.976 | 0.980 |
| | $R^2$ | 0.970 | 0.951 | 0.794 | 1.000 | 0.859 | 0.982 | 0.949 | 0.977 | 0.982 |
| | IA | 0.992 | 0.988 | 0.948 | 1.000 | 0.964 | 0.996 | 0.986 | 0.995 | 0.996 |
| | MIA | 0.913 | 0.891 | 0.771 | 0.995 | 0.811 | 0.939 | 0.880 | 0.933 | 0.940 |
| Kebribeyah | $\chi^2$ | 0.072 | 0.229 | > 100 | 0.001 | 11.88 | 0.103 | 0.213 | 0.058 | 0.063 |
| | RMSE | 31.67 | 45.15 | 60.09 | 1.248 | 55.56 | 36.51 | 47.19 | 29.78 | 30.60 |
| | K-S | 0.063 | 0.073 | 0.092 | 0.067 | 0.094 | 0.059 | 0.086 | 0.065 | 0.068 |
| | CE | 0.879 | 0.754 | 0.563 | 1.000 | 0.627 | 0.839 | 0.731 | 0.893 | 0.887 |
| | $R^2$ | 0.881 | 0.762 | 0.598 | 1.000 | 0.649 | 0.843 | 0.739 | 0.896 | 0.892 |
| | IA | 0.981 | 0.958 | 0.922 | 1.000 | 0.931 | 0.976 | 0.943 | 0.984 | 0.983 |
| | MIA | 0.861 | 0.795 | 0.722 | 0.995 | 0.737 | 0.845 | 0.761 | 0.874 | 0.870 |
| Tuluguled | $\chi^2$ | 0.006 | 0.067 | > 100 | 0.001 | 4.435 | 0.007 | 0.057 | 0.015 | 0.008 |
| | RMSE | 5.621 | 13.95 | 39.01 | 1.194 | 29.74 | 6.515 | 26.19 | 12.84 | 9.447 |
| | K-S | 0.072 | 0.040 | 0.050 | 0.065 | 0.048 | 0.064 | 0.046 | 0.080 | 0.073 |
| | CE | 0.997 | 0.979 | 0.833 | 1.000 | 0.903 | 0.995 | 0.925 | 0.982 | 0.990 |
| | $R^2$ | 0.997 | 0.979 | 0.843 | 1.000 | 0.907 | 0.995 | 0.935 | 0.982 | 0.990 |
| | IA | 0.999 | 0.996 | 0.971 | 1.000 | 0.981 | 0.999 | 0.986 | 0.997 | 0.998 |
| | MIA | 0.973 | 0.938 | 0.829 | 0.995 | 0.864 | 0.970 | 0.883 | 0.945 | 0.959 |
| Flatirons | $\chi^2$ | 0.012 | 0.040 | 0.119 | 0.001 | 0.031 | > 100 | > 100 | > 100 | 0.181 |
| | RMSE | 11.12 | 27.08 | 44.29 | 1.504 | 25.35 | 58.39 | 76.77 | 76.78 | 46.72 |
| | K-S | 0.093 | 0.112 | 0.069 | 0.092 | 0.078 | 0.153 | 0.242 | 0.242 | 0.117 |
| | CE | 0.996 | 0.977 | 0.938 | 1.000 | 0.980 | 0.892 | 0.813 | 0.813 | 0.931 |
| | $R^2$ | 0.997 | 0.978 | 0.945 | 1.000 | 0.981 | 0.896 | 0.814 | 0.814 | 0.934 |
| | IA | 0.999 | 0.997 | 0.996 | 1.000 | 0.998 | 0.986 | 0.976 | 0.976 | 0.992 |
| | MIA | 0.977 | 0.947 | 0.935 | 0.998 | 0.960 | 0.882 | 0.845 | 0.845 | 0.913 |
| Anholt | $\chi^2$ | 0.037 | 0.066 | > 100 | 0.001 | > 100 | 0.010 | 0.023 | 0.017 | 0.011 |
| | RMSE | 0.160 | 0.233 | 0.506 | 0.013 | 0.406 | 0.102 | 0.151 | 0.069 | 0.084 |
| | K-S | 0.055 | 0.040 | 0.064 | 0.040 | 0.062 | 0.041 | 0.030 | 0.046 | 0.045 |
| | CE | 0.979 | 0.957 | 0.796 | 1.000 | 0.869 | 0.992 | 0.982 | 0.996 | 0.994 |
| | $R^2$ | 0.982 | 0.959 | 0.818 | 1.000 | 0.878 | 0.992 | 0.982 | 0.996 | 0.995 |
| | IA | 0.997 | 0.993 | 0.969 | 1.000 | 0.978 | 0.999 | 0.997 | 0.999 | 0.999 |
| | MIA | 0.947 | 0.917 | 0.823 | 0.996 | 0.853 | 0.967 | 0.946 | 0.977 | 0.974 |

The results of unbounded indicators in some distributions increase significantly. In this case, the distribution cannot predict the measurement data, and the value of > 100 is indicated in the table. In addition, the results in the table are rounded, so, for example, a value of 1.000 does not indicate the perfect fitting of the results. From Table 4, ranking wind sites according to different criteria doesn't reach the same result. For example, in Khaf, according to $\chi^2$ indicator, the Weibull distribution fits better with the generalized extreme distribution, while if one considered the $CE$ indicator, the result would be opposite. However, the Kernel has the best goodness of fit results in all wind sites and in all indicators. The result of the proposed Rayleigh distribution is not in the top 3 at any of the wind sites, showing a lack of accuracy in prediction. The results of $CE$ and $R^2$ have the most consistency with the overall indicators' results. $CE$ distinct results are more significant than $R^2$. The coefficient of efficiency is considered a present indicator in the rest of the paper.

As stated before, the wind speed at different heights is needed in the study of site assessment. The wind speed data at different heights should be derived artificially from other heights. In order to project data to a specific height, it needs to consider the wind shear. Wind speed projection according to power and log law is performed with different methods. The results of the observed efficiency coefficient and the calculated one by Kernel distribution are presented in Table 5.

Table 5: Coefficient of efficiency in different wind shear at selected wind sites

| Site | Distribution function | | | | | |
|---|---|---|---|---|---|---|
| | Obs | PMAS | LMAS | PP0 | PP1 | PP2 |
| Khaf | 0.9783 | 0.9671 | 0.9672 | 0.9673 | 0.9663 | 0.9717 |
| Mil nader | 0.9975 | 0.9937 | 0.9941 | 0.9897 | 0.9898 | 0.9897 |
| Shourjeh | 0.9990 | 0.9988 | 0.9989 | 0.9990 | 0.9987 | 0.9982 |
| Bafrajerd | 0.9961 | 0.9953 | 0.9953 | 0.9954 | 0.9954 | 0.9957 |
| Moaleman | 0.9986 | 0.9950 | 0.9943 | 0.9955 | 0.9957 | 0.9954 |
| Sujawal | 0.9999 | 0.9973 | 0.9962 | 0.9976 | 0.9975 | 0.9982 |
| Thanh Hai | 0.9966 | 0.9976 | 0.9973 | 0.9975 | 0.9974 | 0.9975 |
| Aysha | 0.9997 | 0.9984 | 0.9984 | 0.9983 | 0.9987 | 0.9987 |
| Gode | 0.9999 | 0.9852 | 0.9844 | 0.9860 | 0.9887 | 0.9933 |
| Kebribeyah | 0.9998 | 0.9986 | 0.9982 | 0.9984 | 0.9983 | 0.9990 |
| Tuluguled | 0.9998 | 0.9992 | 0.9991 | 0.9992 | 0.9992 | 0.9984 |
| Flatirons | 0.9999 | 0.9971 | 0.9985 | 0.9906 | 0.9843 | 0.9817 |
| Anholt | 0.9999 | 0.9997 | 0.9997 | 0.9997 | 0.9997 | 0.9996 |

Obs: Observation data
PMAS: Power exponent mean annual wind speed
LMAS: Log law mean annual wind speed
PP0: Power exponent polynomial zero degree fitted
PP1: Power exponent polynomial one degree fitted
PP2: Power exponent polynomial two degree fitted

The wind speed at all sites was projected at 90 meters. To project wind speed, a power law with an average power exponent is considered. The calculated power exponent and coefficient of efficiency at 90 meter heights are presented in Table 6.

Table 6: Power law exponent, coefficient of efficiency and mean annual wind speed of projected wind speed to 90 meters height

| Wind site | $\alpha$ | CE | Mean annual wind speed(m/s) |
|---|---|---|---|
| Khaf | 0.1327 | 0.8934 | 10.95 |
| Mil nader | 0.1834 | 0.9455 | 7.96 |
| Shourjeh | 0.0747 | 0.9895 | 7.48 |
| Bafrajerd | 0.0130 | 0.9952 | 6.44 |
| Moaleman | 0.2143 | 0.9164 | 7.34 |
| Sujawal | 0.2102 | 0.9943 | 7.62 |
| Thanh Hai | 0.2237 | 0.9947 | 6.59 |
| Aysha | 0.1373 | 0.9979 | 8.35 |
| Gode | 0.2255 | 0.9941 | 7.30 |
| Kebribeyah | 0.1450 | 0.9949 | 7.86 |
| Tuluguled | 0.1725 | 0.9972 | 7.10 |
| Anholt | 0.1153 | 0.9993 | 9.08 |
| Flatirons | 0.1248 | 0.9997 | 4.81 |

The wind sites based on their mean annual wind speed at projected height are classified into IEC categories I, II, and III. The PDFs of IEC classes, which use Rayleigh distribution to categorize wind sites, are plotted in Figure 2. Most of the wind sites have been categorized into IEC Classes II and III. In IEC Class I, the offshore site has a higher recurrence at an around-rated wind speed compared to IEC, while the onshore site has a higher recurrence at an over-rated wind speed. In IEC Class II, all sites except Mil Nader have a higher recurrence at the rated wind speed.

The equivalent dynamic load of the pitch bearing in long-term conditions, as well as the wind turbine's life expectancy of 20 years in nominated wind sites and IEC classes, were calculated. Subsequently, the equivalent dynamic loads were distributed into bins to create the load duration distribution (LDD) of the equivalent dynamic loads. LDD shows the contribution of different load levels. The results of the equivalent dynamic load duration distribution in selected wind sites and IEC classes are presented in Figures 3, 4, 5. According to IEC, results are categorized according to annual mean wind speed classes (I, II, and III) and wind speed turbulence (A, B, and C) according to IEC 61400-1 [7]. The results show the contribution of load levels in different wind conditions. In some cases, the contribution of higher equivalent dynamic loads in wind sites exceeds the IECs. It is expected that higher contribution in larger loads will result in a lower life.

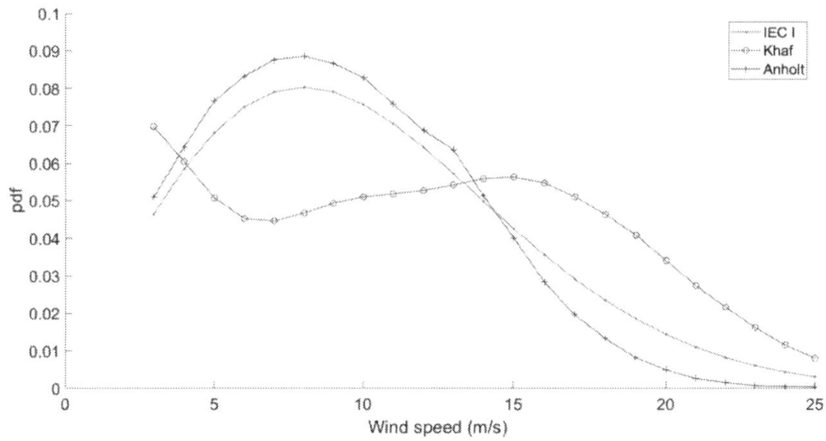


(a) IEC I category

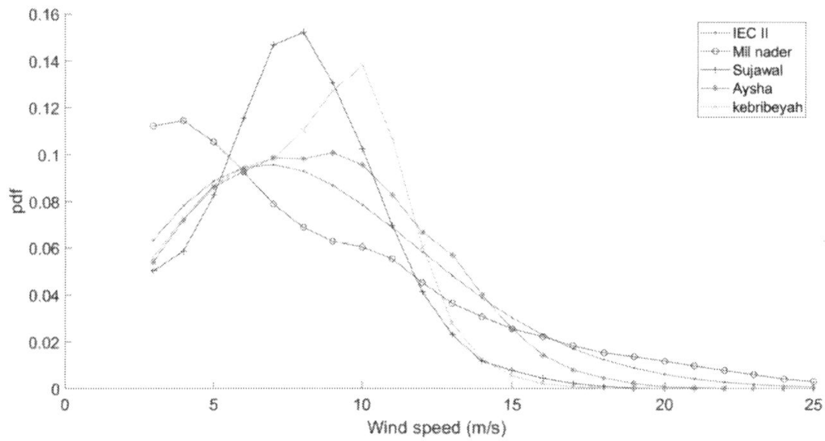


(b) IEC II category

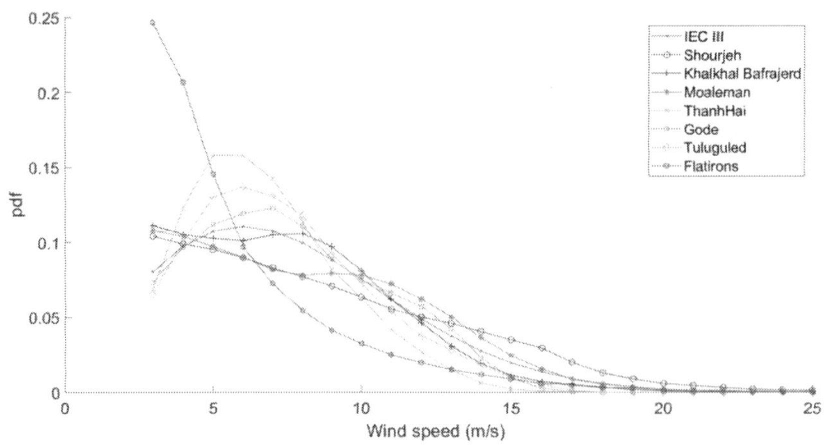


(c) IEC III category

Figure 2: Categorized wind site pdf according to IEC 61400-1 at projected height in category (a) IEC I, (b) IEC II, (c) IEC III

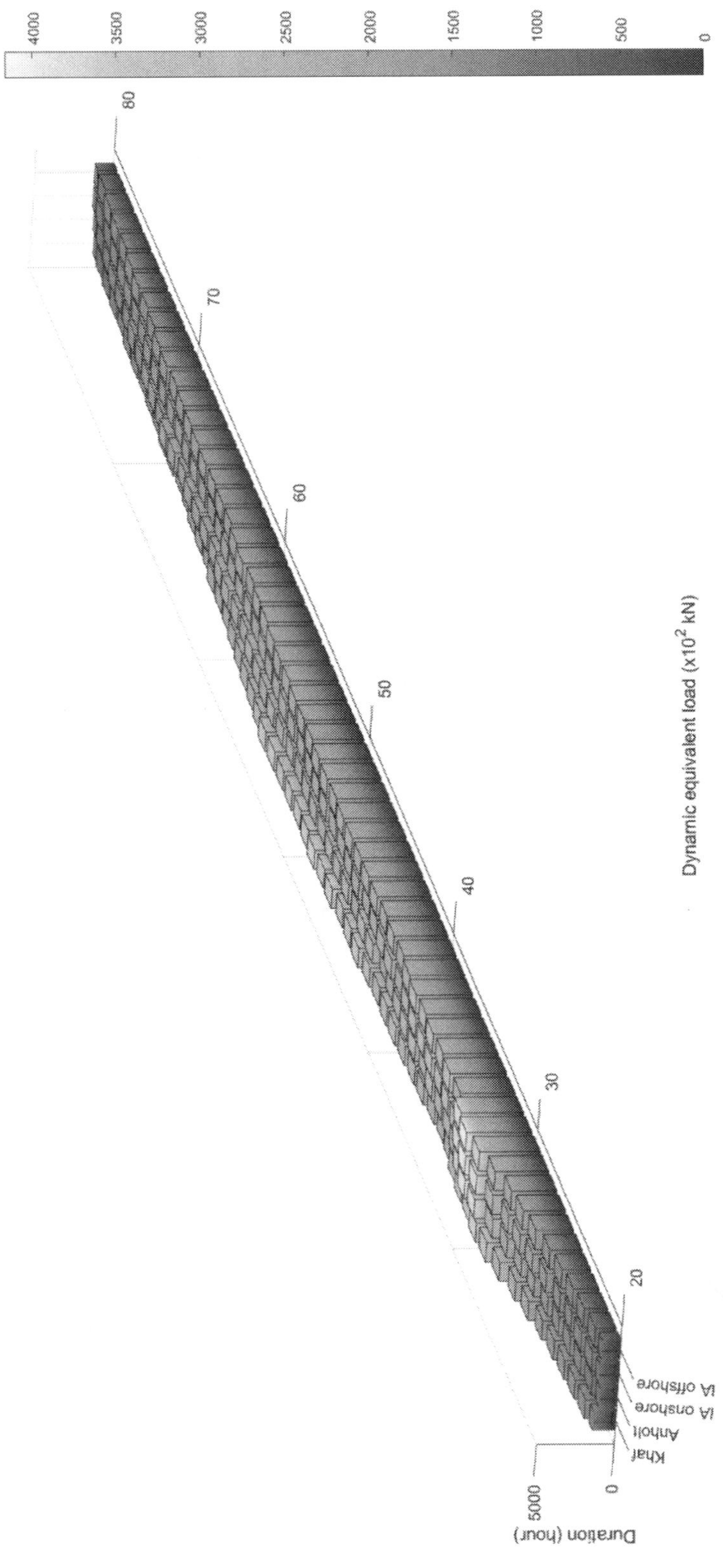


Figure 3: Dynamic equivalent load duration distribution in selected wind sites and IEC class I

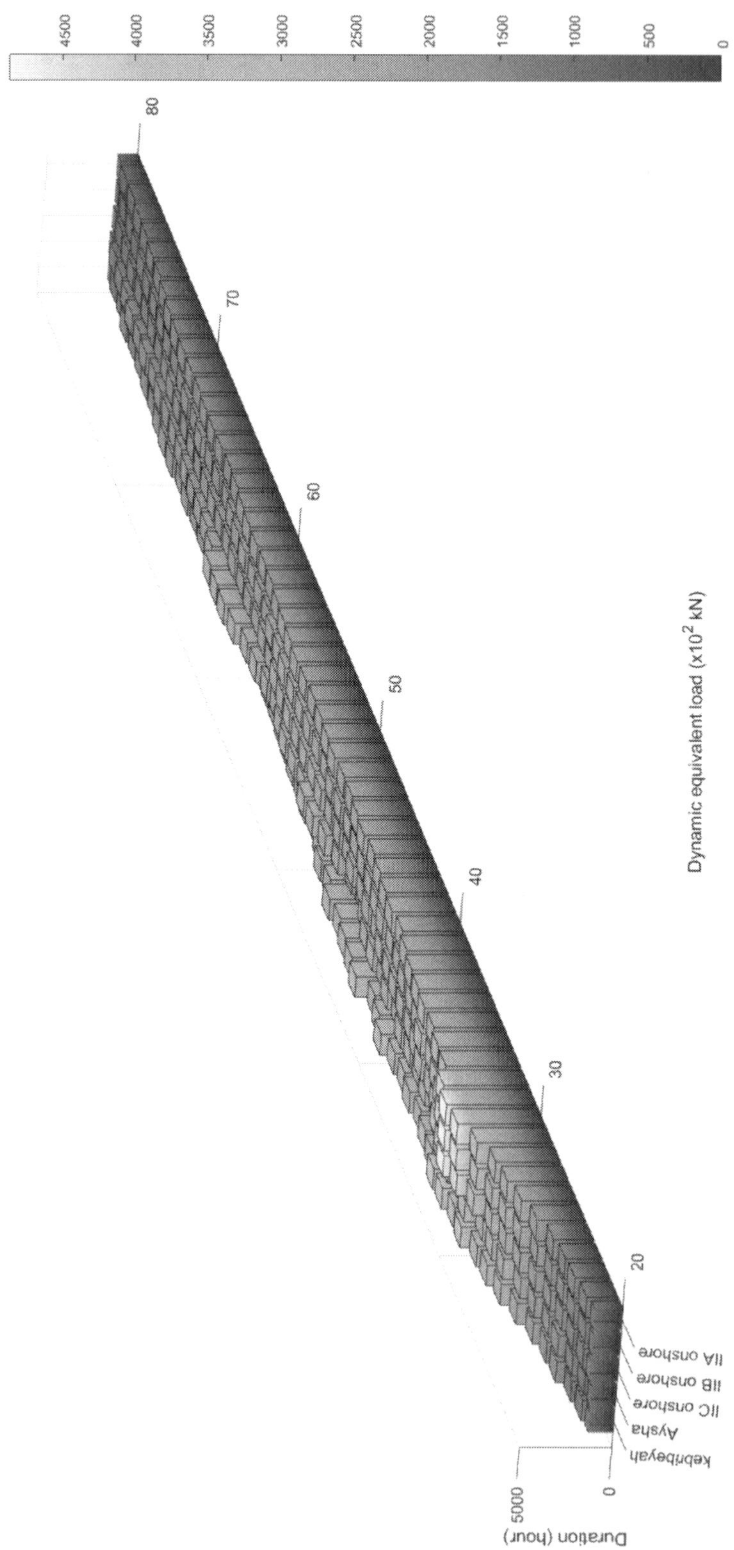


Figure 4: Dynamic equivalent load duration distribution in selected wind sites and IEC class II

Journal of Physics: Conference Series **2507** (2023) 012021 doi:10.1088/1742-6596/2507/1/012021

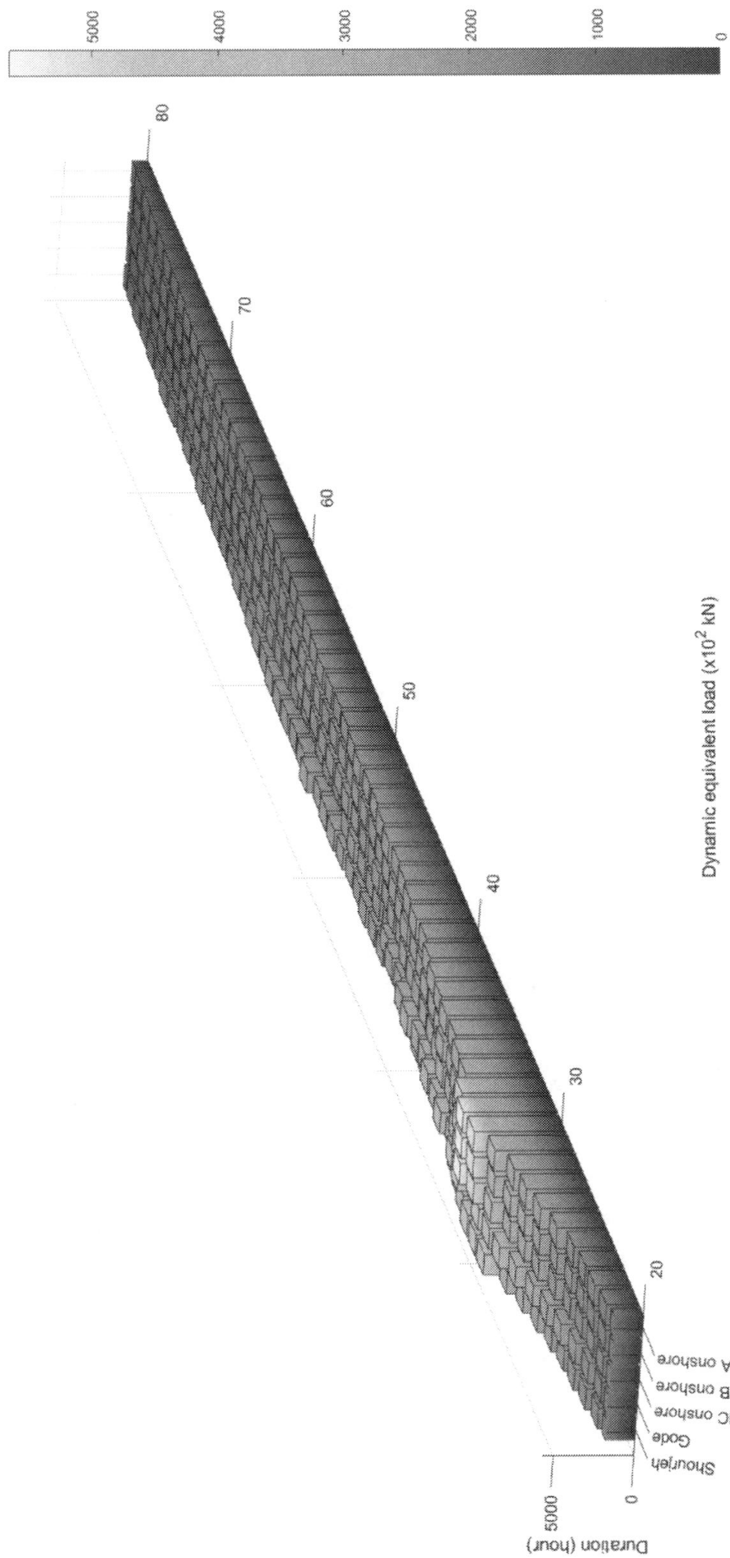


Figure 5: Dynamic equivalent load duration distribution in selected wind sites and IEC class III

In order to compare bearings in different wind sites' conditions, life ratios of bearings in IEC categories with respect to wind sites "$Lr_{IEC,WS}$" are calculated. The life ratio results are presented in Figure 6 and Table 7. The results calculated the life between bearings in IEC categories and nominated wind site conditions. Therefore, the ratio in each bar above one stated that the bearing designed for related IEC conditions is suitable for the mentioned wind site.

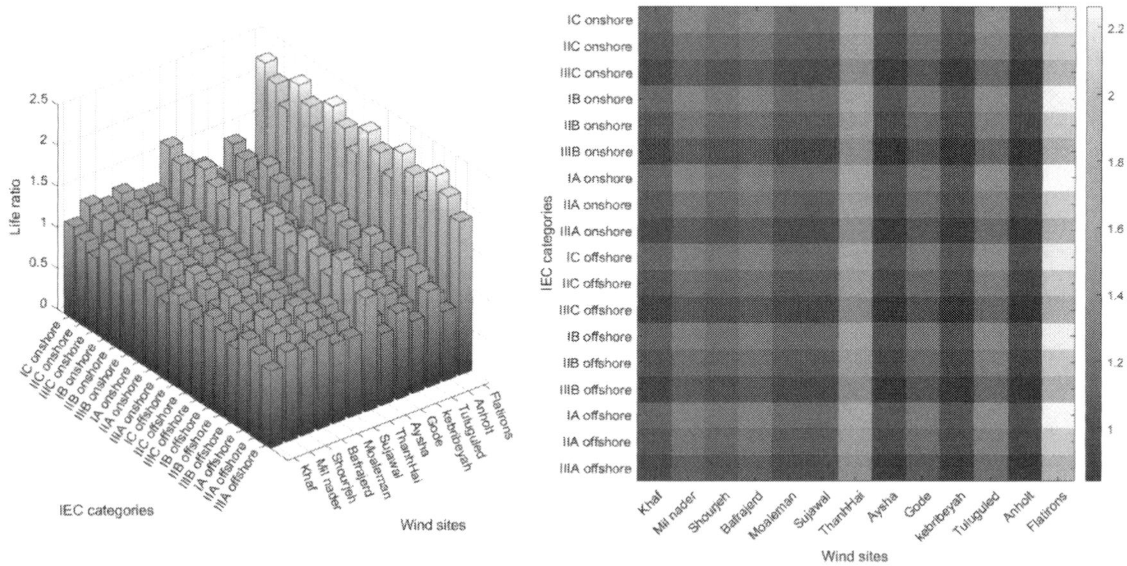


Figure 6: Life ratio factor respect to IEC classes (onshore and offshore) in nominated wind sites

**Life ratio (Lr)**

| IEC categories | Khaf | Mil nader | Shourjeh | Bafrajerd | Moaleman | Sujawal | ThanhHai | Aysha | Gode | kebribeyah | Tuluguled | Flatirons | Anholt |
|---|---|---|---|---|---|---|---|---|---|---|---|---|---|
| IC onshore | 1.13 | 1.32 | 1.23 | 1.31 | 1.17 | 1.16 | 1.66 | 1.04 | 1.26 | 1.05 | 1.39 | 2.24 | 1.01 |
| IIC onshore | 1.04 | 1.22 | 1.14 | 1.21 | 1.08 | 1.08 | 1.53 | 0.97 | 1.17 | 0.97 | 1.29 | 2.07 | 0.94 |
| IIIC onshore | 0.94 | 1.09 | 1.02 | 1.09 | 0.97 | 0.97 | 1.37 | 0.87 | 1.05 | 0.87 | 1.16 | 1.86 | 0.84 |
| IB onshore | 1.13 | 1.32 | 1.24 | 1.32 | 1.17 | 1.17 | 1.66 | 1.05 | 1.26 | 1.06 | 1.40 | 2.25 | 1.02 |
| IIB onshore | 1.05 | 1.22 | 1.14 | 1.22 | 1.08 | 1.08 | 1.54 | 0.97 | 1.17 | 0.98 | 1.29 | 2.08 | 0.94 |
| IIIB onshore | 0.94 | 1.09 | 1.02 | 1.09 | 0.97 | 0.97 | 1.38 | 0.87 | 1.05 | 0.87 | 1.16 | 1.86 | 0.84 |
| IA onshore | 1.14 | 1.33 | 1.25 | 1.33 | 1.18 | 1.18 | 1.67 | 1.06 | 1.27 | 1.06 | 1.41 | 2.26 | 1.03 |
| IIA onshore | 1.05 | 1.23 | 1.15 | 1.22 | 1.09 | 1.09 | 1.55 | 0.97 | 1.18 | 0.98 | 1.30 | 2.09 | 0.95 |
| IIIA onshore | 0.94 | 1.10 | 1.03 | 1.10 | 0.98 | 0.97 | 1.39 | 0.87 | 1.05 | 0.88 | 1.17 | 1.87 | 0.85 |
| IC offshore | 1.12 | 1.31 | 1.23 | 1.30 | 1.16 | 1.16 | 1.65 | 1.04 | 1.25 | 1.05 | 1.39 | 2.23 | 1.01 |
| IIC offshore | 1.04 | 1.22 | 1.14 | 1.21 | 1.08 | 1.08 | 1.53 | 0.96 | 1.16 | 0.97 | 1.29 | 2.07 | 0.94 |
| IIIC offshore | 0.93 | 1.09 | 1.02 | 1.09 | 0.97 | 0.97 | 1.37 | 0.87 | 1.04 | 0.87 | 1.15 | 1.86 | 0.84 |
| IB offshore | 1.13 | 1.31 | 1.23 | 1.31 | 1.17 | 1.16 | 1.65 | 1.04 | 1.26 | 1.05 | 1.39 | 2.24 | 1.01 |
| IIB offshore | 1.04 | 1.22 | 1.14 | 1.21 | 1.08 | 1.08 | 1.53 | 0.97 | 1.17 | 0.97 | 1.29 | 2.07 | 0.94 |
| IIIB offshore | 0.94 | 1.09 | 1.02 | 1.09 | 0.97 | 0.97 | 1.38 | 0.87 | 1.05 | 0.87 | 1.16 | 1.86 | 0.84 |
| IA offshore | 1.14 | 1.32 | 1.24 | 1.32 | 1.18 | 1.17 | 1.67 | 1.05 | 1.27 | 1.06 | 1.40 | 2.25 | 1.02 |
| IIA offshore | 1.05 | 1.23 | 1.15 | 1.22 | 1.09 | 1.09 | 1.54 | 0.97 | 1.17 | 0.98 | 1.30 | 2.09 | 0.94 |
| IIIA offshore | 0.94 | 1.10 | 1.03 | 1.10 | 0.98 | 0.97 | 1.38 | 0.87 | 1.05 | 0.88 | 1.16 | 1.87 | 0.85 |

Wind sites

Table 7: Life ratio $Lr_{IEC,WS}$

The results show that wind sites such as Moaleman and Aysha are categorized according to their annual mean wind speed as IEC III and II, respectively, but their bearing life is less than that of related IECs. The results show that, although the contribution of overrated wind speed in Khaf is greater than that of IEC classes I and II, the IEC class II bearing has an acceptable life ratio. In addition, despite the high annual wind speed in Khaf, it is possible to use IEC Class II pitch bearings. The result of the life ratio of the Anholt offshore wind site compared to related IEC classes is close.

## 5. Conclusions

The wind speed distribution at offshore and onshore wind sites was studied. It is observed that, despite the fair performance of Rayleigh distribution in offshore wind sites, such distribution leads to greater uncertainty in wind distribution and load estimation in onshore sites. This is especially of interest since Rayleigh distribution is the preferred and most commonly used distribution in the wind turbine design standards. It is found that other distributions, for instance Kernel, perform well both in onshore and offshore wind sites, while using the Weibull distribution is also acceptable.

Furthermore, a calculation between the load and life of the pitch bearing and the wind speed is developed, and uncertainty in the loads based on the wind speed model is studied. The results illustrate the influence of wind speed on the pitch bearing loads and life. Pitch bearing life ratio results show that implementing IEC category-designed pitch bearings could result in an overestimate of bearing life compared to wind-site-designed pitch bearings. Moreover, pitch bearings with a lower IEC class design could tolerate the loads of wind sites with a higher annual wind speed.

## Acknowledgement

The authors gratefully acknowledge the financial support of the Research Council of Norway through the InteDiag-WTCP project (Project Number 309205).

## References

[1] J. Carta, P. Ramırez, and S. Velazquez. A review of wind speed probability distributions used in wind energy analysis. *Renewable and Sustainable Energy Reviews*, 13:933–955, 2009.

[2] O. Alavi, K. Mohammadi, and A. Mostafaeipour. Evaluating the suitability of wind speed probability distribution models: A case of study of east and southeast parts of iran. *Energy Conversion and Management*, 119:101–108, 2016.

[3] C. Jung and D. Schindler. Wind speed distribution selection – a review of recent development and progress. *Renewable and Sustainable Energy Reviews*, 119:109290, 2019.

[4] H. Shi, N. Xiao Z. Dong, and Q. Huang. Wind speed distributions used in wind energy assessment: A review. *Frontiers in Energy Research*, 9:769920, 2021.

[5] M. Ahsan ul Haq, S. Choudhary, A. AL-Marshadi, and M. Aslam. A new generalization of lindley distribution for modeling of wind speed data. *Energy Reports*, 8:1–11, 2022.

[6] GL. GL-IV-1: Guideline for the certification of wind turbines, 2010.

[7] IEC. IEC-61400-1: Wind energy generation system, part 1: Design requirements, 2019.

[8] E. K. Akpinar and S. Akpinar. A statistical analysis of wind speed data used in installation. *Energy Conversion and Management*, 46:515–532, 2005.

[9] T. P. Chang. Estimation of wind energy potential using different probability density functions. *Applied Energy*, 88:1848–1856, 2011.

[10] C. Dao, B. Kazemtabrizi, and C. Crabtree. Wind turbine reliability data review and impacts on levelised cost of energy. *Wind Energy*, 22(12):1848–1871, 2019.

[11] D. K. Andreasen, C. Rodenas-Soler, U. Oertel, K. Krügel, I. Reinares, I. S. Mendia, J. H. Nielsen, A. Olsen, A. Tinni, D. Vizireanu, J. Cheaytani, and P. Bousseau. WP2 Wind Turbine diagnosis/prognosis solution for a New Design. Physical D2.4 Portability of failure mode detection/prognosis orientations. Technical report, 2021.

[12] T. Harris, J.H. Rumbarger, and Butterfield C.P. Wind Turbine Design Guideline DG03: Yaw and Pitch Rolling Bearing Life. Technical report, NREL/TP-500-42362, National Renewable Energy Lab.(NREL), Golden, CO (United States), 2009.

[13] L. Wöll, G. Jacobs, and A. Kramer. Lifetime Calculation of Irregularly Oscillating Bearings in Offshore Winches. *Modeling, Identification and Control*, 39(2):61–72, 2018.

[14] G. Breslau and B. Schlecht. A fatigue life model for roller bearings in oscillatory applications. *Bearing World Journal*, 5:65–80, 2020.

[15] DNV. DNV-ST-0361, machinery for wind turbines, 2016.

[16] J. Yu, Y. Fu, Y. Yu, S. Wu, Y. Wu, M. You, S. Guo, and M. Li. Assessment of offshore wind characteristics and wind energy potential in bohai bay, china. *Energies*, 12(15), 2019.

[17] L. J. Bain and C. E. Antle. Estimation of parameters in the weibull distribution. *Technometrics*, 9:621–627, 1967.

[18] C. Dawson, R. Abrahart, and L. See. Hydrotest: a web-based toolbox of evaluation metrics for the standardised assessment of hydrological forecasts. *Environmental Modelling & Software*, 22(7):1034–1052, 2007.

[19] K. Mohammadi, O. Alavi, A. Mostafaeipour, N. Goudarzi, and M. Jalilvand. Assessing different parameters estimation methods of weibull distribution to compute wind power density. *Energy Conversion and Management*, 108:247–265, 2016.

[20] D. R. Legates and Gregory J. McCabe Jr. Evaluating the use of goodness-of-fit measures in hydrologic and hydroclimatic model validation. *WATER RESOURCES RESEARCH*, 35:233–241, 1999.

[21] C. G. Justus and A. Mikhail. Height variation of wind speed and wind distributions statistics. *Geophysical Research Letters*, 3:261–264, 1976.

[22] J. Jonkman, S. Butterfield, W. Musial, and G. Scott. Definition of a 5-MW reference wind turbine for offshore system development. Technical report, National Renewable Energy Lab.(NREL), Golden, CO (United States), 2009.

[23] NREL. Nrel 5mw reference turbine openfast model. `https://github.com/OpenFAST/r-test/tree/main/glue-codes/openfast/5MW_Baseline`, 2022. [Online; accessed 25-August-2022].

[24] A. Rezaei, Y. Guo, J. Keller, and A. R. Nejad. Effects of wind field characteristics on pitch bearing reliability: a case study of 5 mw reference wind turbine at onshore and offshore sites. *Forschung im Ingenieurwesen*, Under publication(-):1–18, 2023.

[25] NREL. Openfast. `https://github.com/OpenFAST/openfast`. [Online; accessed 2-August.-2022].

[26] J. Keller and Y. Guo. Rating of a pitch bearing for a 1.5-MW wind turbine. Technical report, NREL/TP-5000-82462, National Renewable Energy Lab.(NREL), Golden, CO (United States), 2022.

[27] O. Menck, M. Stammler, and F. Schleich. Fatigue lifetime calculation of wind turbine blade bearings considering blade-dependent load distribution. *Wind Energy Science*, 5(4):1743–1754, 2020.

[28] Renewable Energy and Energy Efficiency Organization (SATBA). `http://www.satba.gov.ir/en/`, 2022. [Online; accessed 24-May-2022].

[29] World Bank Group. Pakistan - wind measurement data. `https://energydata.info/dataset/pakistan-wind-measurement-data`, 2023. [Online; accessed 20-January-2023].

[30] GIZ. Vietnam - wind measurement data. `https://energydata.info/dataset/vietnam-wind-measurements-giz`, 2023. [Online; accessed 20-January-2023].

[31] World Bank Group. Ethiopia - wind measurement data. `https://energydata.info/dataset/ethiopia-wind-measurement-data`, 2023. [Online; accessed 20-January-2023].

[32] Ørsted. Green solutions: Offshore wind data. `https://orsted.com/en/our-business/offshore-wind/wind-data`, 2022. [Online; accessed 4-June-2022].

[33] D. Jager and A. Andreas. NREL National Wind Technology Center (NWTC): M2 Tower; Boulder, Colorado (Data);. Technical report, NREL Report No. DA-5500-56489, 1996.

# Wind tunnel test of airfoil with erosion and leading edge protection

C Bak[1], A S Olsen[1], A M Forsting[1], M H Bjerge[2], M E Handberg[3], H Shkalov[3]

[1] DTU Wind and Energy Systems, Frederiksborgvej 399, 4000 Roskilde, Denmark
[2] Rope Robotics, Lokesvej 4, 8230 Åbyhøj, Denmark
[3] Wind Power Lab, St. Kongensgade 59D, 1st floor, 1164 Copenhagen K, Denmark

E-mail: chba@dtu.dk

**Abstract.** This paper describes wind tunnel tests of a NACA $63_3 - 418$ airfoil with erosion and leading edge protection. Measurements are carried out at high Reynolds number ($Re = 5$ million) representing modern wind turbines. Three examples of deviations from the perfect airfoil surface are shown. It is seen how the presence of a roughness mesh degrades the aerodynamics and that the presence of the mesh is more important than the actual topology of the mesh. That is also the case for the stall strips where a small strip influences the performance slightly less than a big stall strip, but the presence of the stall strip alone is influencing the performance significantly. Finally, a simulated leading edge protection (LEP), represented by a sheet of paper, can influence the performance significantly as the paper leads to a backward facing step. Furthermore, the measurements showed that correct mounting of LEP is important to avoid too big losses in aerodynamic performance. Investigating the impact of reduced airfoil performance for the rotor performance showed losses in annual energy production of between 0.3% and 4.0%. All in all the wind tunnel tests reflected that leading edge damages have a significant impact on the aerodynamic performance.

## 1. Introduction

Erosion and contaminated leading edges of blades cause a significant uncertainty for the annual energy production (AEP). The power and the energy output from the wind turbines are measured, but it is a big challenge to make any final conclusions on the energy losses. This is due to the stochastic nature of the wind, which results in uncertainties in the relation between wind speed and power. This challenge is discussed intensively in these years and much effort is put into providing methods to determine the power losses in a precise and reliable manner. Since inspections of the blades are carried out on a regular basis it will be valuable to provide knowledge about how the aerodynamic performance is influenced by erosion, but also leading edge protection (LEP). In this way the power losses can be predicted by summing up the influence section by section along the blade. Investigations have been carried out to predict the power losses ([1], [2], [3], [4], [5]), but also to measure the losses in wind tunnels ([6], [7], [8], [9], [10],). Different overviews of the problem are given and solutions are proposed ([11], [12], [13]). In this work the wind turbine service providers Wind Power Lab and Rope Robotics have together with DTU carried out investigations of how leading edge roughness (LER) influence the aerodynamic performance. More information about the aerodynamic investigations in this project that was called the LERAP project (Leading Edge Roughness And Repair) can be found in three publications, [14], [15] and [16]. A part of this was wind tunnel tests that were carried out in the large *Poul la Cour Tunnel* at Reynolds numbers between 3 and 7 million corresponding to wind turbines of between 1 and 7 MW with Reynolds numbers of 7 million being very high compared to other wind tunnels in the world. In the tests performance is measured of leading edges where the glass fiber is exposed, where small damages protrude from the surface and where LEP is mounted.

## 2. Method

Wind tunnel tests were carried out in the *Poul la Cour Tunnel (PLCT)* on a NACA $63_3-418$ airfoil with a chord length of 1.0m and with different types of simulated LER and LEP.

### *2.1. The wind tunnel*

A sketch of the *PLCT* is seen in Figure 1.

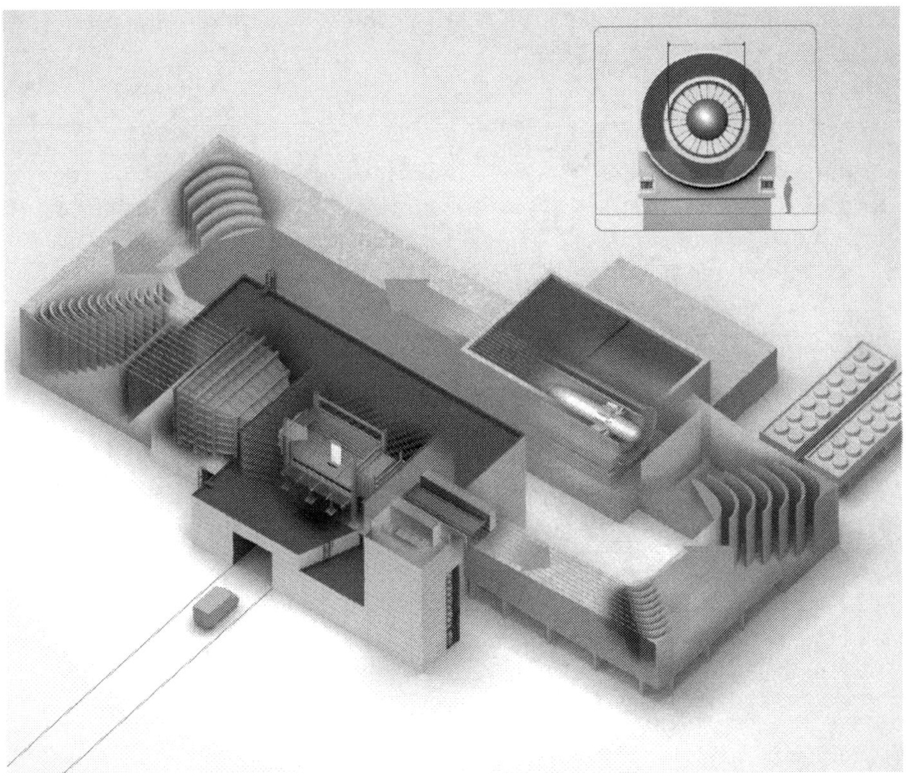

**Figure 1.** Sketch of the Poul la Cour Tunnel. The air is flowing anti-clockwise in the closed return wind tunnel with the closed test section

*PLCT* has a test section with the size width x height x length = 3.0m x 2.0m x 9.0m and the turbulence level is $TI < 0.1\%$. With velocities up to 105m/s, Reynolds numbers (Re) up to 7 million can be obtained with a chord length of 1.0m. Two different configurations of the wind tunnel exist: The aerodynamic and the aeroacoustic. The walls of the test section are hard in the aerodynamic configuration and they are made of Kevlar in the aeroacoustic configuration.

The airfoil is mounted in a turntable. Lift is measured at the airfoil surface and at the test section walls and the drag is measured with a wake rake with 96 pressure tubes. A photo of an airfoil in the aerodynamic configuration of the test section is seen in Figure 2.

**Figure 2.** A photo of the airfoil with 1.0m chord in the test section. The airfoil is mounted in turntables in the floor and in the ceiling.

### *2.2. The airfoil configurations*

A common way of simulating LER in wind tunnel tests is to mount zigzag tape close to the leading edge on both the suction side and the pressure side. However, LER is often due to erosion that reminds of a sandblasted surface. Therefore, erosion is in this investigation simulated by mounting fine and rough meshes that originally should be used to grind surfaces. These meshes are covering the leading edge from $x/c = 3.6\%$ at the pressure side to $x/c = 3.6\%$ at the suction side, see Figure 3.

**Figure 3.** Photo of two types of meshes mounted at the leading edge. Left (a): Fine mesh, Right (b): Rough mesh.

Also, protrusions are simulated using triangular shaped wedges, also known as stall strips, with heights of 1mm, 2mm and 3mm and positioned at the very leading edge, see Figure 4.

Finally, LEP was simulated by using a paper that similar to the meshes is covering the leading edge from $x/c$=3.6% at the pressure side to $x/c$=3.6% at the suction side. The thickness of the

**Figure 4.** Photo of a stall strip mounted at the leading edge.

paper is 0.8mm. A photo of the configuration is seen in Figure 5

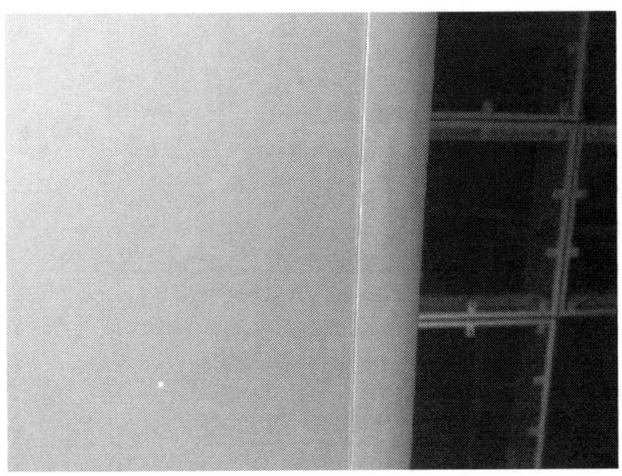

**Figure 5.** Photo of paper mounted at the leading edge to simulate leading edge protection.

The configurations were measured at $Re$ = 3, 5 and 7 million, however only results for $Re$=5 million are shown in this paper.

### *2.3. Prediction of losses in annual energy production*

A method to predict the annual energy production (AEP) loss in a very easy way is described by Bak [18]. The model was developed because it was realized that wind turbine owners sometimes have very little information about the wind turbine. In contrast to wind turbine manufacturers that have advanced models for the wind turbines with knowledge about blade shapes, airfoil shapes, aerodynamic airfoil characteristics etc., some wind turbine owners might only have knowledge about a few parameters for the wind turbine. Thus, when inspections of the blades are made and damages are observed at the leading edge, it can be hard for the wind turbine owner to judge whether a damage is harmful for the AEP or not.

That is the reason that a simple model has been created. The model is based on an approximate method to predict the AEP losses based on knowledge of only the rated power, the rotor radius, the air density, the wind climate (the Weibull distribution) and the loss in lift-drag ratio. Thus, the model does not make very exact predictions, but can within 10% precision predict the loss despite using only very few input parameters. In this way a wind turbine owner can estimate the loss in AEP which can be used as input to a decision of repair.

## 3. Results

In this section results from the wind tunnel tests are shown, and also predictions of corresponding losses in annual energy production under certain assumptions are shown.

### *3.1. Wind tunnel tests*

In Figure 6 is shown how a fine and a rough mesh at the leading edge influence the aerodynamic characteristics.

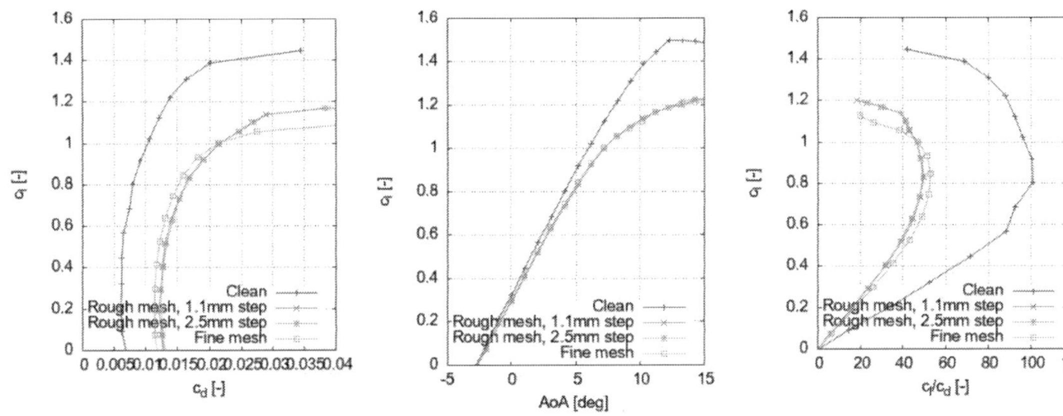


**Figure 6.** Aerodynamic performance of the NACA $63_3-418$ airfoil with meshes mounted at the leading edge. Left: $c_l$ as a function of $c_d$, Mid: $c_l$ as a function of angle of attack, $AoA$, Right: $c_l$ as a function of $c_l - c_d$ ratio. Apart from the performance with meshes, the performance of the clean airfoil is seen.

It is seen how maximum lift is reduced significantly with a $\Delta c_l$ of around 0.3. An interesting result is that despite of the finer mesh the reduction in maximum lift is the same. The drag is increased significantly for both meshes, i.e. around a doubling. The finer mesh results in a slightly lower drag than for the rough mesh, however not significantly lower.

In Figure 7 different heights of stall strips mounted at the very leading edge are shown and compared to a clean airfoil.

It is seen that maximum lift is reduced significantly and that the reduction is bigger the higher the stall strip is. However, the presence of a stall strip makes a big difference and therefore even the 1mm stall strip shows a significant reduction in maximum lift. The drag is increased significantly, but not as much as for the meshes. An interesting observation is the lower drag for the two higher stall strips at low angles of attack around $AoA$=0deg, that is likely because the stagnation point is very close to the stall strip.

In Figure 8 papers simulating LEP is shown.

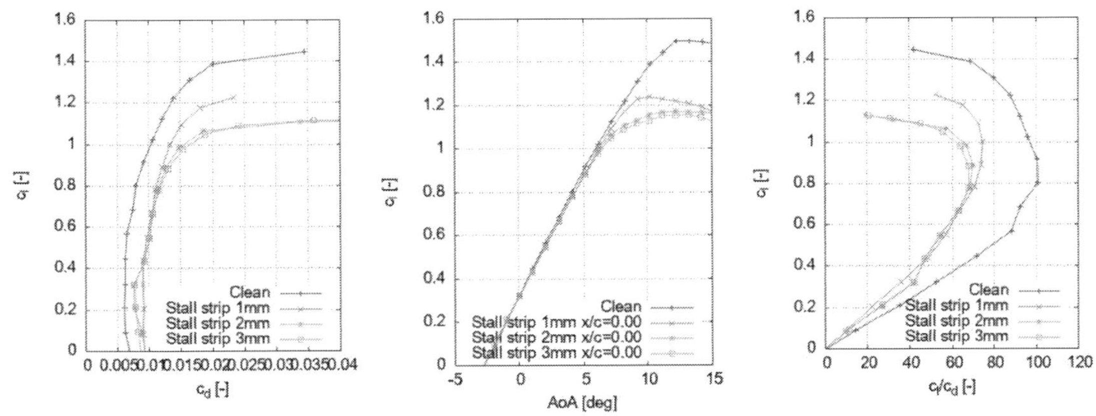


**Figure 7.** Aerodynamic performance of the NACA $63_3-418$ airfoil with stall strips mounted at the leading edge. Left: $c_l$ as a function of $c_d$, Mid: $c_l$ as a function of angle of attack, $AoA$, Right: $c_l$ as a function of $c_l - c_d$ ratio. Also, the performance with the clean airfoil is seen.

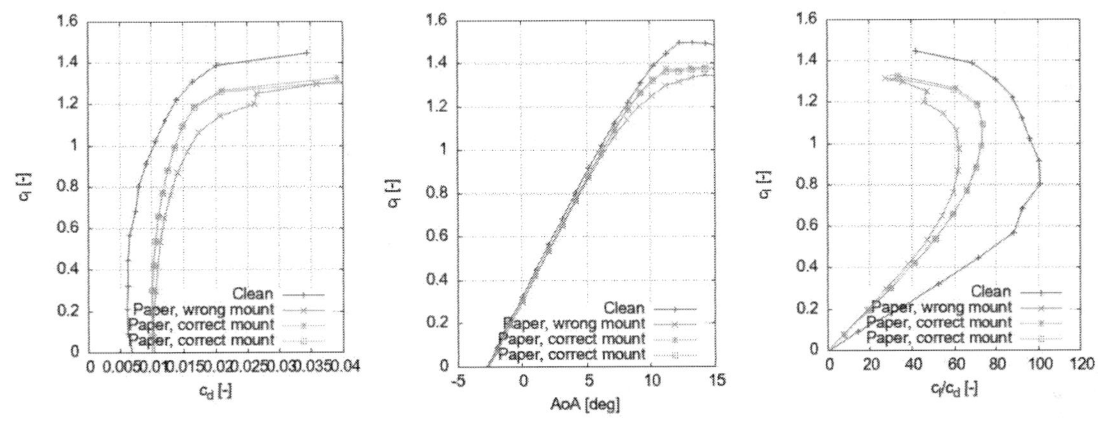


**Figure 8.** Aerodynamic performance of the NACA $63_3-418$ airfoil with paper mounted at the leading edge. Left: $c_l$ as a function of $c_d$, Mid: $c_l$ as a function of angle of attack, $AoA$, Right: $c_l$ as a function of $c_l - c_d$ ratio. Also, the performance with the clean airfoil is seen.

The paper is very glossy so the surface of the paper is not expected to cause any extra drag. However, the backward facing step at the pressure and suction side at $x/c$=3.6% is expected to show extra drag. In the tests the paper that was used turned out to be challenging to mount. The plot shows how mounting errors can affect both lift and drag when this is compared to a test where the mounting is more successful. From the two measurements with correctly mounted paper it is clear that there is a reduction in maximum lift and that drag increases significantly. It is important to state that LEP not necessarily will result in significantly lower lift or higher drag (see [17]), but if it is not designed properly as shown in these tests, it can result in a significant degradation of the aerodynamic performance.

An overview of the loss in maximum lift, $c_{l,max}$, and maximum lift-drag ratio, $(c_l/c_d)_{max}$, is shown in Table 1.

**Table 1.** Maximum lift, $c_{l,max}$, and maximum lift-drag ratio, $(c_l/c_d)_{max}$, for the different configurations

| Configuration | $c_{l,max}$ | $(c_l/c_d)_{max}$ |
|---|---|---|
| Clean | 1.50 | 100.9 |
| Fine mesh | 1.19 | 53.0 |
| Rough mesh (1.1mm step) | 1.19 | 49.7 |
| Rough mesh (2.5mm step) | 1.19 | 49.1 |
| Stall strip 1mm | 1.22 | 74.8 |
| Stall strip 2mm | 1.17 | 69.8 |
| Stall strip 3mm | 1.15 | 68.1 |
| Paper (correct mount) | 1.36 | 74.1 |
| Paper (wrong mount) | 1.32 | 62.2 |

**Table 2.** AEP loss due to imperfections of the leading edge in percent of a clean rotor in a wind climate with Weibull parameters $A = 8m/s$ and $k = 2$. The rotor has a rated power of 2MW, the diameter is 90m and the air density is $1.225kg/m^3$

| Configuration | Outer 10% radius | Outer 20% radius | Outer 30% radius |
|---|---|---|---|
| Fine mesh | 1.0 | 2.3 | 3.4 |
| Rough mesh (1.1mm step) | 1.1 | 2.6 | 3.9 |
| Rough mesh (2.5mm step) | 1.2 | 2.7 | 4.0 |
| Stall strip 1mm | 0.3 | 0.8 | 1.2 |
| Stall strip 2mm | 0.5 | 1.1 | 1.6 |
| Stall strip 3mm | 0.5 | 1.2 | 1.7 |
| Paper (correct mount) | 0.4 | 0.8 | 1.2 |
| Paper (wrong mount) | 0.7 | 1.5 | 2.3 |

*3.2. Predictions of loss in annual energy production*

Based on the simplified AEP loss model a specific wind turbine size was chosen to demonstrate how the results from the wind tunnel tests impact the wind turbine AEP. Thus, the maximum lift-drag values from the tests are used as input to the simplified model. Table 2 presents the AEP loss based on the results from the wind tunnel tests.

As seen in the table it is clear that a rough leading edge represented by the fine and the rough meshes is very bad for the aerodynamics leading to significant losses in AEP. Despite of stall strips being a distinct imperfection these are not as bad as the rough leading edge. However, the stall strips have a smooth and regular shape which might be the reason for the limited losses. Finally, the results show that mounting leading edge protection should be carried out with caution because a wrong mount can result in a significant loss in performance. However, according to [17] solutions exist to make smooth transitions from LEP to the original airfoil.

Experience from predictions, see e.g. [19], shows that the higher the mean wind speed is on a site the smaller the AEP loss will be. Thus, at sites with a Weibull $A$ parameter greater than 8 the losses will be smaller and for $A$ smaller than 8 the losses will be bigger.

## 4. Conclusions

The presented measurements are carried out at rather high Reynolds numbers representing modern wind turbines. Three examples of deviations from the perfect airfoil surface are shown. It is seen how the presence of a roughness mesh degrades the aerodynamics and that the presence of the mesh is more important than the actual topology of the mesh. That is also the case for the stall strips where a small strip influences the performance slightly less than a big stall strip, but the presence of the stall strip alone is influencing the performance significantly. Finally, a simulated LEP can influence the performance significantly where a backward facing step is present and the measurements showed that correct mounting of LEP is important to avoid too big losses in aerodynamic performance. All in all the wind tunnel tests reflected how damages at the leading edge can result in a significant reduction of the aerodynamic performance.

## References

[1] Sareen A, Sapre C A and Selig M S 2014 Effects of leading edge erosion on wind turbine blade performance Wind Energy, 17, Issue 10, pp. 1531-1542.
[2] Standish K, Rimmington P, Laursen J and Paulsen H N 2010 Computational Prediction of Airfoil Roughness Sensitivity. In: 48th AIAA Aerospace Sciences Meeting and Exhibit, AIAA, paper no. 2010-0460
[3] Kruse E K, Sørensen N N and Bak C 2018 Predicting the Influence of Surface Protuberance on the Aerodynamic Characteristics of a NACA 633-418 J Physics: Conference Series, 1037, Issue 2, pp. 022008
[4] Bak C, Gaunaa M, Olsen A S and Kruse E K 2016 What is the critical height of leading edge roughness for aerodynamics? J Physics: Conference Series, 753, Issue 2, pp. 022023
[5] Kruse E K 2019 A Method for Quantifying Wind Turbine Leading Edge Roughness and its Influence on Energy Production. LER2AEP PhD Thesis, DTU Wind Energy
[6] Ehrmann R S, Wilcox B and White E B 2017 Effect of Surface Roughness on Wind Turbine Performance In: Sandia National Laboratories, SAND2017-10669
[7] Maniaci D C, White E B, Wilcox B, Langel C M, van Dam C P and Paquette J A 2016 Experimental Measurement and CFD Model Development of Thick Wind Turbine Airfoils with Leading Edge Erosion J Physics: Conference Series, 753, Issue 2, pp.022013 The Science of Making Torque from Wind (TORQUE 2020) Journal of Physics: Conference Series 1618 (2020) 052050 IOP Publishing doi:10.1088/1742-6596/1618/5/052050 10
[8] Gaudern N 2014 A practical study of the aerodynamic impact of wind turbine blade leading edge erosion J Physics: Conference Series, 524, Issue 1, pp. 012031
[9] Veraart M L W 2017 Deterioration in aerodynamic performance due to leading edge rain erosion Master's thesis. DTU Wind Energy and Wind Energy Research Group Faculty of Aerospace Engineering Delft University of Technology
[10] Kruse EK, Bak C, Olsen AS. Wind tunnel experiments on a NACA 633-418 airfoil with different types of leading edge roughness. Wind Energy. 2021;24(11):1263-1274. https://doi.org/10.1002/we.2630
[11] Sagol E, Reggio M and Ilinca A 2013 Issues concerning roughness on wind turbine blades Renewable and Sustainable Energy Reviews, 23, pp. 514–525
[12] Zidane I F, Saqr K M, Swadener G, Ma X and Shehadeh M F 2016 On the role of surface roughness in the aerodynamic performance and energy conversion of horizontal wind turbine blades: a review Int J Energy Research, 40, Issue 15, pp 2054-2077
[13] Bech J I, Hasager C B and Bak C 2018 Extending the life of wind turbine blade leading edges by reducing the tip speed during extreme precipitation events Wind Energy Science, 3, Issue 2, pp. 729-748
[14] Olsen A S, Beckerlee J S, Ildvedsen S B, Bak C, Wind Tunnel Measurements of the NACA63-418 Airfoil LERAP Project: Tests from the Poul la Cour Tunnel. DTU Wind Energy. 2021, DTU Wind Energy I No. I-1216 https://doi.org/10.11581/DTU.00000266
[15] Forsting A M, Olsen A S, SN N, Bak C, The impact of leading edge damage and repair on sectional aerodynamic performance. In Proceedings of AIAA SCITECH 2023 Forum [0968] Aerospace Research Central (ARC). https://doi.org/10.2514/6.2023-0968
[16] Forsting A M, SN N, Bak C, Olsen A S, LERAP: Leading Edge Repair and Performance. Commissioned by The Energy Innovation Cluster. 2022, DTU Wind and Energy Systems. DTU Wind Energy I No. I-1212 https://doi.org/10.11581/DTU.00000264
[17] Grasso F, Bak C, Smærup A, Ravnkilde L, Johansen RK, Leading Edge Protection Impact on Airfoil Performance: An Experimental Investigation, AIAA 2022-0277, AIAA SCITECH 2022 Forum, January 3-7, 2022, San Diego, CA & Virtual, https://doi.org/10.2514/6.2022-0277
[18] Bak C, A simple model to predict the energy loss due to leading edge roughness, In Turbine Technology; Artificial Intelligence, Control and Monitoring. IOP Publishing. 2022. 032038. (Journal of Physics: Conference Series; No. 3, Vol. 2265). doi: 10.1088/1742-6596/2265/3/032038
[19] Bak C, Forsting AM, Sørensen NN. The influence of leading edge roughness, rotor control and wind climate on the loss in energy production. Journal of Physics: Conference Series. 2020;1618(5):052050 . doi: 10.1088/1742-6596/1618/5/052050

# Investigation of the dynamic inflow effects due to collective and individual pitch steps on a wind tunnel setup

**A Langidis[1], V Petrović[1], S Mancini[2], K Boorsma[2], G Schepers[2,3] and M Kühn[1]**

[1] ForWind, Institute of Physics, University of Oldenburg, Küpkersweg 70, 26129 Oldenburg,Germany

[2] TNO, Wind Energy group, Petten, 1755 LE, the Netherlands

[3] Hanze University of Applied Sciences, Institute of Engineering, Groningen, 9747 AS, the Netherlands

E-mail: apostolos.langidis@uol.de

**Abstract.** Dynamic inflow effects occur due to the rapid change of the rotor loading under conditions such as fast pitch steps. The paper presents a setup suitable for the investigation of those effects for non-axisymmetric rotor conditions, namely individual pitch steps. Furthermore, insights into the relevant phenomena are gathered. An individual pitch control capable model wind turbine is set up in a wind tunnel in order to conduct measurement under controllable conditions. During the execution of the collective and individual pitch steps, the loads and the operational parameters are recorded by the onboard sensors. Meanwhile, simulations engineering aeroelastic codes are run in order to evaluate their accuracy for predicting the relevant phenomena. Results show distinct behaviour of the rotor loads during an individual pitch step, which differs from the loads under collective steps. The free vortex wake simulations are able to predict the turbines' response satisfactory while the blade element momentum tools show deviations from the measurements. The findings serve as a basis for discussion and future work.

## 1. Introduction

The dynamic inflow effect is a term that describes the delay in the wake flow to reach a new equilibrium state after a rapid change in the rotor loading. This can be induced by conditions such as rapid pitch steps or wind gusts and manifests as dynamic behaviour of the loads during the transition time. More specifically, in the case of pitch steps, this leads to load overshoots.

It is important to take this phenomenon into account in the wind turbine design stage in order to have an accurate estimation of the loads a turbine is going to experience during its operational lifetime. In addition, the proper understanding of these can be of great use in the development of turbine controllers where blade pitching is employed. As the trend of wind turbine design pushes for machines with ever larger rotor diameters, understanding and modelling of the relevant phenomena becomes of great importance.

The extensive load envelopes which are required to be calculated for a new wind turbine are typically simulated with Blade Element Momentum (BEM) theory based codes. In their baseline version though, these are not capable of reproducing such dynamic phenomena. Thus, engineering correction models such as the ECN [1] and the Øye [2] have been proposed based on measurement data and have been successfully implemented in the majority of these tools. More recently, improvements on these models have been suggested as in [3] and [4]. However, as the experimental datasets which can be used for the improvement of those models remain limited, additional experimental investigations are necessary. Measurements conducted in the controllable and reproducible conditions of a wind tunnel are rather suitable for this aim. Some of the most important measurement campaigns that have been performed in the past were the NREL measurements in the NASA Aimes wind tunnel [5] and MEXICO project [6]. In a recent study, conducted in the Turbulent Wind Tunnel of ForWind – University of Oldenburg (FW-OL), further insights were given in the physical understanding of the dynamic inflow process due to collective pitch steps and the fidelity of the available models [7].

However, the relevant research has been focused until now on situations where axial symmetry on the rotor is observed. This condition is preserved, for example, in the case of the collective pitch steps of the rotor blades. Situations where there are asymmetric changes in the rotor loading, such as during individual pitch steps, have not been investigated up to date. Furthermore, due to the trend of an increasing size of the rotors, the effect of the wind shear becomes also more apparent as rotor blades encounters varying wind along their rotation.

The current work is a contribution in the direction of filling this gap of knowledge by experimentally investigating the dynamic inflow effects due to individual pitch steps. First, a wind tunnel setup is presented which is able to generate those conditions and is thus suitable for such studies. Subsequently, individual pitch steps of a model wind turbine were performed in the wind tunnel, and the measured loads are compared to collective pitch maneuvers, to preliminarily evaluate the success of existing engineering tools in simulating them.

In the following section, the employed test setup in a wind tunnel is described in detail, followed up by the measurement cases and the simulation models (section 2). Next, the results are presented in section 3 and compared to simulations by representative engineering, BEM-based tools with the focus on the rotor torque and blades' bending moments. Finally, in section 4, the conclusions and the directions for future work are discussed.

## 2. Methods

The measurement setup which was employed for the current investigations is throughout presented in section 2.1. Next, the pitch steps that were performed by the model are described, together with the experimental conditions in section 2.2. Finally, an overview of the simulations setup and the detailed cases runs are given in section 2.3.

### *2.1. Measurement setup*

The experiments are conducted in the Turbulent Wind Tunnel of FW-OL which is a closed loop wind tunnel with a 3 m by 3 m cross-section. The length of the test section is 30 m and can be operated in both closed and open jet arrangements, of which the latter was chosen for the current setup. At the inlet of the tunnel, a unique active grid [8] is installed, which gives the capabilities to create tailor-cut wind regimes such as shear flow and wind gusts.

Inside the test section, the Model Wind Turbine Oldenburg 1.8 (MoWiTO) is installed, at a distance of approximately 4.7 m from the active grid (see figure 1). MoWiTO is a scaled model of the reference NREL 5MW machine with its design objective being the preservation of the design Tip Speed Ratio (TSR) and the lift distribution along the blade span. Its rotor extends 1.8 m in diameter, which translates into a geometrical scaling ratio of 1/70 and a time scaling ratio of 50. More information on the design of the turbine can be found in [9].

MoWiTO is capable of individual pitch and torque control and features extensive measurement instrumentation, including among others, strain gauges for measurement of the flapwise blade bending moments, a torque meter on the shaft and encoders for the rotor speed

**Figure 1.** Experimental setup with MoWiTO in the wind tunnel.

and azimuthal position of the rotor. An important feature of the turbine are the separate servomotors that actuate the pitching mechanism of each blade, thus providing individual pitch control (IPC) capabilities.

*2.2. Measurement matrix and data processing*

The dynamic inflow effect needs, as discussed in the introduction, special conditions where the rotor loading is changing rapidly. Because of that reason and in order to have a solid reference to previous work, it was opted to perform a similar pitch step with the work of Frederik Berger et al. [7]. The blades are prescribed to pitch from -1° to 5° (from high to low load) and then, back to the original position (from low to high load). Each step requires approximately 70 ms to be executed. Between each actuation of the motors, there is a time interval of 5 s. Each data set of measurements was approximately 10 minutes long containing about 40 repetitions of the afore-described maneuvers.

Next, similar maneuvers are performed but first with only one and then with two blades pitching. However, in the current work, only the collective and the individual blade pitch step are in focus. The trajectories of the pitch motors can be seen in figure 2.

All tests were performed for constant rotational speed (restricted to 480 RPM by the generator load-adjusting controller). The cases that were analyzed in this study were under a wind of 6.1 m/s. The onboard instrumentation records all relevant signals in real-time.

In order to extract the representative loads that correspond to each pitch step case, we ensemble and average the loads from each maneuver repetition. The encoder signals for the pitch motors are used in order to spot the point that each step – either to high or to low load – is initiated. The average of these isolated repetitions is considered the representative behaviour for each case.

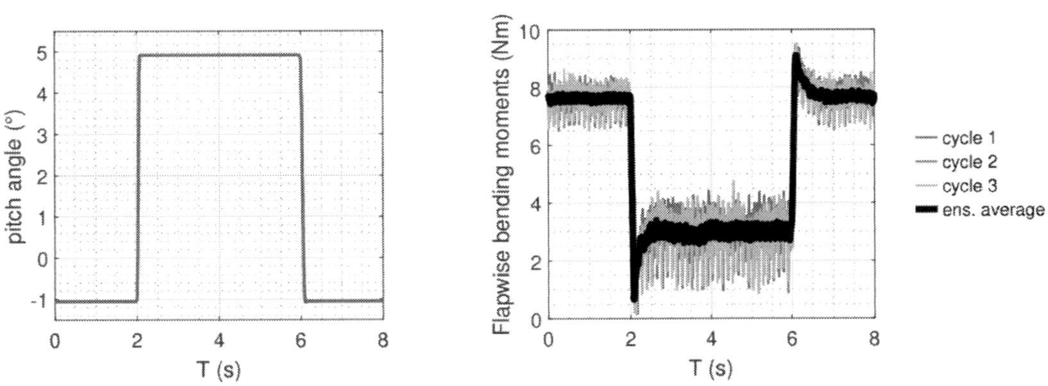


**Figure 2.** Left: The prescribed pitch step trajectory cycle for all blades that execute the step maneuvers. Right: Loads from isolated pitch step cycles and the ensembled average from those. Here for the collective pitch step case.

### *2.3. Simulation models*

The experimental results are compared against the state-of-the-art BEM and free vortex wake (FVW) solvers implemented in TNO AeroModule (AM [10]). A rigid model of the MoWiTO turbine is used in the simulations. Rotational effects were already included in the airfoil polar data thus no additional 3D correction was applied in AM. Snel's first-order model [11] was used to account for dynamic stall effects in both BEM and AWSM (AM's FVW model [12]) simulations. To compare with the experiment, the ensemble-averaged individual blade pitch and rotor speed time histories obtained from the wind tunnel measurements were prescribed in the simulations. As the active grid was not used in this experiment, the inflow was assumed steady and uniform with the same mean wind speed as measured in the wind tunnel.

In the AWSM simulations, the unsteady wake convection, and thus the rotor plane induction, is directly resolved by taking into account the local velocity induced by the shed and trailed vortices in the wake. This means that non-uniform dynamic inflow effects are inherently modeled. The BEM method, instead, requires engineering dynamic inflow models to account for wake unsteadiness and it is not clear how these models perform in non-uniform conditions (like those induced by an individual pitch step). Several state-of-the-art dynamic inflow models for BEM have been recently implemented in AM and their relative performance has been compared in detail [13]. The traditional single-constant dynamic inflow model from ECN [1] and the more recent two-constant model from DTU [14] are used in this work to verify their capability to model non-uniform dynamic wake effects.

## 3. Results

The data that was acquired and processed (as described in section 2.2), is here presented and evaluated. The measurement data from different test cases are presented and discussed in section 3.1, and the comparison with simulation results is provided in section 3.2.

### *3.1. Individual and collective pitch comparison*

The loads on the blade roots as recorded with the strain gauges during the individual pitching of one blade are presented in figure 3. It is clear that even for this small change in rotor thrust, overshoots in the flapwise moment of the pitching blade (Nr. 2) are occurring. Additionally, due to the reduced tangential induction of the pitched blade, the blades following during the

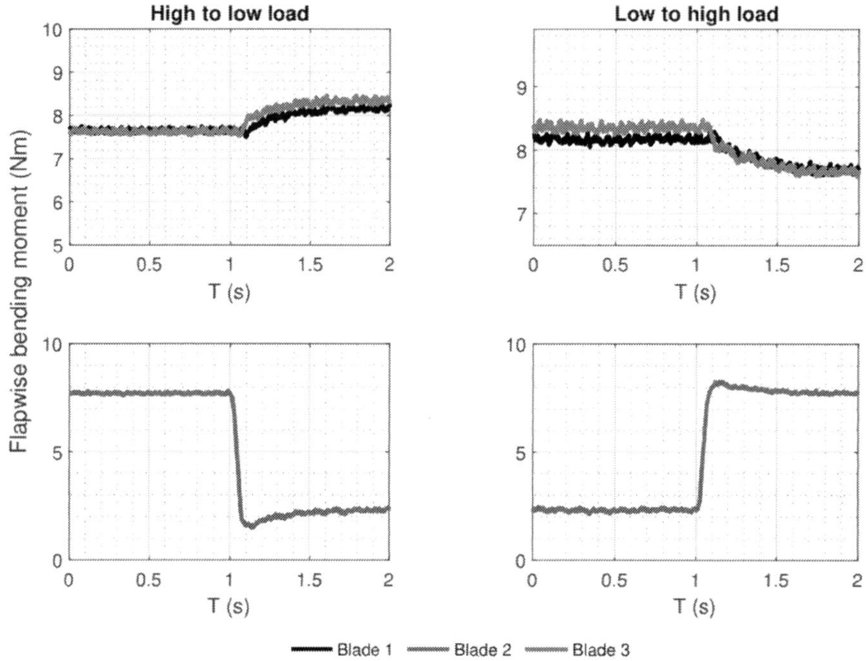


**Figure 3.** Loads on the wind turbine model during individual pitch steps. Blades 1 and 3 remain stationary, while blade 2 is actuated.

rotation, encounter increased tangential wind velocities. This could serve as an explanation for the increased loads of these blades, as it is recorded from the experimental procedure.

In figure 4, selected operational quantities – the rotor torque and the flapwsise bending moments for blade 2 – for the two cases are being plotted against each other. The loads that were recorded on one specific blade are chosen to be compared so that the inconsistencies because of sensors and pitch mechanism discrepancies are limited. The loads are compared only for the blade that is performing a maneuver (as for the individual pitch step, two of the three blades remain still). In the figure, it is set that $t = 1\,\mathrm{s}$ is the instant that the pitch actuation initiates.

As it is expected, the low load conditions (which correspond to all blades being pitched to $5^{\circ}$ for the collective case and only blade 2 to the same position for the individual step) are different for the two cases. For the symmetric case, where the total change of the rotor induction is higher, the difference in the loads is higher, resulting in lower rotor torque (and thrust) in the new equilibrium. Correspondingly, the load overshoots are substantially higher than in the asymmetrical case.

### *3.2. Comparison with simulation models*

The results for all blades for the individual pitch step together with the corresponding simulation results are being plotted in figure 5. For the collective case, results are only plotted for blade 2 in figure 6, for the reason of better comparison.

For the collective steps, the simulations generally show good agreement, with the higher fidelity AWSM simulation matching the experimental recordings slightly better. The BEM simulations are slightly less accurate, with the ECN model overpredicting the load overshoots, while the DTU model seems to converge faster to the new steady state. The observations are

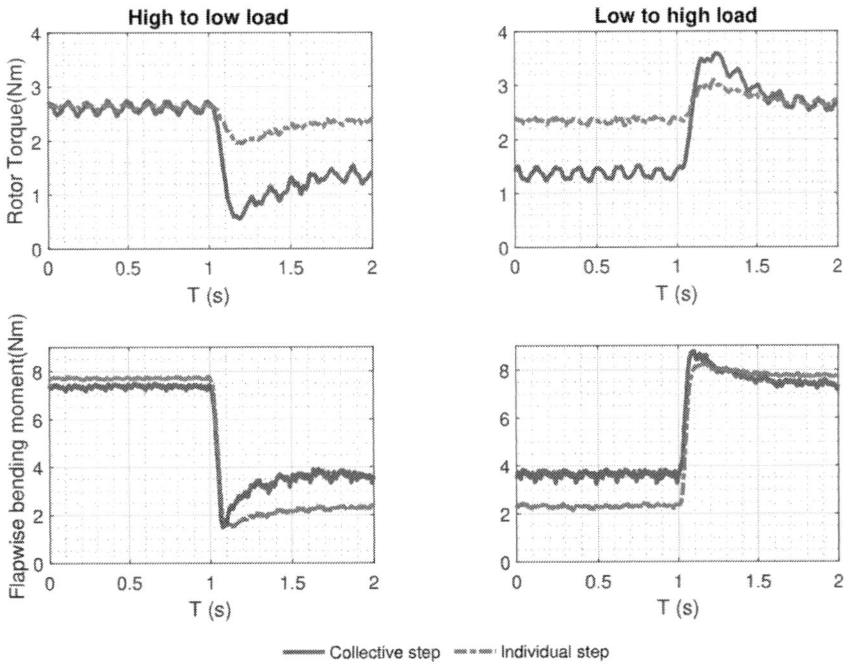


**Figure 4.** Loads on the wind turbine model during individual and collective pitch steps. Top two plots show the change of rotor torque during pitch steps from high to load regime and vice versa. The two figures at the bottom show the flapwise bending moments for the pitching blade no 2 under the same conditions.

in line with previous comparisons of models for similar conditions. [13]

This is not, however, the case when comparing the BEM-based simulations with the experimental reference for the case of asymmetrical pitching. When pitching for high to low loads, the new steady loads differ from the simulated ones. This could be attributed to the fact that the local induction changes are not modeled in those tools. It can be noted that the loads on the steady blades increase after the single blade pitches, which is not being predicted by the BEM tools. Furthermore, BEM tools predict for steady blades load overshoots similar to the pitched blade, which is not observed in the experiments. The AWSM simulation showcases satisfactory agreement in the prediction of the loads on all three blades.

## 4. Conclusions and outlook

In the current paper, the measurement setup for the investigation of the dynamic inflow effect was presented. The capability of producing such phenomena was successfully showcased for both conditions of axial symmetry and asymmetry on the rotor loading. This was realised by performing collective and individual pitch steps under steady flow and rotational speed conditions.

The analysis and the evaluation of the recorded data prove that the case of the individual pitch step differs from the collective one even in the level of the load overshoots when a single blade is examined. Adding to that, the loads on the unpitched blades are affected differently by the pitched blade. The AWSM simulations were shown to be able to reproduce the observed phenomena.

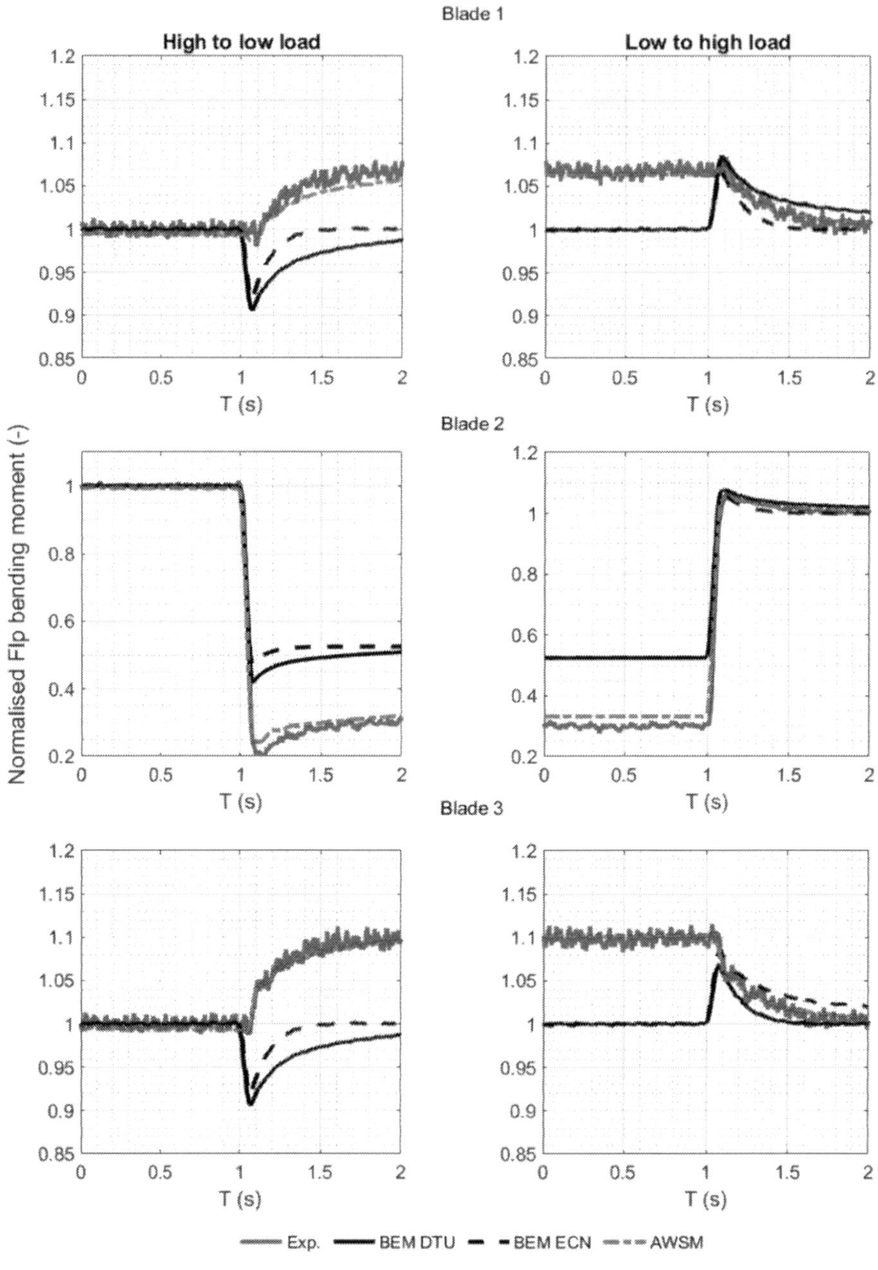


**Figure 5.** Comparison of blade loads during individual pitch step between the experiment and the AWSM and BEM simulations. In the left column are steps from -1° to 5° and in the right the reverse.

The comparison of the experimental data with the simulation results from standard BEM-based engineering tools for modeling such phenomena demonstrates their deficiencies and the

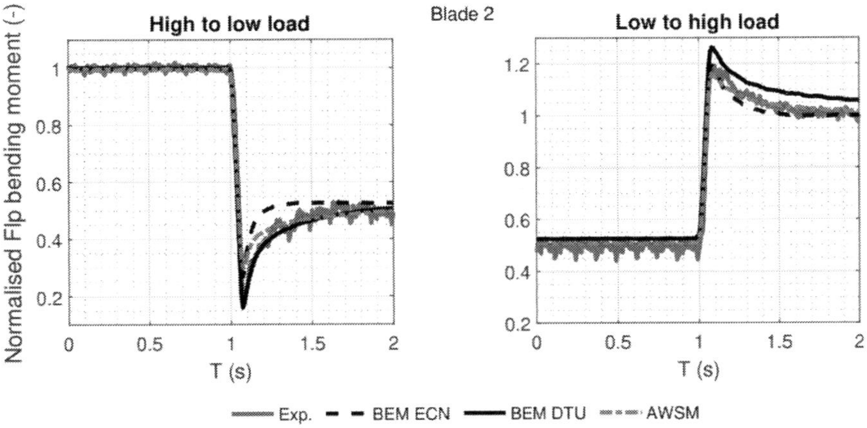


**Figure 6.** Comparison of blade loads during collective pitch step between the experiment and the AWSM and BEM simulations. On the left side are steps from -1° to 5° and on the right the reverse.

need for improvement of the relevant models. Such improvements could be applied to the rotor disk modeling, in order to account for the non-uniformity of the rotor disk loading and the interaction between the blades. In general, data from such measurements are suitable for improving the performance of the existing dynamic inflow models.

Future work will be focused on these aspects while additional measurement data could serve as a database for benchmarking the relevant tools. Measurements under different pitch regimes, such as variations of pitch steps and non uniform inflows, like wind shear can serve as reference for the improvement of the models. Wind tunnel campaigns with more elaborate measurement setups can also contribute to a better understanding of the flow during those maneuvers and thus, the proper physical modeling of dynamic inflow. Employing non-intrusive techniques such as Laser Doppler Anemometry and Particle Image Velocimetry can be a valuable tool for this scope.

## Acknowledgments

This work is partly funded by the Federal Ministry for Economic Affairs and Climate Action according to a resolution by the German Federal Parliament (project "DIMOR" Ref. Nr. 03EE2042 ) and the Public-Private Partnership (PPP) Allowance from the the Dutch Ministry of Economic Affairs and Climate Policy (EZK).

## References

[1] Snel H and Schepers J 1992 *Journal of Wind Engineering and Industrial Aerodynamics* **39** 267–281 ISSN 0167-6105
[2] Oeye S 1990 *Proceedings of the third IEA symposium on the aerodynamics of wind turbines* (Harwell,United Kingdom) pp 1–15
[3] Pirrung G R and Madsen H A 2018 *Wind Energy Science* **3** 545–551
[4] Yu W, Tavernier D, Ferreira C, van Kuik G A M and Schepers G 2019 *Wind Energy* **22** 1433–1450
[5] Hand M M, Simms D A, Fingersh L J, Jager D W, Cotrell J R, Schreck S and Larwood S M 2001 *NREL / TP-500-29955*
[6] Snel H, Schepers G and Siccama N 2009 *47th AIAA Aerospace Sciences Meeting including The New Horizons Forum and Aerospace Exposition*
[7] Berger F, Onnen D, Schepers G and Kühn M 2021 *Wind Energy Science* **6** 1341–1361 ISSN 2366-7451

[8] Neuhaus L, Berger F, Peinke J and Hölling M 2021 *Experiments in Fluids* **62** 130 ISSN 1432-1114
[9] Berger F, Kröger L, Onnen D, Petrović V and Kühn M 2018 *Journal of Physics: Conference Series* **1104** 012026 ISSN 1742-6588
[10] Boorsma K, Grasso F and Holierhoek J 2011 Enhanced approach for simulation of rotor aerodynamic loads Tech. Rep. ECN-M–12-003 ECN Petten, Netherlands
[11] Snel H 1997 *Conference proceedings European Wind Energy Conference* (Dublin, Ireland) pp 429–433
[12] van Garrel A 2003 Development of a wind turbine aerodynamics simulation module Report ECN-C–03-079 ECN
[13] Mancini S, Boorsma K, Schepers G and Savenije F 2023 *Wind Energy Science* **8** 193–210
[14] Madsen H A, Larsen T J, Pirrung G R, Li A and Zahle F 2020 *Wind Energy Science* **5** 1–27

# Predictive maintenance of wind turbine's main bearing using wind farm SCADA data and LSTM neural networks

**Y Vidal [1,2], B Puruncajas [1,3], F Castellani[4] and C Tutivén[3,5]**

[1] Control, Data, and Artificial Intelligence (CoDAlab), Department of Mathematics, Escola d'Enginyeria de Barcelona Est (EEBE), Universitat Politècnica de Catalunya (UPC), Campus Diagonal-Besós (CDB), Eduard Maristany, 16, 08019 Barcelona, Spain
[2] Institute of Mathematics (IMTech), Universitat Politècnica de Catalunya (UPC), Pau Gargallo 14, 08028 Barcelona, Spain
[3] ESPOL Polytechnic University, Escuela Superior Politécnica del Litoral, Faculty of Mechanical Engineering and Production Science (FIMCP), Mechatronics Engineering, Campus Gustavo Galindo Km. 30.5 Vía Perimetral, P.O. Box 09-01-5863, Guayaquil, Ecuador
[4] Department of Engineering, University of Perugia, Perugia, Italy
[5] Universidad Ecotec, Km. 13.5 Samborondón, Samborondón, EC092302, Ecuador.

E-mail: yolanda.vidal@upc.edu, bpurunca@espol.edu.ec, francesco.castellani@unipg.it, cjtutive@espol.edu.ec

**Abstract.** Field failures of wind turbine main bearings cause unwanted downtime and significant maintenance costs. Currently, this industry seeks to increase its reliability, for which condition monitoring and predictive maintenance systems have been adopted. In most industrial wind farms, the integrated Supervisory Control and Data Acquisition (SCADA) system provides data that is stored averaged every 10 minutes that can be used to quantify the health of a wind turbine (WT). This research presents a framework for the analysis of data collected from the SCADA system of an operating wind farm, aiming to early detect the main bearing failure using a Long-Short-Term Memory (LSTM) neural network. For prediction, SCADA variables of the temperature of turbine components near the main bearing, rotor speed, ambient temperature, and generated power are taken into account. The results show that the proposed methodology can detect the target failure up to 4 months in advance of the fatal breakdown. The results obtained confirm the applicability of the proposed model in real scenarios that can help the operator with enough time to make more informed maintenance decisions.

## 1. Introduction

Wind energy is one of the most widely used renewable energy resources with low environmental impact in the world for the generation of electricity. High growth is estimated worldwide, with 1000 GW installed by 2050 with a WT installation rate of 200 GW/year [1]. The main challenge of wind energy is to achieve low operating and maintenance costs (O&M). It is estimated that O&M in wind farms can represent 30% of the total cost of energy due to its remote location, difficult transportation, components and logistics costs, and downtime [2]. One of the fundamental elements of the wind turbine rotation mechanisms are bearings. These can be divided into pitch bearings, yaw bearings, transmission bearings (main bearing and gearbox bearings), and generator bearings [3]. Bearings are commonly subjected to harsh environments, including vibration and shock under varying wind speeds. This has led to bearings operating beyond their limits, which explains the high failure rate of these components [4]. Recently, data show that main bearing failure rates (over a 20-year life) can be as high as 30% [5]. The industry identified main bearing failure as the second largest reliability challenge after WT gearboxes [6].

In general, bearing failures can be classified into fatigue, wear, corrosion, plastic deformation, electrical erosion, cracking, and fracture failure modes. There are different causes and behaviors for these modes, such as deformation, tension, craters, and fractures [7]. Mechanical failures are often accompanied by increased heat loss. In bearings, failures occur with increasing temperature and indicate reduced performance or imminent failure [8]. Most industrial wind farms operate through supervisory control and data acquisition (SCADA) systems, which record monitoring information from different components of the WT, such as wind speed, generated power, and bearing temperature. Therefore, the temperature signals from the SCADA data can provide information on the performance of the main bearing. The recorded data create an opportunity to process the collected time series data for various applications, such as the diagnosis, detection, or prognosis of WT failures [9].

In the literature, several works address failure detection through the use of SCADA data in WTs in operation. For example, in [10], the prediction of the main bearing failure has been carried out on two wind farms, with a total of 84 WTs, where four WTs have the failure. Based on the principles of Ensemble Learning, the anticipation of failure is obtained in no less than one month. In [11], a study is carried out based on several machine learning techniques to predict bearing failure in the gearbox; a wind farm with 13 WTs is used, where three WTs have bearing failures. The best model obtained is an LSTM network with a false alarm rate of 50% and one month of anticipation of failure. In [12], a hybrid model is made to predict fatigue in the main bearings, where the part of the bearing that suffers fatigue consists of known physical formulations, and the unknown degradation of the grease is represented by deep neural networks. The tests are carried out on 10 WTs, proposing regreasing intervals to extend the useful life of the bearings. The studies mentioned above used and validated their methodology in real wind farms; however, the results do not show failure, if not less than a month after failures occur.

In this work, in contrast to the aforementioned works, it has been possible to detect a main bearing failure four months in advance to the fatal breakdown of the component. The proposed methodology works with a normality model based on the use of SCADA data from wind farms composed of 12 WTs. It should be noted that no additional information provided by the SCADA data is used. Additionally, this methodology has not worked with labeled data due to the difficulty in obtaining data from the failure under study and other aspects associated with possible errors in the process. Therefore, the model can be used in any WT that uses SCADA data, even if this type of fault never occurred in the past. The signals of external sensors provided by WT SCADA are used to capture hidden trends in the main bearing temperature. The LSTM neural network has been chosen for modeling due to its characteristic of capturing long-range dependencies and nonlinear dynamics.

The contribution of this research is as follows: i) propose a methodology for the prediction of main bearing failure based on the results obtained in a wind farm in operation, ii) design and develop an efficient deep learning model to predict long-term time series (the incipient fault has been detected 4 months in advance of the fatal breakdown of the component), iii) carry out a comparative analysis in a wind farm where one WT is affected by the failure under study, another turbine has another type of failure, and the rest are healthy.

The presented document has the following structure: Section 2 carries out an analysis of the SCADA data to be selected, as well as a complete statement of the proposed methodology, while Section 3 presents the results and discussion. The document ends in Section 4 with possible future directions.

## 2. The proposed methodology

The proposed approach for the early prediction of main bearing failure is based on the creation of a normality model by using an LSTM neural network. The SCADA data of the selected variables under healthy conditions are used to train the model. Then, when the model predicts the target variable from data that is faulty, this will end with greater errors in the predictions. Figure 1 shows the normality model approach.

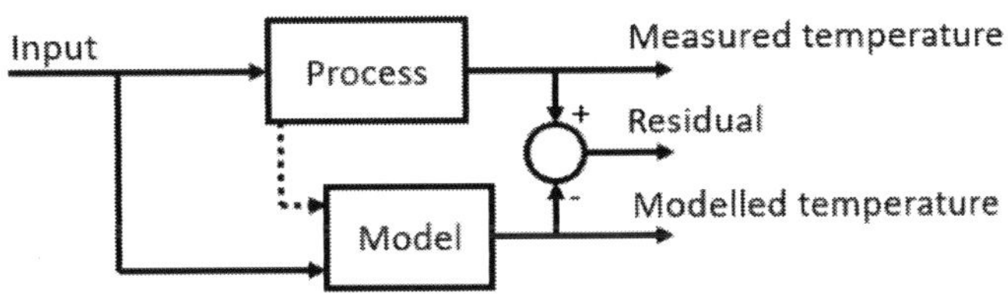


**Figure 1.** Normality model. When already trained (only with healthy data) the inputs are data that may or may not be healthy; the output shows the real measured SCADA temperature and the estimated (modelled) temperature by the LSTM network. In the middle is the residual (error that can be higher if the data is not healthy).

The methodology used to derive the proposed approach is the following: 1) SCADA data are described and analyzed to select the variables to be used for the creation of the normal behavior model; 2) treatment of outliers and empty data is considered; 3) data partition into train, validation and test datasets is performed; 3) data normalization and reshape is made; 4) the LSTM architecture design for the specific problem is created; 5) the fault indicator for the early prediction of the main bearing failure is developed and described; 6) test on a real SCADA dataset from an operational wind farm is performed.

### *2.1. SCADA data set*

The SCADA data used in this study correspond to a wind farm commissioned in Spain in 2006. The wind farm has 12 operational WTs, where each wind turbine has a nominal power of 1500kW, a diameter of 77 $m$, IEC IIa class, a swept area of 4657 $m^2$, and wind speed range for energy production between 3.5 $m/s$ and 25 $m/s$. WT SCADA data variables can be grouped into environmental, electrical, component temperature, hydraulic, and electrical variables. The maximum, minimum, and standard deviation values are available in 10-minute time periods for the SCADA data. For the study, continuous operational data from the wind farm were collected from February 2017 to November 2018.

*2.1.1. Data analysis* In the Introduction, it was described the various failure modes of the main bearings, which in many cases lead to a temperature increase. For this reason, the SCADA temperature variables are selected near the main bearing. In particular, the selected SCADA variables are the low-speed shaft temperature, the bearing noncoupling side temperature, the gearbox temperature, and the generator temperature. Finally, also the generated real power and rotor speed are selected, which provide information about the operating regions of the WT, and the ambient temperature due to its influence on all the subsystems of the WT. The selected variables are detailed in Table 1 (note that each variable has a range of operating values). Figure 2 shows the readings of the SCADA variables selected.

**Table 1.** Selected SCADA variables with their respective description and value ranges.

| Variable | Description | Range | Units |
|---|---|---|---|
| Pot | Generated real power | [0, 2000] | kW |
| TempAmb | Ambient temperature | [−5, 40] | °C |
| TempCojLOA | Bearing non-coupling side temperature | [0, 120] | °C |
| TempEjeLento | Low-speed shaft temperature | [0, 120] | °C |
| TempGen | Generator temperature | [0, 175] | °C |
| TempRodamMultip | Gearbox temperature | [0, 120] | °C |
| VelRotor | Rotor speed | [0, 50] | rpm |

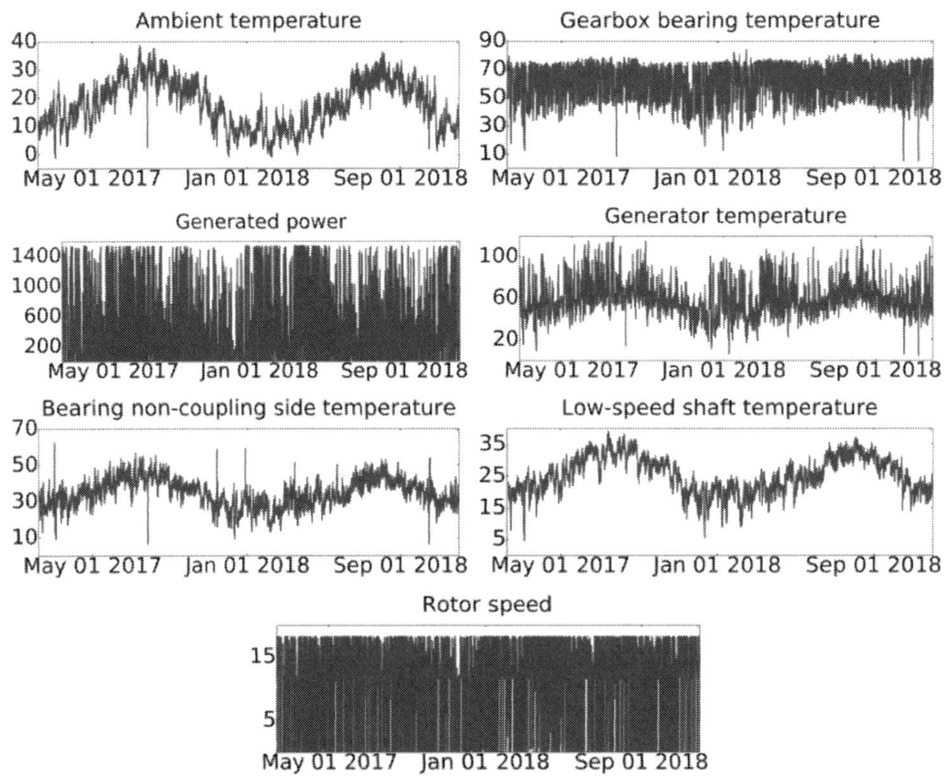


**Figure 2.** Example of the seven SCADA variables selected to develop the normality model.

*2.1.2. Data cleaning* Real SCADA data have unavoidable outliers from different WT readings. In this work, data cleaning is carried out in such a way that information is not lost, since it could cause loss of information for the prediction of failures. The strategy used filters the data from different sensors using the ranges defined for the different sensors (see Table 1).

Another problem in SCADA data is missing values due to sensor malfunction; when added to the filtered data range of the aforementioned outliers, missing values increase. The imputation strategy used to solve this problem is the use of a piecewise cubic Hermite interpolation polynomial (pchip). This type of interpolation works with known points and specific slopes at the interpolation points. The curve obtained from pchip preserves the trend of the data, respecting the monotonicity and guaranteeing at least the first derivative.

*2.1.3. Train, validation, and test splitting* For the development of the proposed early prediction model, the following steps will be followed: (1) divide the data for training, validation, and testing, (2) train the neural network with the training data and validate the model with the validation data, (3) evaluate the model with the test data. This section will focus in the first step; the remaining steps will be explained throughout the document.

The data have been divided so that its time series have not been broken in time (the information has not been mixed); consequently, the training and validation data correspond to the year 2017, while the test data correspond to the year 2018. Finally, the division is detailed in Figure 3; note that this division has been made for the entire wind farm.

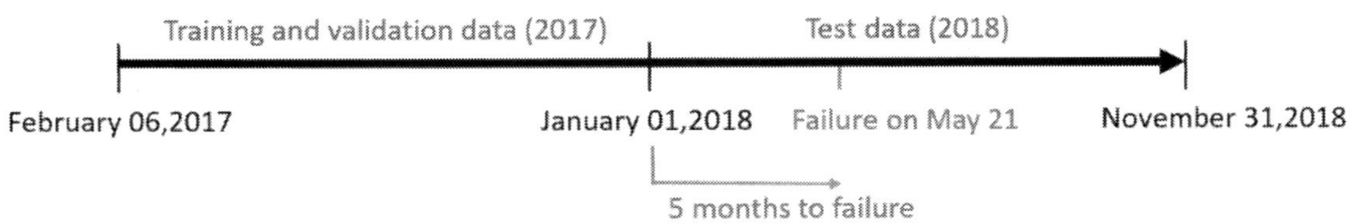


**Figure 3.** Data distribution for WT2.

Data from 2017 have been divided into 90% for training and 10% for validation, obtaining 42,481 samples for training and 4,609 samples for validation. The data from 2018 is used for testing, obtaining 47,953 samples.

*2.1.4. Data normalization* The SCADA data of the selected variables have different magnitudes due to the different nature of the measurements. In deep learning and machine learning applications, it is recommended to scale data to facilitate learning [13]. Therefore, the maximum-minimum scaling has been selected, guaranteeing data in the range [0, 1]. It is a simple technique, and its only drawback is dealing with outliers, which it has already resolved by range filtering the data. Normalization of the data has been carried out so that the maximum and minimum values have been taken from the training data and used to normalize the validation and testing data.

*2.1.5. Data arrangement* Data have been ordered so that a sample has a length of 144 time steps, corresponding to one day, with the intention that the network learns the temporal trend characteristics of one day of operation. The next step is to reshape the data to be ready as input for the LSTM neural network. For this, seven input data are defined, which are shown in Table 1. The table 2 shows the input data array of the LSTM neural network, where $k$ represents the sample number and the instants of time are defined from $t-144$ to $t-1$.

For the output of the neural network, the target is the SCADA variable corresponding to the low speed shaft temperature at the time instant $t$ (at the end of the day).

*2.2. LSTM*

In recent years, deep learning has proven its powerful hands-on learning ability in conjunction with the superiority of big data processing, attracting attention from various fields. LSTM networks have significant advantages over other artificial intelligence techniques due to its memory capacity over time series [14]. The LSTM neural network is a type of recurrent neural network (RNN) that solves the problem of gradient vanishing while preserving the quality of the RNN for processing sequential data [15]. The LSTM neural network decides the update of the information through the architecture of its cell. The reader is referred to the excellent reference

**Table 2.** Data matrix where columns represent the seven SCADA variables, rows represent 144 timestamps, and the value of $k$ represents the sample number.

| | **SCADA variable 1** | **SCADA variable 2** | **. . .** | **SCADA variable 7** |
|---|---|---|---|---|
| $\mathbf{X}^{(k)} =$ | $y^{(k)}_{t-1,1}$, $y^{(k)}_{t-2,1}$, $\vdots$, $y^{(k)}_{t-144,1}$ | $y^{(k)}_{t-1,2}$, ${}^{(k)}_{t-2,2}$, $\vdots$, $y^{(k)}_{t-144,2}$ | $\cdots$ | $y^{(k)}_{t-1,7}$, $y^{(k)}_{t-2,7}$, $\vdots$, $y^{(k)}_{t-144,7}$ |

[16] for a comprehensive explanation of the inference formulas for the LSTM network, as well as its fundamentals.

*2.2.1. LSTM model* A many-to-one LSTM neural network has been chosen due to the approach proposed in this work. For the input of the network, there is a sequence of 144 data and an output corresponding to the temperature of the low-speed shaft temperature at the instant of time $t$. To choose the best LSTM neural network model, tests were performed with a unidirectional LSTM neural network and a bidirectional LSTM neural network. The results showed similarities, so the LSTM unidirectional neural network was chosen because of its lower computational cost. The unidirectional LSTM network architecture has a hidden layer, and the hyperparameters are as follows.

The optimal number of units in terms of time, computational cost, and results in the hidden layers of the LSTM cells is 100. The batch size is selected to be 64, a learning rate of 0.01 is defined, and 200 epochs are used to train the network. Finally, the mean square error (MSE) has been selected as the loss function of the neural network. Figure 4 shows the architecture of the LSTM network.

*2.2.2. Trained model* The realization of the model has been done with the PyTorch programming language [17] on a laptop with a NVIDIA GeForce RTXTM2060 video card, a ninth generation Intel i7 processor, 16 GB RAM and a Windows 10 operating system. The training lasted 31 minutes for each wind turbine.

### *2.3. Fault Indicator (FI)*

The early failure indicator is based on the generation of a nominal residual by comparing the measurements of the physical variable of the system $y_t$ (temperature of the low-speed shaft at the time instant $t$) with their estimate $\hat{y}_t$ (output of the LSTM network). In this work, the residual value is $|y - \hat{y}|$. When considering the uncertainty of the model, the residual generated is not enough to establish an alarm signal through a threshold; there is a risk of generating false alarms.

To solve this problem, a simple moving average (SMA) filter is implemented to smooth the residual shape, removing sudden changes from the residual. The SMA filtering process has been implemented through a moving window of sizes 144 and 1008; that is, one day and one week of data. Fault detection is activated when the SMA of the residual is more significant than a threshold. In particular, the mean $\mu$ and the standard deviation $\sigma$ of the SMA of the training residual are calculated. Finally, the threshold is defined as:

$$threshold = \mu + \kappa\sigma. \tag{1}$$

Note that by adjusting the value of $\kappa$ it allows for threshold tuning.

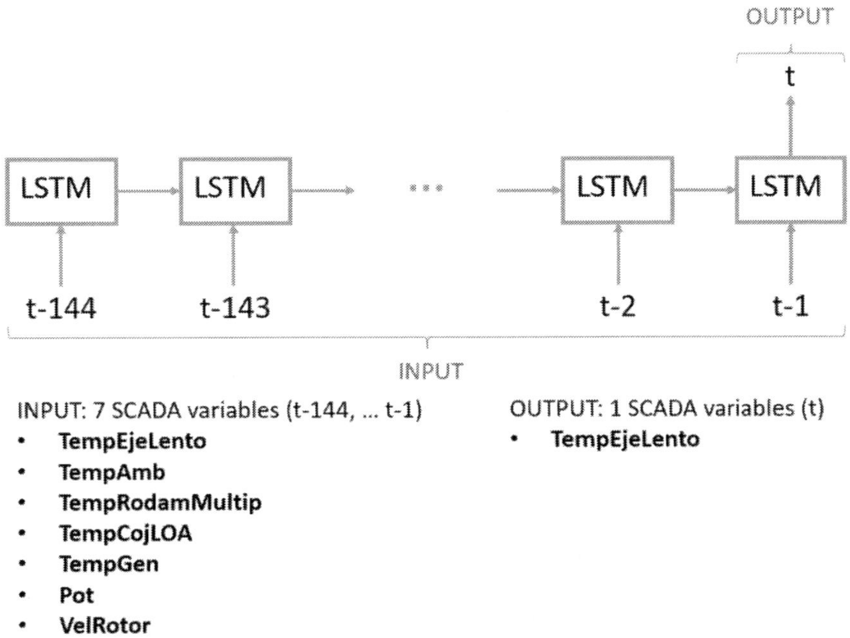


**Figure 4.** Many-to-one LSTM architecture.

## 3. Results and Discussion

The presented section describes the results obtained from a proposed methodology based on alarm activations when the FI exceeds a threshold. Table 3 summarizes the alarms activated in a wind farm with different values of SMA and thresholds. Only one wind turbine (WT2) has experienced a failure of interest that occurred on May 21, 2018.

To fine-tune the smoothing of the SMA and the decision threshold, the task of smoothing the FI is performed using only training and validation data to minimize the number of false alarms. Two SMA values are used, one with 144 data (a day) and the other with 1008 data (a week). With SMA values of 144 and $\kappa$ of 3 ($\mu + 3\sigma$), eleven alarm activations are obtained, but to improve the results, the value of $\kappa$ is changed to 6 ($\mu + 6\sigma$), which results in six alarms. The results are further improved by increasing the SMA to 1008, and tests are carried out with $\kappa$ values of 3 and 6, with the latter providing the best results.

Figure 5 shows the best SMA result (weekly smoothing, 1008 data) of the residual curve in training, validation, and testing in the wind farm in detail. For the WT2, an anomaly is detected on February 18, receiving an alarm four months before the total breakdown of the component. The detected anomaly is due to a possible initial failure (initial crack, friction,...), which has been detected months in advance of the fatal breakdown of the component. There is also an alarm activation in WT8, which is related to a different component, i.e., a gearbox replacement carried out on the WT8 from March 22 to April 11. Therefore, it is not completely a false alarm. In fact, it is noteworthy that there are no false alarms in a 2-year period over a whole wind farm, which are excellent results.

In summary, the proposed methodology based on alarm activations when the FI exceeds a threshold shows promising results for detecting anomalies in wind farms. The fine-tuning of the smoothing of the SMA and the decision threshold is critical to reduce the number of false alarms. The results obtained from the methodology include an early detection of a failure of interest in a wind turbine, which may help to prevent significant financial losses due to unexpected downtimes.

**Table 3.** Experimental summary of SMA and threshold value over the training and validation datasets. The activated alarms are presented with an × mark.

| **WT** | **SMA(144)** | | **SMA(1008)** | |
|---|---|---|---|---|
| | $\mu + 6\sigma$ | $\mu + 3\sigma$ | $\mu + 6\sigma$ | $\mu + 3\sigma$ |
| WT1 | - | × | - | × |
| WT2 | × | × | × | × |
| WT3 | × | × | - | - |
| WT4 | - | × | - | × |
| WT5 | - | × | - | - |
| WT6 | - | × | - | × |
| WT7 | × | × | - | × |
| WT8 | × | × | × | × |
| WT9 | - | × | - | × |
| WT10 | × | × | - | × |
| WT11 | - | - | - | - |
| WT12 | × | × | - | - |

## 4. Conclusions

The proposed methodology for the early prediction of main bearing failure using SCADA data from a wind farm yielded several key findings, which are summarized below.

Firstly, the analysis showed that the low-speed shaft temperature and the non-coupling side temperature were found to be indicative of the main bearing failure. This finding is significant as it can help the maintenance team to identify early warning signs of main bearing failure and take corrective actions before it becomes a more significant problem.

Secondly, the Long Short-Term Memory (LSTM) architecture design used in the proposed methodology proved to be effective, and the proposed fault indicator demonstrated a high level of accuracy in detecting the main bearing failure. LSTM is a type of recurrent neural network that can learn long-term dependencies in time-series data, making it particularly well-suited for analyzing SCADA data from wind turbines. The high accuracy of the fault indicator in detecting main bearing failure is significant, as it can help the maintenance team to focus their attention on the affected turbines and take corrective actions proactively.

Thirdly, the comparative analysis conducted on a wind farm with one WT affected by the failure, another turbine with a different type of failure, and the rest being healthy showed that the methodology was able to identify the affected WT accurately and early. This finding is crucial as it can lead to reduced downtime and maintenance costs, as corrective actions can be taken before the failure becomes more severe.

Fourthly, the results demonstrate that the stated approach is effective in detecting a main bearing fault that resulted in a significant increase in temperature. Although only one failure was available in the investigated wind park data, which is insufficient for statistical analysis, any bearing fault leading to heat release might be detectable by the proposed strategy. However, to more extensively investigate the performance of the model, it is necessary to apply the model to other wind parks with main bearing failure issues. Therefore, future work will test the model on a larger dataset to assess its performance in different scenarios and draw more generalizable conclusions

Finally, note that having few false alarms is crucial in any alarm system, especially in the context of wind turbines, as it can significantly affect the performance and productivity of the maintenance team. False alarms can lead to alarm fatigue, a condition where the maintenance team becomes desensitized to alarms due to their frequent occurrence. Alarm fatigue can lead to a decrease in the maintenance team's response time to real alarms, potentially resulting in an increase in downtimes, which can lead to significant financial losses for the wind farm. The proposed methodology, which is based on alarm activations when the FI exceeds a threshold, aims to minimize the number of false alarms by fine-tuning the smoothing of the SMA and the decision threshold. As described in this section, the methodology was tested on a wind farm with 12 wind turbines over a period of two years, and no real false alarms were detected during this period. The absence of false alarms in the proposed methodology is a significant advantage, as it ensures that the maintenance team is not bombarded with unnecessary alarms, which can lead to alarm fatigue. This enables the maintenance team to focus their attention on real alarms and respond to them promptly, minimizing downtimes and maximizing the productivity of the wind farm.

In summary, the proposed methodology for the early prediction of main bearing failure using SCADA data from a wind farm demonstrated several significant findings, including the identification of key indicators of main bearing failure, the effectiveness of the LSTM architecture design, and the ability to accurately identify affected turbines early. These findings are critical as they can help to improve the productivity and performance of wind turbines, reduce maintenance costs, and prevent downtime.

## 5. Acknowledgments
This work is partially funded by the Spanish Agencia Estatal de Investigación (AEI) - Ministerio de Economía, Industria y Competitividad (MINECO), and the Fondo Europeo de Desarrollo Regional (FEDER) through the research project PID2021-122132OB-C21; and by the Generalitat de Catalunya through the research project 2021 SGR 01044.

## 6. References
[1] IRENA I 2019 *Abu Dhabii*
[2] Crabtree C J, Zappalá D and Hogg S I 2015 *Proceedings of the Institution of Mechanical Engineers, Part A: Journal of Power and Energy* **229** 727–746
[3] Liu Z and Zhang L 2020 *Measurement* **149** 107002
[4] Saidi L, Ali J B, Bechhoefer E and Benbouzid M 2017 *Applied Acoustics* **120** 1–8
[5] Hart E, Turnbull A, Feuchtwang J, McMillan D, Golysheva E and Elliott R 2019 *Wind Energy* **22** 1534–1547
[6] Keller J, Sheng S, Cotrell J and Greco A 2016 Wind turbine drivetrain reliability collaborative workshop: a recap Tech. rep. National Renewable Energy Lab.(NREL), Golden, CO (United States)
[7] Encalada-Dávila Á, Puruncajas B, Tutivén C and Vidal Y 2021 *Sensors* **21** 2228
[8] Feng Y, Qiu Y, Crabtree C J, Long H and Tavner P J 2013 *Wind Energy* **16** 728–740
[9] Marti-Puig P, Blanco-M A, Cárdenas J J, Cusidó J and Solé-Casals J 2019 *Energies* **12** 453
[10] Beretta M, Julian A, Sepulveda J, Cusidó J and Porro O 2021 *Sensors* **21** 1512
[11] Desai A, Guo Y, Sheng S, Phillips C and Williams L 2020 Prognosis of wind turbine gearbox bearing failures using scada and modeled data *Annual Conference of the PHM Society* vol 12 pp 10–10
[12] Yucesan Y A and Viana F A 2021 *Computers in Industry* **125** 103386
[13] Bhanja S and Das A 2018 *arXiv preprint arXiv:1812.05519*
[14] Choe D E, Kim H C and Kim M H 2021 *Renewable Energy* **174** 218–235
[15] Chung D W, Ko J H and Yoon K Y 2022 *Journal of Electrical Engineering & Technology* 1–15
[16] Sherstinsky A 2020 *Physica D: Nonlinear Phenomena* **404** 132306
[17] Paszke A, Gross S, Massa F, Lerer A, Bradbury J, Chanan G, Killeen T, Lin Z, Gimelshein N, Antiga L *et al.* 2019 *Advances in neural information processing systems* **32**

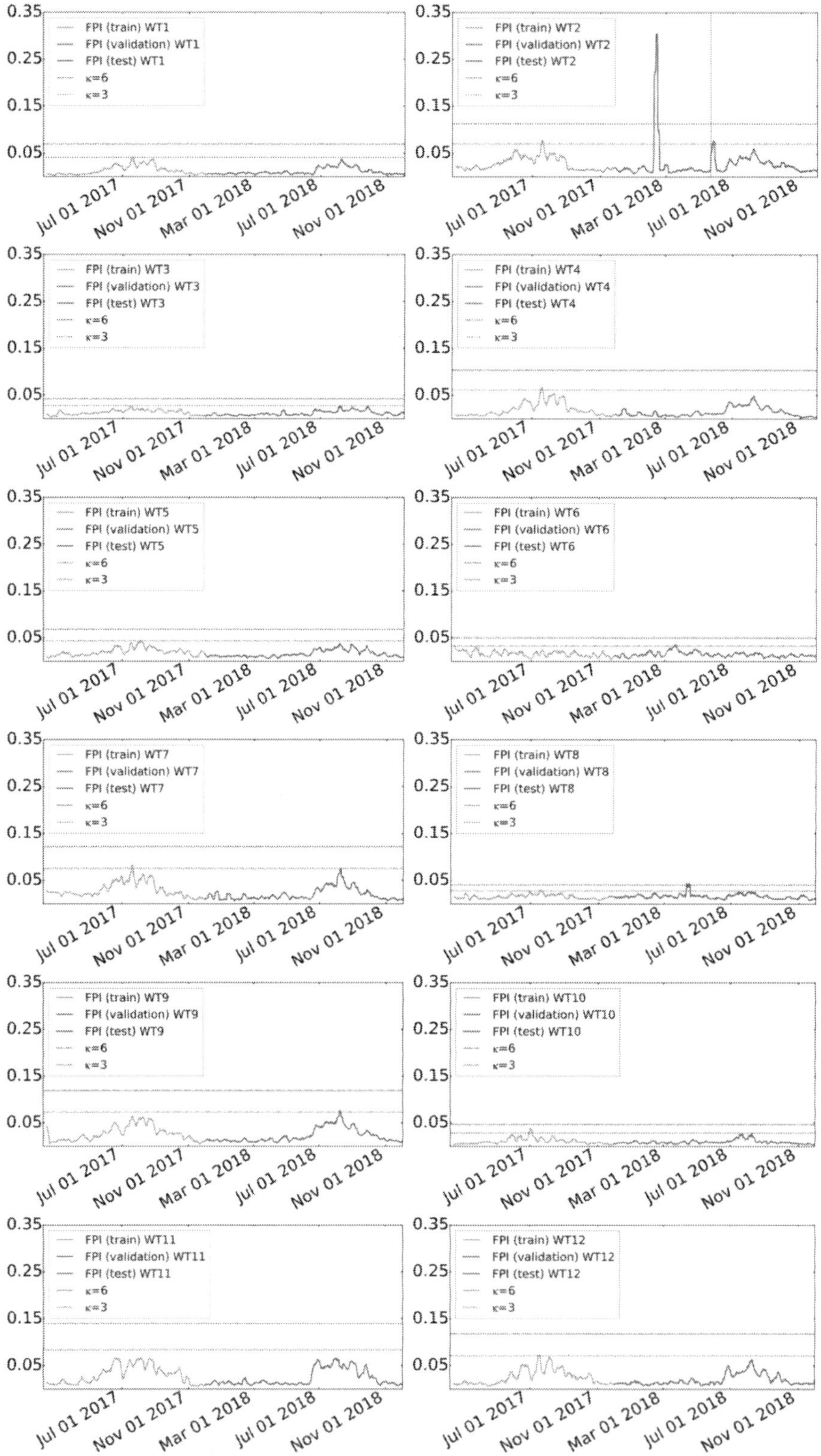


**Figure 5.** Results obtained over training, validation, and test datasets. The thresholds with values of $\kappa$ equal to 6 and 3 are shown for each WT.

# Weather-dependent passive thermography and thermal simulation of in-service wind turbine blades

**Somsubhro Chaudhuri**[1], **Michael Stamm**[1], **Rainer Krankenhagen**[1]
[1]Bundesanstalt für Materialforschung und -prüfung, Germany
E-mail: `somsubhro.chaudhuri@bam.de`

**Abstract.** To cope with the increase in the manufacturing and operation of wind turbines, wind farm operators need inspection tools that are able to provide reliable information while keeping the downtime low. Current inspection techniques require the wind turbine to be stopped. This work presents the current progress in the project EvalTherm, in which passive thermography is evaluated as a possible non-destructive inspection tool for operational wind turbine blades (WTBs). A methodology to obtain thermal images of rotating WTBs has been established in this project. However, the quality of the results is heavily dependent on various aspects such as weather conditions, information on the inspected WTB, damage history, etc. In this work, a section of a used WTB is simulated using finite-element modelling (FEM) as well as experimentally tested for evaluating the accuracy of the model. Such a model will provide insight into the potential thermal response of a certain structure (with specific material properties) in given weather (boundary) conditions. The model is able to provide satisfactory predictions of the temporal thermal response of the structure, as well as indicate what thermal contrast(s) transients result from artificial defects introduced in the structure.

## 1. Introduction

To achieve the carbon neutrality goals set at COP26, the number of wind turbines in operation and construction is exponentially increasing [1] (currently at 837 GW worldwide in 2021 [1]). This increases the effort of maintaining such infrastructure for the operators of wind turbine farms, both on-shore and off-shore [2]. This is further exacerbated by the complex structure of wind turbine blades (WTBs) that makes inspection and evaluation of findings a challenge. WTBs are multi-material (glass/carbon fibre reinforced polymer G/CFRP, balsa wood or PVC foam, glue, etc.) structures based on specific, proprietary designs [1, 3]. Approximately 65% of all failure incidents related to wind turbines are related with WTBs [4, 5]. To avoid premature WTB failure, a range of inspection techniques have been developed and currently used in operation [3, 4, 6, 7]. Infrared thermography (IRT) is one of them [8, 9, 10, 11]. The work presented here is part of an ongoing multi-partner project titled "EvalTherm": the evaluation of passive thermography as a non-destructive inspection tool of WTBs in operation [12]. This paper specifically discusses the aspect of performing ground-based passive thermography on WTBs and the corresponding issues. Finite-element (FE) based simulations are performed using COMSOL Multiphysics® to simulate the thermal response of a WTB. This enables introducing known defects in the FE model and simulating their thermal response. Field measurements are compared with the simulation results to possibly link defect signatures observed in the field with the simulation results of artificial defects. Apart from passive thermography, other

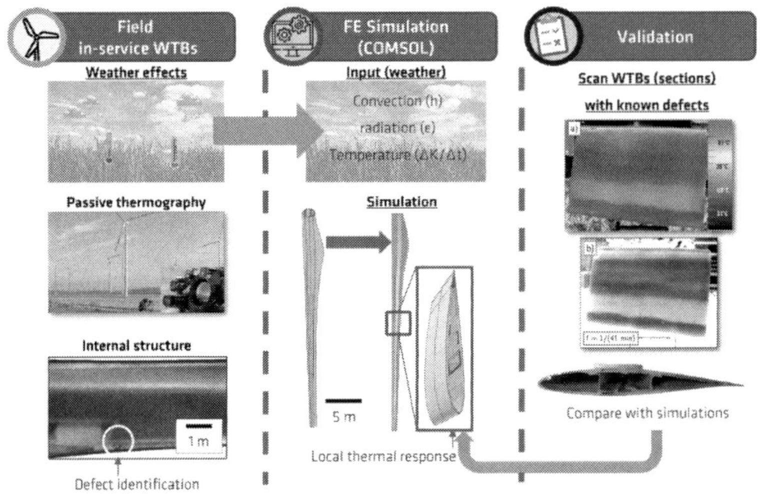


**Figure 1.** Schematic of the EvalTherm workflow.

partners of the EvalTherm project will be working on comparing the results obtained from passive thermography with active thermography results and on additional aspects crucial for bringing this technology into service. However, this is beyond the scope of this paper.

## 2. Approach

To understand and simulate the thermal behaviour of a WTB in operation, not only the external conditions but also the entire internal structure of the WTB must be known. Since the expected, and observed, defect related thermal contrasts in relation to usual surface temperature distributions on WTBs are low (<1 K) [10, 13, 14, 15]. Even minor details of the inner structure can have a large impact on surface temperatures.

Recently, a lab experiment was performed on a WTB section with the objective of linking experimental measurements and FE simulations using COMSOL Multiphysics [16]. It turned out that even a difference of 0.5 cm for a shell thickness of 2 cm strongly influences the thermal detectability of inner features like beam bonding (not reported so far). Unfortunately, such detailed information is usually not available for the wind turbine operator or the inspection companies. In order to perform useful thermal simulations focus is given on cut sections of old blades where the structural details are known from the cross-section views [16].

In addition, a scalable FEM model of an entire rotor blade was developed based on a typical structure. The goal is a general blade model which can be fitted to a specific design by a range of geometrical parameters and shape factors. It will be described in more detail in a later report. Here, we will focus on the cut part of a WTB which is sufficient to investigate the spatial and temporal evolution of thermal contrasts on the outer surface, at least in a first approximation. Later, if a suited wind turbine with sufficient information about the inner blade structure is found, the FEM simulations will be extended to the qualitative simulations of thermal contacts.

The running activities of the project are summarised in the following scheme (Figure 1). Field inspection of in-service WTBs is performed using ground-based passive thermography. In parallel, a simulation of the WTB structure with input parameters and boundary conditions based on measurements performed during corresponding field measurements is developed to predict the thermal response of the WTB. Comparing these simulations with real data acquired with passive and active thermography allows the validation of simulated thermal responses, and thus provide a method of predicting possible thermal contrasts in a range of weather conditions.

**Figure 2.** A schematic of the IRT camera setup.

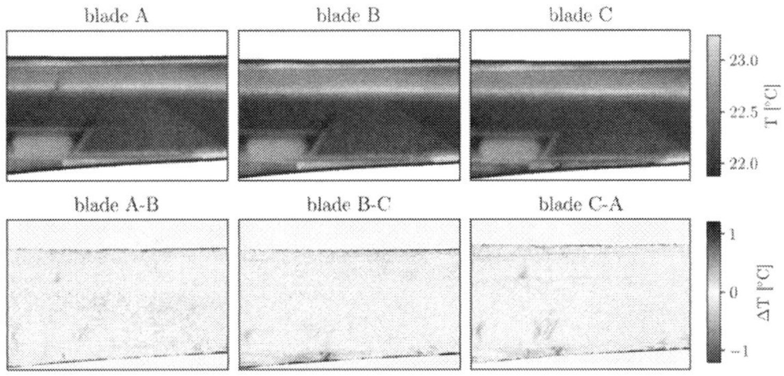


**Figure 3.** TOP: Surface temperature of 3.6 m long section of a WTB; BOTTOM: temperature differences between the different blades. Taken from [16].

The field inspection process is briefly described in section 3 to provide the overarching concept being developed in this project, lab measurements are described in section 4, and initial FE model validation results are shown in section 5. Section 6 summarises the conclusions from this work and outlines the next steps in the ongoing EvalTherm project.

## 3. Field inspection of in-service WTBs

Field inspection of in-service WTBs is performed using ground-based passive thermography (Figure 2). As an example, an in-service wind turbine with 35 m long WTBs was scanned during the month of August in central Germany. The wind turbine was in regular operation and not stopped for the inspection procedure. The IRT camera used is an ImageIR 8800 long-wave IR camera from Infratec GmbH. Camera specifications are provided in Table 1. The table also includes specifications when the IR camera is used for lab measurements (described in section 4.2.1). The camera is set up on a pan-tilt unit (PTU) which allows for programmable camera panning to automatically capturing the rotating WTBs. With such a semi-automatic measurement setup, the data acquisition is fast and takes about three minutes of scanning time (excluding approximately 5-10 minutes of moving the setup to the other side of the WTBs) for the suction and pressure side respectively.

In the shown scenario (Figure 3), it was attempted to capture internal structure of the blade while the heat source, the Sun, is shining on the opposite side of the scanned blade. Special attention is given to identifying optimum weather conditions for obtaining the best possible thermal contrast. Thermal images of 3.6 m long sections of the WTB are taken from the ground at a distance to the tower of 90 m and are shown in Figure 3. Here, some details of the internal structure of the WTB are visible. Using a specifically developed and patented post-processing workflow where the temperature differences of the three blades are taken [10, 16], anomalies in the structure of the blade can be identified and marked.

## 4. WTB section lab measurements

The purpose of performing lab measurements is to be able to limit the number of influencing factors involved in the field, in order to better understand the effect of each individual factor, and subsequently benchmark an FE model. It is also worth mentioning that it is challenging to obtain accurate WTB design documents from manufacturers due to commercial reasons like intellectual properties on the part of manufacturers. Thus, lab measurements of used WTBs become a

**Table 1.** Camera and measurement specifications for lab measurements and field inspection..

| **Parameter** | Lab experiment | Field measurement |
|---|---|---|
| Detector | Cooled Hg1-xCdxTe | |
| Wavelength | 8-9.2 µm | |
| Detector resolution | 640 x 512 pixels, pixel pitch: 16 µm | |
| Integration time | 140 µs | |
| Calibrated temperature range | 0-60°C | |
| NETD | 47 mK | |
| Assumed emissivity | 1 | |
| Objective focal length | 25 mm | 200 mm |
| Distance to object | 3.05 m | 90 m |
| Field of view | 1.25 x 0 .99 m | 4.6 x 3.7 m |

feasible alternative. Stamm and Krankenhagen [16] have performed these measurements for a specific sample extracted from a used WTB, where half of the width of the blade was removed for simplifying the problem and also for observing the inner section of the WTB. In this work, a full section of a used WTB is tested. The dimensions of the specimen and a cross-sectional image are shown in Figure 4. The section is 1 m long and has a maximum chord length of 765 mm.

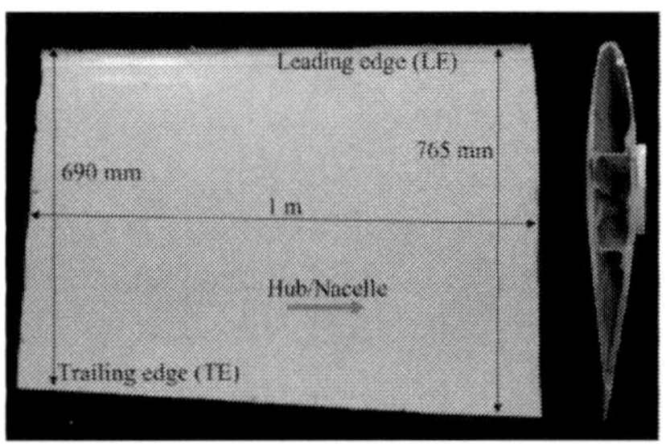


**Figure 4.** Schematic of the rotor blade section showing the dimensions and the cross-section.

### *4.1. FE model*

COMSOL Multiphysics software package version 6.1 with Heat Transfer module was used for FE modelling. For defining the geometry of the WTB section as accurately as possible, detailed measurements of the cross-section shown in Figure 4 were taken. This included the different materials that form the blade such as glass fibre reinforced plastic (GFRP), sandwich foam, resin or glue, and the skin, shown in Figure 5. Thermal properties of the different materials have been taken from [16] and are provided in Table 2. Experimental validation of these parameters is planned in next steps of the project. It is important to note that the GFRP is assumed to behave like an isotropic material when it comes to macroscopic thermal effects which are of interest in this study. Also, the skin is given the same material properties as the GFRP for the sake of simplicity. The influence of radiant cooling (with an emissivity of 0.95 as an influence of the coating on the skin) was included on the irradiated surface (the skin).

Different types of simulations have been performed for the WTB section, including the simulation of thermal measurements performed in the lab as well as measurements performed outside. They are explained in detail in section 4.2. The FE mesh has been generated within COMSOL. For the sake of brevity, the mesh construction is not discussed in this paper, but will be presented with a mesh study in a following report.

Journal of Physics: Conference Series **2507** (2023) 012025 doi:10.1088/1742-6596/2507/1/012025

**Table 2.** Thermal properties.

| Material | Thermal conductivity $k$ $Wm^{-1}K^{-1}$ | Mass density $\rho$ $Kgm^{-3}$ | Heat capacity $C_p$ $Jkg^{-1}K^{-1}$ |
|---|---|---|---|
| GFRP | 0.35 | 1800 | 1000 |
| Foam | 0.03 | 35 | 1300 |
| Glue | 0.28 | 1300 | 1280 |

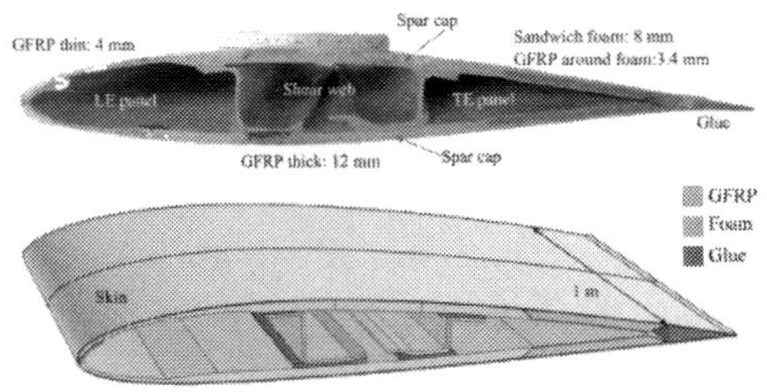


**Figure 5.** Schematic of the cross-section showing the different materials and thickness distribution.

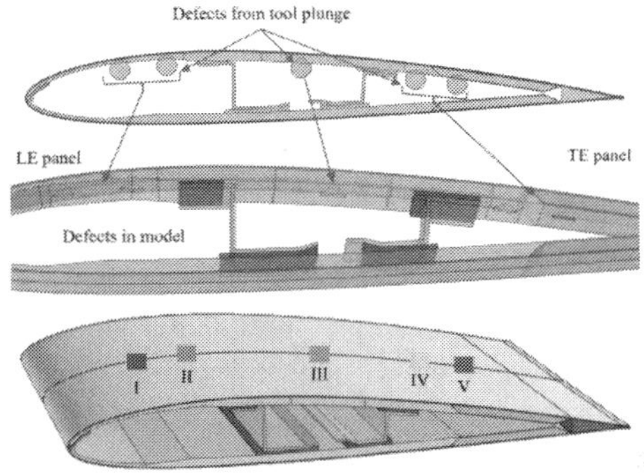


**Figure 6.** Schematic showing the introduction of defects into the COMSOL model.

As this study is an evaluation trial of the methodology of studying the effect of defects on the thermal response of the WTB section both experimentally and in simulations, defects have been machined in the WTB section using a Dremel multi-purpose tool. Essentially, semi-elliptical troughs were milled on inner surfaces as artificial defects . It is understood that this is not strictly representative of a real defect but rather a simplified loss of material thickness. However, in the next steps of this project, WTB sections with known and documented realistic defects will be scanned and modelled using the developed methodology. This is beyond the scope of this paper. In the COMSOL model, the defects are generated using a similar method where the intersecting elements of the WTB with the milling tool are removed to create the groove-like defect(s), see Figure 6. The defects are numbered I-V. Defects I and III are used as examples in section 5. The dimensions are given in Table 3. This technique (along with the correct choice of mesh elements - tetrahedral in this case) allows for complex defect configurations such as defect V in the TE panel going through both the foam and the inner GFRP skin. Additionally, such a model allows a relatively straightforward comparison between the thermal response of the WTB section without and with defect(s).

The following boundary conditions for the heat transfer module in COMSOL were used:

(1) Radiation: the value of radiation was obtained using a Hukseflux Pyranometer model SR-03. It was obtained in $Wm^{-2}$.

(2) Initial temperature: It can be assumed, that the measurements are performed when the specimen is in a thermal steady state, hence the surface temperature of the specimen is equal to the inner temperature of the specimen. This is generally equal to the air temperature in the lab where the specimen was stored. In the case of outdoor measurements, the specimen was stored outside overnight, and the initial temperature was taken as the temperature of the surface of the specimen at the time of thermal scanning.

(3) Ambient temperature: for lab measurements, this was set to the air temperature regulated by the air conditioning system (21.5°C). For external measurements, this was measured.

**Table 3.** Defect characteristics.

| Defect # | Depth [mm] | Length [mm] | Width [mm] |
|---|---|---|---|
| I | 4 | 15-18 | 8 |
| II | 4 | 15-18 | 8 |
| III | 6 | 40-45 | 8 |
| IV | 5 | 30-35 | 8 |
| V | 5 | 30-35 | 8 |

### *4.2. Experimental setup*

To compare with the results obtained from the COMSOL model, the WTB section is setup in lab conditions as well as outside. Both are described briefly below.

*4.2.1. Lab measurement* The WTB section is setup in lab conditions with controlled air temperature. The heat source is a SuperBeam 1200 rated 1200 W, which is used as a (lab) substitute for the Sun. The primary disadvantage of this setup is that it is not possible to replicate the homogenous heating by the Sun with an artificial heat source. Thus, each defect location was heated and scanned separately and compared with the FE simulation in which a homogenous heating across the surface of the specimen (subject to the curvature of the surface) is considered. A basic schematic is shown in Figure 7. A pyranometer was used to measure the intensity of the heating provided by the SuperBeam in $Wm^{-2}$, such that the values can be used as input for the COMSOL model.

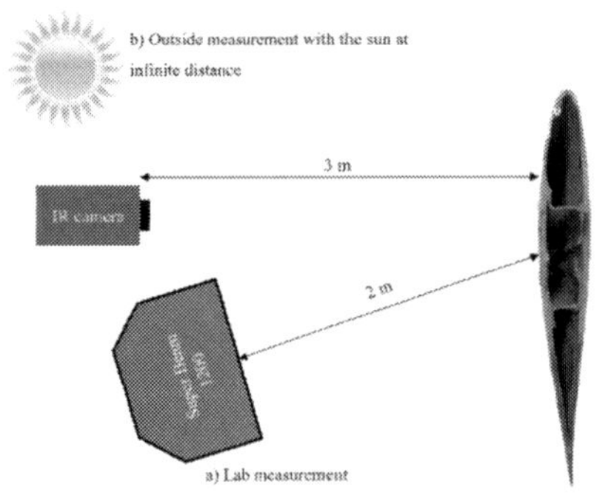


**Figure 7.** Basic schematic of the IR camera, specimen, and heat source setup; a) lab measurement with SuperBeam 1200; b) outside measurement with the sun..

## 5. Results and discussion

In total, three different kinds of experiments were performed. Details are provided in Table 4. All the three tests have the same specimen and defects. The defects are detailed in Table 3. It is important to highlight that it was expected and confirmed, that the boundary conditions strongly influence the detectability of defects with different characteristics. The experimental results are compared with the simulations. For the sake of brevity, results of Tests #1 and #3 are presented here. Test #1 represents a case of active thermography where the user actively

**Table 4.** Table of the three different types of tests performed.

| Test ID | Test location | Ambient temperature at beginning of test | Specimen temperature at beginning of test | Source of radiation |
|---|---|---|---|---|
| Test #1 | Lab | 21.6°C | 23.7°C | SuperBeam |
| Test #2 | Lab | 21.6°C | 5°C | None (heating from ambient air) |
| Test #3 | Outside | 1°C (gradually increased with time) | 3°C | Sun |

controls the heat source (SuperBeam). Test #3 is passive thermography with the Sun being the source of heating.

### 5.1. *Test #1*

For Test #1, the specimen was stored in the lab and heated for a specific period with the SuperBeam. As homogenous heating on the entire surface of the WTB is not possible in this arrangement, results shown here focus on defect I (from Figure 5) located in the leading edge and thinnest GFRP section. For the first 60 seconds of the measurement, no heating is turned on. Henceforth, 10 minutes of heating is provided by turning on the SuperBeam to full rated power. From the Pyranometer, it could be seen that the SuperBeam at a distance of 2 m to specimen provided an irradiation of 1200-1300 $Wm^{-2}$. Using optical spectrometry, preliminary reflection measurements of the coating of similar WTB blades were performed. Results showed that such WTB coatings offer an average of 50% reflection in the long wave infrared spectrum of the sun. This reflection was accounted for in the boundary conditions used in the COMSOL model for Test #1.

Figure 8 presents a thermogram of the specimen taken once the SuperBeam has been turned off after 10 min heating but remained for approximately 5 minutes in front of the specimen. The turning off of the SuperBeam is indicated as "End of heating" and is highlighted in Figure 9 and Figure 10. It is shown as a region and not a singular point as the heat source is manually reduced in intensity from 100% to 0%, thus it is not instantaneous. Due to the reduced thickness of GFRP above the defects as compared to the surrounding bulk material, a thermal contrast appeared after a certain period of heating (100+ seconds), and the defect was visible in the IR data without additional image post-processing. Figure 9 presents the temporal temperature distribution obtained from lab measurements as well as from the COMSOL simulation at Defect I. Even though the absolute temperature is not the same, the simulation was satisfactorily able to predict the shape of the temperature transient at the specimen surface. The difference in peak temperature is likely to be attributed to inaccuracies in the material properties (not just of the GFRP, but also of surrounding material) and boundary conditions (in the room). Another interesting location is the anomalous heating in the region between 750-900 seconds of scanning. This is attributed to residual infrared radiation from the SuperBeam even after it was turned off (because of the hot halogen lamp). After the heating, the face of the SuperBeam heat source was turned away from the specimen. It was covered with black fabric to reduce the added reflection on the WTB section at approximately 900 seconds of the recording. This highlights the strong influence of a range of boundary conditions (other than the obvious) on the measurements, confirming what previous authors have also acknowledged in such experiments.

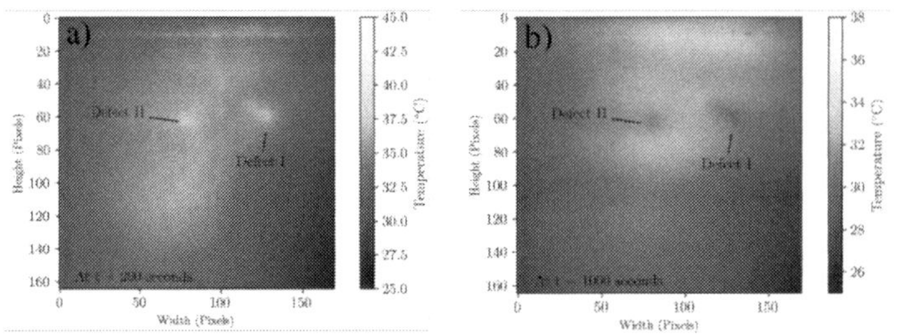


**Figure 8.** Test #1: Section of WTB which contains defects. a) Thermogram is taken at time of maximum thermal contrast ($\Delta T$, Figure 10)
; b) Thermogram is taken approximately 5 minutes after the heat source is turned off.

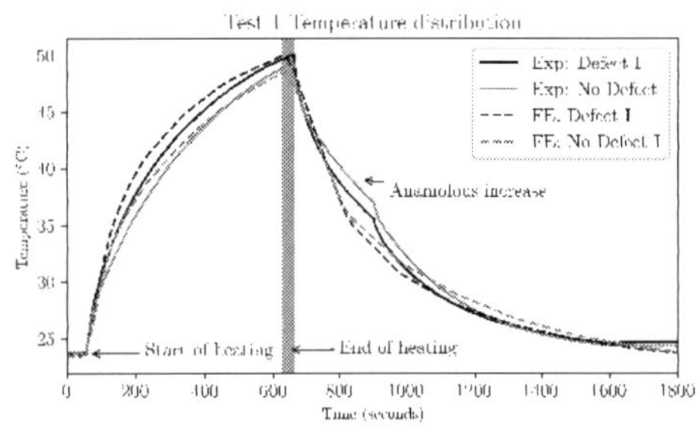


**Figure 9.** Temperature distribution from experimental data and simulation data of Test #1.

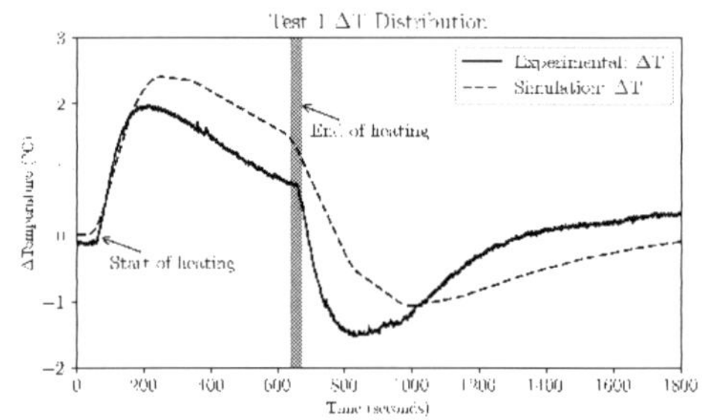


**Figure 10.** Distribution of the temperature difference in the presence and absence of a defect ($\Delta T$) of Test #1.

Figure 10 comprises the same data sets but shows the difference between a defect region and a sound region. This thermal contrast ($\Delta T$) is the actual signal in thermographic defect detection. For the experiment, the results showed that maximum $\Delta T$ was achieved at approximately 200 seconds of the measurement, which highlights that ideally the test could be stopped after this exposure. Figure 8*a*) shows the thermogram at this instant. If the defect related $\Delta T$ is higher than the thermal resolution of the camera (see Table 1) and other external noise like reflections or inhomogeneous convection, it should be possible for the defect to be detected without extensive post-processing. Thermograms in Figure 8*a*–*b* have not been post-processed (apart from defining a certain temperature range for the colour scheme) and show the defects to be distinguishable. Additionally, Figure 10 also shows the simulated $\Delta T$ for the same experimental conditions. It can be observed that the FE simulation over-predicts the $\Delta T$, but provides a reasonable estimation of the contrast transient, especially in terms of a peak early in the heating process. The authors assume an increased lateral heat conductivity as the reason for this deviation. The anisotropy of the thermal conductivity in GFRP is known and was reported earlier in [14]. The lateral diffusion of a hot spot reduces its maximum intensity and thus the $\Delta T$. This effect was not regarded in the simulation leading to an enhanced simulated $\Delta T$. Such a combination of experimentally measured thermal properties followed by thermal simulation is not readily available in the literature and it is planned in the future work of the EvalTherm project.

### *5.2. Test #3*

For Test #3, the specimen was kept outside overnight. Before scanning, the inside of the specimen was at 1 °C. To protect the specimen from the Sun, the specimen was covered during the camera setup. However, the outer layer reached (not intended for the experiment) approximately 5 °C (due to the Sun's radiation) before the measurements could begin. This was accounted for in the COMSOL simulation. Figure 11 is a thermogram of the specimen with defects III and I visible. Defect III is in the thickest section (12 mm) of the GFRP, and this defect was not visible in the unprocessed thermogram in Tests #1 and #2. This is attributed to the relatively stronger thermal flux generated due to the homogenous irradiation of the Sun (in contrast to the SuperBeam) on the surface of the WTB and the relatively colder air temperature of approximately 1 °C (see Table 4). This also enables the internal structure of the WTB to be visible without any additional post-processing. However, post-processing can help mitigate (to a certain extent) effects of strong reflections as well as noise in the image due to dead camera pixels. Irregularities in the internal structure can be visualized as well, but this is beyond the scope of this paper.

Figure 12 presents the temporal temperature distribution obtained experimentally at the location of defect III and a location in the same material without any defect. These are compared with the simulation data. As expected, the temperature measured at the surface increases with time due to the radiation from the Sun. The simulation results are satisfactorily able to predict trends in the thermal response of the WTB section. The temperature profile is different from Test #1 (Figure 9) as the recording is taken for a period of 30 minutes with the specimen exposed to the Sun (in Test #1 the source of heat is turned off after 10 minutes). The simulation results for Test #3 have a deviation in the results, specifically the rate of temperature increase in the first half of the test. It is important to highlight the incremental number of boundary conditions that arise to outside measurements, and only some can be incorporated in the simulations. Such factors are namely air temperature, wind speed, convection (free or forced), irradiation from the Sun, reflection from buildings, etc. The difference between the experiment and simulation can thus be attributed to this. As it is not always possible to measure every parameter, a parametric study would be a possible way of understanding which values should be prioritized (in addition to the parameters already measured such as air temperature and irradiation).

Figure 13 shows the resulting thermal contrast ($\Delta T$) due to the presence of defect III (black). The $\Delta T$ is approximately 0.3 K which, from experience, is close to what is the detection limit in the field (see Figure 3). This indicates the possibility for defect detection without sophisticated image post processing (Figure 11). In the simulation, $\Delta T$ is constant during the duration of the experiment for defect III, which is not seen in the $\Delta T$ observed for defect I (blue in Figure 13). The authors attribute this to the difference in material thickness at the defect location. The thicker the material, the longer it would take for a homogenous temperature distribution to occur (thus loss of $\Delta T$). If the experiment had been allowed to run longer than 30 minutes, a decline in $\Delta T$ could be expected for Defect III (such a trend is seen in the simulation). This behaviour is seen in Defect I, where with time, the contrast is slowly lost (the GFRP section around Defect I is 3 times thinner than Defect III). The simulations provide a reliable estimate of the $\Delta T$ transient. For Defect III, the simulation predicts an eventual reduction in $\Delta T$, which is not seen in the experiments. This could be attributed to the anisotropic behaviour of the GFRP material, specifically the anisotropy in thermal conductivity. Due to the directional construction of GFRP, it is plausible that with use (the WTB section tested is a used section with an unknown load history) the thermal conductivity has also altered. This has not been accounted for in the simulation.

## 6. Conclusions and Future Work

The primary aim of this work was to evaluate the accuracy of the FE model and possibly extract information regarding thermal contrast resulting due to defects. The FE models can provide indicative trends of the thermal response of the tested WTB section, provided the boundary conditions are recorded as accurately as possible. Material properties play a critical role and

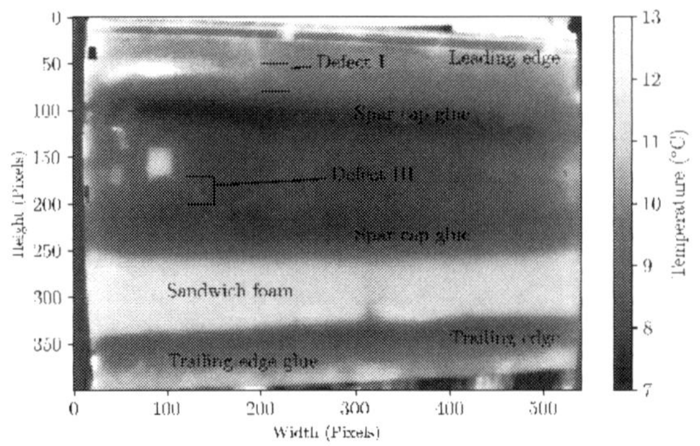


**Figure 11.** Test #3: Thermogram of the specimen with defect III visible.

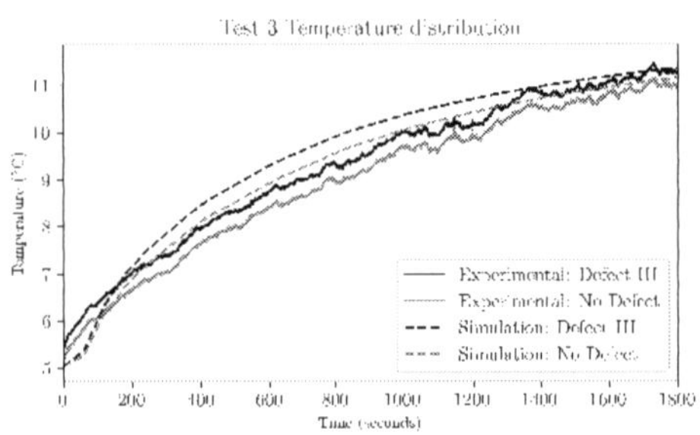


**Figure 12.** Temperature distribution from experimental data and simulation data of Test #3.

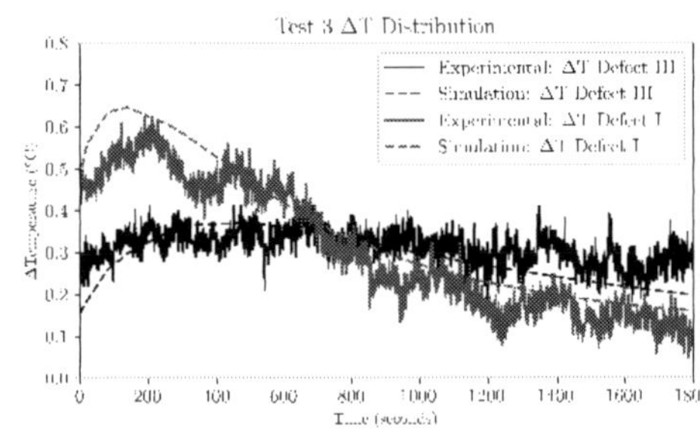


**Figure 13.** Distribution of the temperature difference in the presence and absence of a defect ($\Delta T$) of Test #3.

should be measured for individual materials to improve the accuracy of the FE model. The thermal contrasts obtained are sufficient to visualize the defects without any additional image post-processing. However, post-processing could be beneficial for removing noise and segmenting the internal structure in the images.

To further improve upon this work, the following future work is planned:

- The defects produced in this work are not representative of real defects. It is planned in this project to procure specimens that contain known defects which better represent reality. Also, it is planned to include defect data from other NDT techniques such as X-ray computed tomography.
- Experimental evaluation of thermal material properties which also includes the measurement of reflectance of the coating used on WTBs.
- The long-term aim of the project is to extend the FE modelling to full-scale WTBs, in line with the already implemented methodology of field inspection of in-service WTBs and include the influence of weather conditions.

**Acknowledgments**

The results presented were obtained within the EvalTherm project and the authors would like to thank the project partners for their cooperation. Special thanks to Julien Lecompagnon for his guidance in data processing and formatting.

Journal of Physics: Conference Series **2507** (2023) 012025 doi:10.1088/1742-6596/2507/1/012025

## References


[1] Global Wind Energy Council (GWEC). Global wind report 2022. Report, GWEC, 2022.

[2] Wenxian Yang, Peter J. Tavner, Christopher J. Crabtree, Y. Feng, and Y. Qiu. Wind turbine condition monitoring: technical and commercial challenges. *Wind Energy*, 17(5):673–693, 2014.

[3] Y. Du, S. Zhou, X. Jing, Y. Peng, H. Wu, and N. Kwok. Damage detection techniques for wind turbine blades: A review. *Mechanical Systems and Signal Processing*, 141, 2020.

[4] M. Civera and C. Surace. Non-destructive techniques for the condition and structural health monitoring of wind turbines: A literature review of the last 20 years. *Sensors*, 22(4), 2022. Export Date: 30 September 2022; Cited By: 6.

[5] Sander R. Brouwer, Saad H. S. Al-Jibouri, Ibsen Chivatá Cárdenas, and Johannes I. M. Halman. Towards analysing risks to public safety from wind turbines. *Reliability Engineering & System Safety*, 180:77–87, 2018.

[6] I. Amenabar, A. Mendikute, A. López-Arraiza, M. Lizaranzu, and J. Aurrekoetxea. Comparison and analysis of non-destructive testing techniques suitable for delamination inspection in wind turbine blades. *Composites Part B: Engineering*, 42(5):1298–1305, 2011.

[7] Renaldas Raišutis, Elena Jasiuniene, Reimondas Sliteris, and A. Vladišauskas. The review of non-destructive testing techniques suitable for inspection of the wind turbine blades. *Ultrasound*, 63, 2008.

[8] D. Traphan, I. Herráez, P. Meinlschmidt, F. Schlüter, J. Peinke, and G. Gülker. Remote surface damage detection on rotor blades of operating wind turbines by means of infrared thermography. *Wind Energ. Sci.*, 3(2):639–650, 2018. WES.

[9] H. Sanati, D. Wood, and Q. Sun. Condition monitoring of wind turbine blades using active and passive thermography. *Applied Sciences (Switzerland)*, 8(10), 2018. Export Date: 30 September 2022; Cited By: 22.

[10] M. Doroshtnasir, T. Worzewski, R. Krankenhagen, and M. Röllig. On-site inspection of potential defects in wind turbine rotor blades with thermography. *Wind Energy*, 19(8):1407–1422, 2016.

[11] C. Galleguillos, A. Zorrilla, A. Jimenez, L. Diaz, Á L. Montiano, M. Barroso, A. Viguria, and F. Lasagni. Thermographic non-destructive inspection of wind turbine blades using unmanned aerial systems. *Plastics, Rubber and Composites*, 44(3):98–103, 2015. Export Date: 30 September 2022; Cited By: 33.

[12] BAM. Project webpage: Evaltherm - passive thermography for the detection of rotor blade damage on wind turbines, 2020.

[13] T. Worzewski, R. Krankenhagen, M. Doroshtnasir, M. Röllig, H. Steinfurth, and C. Maierhofer. Forschung zur thermografischen zustandsinspektion von offshore rotorblättern. *Wind-Kraft-Journal*, (February), 2014.

[14] Tamara Worzewski, Rainer Krankenhagen, Manoucher Doroshtnasir, Mathias Röllig, Christiane Maierhofer, and Henrik Steinfurth. Thermographic inspection of a wind turbine rotor blade segment utilizing natural conditions as excitation source, part i: Solar excitation for detecting deep structures in gfrp. *Infrared Physics & Technology*, 76:756–766, 2016.

[15] Tamara Worzewski, Rainer Krankenhagen, and Manoucher Doroshtnasir. Thermographic inspection of wind turbine rotor blade segment utilizing natural conditions as excitation source, part ii: The effect of climatic conditions on thermographic inspections – a long term outdoor experiment. *Infrared Physics & Technology*, 76, 2016.

[16] M. Stamm and R. Krankenhagen. Weather-dependent passive thermography of unheated wind turbine blades. In *Proc.SPIE*, volume 12109, page 121090E, 2022.

# AUTHOR INDEX

**Institute of Physics**
Dirac House, Temple Back
Bristol BS1 6BE UK

ISSN: 1742-6588
ISBN 978-1-7138-7463-8

9 781713 874638